YEARBOOK OF SCIENCE AND THE FUTURE
1998

YEARBOOK OF SCIENCE AND THE FUTURE
1998

Encyclopædia
Britannica, Inc.

Chicago

Auckland
London
Manila
Paris
Rome
Seoul
Sydney
Tokyo

1998
Yearbook
of
Science
and
the Future

Library of Congress Catalog Card Number: 69-12349
International Standard Book Number: 0-85229-657-6
International Standard Serial Number: 0096-3291

Editor
Charles Cegielski

Associate Editor
Adelheid Fischer

Contributing Editors
David Calhoun, Arthur Latham, Melinda C. Shepherd, Karen Sparks

Special Editorial Consultant
Michael Woods

Creative Director
Bob Ciano

Operations and Budget Manager
Diana M. Pitstick

Senior Picture Editor
Kathy Creech

Art Director
Steven Kapusta

Picture Editor
Sylvia Ohlrich

Senior Graphics Editor
Michael Kocik

Designers
Kathryn Diffley, John L. Draves, Jon Hensley

Art Staff
Michelle Burrell, Karen M. Farmer

Director, Geographic Information Services
Barbra A. Vogel

Cartography Staff
John E. Nelson, Michael D. Nutter, Antonio Perez

Manager, Copy Department
Sylvia Wallace

Copy Supervisors
Lawrence Kowalski, Barbara Whitney

Copy Staff
Linda Cifelli, Letricia A. Dixon, Sandra Langeneckert, Afrodite Mantzavrakos, Maria Ottolino Rengers

Manager, Production Control
Mary C. Srodon

Production Control Staff
Marilyn L. Barton

Manager, Composition/Page Makeup
Melvin Stagner

Supervisor, Composition/Page Makeup
Michael Born, Jr.

Technical Analyst
Bruce David Walters

Composition/Page Makeup Staff
Griselda Cháidez, Carol A. Gaines, Thomas J. Mulligan, Gwen E. Rosenberg, Tammy Yu-chu Wang Tsou, Danette Wetterer

Director, Information Management
Carmen-Maria Hetrea

Index Supervisor
Lisa Strubin

Index Staff
Darrin A. Baack, Stephen S. Seddon

Librarian
Shantha Uddin

Assistant Librarian
Robert Lewis

Secretarial Staff
Sara Brant, Julie Stevens

Director, Publishing Technology Group
Mary Voss

Publishing Technology Group
Steven Bosco, Troy Broussard, James Burke, Sheila Simon, Vincent Star

Encyclopædia Britannica, Inc.

Chairman of the Board
Jacob E. Safra

Chief Executive Officer
Constantine S. Yannias

Chief Operating Officer
James E. Goulka

Editor in Chief
Robert McHenry

Director of Yearbooks
Charles P. Trumbull

Director of Production
Marsha Mackenzie

foreword

"Scientists suggest life on Mars." "Ewe cloned from adult sheep udder." "Researchers create 'laser' beam of atoms." "Plant fiber transformed into fake fat." "Space probe finds possible ocean of water on moon of Jupiter." "Hundreds of African lake fish species discovered to have evolved in 12,000 years." Statements with such potential for astonishment may seem altogether appropriate as tabloid headlines or, at least, ideas for science-fiction stories. What makes them truly astonishing, however, is not that the events so described are beyond the realm of reason but, paradoxically, that they actually happened—and, moreover, that they all happened in the short space of about a year.

This amazingly productive period of scientific accomplishment and discovery is thoroughly covered in Encyclopædia Britannica's *1998 Yearbook of Science and the Future*. In the Year in Review section, some 50 articles, led off by a specially written OVERVIEW essay, focus on the major events of the past year—all of the above-mentioned developments and much more—while 12 illustrated feature articles take an in-depth, long-term look at some of the most important accomplishments

and pressing issues in science today. In the review articles ASTRONOMY, EARTH SCIENCES, and LIFE SCIENCES, for example, expert contributors bring their varied emphases and interpretations to the claim by NASA scientists that a meteorite believed to be from Mars contains mineral, biochemical, and fossil evidence of life. The same discovery is approached from yet another perspective in the feature article LIFE ON THE EDGE, which takes up the question of life on other planets in terms of the no-less-remarkable discoveries in recent years of organisms on Earth that thrive deep underground, in the boiling water of hot springs, in salt-saturated brine pools, and in other hostile environments once thought too forbidding for life as we know it.

Other of the yearbook's feature articles deal with the mysterious line of extinct humans called the Neanderthals and their place in human evolution; the work of the International Rice Research Institute in the Philippines to reduce hunger and poverty in the less-developed, rice-dependent nations of the world; and, in a photo essay, the unique achievements of a nature photographer with a passion for imaging the wing patterns of butterflies and

moths. Two mutually complementary features explore our ambitious, although often dubiously successful, attempts to know the future. One discusses the field of modern futures studies, its historical roots, and its contributions; the other offers answers to the question of why we repeatedly have fallen short of foreseeing the full impact of our most profound and far-reaching innovations. Yet another pair of features report on some of the more ominous findings of science—that environmental pollution may be reducing the genetic ability of future generations of living species to adapt to change and that chronic sleep deprivation is making us less efficient and prone to illnesses and accidents, with potentially disastrous consequences.

The accelerating technological growth and change that mark the 1990s has inspired concomitant changes in the way Encyclopædia Britannica produces its yearbooks. This volume is the first *Yearbook of Science and the Future* to be edited and designed by means of a new personal-computer-based publishing system, which replaces a collection of very antiquated mainframe-computer equipment and makes the book's text and im-

ages much more amenable to electronic forms of publishing than previously had been possible. From the start, we intended to make the effects of the switch to the new system, which required hard work and long hours from a great many people, as unobtrusive as possible. Consequently, the highest compliment that we can expect to elicit from our readers about the changeover is "What changeover?" On the other hand, one alteration in the book intended to be noticed is the addition of a new bibliographic article entitled RECENT BOOKS OF SCIENCE.

As always, we hope that the yearbook informs and delights you. The abundance of scientific developments in the past year helped make it an especially exciting and challenging volume to produce. In the feature article TO GLIMPSE TO-MORROW, noted scientific prophet Arthur C. Clarke is quoted as having said, "Anything that is theoretically possible will be achieved in practice, no matter what the technical difficulties, if it is desired greatly enough." The past year certainly proved Clarke right. Now, I wonder, what will our desires make possible next year?

—Charles Cegielski, Editor

contents

8

56

186

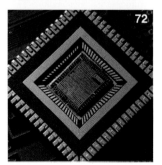

72

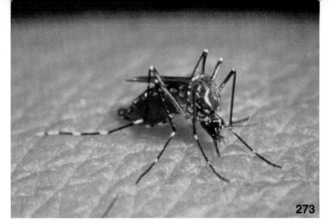

273

399

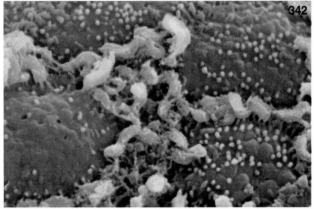

342

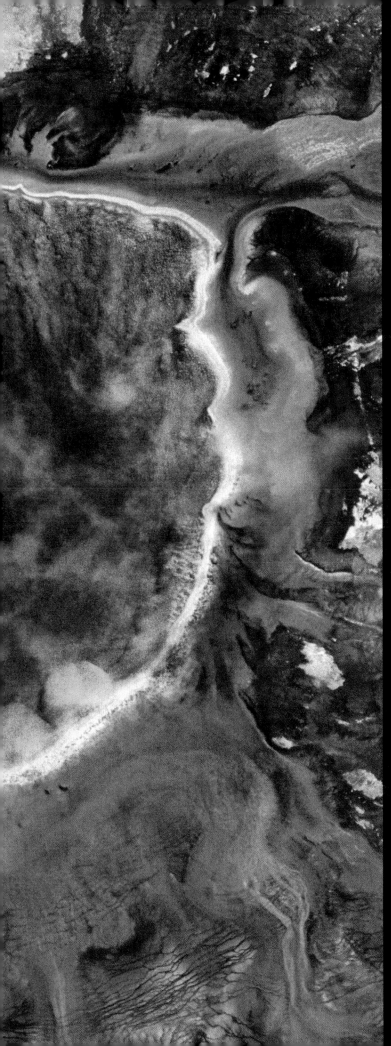

Life on the Edge

by Michael Woods

They are the stuff of science fiction, but now fiction has become fact. Microbes discovered in some of the most inhospitable places on Earth are transforming the way we think about the world while providing solutions to many of our most difficult problems.

The hot springs of Yellowstone National Park harbor whole new worlds of microbes, some of which survive at the boiling point of water.

Charles O'Rear—Westlight

Most organisms on Earth, including warm-blooded animals, are mesophiles; that is, they thrive in a relatively narrow range of moderate environmental conditions. The majority of animals and flowering plants, for instance, cannot survive beyond 50° C. (To convert degrees Celsius to degrees Fahrenheit, multiply by 1.8 and add 32; thus, 50° C equals 122° F.) On a pH scale—the measure of acidity and alkalinity—most organisms realize optimal growth in environments whose pH registers in a mid-range between 5 and 9, deviating little from a pH reading of 7, which is considered neutral. Furthermore, when it comes to pressure, most terrestrial animals and plants, as well as many aquatic organisms, live comfortably at normal atmospheric pressure (about 100 kilopascals, or 15 pounds per square inch).

The discovery of new microbes that thrive in extreme environments, however, has turned this assumption upside down. In the past three de-

cades, scientists have cataloged an amazing number of microbes—some of them bacteria but many now recognized as belonging to a distinct category of life known as archaea—that are immune to conditions that spell instant death for ordinary forms of life. These organisms are called extremophiles, after their proclivity for brutal environments. Some of these organisms not only tolerate harsh conditions but, like a special group of extremophiles known

as obligate extremophiles, require them in order to survive.

Extremophiles defy death by thriving in temperatures above the boiling and below the freezing points of water. They survive conditions more acidic than battery acid and more caustic than household ammonia. Others flourish in salt marshes 30 times the salinity of the Pacific Ocean, smoldering heaps of coal waste, hydrothermal vents on the deep ocean floor where crushing

pressure and searing heat are a fact of daily life, active volcanic craters, radioactive waste from nuclear reactors, and hot petroleum reservoirs three kilometers (two miles) below the Earth's surface where temperatures reach 110° C.

The discovery of extremophiles has had profound theoretical and practical implications. Their existence has altered fundamental scientific conceptions about the origins and boundaries of life. In 1995, for example, researchers discovered a community of organisms 1,000 meters (3,300 feet) underground near the Columbia

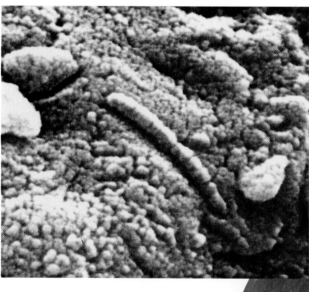

Microbes that inhabit harsh places on Earth have revived speculation that life may exist on other planets. In 1996 NASA scientists discovered tubelike structures (above), less than 1/100 the width of a human hair, in a meteorite from Mars. Scientific speculation that the structures were fossilized microorganisms fueled worldwide debate about the possibility of life on Mars (right).

(Above) NASA; (right) JPL/NASA

Michael Woods is Science Editor in the Washington Bureau for the Toledo *(Ohio)* Blade *and the* Pittsburgh *(Pennsylvania)* Post Gazette.

River in Washington. These organisms, called SLiMEs (subsurface lithoautotrophic microbial ecosystems), live in the absence of sunlight, deriving their energy from water and basalt.

Some scientists now speculate that the first life forms on Earth could have been terrestrial extremophiles similar to SLiMEs. They suggest that these organisms could have existed before photosynthesis evolved about 2.8 billion years ago. According to Blaine Metting of the U.S. Department of Energy's (DOE's) Subsurface Science Program, "Life may have originated independently of sunlight and come to the surface, rather than vice versa."

This theory lent credence to speculation in 1996 about possible traces of microbial life in a meteorite from Mars. Planetary experts argued that if extremophiles could thrive in the harsh conditions that prevailed three billion years ago on Earth, they might easily have survived the conditions that existed on Mars when the meteorite was expelled from the planet's surface several billion years ago. Indeed, some scientists endorse the idea proposed by Thomas Gold of Cornell University, Ithaca, New York, that several other planets in our own solar system harbor microbial life—if not on the surface, then deep within the recesses of planetary rock. In a 1992 report in the *Proceedings of the National Academy of Sciences,* Gold theorized that organisms similar to terrestrial extremophiles may be "widely disseminated" in the universe.

While these death-defying microbes have helped lend credibility to theories of life on other planets, they have also forced scientists to recognize the existence of terrestrial life in the nether regions of Earth, referred to as the deep biosphere. In the past scientists assumed that life thrived primarily

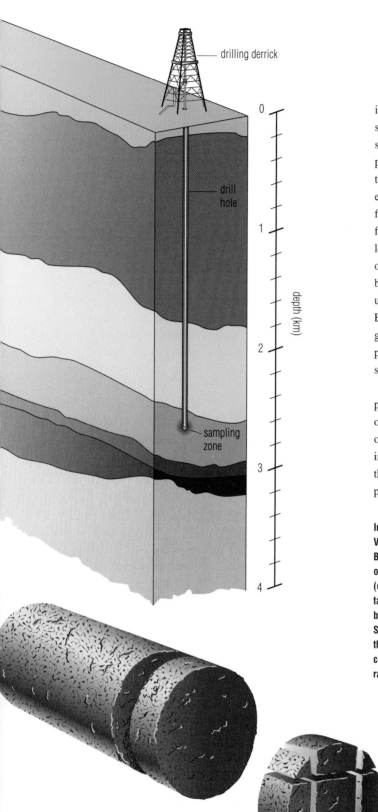

drilling derrick

drill hole

sampling zone

depth (km)

0

1

2

3

4

in the thin shell of atmosphere, soil, and water near the Earth's surface. But deep-drilling projects now have established that microbes, many of them extremophiles, flourish in dark fluid-filled pores, cracks, and fissures several kilometers below the surface. Some microbiologists now estimate that the biomass of microbial life in the upper few kilometers of the Earth's crust may even be greater than that of animals, plants, and microbes living in surface ecosystems.

The discovery of extremophiles has not only broadened our view of the world but also opened up new possibilities for improving human health and the environment. Researchers predict that extremophiles also

will have major industrial and commercial applications, among them extracting metals from ores, generating renewable energy, treating sewage, and cleaning up pollution. They also may be a source of superactivated enzymes that can be used in biotechnology and the production of foods, drugs, chemicals, and other products.

SCIENCE'S HIDDEN FRONTIER

Until recent times extremophiles had been largely overlooked by scientists—for a variety of reasons. For the most part, scientists simply neglected to look for microorganisms in inhospitable

In 1995 scientists drilling in Virginia's Taylorsville Triassic Basin discovered the microorganism *Bacillus infernus* (opposite) in a rock core (below) taken from 2,700 m (8,850 ft) beneath the Earth's surface. Scientists have raised concerns that these organisms may help spread contamination from underground radioactive waste sites.

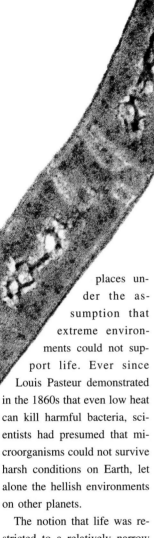

David Boone, Oregon Graduate Institute and Henry Aldrich, University of Florida

places under the assumption that extreme environments could not support life. Ever since Louis Pasteur demonstrated in the 1860s that even low heat can kill harmful bacteria, scientists had presumed that microorganisms could not survive harsh conditions on Earth, let alone the hellish environments on other planets.

The notion that life was restricted to a relatively narrow range of moderate conditions began to crumble in the late 1960s, although there had been hints to the contrary decades earlier. In 1926, for instance, Edson S. Bastin and Frank E. Greer of the University of Chicago cultured bacteria discovered in an oil deposit hundreds of meters below the surface. They speculated that the microbes were archaebacteria, descendants of ancient, primitive bacteria buried with decaying vegetation 300 million years ago. Only recently have scien-

tists come to the conclusion that these archaebacteria are not merely primitive forms of ordinary bacteria. Rather they belong to an entirely new superkingdom of organisms known as Archaea. For decades archaebacteria had been mislabeled, in large part because under a microscope they look similar to bacteria.

This new thinking about life in extreme environments was stimulated by the early work of such researchers as Thomas Brock of the University of Wisconsin at Madison, who in 1966 detected microbes in a hot spring in Yellowstone National Park. One organism lived in water whose temperature measured 70° C. In 1967 Brock identified another microbe that lived in a 100° C spring—the boiling point of water.

Since then, scientists have identified dozens of previously unknown microbes in some of the most inaccessible and hostile places on Earth, including hydrothermal vents associated with enormous ruptures in the ocean floor. Known as seafloor spreading centers, these giant cracks are formed when hot magma, rising from deep beneath the seafloor, causes great plates in the Earth's crust to slowly drift apart. Seawater seeps into the cracks, mixes

with minerals, and pours back out in springs called hydrothermal vents. Often these vents mark the sites of richly varied marine communities.

In 1977 an expedition led by oceanographers John B. Corliss of Oregon State University and John M. Edmond of the Massachusetts Institute of Technology discovered an entire community living around a spreading center in the Pacific Ocean. Corliss and Edmond viewed the first hydrothermal ecosystem from the U.S. research submarine *Alvin* about 320 kilometers (200 miles) northeast of the Galápagos Islands. Though located at a depth of three kilometers (1.9 miles), far beyond the reach of sunlight, the sea-vent community was surprisingly diverse and colorful. Corliss and Edmond found giant white tube worms (pogonophorans) and pink vent fish (bythitids), as well as an abundance of mussels and white crabs. In the absence of photosynthesis, these self-sufficient, closed-loop ecosystems derive all their energy from bacteria that metabolize the hydrogen sulfide found in the mineral-rich water.

In the 1980s extremophile research was accelerated by the DOE as part of its focus on energy and cleanup. Concerns about groundwater contamina-

tion and other kinds of environmental pollution, for example, surfaced when scientists realized that microbes living in deep rock formations might transport radioactive contamination into groundwater from deep geologic salt beds used as waste repositories. They hypothesized that microbial colonies could produce gases such as carbon dioxide, methane, and hydrogen that build up pressure in waste repositories, forcing contaminated water through underground cracks into groundwater supplies. The microbes also could incorporate radioactive carbon into some of these gases and increase the hazards from these

In the 1860s Louis Pasteur demonstrated that even low heat could kill harmful bacteria in food. New research, however, has challenged the belief that microbes are unable to survive high temperatures.

Brown Brothers

Dave Ward, Montana State University

buildups. A recent study of a proposed underground waste repository in Switzerland, for example, estimated that microbes would produce one million cubic meters (1.3 million cubic yards) of gas.

In 1985 the DOE launched its Subsurface Science Program and began to drill into rock in search of microbial life at a number of sites, including the Savannah River nuclear-materials-processing facility in South Carolina. The results were startling. Researchers detected ubiquitous microbes in core samples taken from depths as great as 2.8 kilometers (1.7 miles).

BIOLOGY IN HARD PLACES

How extremophiles adapt to their harsh environments has largely eluded scientists. Despite the value of extremophiles to basic research and their potential for use in a wide variety of products and processes, scientists know comparatively little about them, partly because they are difficult to cultivate under laboratory conditions. Extremophile research involves building expensive cultivation systems that mimic the temperatures, pressures, and other conditions found in the organisms' natural

habitats. Some of these organisms damage expensive cultivation systems, since they grow by oxidizing metal sulfides, producing insoluble metal oxides that corrode metal reaction vessels and foul glass surfaces.

Not only is it difficult to recreate the habitats of extremophiles in the lab, but the study of their behaviors is complicated by the intricate combination of strategies they use to survive in hostile circumstances, from the structure of

(continued on page 18)

The effluent channels of Octopus Spring in Yellowstone National Park (top) are home to cyanobacteria that form layered green-and-orange mats (center) in water temperatures up to 74° C (165° F). Magnification of the mat's top layer (above) reveals the sausage-shaped cyanobacteria that provide photosynthesized nutrients for threadlike bacterial symbionts.

14

(Inset) Bacteria have been discovered around hydrothermal vents on the deep ocean floor, where temperatures can top 350° C (660° F). Surviving without light or oxygen, these extremophiles oxidize sulfur compounds from hot seawater, making nutrients available to symbiotic organisms such as tube worms (below).

TO THE ENDS
OF THE EARTH

Think of the most inhospitable places on Earth—the bubbling cauldrons of Yellowstone hot springs, the perpetual night of the deep ocean floor, the crevices in solid rock several kilometers beneath the Earth's surface. Until recently, these places have been considered too hostile to support life.

In the past three decades, however, scientists have discovered organisms known as extremophiles in some of the world's most challenging places. These organisms are categorized according to their environmental preferences.

Thermophiles can take the heat. For them, optimum temperatures exceed 45° C. Some like it even hotter. Hyperthermophiles grow best in temperatures above 80° C. These extreme thermophiles can withstand temperatures of at least 140° C. Some authorities believe their outer limits of survival may exceed 150° C.

As a result, many of them live in or near environments associated with volcanic activity, including hot springs, where water temperatures of 99°–100° C approach the boiling point; steam vents, or fumaroles, whose temperatures range from 150° to 500° C; or geothermal vents on the ocean floor, where temperatures may exceed 350° C.

Some thermophiles can be found in more common places, including compost heaps or silage, where the decomposition process raises temperatures to 65° C, or sun-heated surface soils, which may reach 70° C.

Psychrophiles are cold-loving organisms. They thrive in sea ice, frozen Antarctic lakes, cold ocean depths, and other niches whose temperatures register near or below freezing.

Barophiles can withstand extreme pressure, such as that of the ocean floor. In undersea environments, pressure increases by one atmosphere for about every 10 meters of descent. Some barophiles thrive at depths of 4,000 meters (more

than 13,000 feet), which translates to an increase in pressure of 400 atmospheres. Extreme barophiles have been retrieved from depths of 10,000 meters (nearly 33,000 feet), where the pressure is approximately 1,000 atmospheres. These organisms are astoundingly resilient, considering that the recommended limit for scuba divers is approximately 80 meters (250 feet), or about 8 atmospheres of additional pressure.

Acidophiles thrive in extremely acidic conditions. Until recently, scientists were aware of only four organisms that could grow at pH values slightly above 0. (On a pH scale of 0–14, a reading of 7 is considered neutral. Readings below 7 reflect increasing acidity, while those above 7 measure increasing alkalinity.)

Then in 1995 German scientists topped that record with the discovery of two species of archaea in a volcanic pool near a steam vent in Japan. These organisms grew at and even slightly below a pH value of 0. Acidophiles such as *Thiobacillus* and *Sulfolobus* oxidize sulfide minerals and actually produce sulfuric acid as a metabolic by-product. Large numbers of sulfur-oxidizing microbes, including *Thiobacillus,* are present in and around hydrothermal vents on the ocean floor.

Alkalophilic microbes require a pH as high as 11, the equivalent of household ammonia. They thrive in soda deserts and soda lakes such as the Wadi an-Natrun in Egypt and Lake Magadi in Kenya.

Halophiles live in highly saline environments, including evaporation ponds used to harvest salt from sea water, natural salt lakes such as Utah's Great Salt Lake or the Dead Sea in the Middle East, and salt-preserved foods. Some of these organisms survive in saturated salt solutions; that is, the water contains so much salt that no more will dissolve in it. Conventional organisms quickly perish in these solutions, since their high osmotic pressure draws fluids out of living cells.

Some extremophiles tolerate only one extreme environmental condition. Others actually live in niches that combine two or more extremes. Barophiles found in the deep sea, for instance, thrive at hundreds of atmospheres of pressure and temperatures close to freezing. Other organisms thrive near hydrothermal vents on the deep ocean floor in niches characterized by extreme heat and pressure. Thermoacidophiles grow best in environments such as acidic hot springs, where the water may top 75° C and the pH dips below 2. Haloalkalinophiles live in places that concentrate salt and alkalinity, such as soda lakes.

(continued from page 14)

their cell walls to the mechanisms by which they metabolize food.

Researchers, however, have identified a number of survival strategies among extremophiles. Some organisms have unusual physical or chemical features that distinguish them from mesophilic archaea or bacteria, including tougher cell walls or unusual cell membranes. For example, cold-loving extremophiles, or psychrophiles, have membrane lipids rich in unsaturated fatty acids, which keep them more fluid and functional at low temperatures. By contrast, heat-loving extremophiles, or thermophiles, have membrane lipids rich in saturated fatty acids, which form stronger bonds than unsaturated fatty acids and enhance heat resistance. The most heat-resistant kinds, called hyperthermophiles, also contain a special enzyme—reverse gyrase—that causes a supercoiling of DNA and makes it more heat-stable.

Extremophiles also can synthesize chemical products that boost resistance. Some thermophiles, for example, produce cell products such as inositol or glycerate phosphate, which seem to offer some protection against heat. Resistance to extreme conditions also results from adaptations in the folded, three-dimensional structure of enzymes synthesized by extremophiles. In mesophilic organisms, for example, temperatures above $60°$ C normally inactivate enzymes by disrupting the folded structure critical for enzyme function. Some extremophiles, on the other hand, have what scientists dub a salt bridge, a zipperlike series of ionic chemical bonds that reinforces the interior structure so that the enzyme does not unfold, or denature, in harsh environmental conditions. Combined with other adaptations, the salt bridges help confer resistance to multiple factors such as pressure and heat, as in the case of extremophiles that live near deep-sea volcanic vents. In addition to salt bridges, the enzymes of these organisms have a densely packed interior held together by hydrophobic bonds, which

EXTREMOPHILES AND THEIR HABITATS

Category	Representative Microorganism	Habitat	Optimum Growth Conditions	Possible Applications
acidophile	Thiobacillus ferrooxidans	acidic springs; bogs; mine drainage (e.g., Appalachia)	$30°$ C; pH 2.5	leaching metals from ores; leaching pyrite (FeS_2) from coal
alkalinophile	Clostridium thermoalcaliphilum	soda deserts and lakes (e.g., Lake Magadi in Kenya); raw sewage sludge	$48°–51°$ C; pH 9.6–10.1	waste treatment
barophile	Methanococcus jannaschii	deep-sea hydrothermal vents (e.g., vents along Pacific Ocean Ridge)	250 atm; $85°$ C	supplying enzymes for methane production; cleanup of toxic wastes; detergent additive
halophile	Halobacterium salinarium	evaporate brines; natural salt lakes (e.g., Dead Sea)	4–5 M NaCl*; $66°–68°$ C	—
hyperthermophile	Pyrococcus furiosus	areas of volcanic activity (e.g., steam vents; geothermal marine sediments)	$100°$ C; pH 7.0	supplying enzymes for polymerase chain reaction
psychrophile	Micrococcus cryophilus (Psychrobacter immobilis)	polar waters and ice (e.g., Arctic Ocean; Antarctica)	$0°–20°$ C	—
thermoacidophile	Sulfolobus acidocaldarius	acidic hot springs; solfataras (e.g., Pacific islands; Iceland)	$70°–85°$ C; pH 1–3	leaching metals from ores; recycling rubber from waste tires
thermophile	Thermus aquaticus	geothermal vents (e.g., Yellowstone National Park)	$70°–75°$ C	supplying enzymes for polymerase chain reaction

*Concentration measured in molarity.
Portions of this table were prepared with the assistance of Robert M. Kelly and Guy D. Duffaud at North Carolina State University.
Categories reflect the adaptation of some organisms to more than one extreme condition.

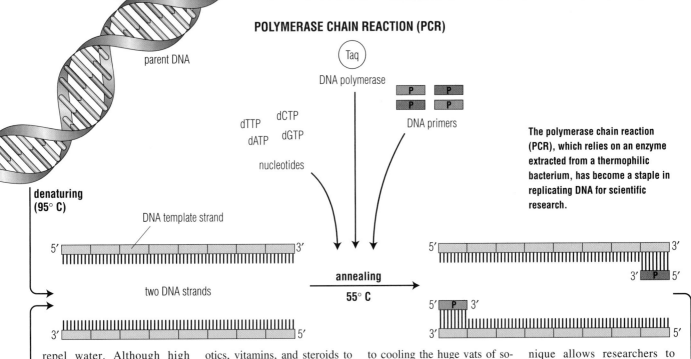

POLYMERASE CHAIN REACTION (PCR)

Taq
DNA polymerase

DNA primers

dTTP dCTP
dATP dGTP

nucleotides

The polymerase chain reaction (PCR), which relies on an enzyme extracted from a thermophilic bacterium, has become a staple in replicating DNA for scientific research.

parent DNA

denaturing (95° C)

DNA template strand

5′ ... 3′

two DNA strands

3′ ... 5′

annealing
55° C

repeat cycle

synthesizing (72° C)

repel water. Although high pressure may destabilize the salt bridges, it strengthens these hydrophobic bonds.

EXTREMOPHILE ENZYMES

Much of the great interest in extremophiles centers on their unique enzymes. Both ordinary mesophilic microbes and archaea secrete enzymes to break complex molecules down into smaller digestible parts. Because enzymes function as biological catalysts, they instigate chemical reactions or speed up processes that normally would occur very slowly. Since ancient times humans have exploited microbes and their enzymes in fermentation processes. Today industrial microbiology uses enzymes to produce scores of common commercial and industrial products, from antibi-

otics, vitamins, and steroids to amino acids and citric acid. Worldwide about $2 billion worth of enzymes are used in industrial processes each year.

Most of these enzymes, however, are extracted from mesophilic organisms. Thus, they are fragile and can be used only under relatively moderate temperatures, pressures, and pH levels. When these ordinary enzymes are exposed to temperatures above 60°–70° C, for instance, their chemical structure undergoes irreversible changes, and they are rendered inactive.

Hardier enzymes from extremophiles, called extremozymes, are much in demand to produce commercial products more economically and efficiently. In many large-scale industrial fermentation processes that use mesophilic bacteria, for instance, a large share of total production costs goes

to cooling the huge vats of solution so that the vital enzymes are not destroyed. Many chemical reactions in industrial microbiology would run faster and more efficiently at high temperatures, and hotter temperatures also would reduce the need to protect against contamination with other microbes.

POLYMERASE CHAIN REACTION

The most well-known example of extremozymes' potential is found in the polymerase chain reaction (PCR), developed in 1983 by biochemist Kary B. Mullis at Cetus Corp., Emeryville, California. The revolutionary PCR process, which earned Mullis a share of the 1993 Nobel Prize for Chemistry, is a method for duplicating a single strand of DNA into billions of identical copies within a few hours. The tech-

nique allows researchers to generate large quantities of DNA for use in various experiments and procedures. Since its development PCR has been invaluable in scientific research, diagnosing infectious diseases, and analyzing the DNA in blood and other biological traces found at crime scenes.

Key to making PCR a completely automated and inexpensive process is an enzyme extracted from a thermophilic bacterium known as *Thermus aquaticus*. The microbe was discovered by Brock and fellow scientist Hudson Freeze in 1967 in a Yellowstone hot spring located near Old Faithful.

PCR involves three steps, each of which is rapidly repeated several times in the process of replication. In the first step, the "target" DNA fragment is heated to about 95° C.

(continued on page 21)

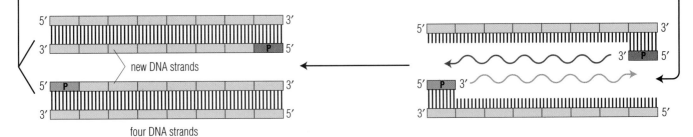

new DNA strands

four DNA strands

ADDING A BRANCH TO THE TREE OF LIFE

Archaea

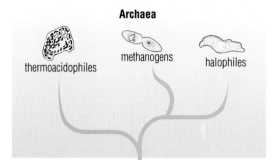

thermoacidophiles methanogens halophiles

Many of the new microbes discovered in extreme environments belong to an entirely new superkingdom of life known as Archaea.

In 1977 Carl R. Woese and his colleagues at the University of Illinois at Urbana-Champaign startled scientists by proposing that archaebacteria, or "primitive" bacteria, are so unlike other organisms, even bacteria, that they constitute a third major group, or superkingdom, of living things. He named this group Archaea. Considered living fossils, remnants of some of the most ancient forms of life, the archaea include a large number of extremophiles, organisms that thrive in some of the harshest conditions on Earth.

Scientists initially had classified archaebacteria as bacteria. But Woese concluded that biochemically and genetically the archaebacteria are as different from bacteria as they are from humans and other eukaryotes.

In mid-1996 a team of researchers from the Institute for Genomic Research, Rockville, Maryland, the University of Illinois, and Johns Hopkins University, Baltimore, Maryland, confirmed Woese's controversial hypothesis about the genetic differences between archaea and other forms of life.

Researchers decoded the genome of *Methanococcus jannaschii,* an archaeon isolated in the early 1980s near a hydrothermal vent more than three kilometers (two miles) below the Pacific Ocean. *M. jannaschii,* which grows without oxygen and requires temperatures of 85° C and pressures of 250 atmospheres (3,700 pounds per square inch), is a methanogen—an organism that consumes molecular hydrogen and carbon dioxide and produces methane, the main component in natural gas. The project, funded by the U.S. Department of Energy's (DOE's) Microbial Genome Program, determined the sequence of chemical subunits in all 1,738 of the microbe's genes.

Scientists found that two-thirds of the microbe's genes were totally new to science. Even more surprising, the data demonstrated that archaea are more closely related to humans than previously thought. Ac-

cording to Woese, "The data confirm what we've long suspected, that the archaea are related to us, to the eukaryotes; they are descendants of the microorganisms that gave rise to the eukaryotic cell billions of years ago."

The DOE program currently is funding projects to sequence and map the genomes of several additional extremophiles. These include *Pyrococcus furiosus,* a marine hyperthermophile that thrives at 100° C, and *Deinococcus radiodurans,* which has a high resistance to radioactivity. Like other extremophiles, they may have practical applications in medicine, industrial processes, and environmental cleanup.

Eucarya

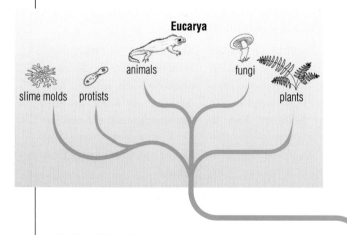

slime molds protists animals fungi plants

Before Woese's announcement, many scientists divided life on Earth into two superkingdoms: the Bacteria, which include single-celled organisms lacking a nucleus, and the Eucarya, whose more complex cells contain a distinct nucleus. This group encompasses plants and animals.

Bacteria

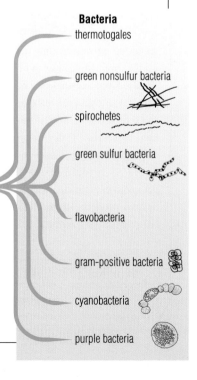

thermotogales

green nonsulfur bacteria

spirochetes

green sulfur bacteria

flavobacteria

gram-positive bacteria

cyanobacteria

purple bacteria

common ancestor

(continued from page 19)

Jean-Loup Charmet

Heating breaks the chemical bonds that bind the two strands of the DNA helix and thus unties the DNA molecule. In the second step, the temperature is reduced, and short strands of "primer" DNA attach to the target, acting as "start" and "stop" signals for the actual copying. Finally, an enzyme called DNA polymerase catalyzes formation of new DNA strands, using the target DNA as the model or template.

Once the first cycle is complete, the two original DNA strands have multiplied into four strands. Then the cycle is immediately repeated, each DNA strand serving as a template for spinning out new copies. After 30–60 cycles, PCR has exponentially magnified the original DNA into a quantity large enough to be identified and studied. By this process, in theory, one molecule of DNA in a blood speck found at a crime scene could be amplified within hours and linked to a suspect.

The heat tolerance of *T. aquaticus* polymerase, called Taq polymerase, was the key to automating the PCR process. It eliminated the need to replace the polymerase with a fresh, active enzyme after each heating step. Taq polymerase also increased the efficiency of the process. All the ingredients in the mixture could be reheated

For centuries people have found practical ways to use microorganisms, including in the making of wine. In a more modern twist, researchers are investigating the use of thermophilic bacteria in the high-temperature fermentation of alcohol.

quickly and repeatedly. Today technicians use a DNA polymerase from another extremophile, *Pyrococcus furiosus*. This Pfu polymerase is even more heat-stable than Taq polymerase and is less likely to introduce errors into the replication process.

COMMERCE AND INDUSTRY

Hyperthermostable enzymes also are used to manufacture more mundane products, such as natural food sweeteners, detergent additives, fabrics, and paper. Xylose isomerase from the bacterium *Bacillus coagulans,* for instance, is used to manufacture high-fructose corn syrup, an important sweetening agent in soft drinks. A protease from *B. licheniformis* is used in some detergents because it can withstand both high temperatures and alkaline environments. Amylase from *B. licheniformis* liquefies starch at temperatures as high as 110° C. Primalco Ltd. Biotec, a bio-

technology firm in Rajamäki, Finland, is commercializing Ecopulp, an extremozyme that survives heat and a highly alkaline environment to bleach wood pulp for kraft paper. The enzyme reduces the need for a polluting bleaching agent, chlorine dioxide, and reduces manufacturing costs by at least 15%. Genencor International of Rochester, New York, is developing an extremozyme for stonewashing denim, the process that gives jeans a worn, faded appearance. Researchers are investigating the use of *Clostridium thermocellum* and several other thermophilic bacteria in the high-temperature fermentation of alcohol. Other thermophiles show promise in the production of many industrially important medicines and chemicals, including antibiotics, amino acids, lactic acid, carotenoids, and acetic acid.

The mining industry also is looking at potential applications of extremozymes, including the microbial extraction, or leaching, of copper, uranium, and other metals from ores and wastes. This bacterial leaching is cheaper than conventional smelting, which requires great inputs of energy. It also reduces operating costs by eliminating the need for equipment to control the release of sulfur oxides and other pollutants into the atmosphere.

Mining researchers are hoping to find a replacement for the acidophilic bacterium *Thiobacillus ferrooxidans*. Though the microbe already is used in industrial leaching, it is sensitive to the high temperatures required in the ore-separation process. Laboratory and other small-scale studies suggest that thermophiles could not only withstand these temperatures but also thrive in hotter conditions, which translates into faster reaction rates and more rapid recovery of ores. By removing and metabolizing sulfur, a hyperthermophile called *Sulfolobus*, for instance, has been proved in preliminary tests to leach molybdenum from molybdenite and copper from the copper ore, chalcopyrite.

RENEWABLE ENERGY

Thermophiles also may play a vital role in the cheap production of renewable fuels. *C. thermocellum*, for example, can directly ferment crude cellulose plant material into ethanol, which eliminates the need for costly intermediate processing steps. Especially active in this renewable energy research is the DOE's Microbial Genome Program. Project researchers are collecting basic genetic information about extremophiles that will lead to new sources of energy as well as methods for cleaning up toxic and radioactive wastes. By mapping extremophile genes (finding the exact location of specific genes on a chromosome) and sequencing them (determining the order of the long chains of molecular units known as nucleotide bases that make up their DNA), researchers hope to study and duplicate the coded information that produces key enzymes.

Extremozymes also are helping to bring the dream of exploiting hydrogen as a clean-

Enzymes derived from extremophiles are used in a variety of commercial processes, including the manufacture of sweeteners for soft drinks (top) and the stonewashing of denim (left).

(Left) Mark Fortenberry—VisionQuest; (above) David Burnett—Contact Press Images

burning energy source closer to reality. Hydrogen currently is produced in several ways, including electrolysis—which involves using electric current to split water into its constituent elements, hydrogen and oxygen—and the processing of hydrocarbons such as natural gas. These procedures currently are too costly for widespread hydrogen production. Researchers at Oak Ridge (Tennessee) National Laboratory are testing two extremozymes in an effort to develop a new and less-expensive process for producing hydrogen. The extremozymes make it possible to produce hydrogen from a relatively inexpensive raw material, the simple sugar glucose. One process uses glucose dehydrogenase obtained from *Thermoplasma acidophilum,* a microbe that lives in smoldering heaps of coal-mine wastes. The enzyme, which removes hydrogen atoms from glucose, remains active at temperatures up to 60° C.

The other process uses a hydrogenase obtained from *P. furiosus,* a microbe found in hydrothermal volcanic vents on the ocean floor. This enzyme, which remains active at temperatures up to 100° C, combines atoms of hydrogen into molecules of hydrogen gas. In removing hydrogen from glucose, the extremozymes do more than produce a hydrogen energy source. They transform glucose into gluconic acid, a by-product that could be marketed to the chemical and food industries, where it is used to manufacture a range of products from paint strippers and medications to cleansers. Researchers are trying to make the economics of the process yet more attractive by adding another enzyme—cellulase—that can decompose the cellulose in waste paper into glucose. Instead of purchasing glucose from an outside source

Researchers are seeking to replace the heat-sensitive acidophile *Thiobacillus ferrooxidans,* currently used in a process to recover metal from low-quality ores, with a hardier extremophile. When mixed in a solution of water and ferric and sulfate ions, the bacteria catalyze chemical reactions that help separate ore from rock. Higher temperatures would result in faster reaction rates and ore extraction.

$H_2SO_4(aq)$	aqueous sulfuric acid
Fe^{3+}	iron(III)
CuS	copper sulfide
O_2	oxygen
Cu^{2+}	copper(II)
SO_4^{2-}	sulfate
Fe^{2+}	iron(II)

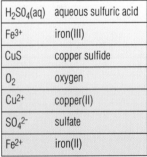

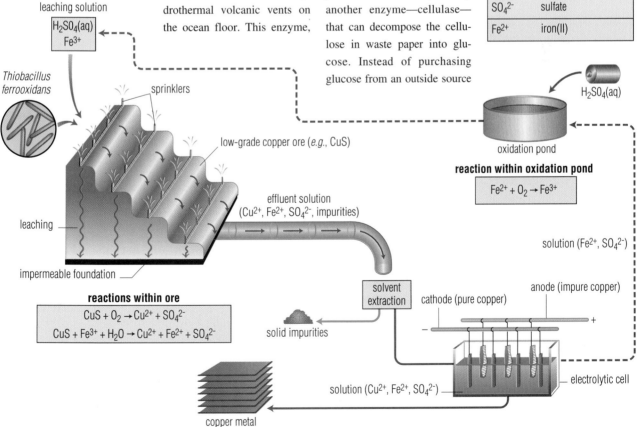

leaching solution
$H_2SO_4(aq)$
Fe^{3+}

Thiobacillus ferrooxidans

sprinklers

low-grade copper ore (*e.g.,* CuS)

leaching

impermeable foundation

reactions within ore

$$CuS + O_2 \rightarrow Cu^{2+} + SO_4^{2-}$$
$$CuS + Fe^{3+} + H_2O \rightarrow Cu^{2+} + Fe^{2+} + SO_4^{2-}$$

effluent solution
(Cu^{2+}, Fe^{2+}, SO_4^{2-}, impurities)

solid impurities

solvent extraction

$H_2SO_4(aq)$

oxidation pond

reaction within oxidation pond

$$Fe^{2+} + O_2 \rightarrow Fe^{3+}$$

solution (Fe^{2+}, SO_4^{2-})

anode (impure copper)

cathode (pure copper)

electrolytic cell

solution (Cu^{2+}, Fe^{2+}, SO_4^{2-})

copper metal

Microbiologist Karl O. Stetter gathers organisms in Iceland for screening by the U.S. company Recombinant BioCatalysis, which explores the microbes' commercial, medical, or industrial applications.

for the production of hydrogen energy, the glucose produced from the decomposed cellulose could be processed into hydrogen.

THE FUTURE

Possibilities for the use of extremophiles will soar as research expands dramatically in the next decade. Several commercial firms already are concentrating on finding applications for extremozymes. One company, Recombinant BioCatalysis, Inc., Sharon Hills, Pennsylvania, isolates and sells extremozymes and other enzymes. The firm is developing methods for the rapid screening of extremozymes to identify those with potential commer-

cial applications. It also maintains large libraries of genetic coding data for enzymes from many different kinds of extremophiles that could be used to clone extremozymes.

This extremozyme research is a worldwide effort, with programs under way in many countries. One of the most ambitious is Japan's Deep-Sea Environment Exploration Program (DEEPSTAR), a 15-year project to retrieve and study organisms from deep under the sea by using a fleet of the world's finest research submarines, including the manned vessels *Shinkai 6500* and *Shinkai 2000* and the remotely operated *Dolphin 3K*. Funding for the first eight years of the project, which began in 1992,

totals $43 million. Of the three submersibles, *Shinkai 6500* can descend the farthest. Diving to depths of 6,500 meters (21,000 feet), the vessel brings about 97% of Earth's deep ocean floor within reach. Their combined resources will have access to areas of the ocean floor far beyond the capabilities of *Alvin,* which has a depth limit of 4,000 meters (13,000 feet).

The Japanese vessels will retrieve microbial samples from deep ocean environments and take them to a sophisticated surface laboratory. Samples will be cultured in automated equipment that reproduces conditions on the deep seafloor. The extremophiles will grow under hundreds of atmospheres of pressure, temperatures from

above the boiling point of water to below freezing, and extremes of pH.

Many challenges lie ahead in efforts to exploit extremophiles and their enzymes. Applications such as PCR, for instance, require such minute amounts of extremozymes that a few grams might meet the world's needs for a year. But some industrial applications may require extremozymes by the ton. Rather than invest in cultivating huge vats of these microbes in their natural conditions, scientists may be able to genetically engineer desirable extremozyme traits into easier-to-grow microbes.

One of the biggest challenges for bioengineers is developing an organism that can thrive in the most hostile environment of all—industrial solvents. These extremophiles would not only supply enzymes for industrial processes that use solvents but help mitigate their dangerous by-products.

To date, only about 500 species of archaea have been identified. Some experts suspect that there may be a million more. According to Gary Olsen of the University of Illinois at Urbana-Champaign, what we currently know about extremophiles is only the tip of the iceberg. "Most of the organisms of the ocean have not been cultivated in a laboratory; in most cases they are not even closely related to anything that has been cultivated in a labora-

The Japanese research vessel *Shinkai 6500* is part of a 15-year effort to research ocean depths, including retrieving new organisms from the ocean floor.

tory," he has pointed out. "We are clueless as to what these things are doing. It's incredible that we're almost completely ignorant about some of the most fundamental processes that underlie the ecology of the planet."

FOR ADDITIONAL READING

■ "The Biosphere Below" in *Earth: The Science of Our Planet,* Daniel Grossman and Setch Shulman (William C. Brown Publishers, 1995).

■ "The Chemistry of Life at the Margins," Faye Flam, *Science* (July 22, 1994, pp. 471–472).

■ "The Deep, Hot Biosphere," Thomas Gold, *Proceedings of the National Academy of Sciences* (July 1992, pp. 6045–49).

■ "Extremozymes: Expanding the Limits of Biocatalysis," Michael W.W. Adams, Francine B. Perler, and Robert M. Kelly, *BIO/TECH-NOLOGY* (July 1995, pp. 662–668).

■ *Geomicrobiology,* Henry L. Ehrlich (Marcel Dekker, Inc., 1996).

■ "Microbes Deep Inside the Earth," James K. Frederickson

and Tullis Onstott, *Scientific American* (October 1996, pp. 68–73).

INTERNET RESOURCES

■ Extremophiles Home Page http://www.rit.edu/~paa0637/extreme.html

■ Life in Extreme Environments Home Page http://www.reston.com/astro/extreme.html

■ U.S. Department of Energy Biological and Environmental Research Program Home Page http://www.er.doe.gov/production/oher/oher_top.html

しんかい 6500

In the Realm of the Giant

by J. Kelly Beatty

After a journey of more than 3.7 billion kilometers, the Galileo spacecraft reached its final destination in December 1995. Since then it has been giving scientists their closest and longest look yet at the planet Jupiter and its moons.

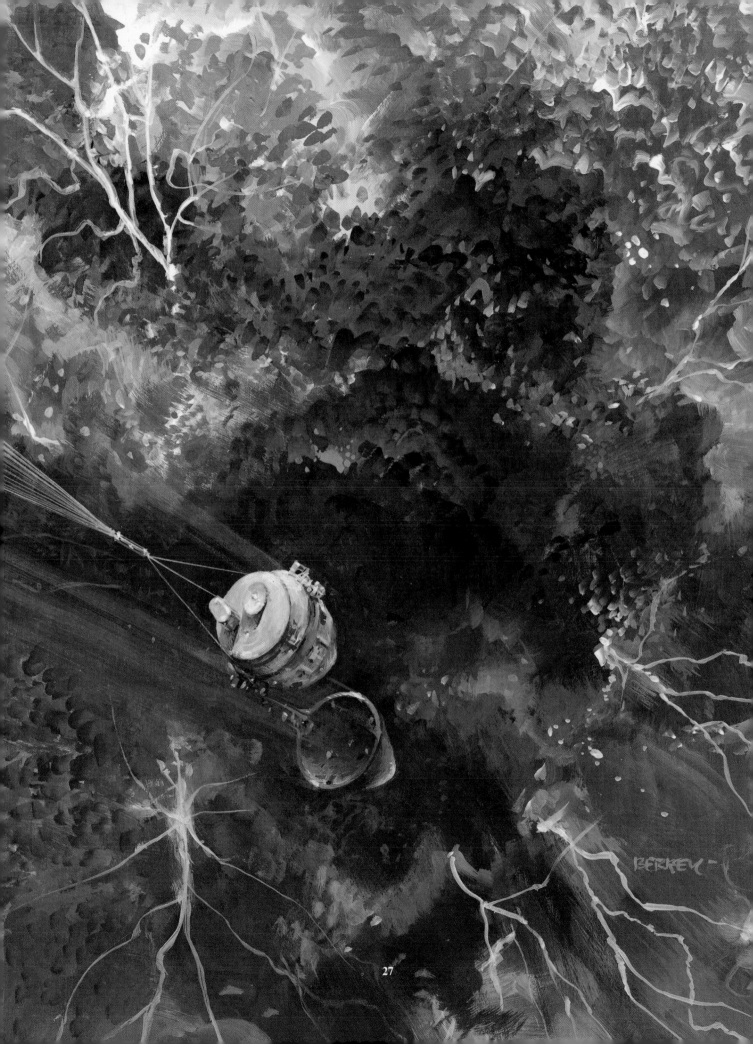

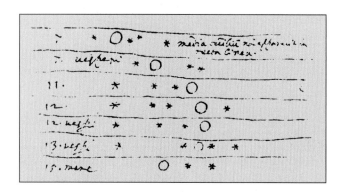

Jupiter and the changing positions of its four large moons, as observed by Galileo Galilei through a small telescope, are recorded over a succession of nights in a portion of his notebook from 1610.

When it comes to picking a destination for interplanetary travel, each world in our solar system has a certain appeal. Venus, cloaked in dense, noxious clouds, is the planet of mystery. Mars once had flowing rivers and may have been an abode of life. Saturn's attraction is its resplendent rings.

Nevertheless, no place offers more variety than giant Jupiter. The largest planet in the solar system, Jupiter gleams in the night sky as a bright, steady beacon that has been recognized since antiquity. Its allure heightened in 1610, when the Italian astronomer Galileo Galilei discovered that Jupiter has

J. Kelly Beatty is Senior Editor, Sky & Telescope *magazine.*

four large satellites. Although this quartet of moons was spotted independently by the German astronomer Simon Marius, who gave them their names— Io, Europa, Ganymede, and Callisto—they came to be called the Galilean satellites. In the centuries that followed, astronomers using Earth-based telescopes found nine more satellites circling Jupiter, and they became ever more intrigued by the planet's bands of dynamic, colorful clouds and its enduring Great Red Spot.

Visits by four spacecraft during the 1970s (the U.S. Pioneers 10 and 11 and Voyagers 1 and 2) and one in 1992 (the multinational Ulysses mission) added firsthand knowledge of a vast magnetic envelope teeming with charged particles, a faint ring, three new moonlets, and a better perspective on the

swirling storms that ripple through the Jovian atmosphere. Being flyby missions, however, the Pioneers and Voyagers could provide little more than snapshots of the goings-on at Jupiter. To really know the place—to understand its complexity—would require adding an artificial satellite to Jupiter's retinue of natural moons, an orbiting sentinel that could study the system for years.

Thus was born Project Galileo, a spacecraft that has been sending spectacular images and other data to waiting scientists since reaching Jupiter in December 1995. To the casual observer Galileo represents just another success story in NASA's long procession of interplanetary expeditions. To those who have worked on and with the mission, however, the arrival at Jupiter marked not only the beginning of its intended assignment but also the end of a harrowing series of misfortunes that dogged the spacecraft all the way to the outer solar system.

Work on Galileo began after the mission was approved by Congress in 1977. That was two years before the twin Voy-

agers would make their revealing flybys, but NASA's scientists and engineers already knew what they wanted. First, Galileo would actually be two spacecraft in one: a larger craft for orbiting Jupiter and a smaller probe to take measurements while plunging into the planet's atmosphere. Second, to make full use of the rocket muscle afforded by the forthcoming U.S. space shuttle system, Galileo would be big—at more than 2.5 metric tons, the largest interplanetary craft ever built by NASA. Third, it would bristle with instruments, 12 on the orbiter and 7 on the probe.

During its development the project encountered technical difficulties and delays, compounded by troubles with the space shuttle. Initially planned for 1982, Galileo's launch was rescheduled for May 1986. Then disaster struck when the space shuttle *Challenger* and its crew were lost to a postlaunch explosion early that year on a cold January day. Galileo became a double victim: the shuttle program was suspended while its serious problems were corrected, and in light of the accident NASA managers decided that the liquid-fueled Centaur rocket that was to boost Galileo to Jupiter from Earth orbit was too dangerous to carry in the shuttle's cargo bay.

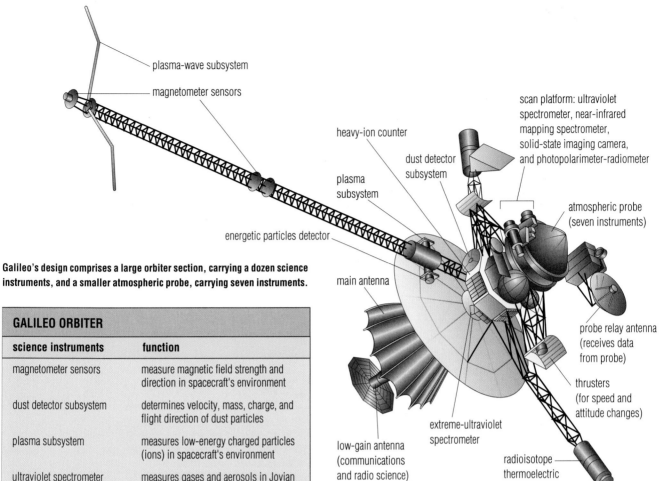

plasma-wave subsystem

magnetometer sensors

scan platform: ultraviolet spectrometer, near-infrared mapping spectrometer, solid-state imaging camera, and photopolarimeter-radiometer

heavy-ion counter

dust detector subsystem

plasma subsystem

atmospheric probe (seven instruments)

energetic particles detector

main antenna

probe relay antenna (receives data from probe)

thrusters (for speed and attitude changes)

low-gain antenna (communications and radio science)

extreme-ultraviolet spectrometer

radioisotope thermoelectric generators (provide electric power)

Galileo's design comprises a large orbiter section, carrying a dozen science instruments, and a smaller atmospheric probe, carrying seven instruments.

GALILEO ORBITER

science instruments	function
magnetometer sensors	measure magnetic field strength and direction in spacecraft's environment
dust detector subsystem	determines velocity, mass, charge, and flight direction of dust particles
plasma subsystem	measures low-energy charged particles (ions) in spacecraft's environment
ultraviolet spectrometer	measures gases and aerosols in Jovian atmosphere and searches for complex molecules
near-infrared mapping spectrometer	gathers spectral data on thermal, compositional, and structural nature of Galilean satellites
solid-state imaging camera	provides high-resolution images in visible light using 1,500-mm telescopic camera
photopolarimeter-radiometer	observes light in visible and infrared wavelengths and provides data on atmospheric composition and thermal-energy distribution
extreme-ultraviolet spectrometer	measures loss of volatile gases from Galilean satellites and studies structure and composition of upper Jovian atmosphere
radio science	employs microwave radio signals transmitted by low-gain antenna for several experiments
heavy-ion counter	measures charged sulfur and oxygen atoms trapped in Jovian magnetic field
energetic particles detector	measures energy, composition, intensity, and angular distribution of high-energy charged particles in spacecraft's environment
plasma-wave subsystem	measures electrostatic and electromagnetic components of plasma waves in Jovian magnetosphere

GALILEO PROBE

science instruments	function
atmosphere structure instrument	provides data about temperature, density, pressure, and molecular weight of atmospheric gases
neutral mass spectrometer	analyzes composition of gases by measuring their molecular weights
nephelometer	locates and measures cloud particles in environment of probe
lightning and radio-emissions detector	searches and records radio bursts and optical flashes generated by lightning in Jovian atmosphere
helium-abundance detector	determines the ratio of hydrogen to helium in Jovian atmosphere
net-flux radiometer	senses differences between flux of light and heat radiated downward and upward at various levels in Jovian atmosphere to provide information on cloud layers and winds
energetic particles instrument	used before atmospheric entry to measure fluxes of charged particles in innermost regions of Jovian magnetosphere and ionosphere

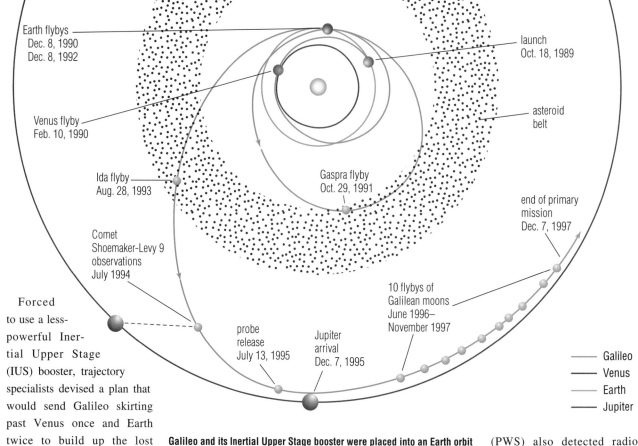

Earth flybys
Dec. 8, 1990
Dec. 8, 1992

launch
Oct. 18, 1989

Venus flyby
Feb. 10, 1990

asteroid belt

Ida flyby
Aug. 28, 1993

Gaspra flyby
Oct. 29, 1991

Comet
Shoemaker-Levy 9
observations
July 1994

end of primary
mission
Dec. 7, 1997

10 flybys of
Galilean moons
June 1996–
November 1997

probe
release
July 13, 1995

Jupiter
arrival
Dec. 7, 1995

Galileo
Venus
Earth
Jupiter

Forced to use a less-powerful Inertial Upper Stage (IUS) booster, trajectory specialists devised a plan that would send Galileo skirting past Venus once and Earth twice to build up the lost speed. This roundabout Venus-Earth-Earth gravity assist (VEEGA) would take much longer to reach Jupiter than the original trajectory and require numerous costly changes to the already completed spacecraft. Galileo finally got its ride into space aboard the shuttle *Atlantis* on Oct. 18, 1989, more than seven years after the launch date initially envisioned.

OPPORTUNISTIC SCIENCE

The VEEGA trajectory took more than six years to deliver Galileo to Jupiter, but along the way the spacecraft was able to do some originally unanticipated sightseeing. Arriving at Venus just under four months after launch, the orbiter used its near-infrared mapping spectrometer (NIMS) to probe deep into the cloud-choked atmosphere. An instrument called the plasma-wave subsystem

Galileo and its Inertial Upper Stage booster were placed into an Earth orbit by the space shuttle *Atlantis* on Oct. 18, 1989 (below). Shortly thereafter, the booster sent the craft on its six-year journey toward Jupiter. Galileo followed a roundabout Venus-Earth-Earth gravity assist (VEEGA) trajectory (above) that involved three planetary flybys and two passes through the asteroid belt. Fortuitously, it was in the right place to make a direct observation of the collision of Comet Shoemaker-Levy 9 with Jupiter in mid-1994.

(PWS) also detected radio static from lightning, confirming a finding made during prior spacecraft visits.

Galileo's two loops past Earth in the Decembers of 1990 and 1992 offered dramatic vistas of our home planet. It also provided the chance for a little scientific whimsy: if Galileo were an alien craft, could it detect the presence of intelligent beings here? The orbiter's instruments found various evidence for life in general including elevated amounts of oxygen in Earth's atmosphere and strangely colored patches on the surface. Its electronic camera failed to see the nighttime glow of city lights, but the PWS detector picked up a few bursts of energy from radio and television broadcasts.

During the long, looping cruise to Jupiter, Galileo passed through the asteroid belt twice, and on each occasion mission controllers directed the spacecraft to reconnoiter an asteroid in its vicinity. Sometimes called minor planets, these rocky objects exist by the thousands between the orbits of Mars and Jupiter. Space scientists still know very little about asteroids other than their sizes and colors. As seen from Earth, one large group, dubbed the S class, has overall colorations (reflection spectra) similar to those of the most common type of meteorite (called ordinary chondrites), which consist of silicate minerals and flecks of iron-nickel metal. Nevertheless, the colors do not match

perfectly, and astronomers wanted to know why. Given Galileo's ability to record spectra at many discrete wavelengths, it was hoped that the spacecraft could determine whether S-class asteroids are, in fact, the source of these meteorites.

The first asteroid rendezvous occurred on Oct. 29, 1991, with asteroid 951 Gaspra. Discovered in 1916 and named for a resort on the Black Sea, Gaspra orbits the Sun at an average distance of 331 million kilometers. (A kilometer is about 0.62 miles.) Galileo

passed by quickly at a range of 1,600 kilometers, taking pictures throughout one of Gaspra's seven-hour spins. The asteroid's elongated shape, measuring 18×10 kilometers, proved a bit larger than expected. The surface bears few impact craters, a hint that sometime within the past 500 million years Gaspra was involved in a serious collision,

Pictures of the Moon were obtained by Galileo during its December 1990 flyby of Earth. The color-coded images depict spectral properties of the lunar surface related to composition or weathering.

which shook it violently and "erased" many craters.

Galileo visited asteroid 243 Ida nearly two years later, on Aug. 28, 1993. More than twice the size of Gaspra, Ida measures 56 kilometers long. Project scientists knew that it held promise as a good test of the asteroid-meteorite connection because Ida's surface spectra appeared to be a close match to those of ordinary chondrites. Based on Galileo spectral data, Ida closely resembles a stony object packed with metallic iron (which makes the surface look slightly

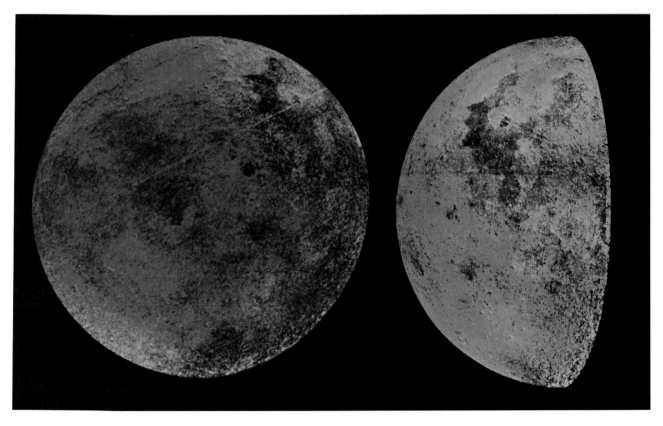

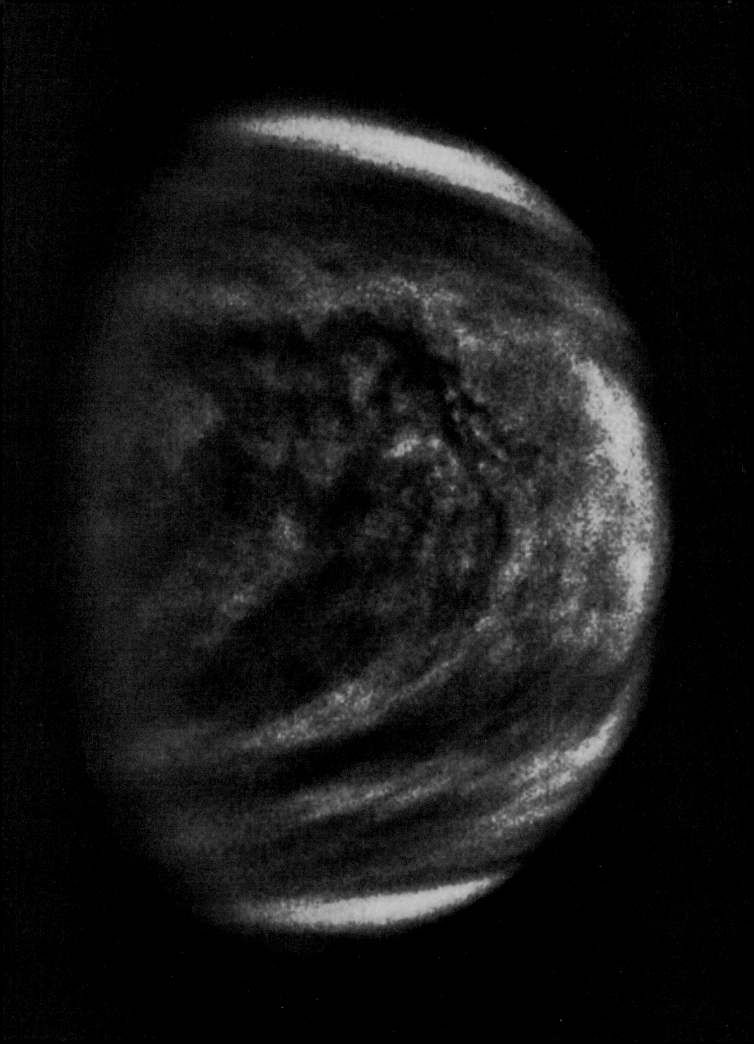

Galileo's February 1990 flyby of Venus offered space scientists another opportunity for planetary imaging. The spacecraft's picture of Venus on the opposite page has been filtered and colorized to highlight subtle cloud features.

brighter at red and near-infrared wavelengths). On the other hand, Ida may indeed be a giant ordinary-chondrite meteorite in disguise, since Galileo found areas of Ida near fresh impact craters that are very close spectral matches to the meteorites. Consequently, many researchers now think that the surface of Ida and, by extension, the surfaces of other S-class asteroids have undergone "space weathering" of some kind that masks their true nature.

Ida provided a surprise for mission scientists in the form of a small moon circling about 100 kilometers away. Measuring about 1.5 kilometers across, the little companion is called Dactyl, named for the beings called Dactyli in Greek mythology who lived on Mount Ida in the company of Zeus. No other asteroid is definitely known to have a satellite, though there have been hints from Earth-based observations. The histories of Ida and Dactyl are probably closely intertwined. Ida is itself a member of a 150-member asteroid "family" thought to represent the breakup of a larger precursor, so perhaps the two were ejected together.

Galileo was still some 17 months from its true destination when it was swept up by an event unprecedented in the history of astronomical observation. In July 1994 fragments of a comet named Shoemaker-Levy 9 struck Jupiter, hitting just out of view on the planet's back side as seen from Earth. Galileo, however, was fortuitously positioned to see the crash site directly. Even though the spacecraft was still about

Ida was the target of Galileo's second asteroid rendezvous, in August 1993. The spacecraft's observations of the 56-kilometer-long rock surprised scientists when they revealed that the body has its own tiny moon, later named Dactyl, orbiting about 100 kilometers away.

240 million kilometers away, its four imaging instruments contributed valuable observations to a worldwide effort mounted to monitor the collision. For example, according to the NIMS instrument the impacts of the largest fragments created fireballs that briefly exceeded 10,000 K (17,500° F)—hotter than the surface of the Sun. (For more information on Galileo's asteroid flybys and Comet Shoemaker-Levy 9's

encounter with Jupiter, see *1996 Yearbook of Science and the Future* Feature Article: AS-TEROIDS: SECRETS LOCKED IN STONE.)

The final major event performed by Galileo before reaching Jupiter occurred on July 13, 1995, when the orbiter and probe parted ways. Without further course correction, both components would have dropped into Jupiter's atmosphere. Thus, on July 27 the orbiter's onboard engine came to life for about five minutes, redirecting the craft onto a course that would carry it to one side of the planet. Except for a brief "wake-up" firing three days earlier, the engine had not been operated since 1984, but it worked as planned.

Both spacecraft were now

poised for arrival, although Galileo's misfortunes were not yet over. Back in April 1991, mission controllers had signaled the orbiter to deploy its 4.8-meter-diameter main communication antenna, which had been stowed like a closed umbrella since launch. (A meter is about 3.28 feet.) The antenna failed to open fully, however, because one or more of its 18 ribs were stuck. Frustrated engineers back on Earth tried a variety of tests and maneuvers to free the snared ribs, but to no avail.

Without its main antenna, Galileo was forced to rely on a smaller, less-directional antenna for communication, and the amount of data that could now be relayed to Earth was limited to a comparative trickle. This contingency mode of transmission was the means by which Galileo had sent back its pictures of Gaspra, Ida, and Comet Shoemaker-Levy 9's demise, and the same strategy would be used for the spacecraft at Jupiter. NASA planners had revised the mission knowing that thousands of images and other planned observations could never be transmitted to Earth. Nevertheless, with careful planning Galileo was still expected to achieve 70% of its scientific objectives.

Another serious problem arose after the probe was re-

JPL/NASA

leased, when the orbiter's tape recorder failed to stop rewinding after a brief picture-taking session. Had the tape actually broken, Galileo would have had no way to store its data before sending them home. Fortunately, the tape was intact, though one section probably became weakened by hours of rubbing against the rewind mechanism. Used carefully, the recorder continued to work well, yet project personnel must have quietly wondered whether the star-crossed orbiter and probe would ever reach Jupiter.

JUPITER AT LAST

Reach Jupiter they did, however, on Dec. 7, 1995. Two critical events took place that day: the probe made its long-awaited plunge into the planet's atmosphere, and the orbiter fired its engine for 49 minutes to slow down enough to become captured by Jupiter's gravity.

Since the probe relied solely on internal batteries for power, it had been completely dormant throughout the long interplanetary cruise. Accelerometers brought it to life as the aerodynamically shaped craft rushed into Jupiter's atmosphere at 47 kilometers per second and endured an abrupt deceleration of 228 times the acceleration of

gravity on Earth. After its parachutes opened and its protective outer shell fell away, the instrumented capsule took readings as it descended a distance of 80 kilometers. The probe's entry site was not far from Jupiter's equator at latitude +6.6°.

Data from the seven instruments aboard were radioed to the orbiter for 58 minutes, until the ambient temperature reached 425 K (152° C, 305° F) and the probe's transmitter succumbed from the heat. At that point the pressure was equal to 24 Earth atmospheres, equivalent to being in Earth's oceans at a depth of 230 meters. Nevertheless, the probe continued to drift downward even after its electronics failed. Its fate was first to melt and then to evaporate away, its atoms ultimately becoming part of the planet. (*See* diagram on page 35.)

Unlike Earth, Jupiter has no solid surface. Having a diameter more than 11 times greater than Earth's and 318 times its mass, the giant planet consists almost entirely of hydrogen and helium with a rock-metal core at an estimated 30,000 K (55,000° F). This composition reflects the materials present in the huge nebula of gas and dust that surrounded the Sun when it and the planets formed more than 4.5 billion years ago. Con-

A sequence of images taken some two seconds apart by Galileo records the luminous impact of a fragment of Comet Shoemaker-Levy 9 on the nightside of Jupiter on July 22, 1994.

sequently, Jupiter's overall abundances of individual elements should closely match those of the Sun, in which hydrogen and helium also predominate. Jupiter's much cooler temperatures, however, allow certain combinations of elements to form compounds that are not found on the Sun. For example, Jupiter's allotment of oxygen probably exists almost entirely as molecules of water (H_2O).

Although hydrogen and helium exist as colorless gases in Jupiter's upper atmosphere, the situation changes deeper down as the pressure and heat build. Theorists believe that the gases gradually transform to a liquid state. At a depth of about 21,000 kilometers, where the pressure is more than three million Earth atmospheres, the hydrogen is thought to lose its molecular character and become a metallic fluid. No longer able to mix freely with hydrogen, the denser helium collects into droplets that settle toward Jupiter's core. This separation releases considerable heat, such that Jupiter actually radiates more energy to space than it receives from the Sun.

What we see as Jupiter's "surface" is actually the top of an opaque, global cloud deck. Before Galileo's arrival, astronomers had presumed the existence of three distinct cloud layers. The uppermost tier, the one seen from Earth, should be crystals of ammonia (NH_3). The layer in the middle should consist of a compound called ammonium hydrosulfide (NH_4SH), with a cloud deck of water at the bottom. All three should exist at pressures from about 0.4 to 5 atmospheres, a range through which the probe descended.

Scientists were elated and, in some cases, very surprised by the results from Galileo's probe. Its instruments found that helium accounts for 14% of the molecules in Jupiter's upper atmosphere, very close to the Sun's value. Apparently not much of the helium has been drawn to deeper levels due to gravitational settling. Unexpectedly, only wisps of the ammonia and ammonium hydrosulfide clouds were seen, and the predicted water cloud was virtually absent. In fact, water was hardly detected at all—its abundance (or, more precisely, that of oxygen) was no more than one-fifth of that found in the Sun. Moreover, the probe detected no lightning in its vicinity, even though such discharges had been expected in an environment of dense water clouds. It did sense pulses of electrostatic energy from lightning thousands of kilometers away, however.

Cosmic chemists do not yet understand why Jupiter's atmosphere was found to be so dry. Perhaps the water somehow ended up in the core as the planet formed. Another explanation may be the unusual atmospheric location through which the probe fell. From Earth this region in the cloud deck looked atypical, a kind of

partial clearing through which extra heat was escaping upward. Astronomers have seen these infrared "hot spots" before in the Jovian atmosphere, although they are rare. As luck would have it, the probe descended directly into one. These spots may be drier than elsewhere in the atmosphere, explaining the dearth of water found by the probe. On the other hand, the probe detected higher proportions of carbon, nitrogen, and sulfur than expected. These elements were

probably delivered by infalling meteorites and comets, although in that case oxygen should have been there, too.

Another dramatic surprise was the strength of the Jovian winds, which was determined by tracking the probe's motion from the orbiter and from sensitive radio antennas on Earth. Instead of dying away with depth, the winds actually picked up speed and remained near 200 meters per second (450 miles per hour) over most of the probe's descent. Because

the winds turned out to be so strong and so consistent over a wide range of altitudes, Galileo scientists now suspect that the motions in Jupiter's dynamic atmosphere are driven by heat escaping from deep in the planet's interior, rather than by the Sun's energy.

Galileo's probe made another interesting discovery three hours before entering the Jovian atmosphere. At a point 50,000 kilometers from Jupiter, the energetic particles instrument (EPI) registered one million hits per second from electrically charged protons, electrons, and beta particles (the nuclei of helium atoms). This newfound radiation belt, about 10 times more intense than the Van Allen belts surrounding Earth, had not been detected before because no previous spacecraft had taken measurements so close to the planet.

A TWO-YEAR SIGHT-SEEING TOUR

When the Galileo orbiter fired its braking rocket in December 1995, it became a captured satellite of Jupiter in a long, looping path that took nearly seven months to complete. This initial orbit had a perijove, the point nearest Jupiter, of only 215,000 kilometers—little more than half the distance be-

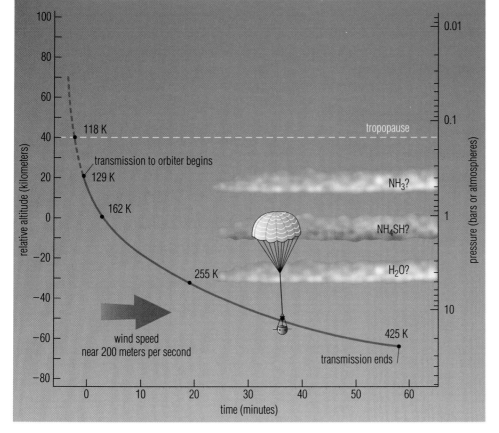

tween the Earth and the Moon. This region lies deep in the planet's magnetosphere, the volume of space dominated by Jupiter's magnetic field, and is densely populated with trapped charged particles. Left in this orbit, the orbiter and its many electronic systems would soon have suffered irreparable harm, so flight controllers used Galileo's engine to alter the orbit. The new perijove was more than three times farther from Jupiter, and the time to circle Jupiter was reduced to a couple of months.

Because of the radiation danger near Jupiter, project scientists did not schedule close passes with Io, the innermost and most colorful of Jupiter's Galilean satellites, during the first two years of the mission. In fact, Galileo passed very close to Io, less than 1,000 kilometers away, on its arrival day, and plans had originally called for a wide variety of scientific studies of the satellite. At that time, however, confidence in the orbiter's tape recorder was shaky, and project managers decided to forego the studies of Io to ensure that data from the descent probe could be recorded with certainty.

During its first two years at Jupiter, through the end of 1997, the orbiter is scheduled

GALILEO'S TOUR HIGHLIGHTS THROUGH 1997			
orbit	satellite	flyby date (universal time)	approximate flyby altitude (kilometers)
1	Ganymede	June 27, 1996	840
2	Ganymede	September 6	255
3	Callisto	November 4	1,105
4	Europa	December 19	695
5	no close flyby	(Jan. 19, 1997)	
6	Europa	February 20	590
7	Ganymede	April 5	3,060
8	Ganymede	May 7	1,585
9	Callisto	June 25	415
10	Callisto	September 17	525
11	Europa	November 6	1,125

Note: Because of a conjunction of Jupiter with the Sun (positioning of the Sun directly between Jupiter and Earth) in late January 1997, mission planners could not schedule a close flyby of a Galilean moon on January 19. The Sun's powerful electromagnetic interference would have severely degraded Galileo's data transmission.

to pass close to one or another Galilean satellite 10 times, generally once each orbit. The encounters are detailed in the Table. Scientific studies have not been limited to those objects on those dates, however; the spacecraft has obtained images and other data for a variety of moons and Jupiter itself whenever the geometry has been favorable.

DYNAMIC IO

Even when seen through terrestrial telescopes, Io has always seemed different than its neighbor worlds. Images from the Voyager spacecraft showed why: the moon is a simmering patchwork of yellow, orange, and black volcanic features. Eruptions are going on all the time (the Voyagers observed 11 of them), driven to heights of 100 kilometers or more by molten sulfur or sulfur dioxide gas. Roughly a third of Io's surface is covered with bright sulfur-based "snow" that has condensed from the belchings of its interior.

Io is so active because of a gravitational tug-of-war going on in its interior. Since it orbits so close to Jupiter, Io is forced to have one hemisphere always facing the planet—just as one side of the Moon always faces Earth. Thanks to small tugs from neighboring Europa and Ganymede, however, the orbit of Io is not a perfect circle. As a consequence, Jupiter's gravity causes a constant, periodic flexing of Io's interior. This tidal energy is dissipated as heat, which keeps the inside of Io very hot.

Galileo passed close enough to Io in December 1995 for the

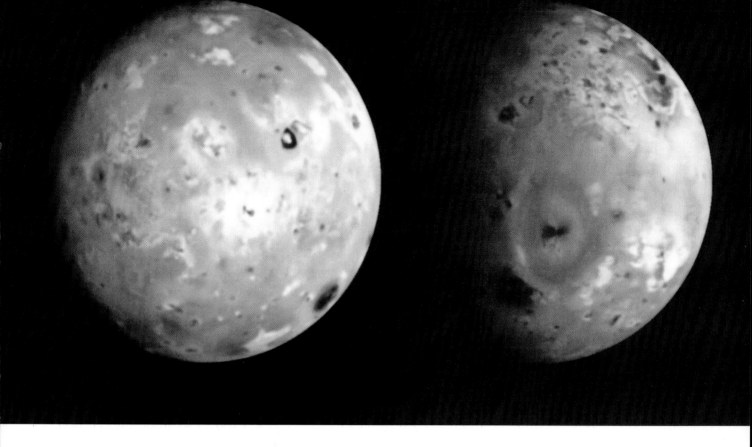

moon's gravity to alter the spacecraft trajectory in a measurable way. Later analysis of the deflection revealed that Io must have a big, dense core consisting either of pure iron or a mixture of iron and iron sulfides. If it is the latter case, the core spans at least half of Io's 3,630-kilometer diameter. Galileo's magnetometers also recorded a disturbance in the Jovian magnetic field in the region of Io. Project scientists are not yet certain of the explanation, but Io's core might be generating a magnetic field of its own.

Even while viewing Io from afar, Galileo has chronicled numerous changes in the volcanic features—not only since the Voyager flybys in 1979 but also from month to month during the orbiter's mission. A few volcanoes have been caught in the act of erupting as well. Around one of the most active sites, named Ra Patera, fresh volcanic deposits cover an area about the size of New Jersey.

Thanks to the incessant bombardment of Io from charged particles, sulfur and oxygen atoms are blasted from its surface and make their way into Jupiter's magnetosphere. A tenuous doughnut-shaped cloud of these atoms envelops the moon's entire orbit, and once they become ionized, they serve as a dominant source of the charged particles populating the magnetosphere.

ENIGMATIC EUROPA

If Io looks like a bubbling pizza, then Europa, the next satellite outward, might be likened to a cracked hard-boiled

Three color-enhanced views of Jupiter's moon Io together reveal about three-quarters of its surface. Since the Voyagers' visits 17 years earlier, large areas of Io have been volcanically resurfaced.

egg. Voyager images showed a bright, ice-covered globe crisscrossed by a complex jumble of dark lines. Those observations prompted widespread speculation that tidal heating of Europa's interior has been maintaining a global ocean of liquid water not far below its surface, and the overlying ice crust has cracked, shifted slightly, and refrozen numerous times.

Galileo's first images of Europa concentrated on the intriguing dark cracks, which sometimes continue for 1,600 kilometers. One type of complex stripe, called a triple band, has a bright streak running down its center, flanked by dark material. Before Galileo's arrival the nature of the bands was not understood. The orbiter's improved views, however, provide some evidence that they are due to geyserlike eruptions, at least in part.

When Galileo passed very near Europa on Dec. 19, 1996, it obtained images hundreds of times sharper than had been possible from the Voyagers' perspective. Some views revealed surface details only 20 meters across. Scientists were surprised to learn that the random pattern of cracks and ridges continued at smaller and smaller scales to the limit of the camera's resolution.

In addition to the network of fractures, the exterior of Europa has been modified in three distinct ways. First, some cracks have actually spread the

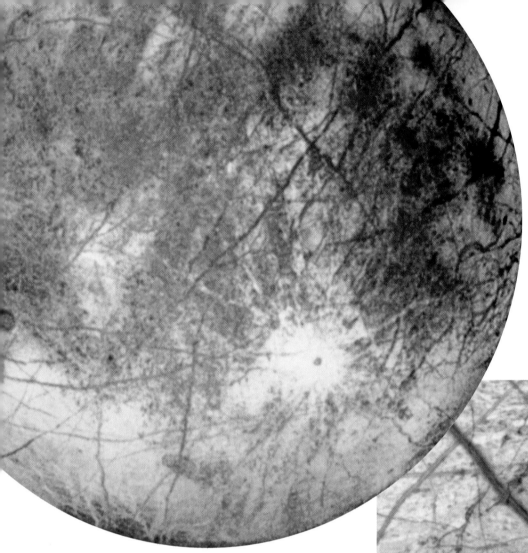

A full-hemisphere Galileo image of Europa (left) reveals an ice-covered globe with a cracked-egg appearance. Scientists speculate that an ocean of water, perhaps global in extent, underlies the ice crust, which has repeatedly fractured, shifted, and refrozen. Some of Galileo's images show an intriguing type of stripe called a triple band (below), with dark margins and a bright center.

crust apart, not unlike the sea-floor spreading that takes place along Earth's mid-ocean ridges. The openings were later filled in from below by slushy water or soft ice. Second, some areas show a chaotic jumble that has locally obliterated the pervasive crack system. Geologists suspect that these areas mark deep-seated sources of heat, places where ammonia and methane (CH_4) have evaporated out of the ice and caused it to collapse. Third, there are clear examples of flows across the surface, indicating that "water volcanoes" were active some time in Europa's past.

Scientists now believe that an ocean of water lies hidden under at least parts of Europa's ice crust. If so, it would be the only world in the solar system known to have such a reservoir. Water is considered essential for the existence of life. Therefore, should an ocean exist, it is conceivable that this Moon-sized world, a mere 3,120 kilometers across, did—and perhaps may still—harbor primitive forms of life. Finding more support for this exciting notion may turn out to be beyond Galileo's capabilities, however, unless the spacecraft were to spot something rare, like an active geyser or eruption of water.

GRAND GANYMEDE

With a diameter of 5,265 kilometers, Ganymede not only ranks as the largest moon in the solar system, but it also is larger than the planets Mercury and Pluto. Like its neighbors Europa and Callisto, Ganymede consists of rock overlain by a thick mantle of water ice.

Ganymede was the first satellite observed at close range by Galileo, and it offered an early surprise. Voyager images had shown that some parts consist of large, dark "seas" that were relatively featureless. Other areas were seen to bear huge systems of bright, parallel grooves that snake for long distances and frequently cross one another. Planetary scientists thought the dark areas to be geologically ancient and the ridge-and-valley systems comparatively fresh. Galileo's views suggest otherwise. Galileo Regio, the most prominent dark area, now appears to have

38

Ancient impact craters seen in a Galileo image of Ganymede's Galileo Regio area (right) testify to the great age of the region, but the unexpected presence of deep furrows suggests multiple episodes of geologic reworking. A Galileo close-up of Ganymede's Uruk Sulcus region (below) reveals a complex mix of more ancient and younger terrain.

been reworked by multiple episodes of shearing and rifting.

One discovery that virtually no one expected was that Ganymede has a dense core and an internally generated magnetic field. Galileo detected the magnetic field's presence with its magnetometers and PWS instrument during two flybys in 1996, and the field appears strong enough to create a good-sized magnetosphere of its own within the Jovian field in which all the Jovian satellites are immersed. Physicists now believe that the core of Ganymede is molten, rich in iron, and churning with enough vigor to create an electromagnetic dynamo. No other moon in the solar system, with the possible exception of Io, is known to have its own magnetic field.

Galileo's ultraviolet spectrometer (UVS) detected a great many hydrogen atoms escaping from Ganymede to space. On the assumption that the hydrogen derives from the breakdown of water molecules, the moon should have large amounts of oxygen either locked up inside the icy crust or hovering over it. (Hydrogen can escape Ganymede's weak gravity because it is a much lighter atom than oxygen.) If hydrogen and oxygen have been going their separate ways since the moon formed, then

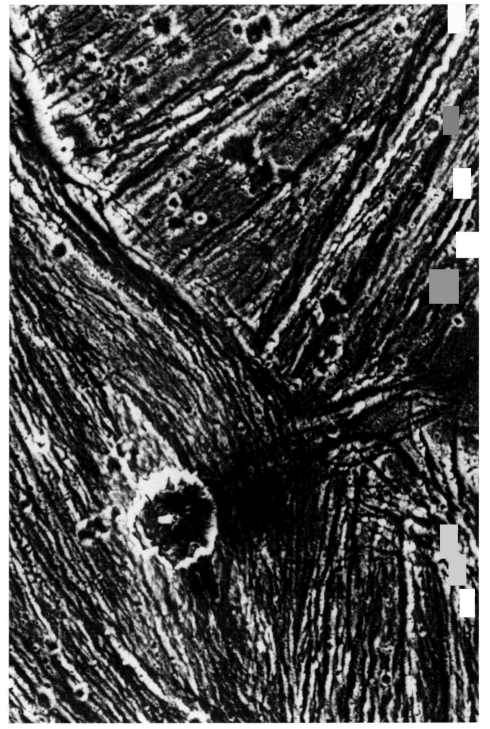

JPL/NASA

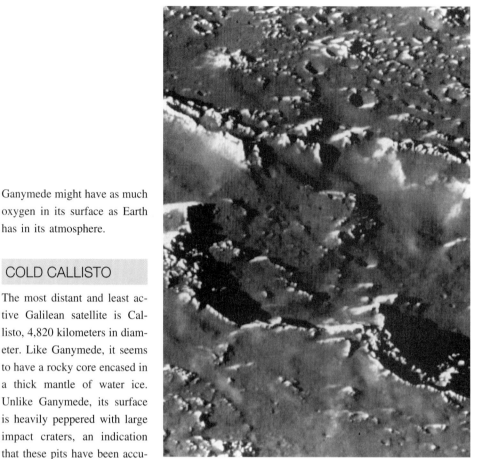

Galileo's observations of Callisto include an image of a chain of craters thought to have been created by a fragmented object. The crater walls are slumped owing to multiple landslides of dark material, which suggests that parts of the moon's surface may be coated with dark dust.

Ganymede might have as much oxygen in its surface as Earth has in its atmosphere.

COLD CALLISTO

The most distant and least active Galilean satellite is Callisto, 4,820 kilometers in diameter. Like Ganymede, it seems to have a rocky core encased in a thick mantle of water ice. Unlike Ganymede, its surface is heavily peppered with large impact craters, an indication that these pits have been accumulating on an otherwise geologically undisturbed surface for billions of years.

Some of the largest impact basins are surrounded by multiple rings, like ripples in a pond that have been frozen in place. Nevertheless, these huge features show few of the classic features of giant impact scars; for example, there are no crater rims or evidence of widespread blankets of ejected debris. It is as if all the elevated features have slumped back to ground level. Such a process is hard to envision given the extreme cold of Callisto's surface, estimated to be 150 K (−123° C, −189° F) or less. At such temperatures ice behaves very much like rock. Given billions of years, however, an ice mountain would tend to flatten out, albeit at a glacial pace.

Another puzzle is that even Galileo's best images show very few small craters on Callisto. This finding runs counter to what is seen on other heavily cratered bodies like the Moon or Mercury—that for every large crater there should be many more smaller ones. Still another provocative bit of information comes from a Galileo image of a crater chain whose walls have been degraded by multiple landslides of dark debris. Some scientists now speculate that parts of the surface may be coated with a layer of dark dust, either from Callisto itself or from the meteorites that have pelted it for billions of years.

VIEWING THE GIANT

One scientific area that has been particularly hard hit by the loss of Galileo's main antenna is the orbiter's study of Jupiter itself. To understand how the planet's atmospheric system of bright "zones" and dark "belts" evolves, project scientists had hoped to combine thousands of images taken through various colored filters into time-lapse movies. Given Galileo's limited communication ability, views of Jupiter now must be chosen carefully. One simple set of measurements radioed back to Earth has shown that a thin haze high in Jupiter's stratosphere is

more opaque in the polar regions than elsewhere. The haze is probably more concentrated over the poles because in those locations magnetospheric particles are funneled along magnetic field lines down into the atmosphere, where they provide an energy source for chemical reactions that create the haze.

Since Galileo's arrival at Jupiter the planet's Great Red Spot has received special attention. Known to telescopic viewers for some 300 years, this huge, baleful storm is at least twice the size of Earth. It rotates counterclockwise, making a complete cycle about every six days, while the wind along its margins races at 100 meters per second (225 miles per hour). Meteorologists are intrigued by the longevity of this spot and of other, smaller ones in the Jovian atmosphere. Perhaps with enough study they will learn whether the energy for their rotation comes from the belt-zone system or from some deep-seated internal source.

Long-term study is what Galileo was designed for, and NASA managers have been thrilled with its many successes. Plans were approved in 1997 to extend the mission beyond its intended two years to concentrate on additional studies of Europa. With nearly $2

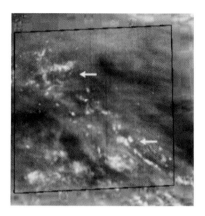

Scientists assembled a series of Galileo images to create a mosaic of Jupiter's Great Red Spot (below) and color-coded it to reveal cloud-top heights. High, thick clouds are white; high, thin clouds are pink. Blue indicates low-altitude clouds. Bright white clouds thought to be similar to thunderheads on Earth appear in two black-and-white images (left), taken 70 minutes apart, that are enlargements of the boxed area below. Arrows show where clouds have formed or dissipated in the intervening time.

billion spent on the program to date, it would seem prudent to let the orbiter study its targets for as long as possible.

Galileo is so large and complex that it may be the last spacecraft of its kind to visit Jupiter. NASA has no firm plans for a follow-up mission, but many concepts are under consideration. One proposed craft, nicknamed the Europa Ice Clipper, would fire a projectile into Europa's surface, causing a plume of debris to be sprayed upward into space. Next, the spacecraft would

swoop within 50 kilometers of Europa's surface to collect some of the icy particles and then return to Earth with the material for analysis. Another idea is to build an "interplanetary submarine" to explore Europa's ocean and search for life there. These and other concepts will take shape once Galileo has finished its exciting mission and planetary scientists have solved some of the many new mysteries Jupiter and its moons have given them.

FOR ADDITIONAL READING

■ *Galileo: Exploration of Jupiter's System,* Clayne M. Yeates *et al.* (NASA, 1985).

■ "The Galileo Mission," Torrence V. Johnson, *Scientific American* (December 1995, pp. 44–51).

■ "Galileo Orbiter" (special section), *Science* (Oct. 18, 1996, pp. 377–403).

■ "Galileo Probes Jupiter's Atmosphere" (special section), *Science* (May 10, 1996, pp. 837–860).

■ *Galileo: The Tour Guide* (Jet Propulsion Laboratory, 1996).

■ "Ida and Company," J. Kelly Beatty, *Sky & Telescope* (January 1995, pp. 20–23).

■ "Into the Giant," J. Kelly Beatty, *Sky & Telescope* (April 1996, pp. 20–22).

INTERNET RESOURCES

■ Project Galileo home page http://www.jpl.nasa.gov/galileo

Photographs, JPL/NASA

*We are running on much less sleep today
than evolution intended humans to have. This sleep debt is making us less efficient,
less mentally acute, and more prone to illnesses and accidents.*

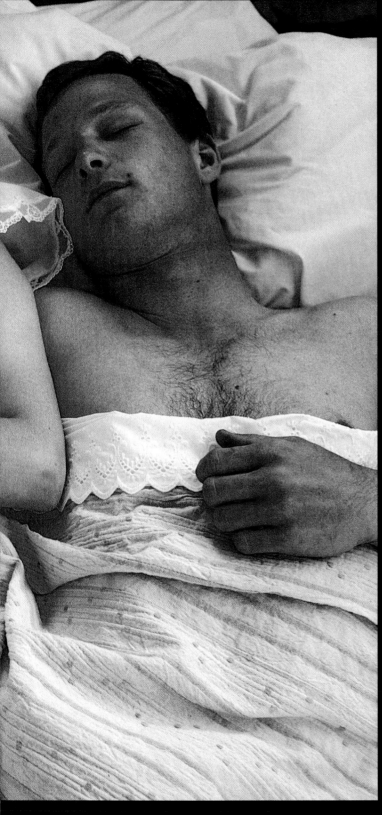

Our Sleepy Society

by
Stanley Coren

Notwithstanding that the average person spends one-third of his or her life asleep, sleep is one of the most misunderstood aspects of human behavior. Many of us today consider the hours spent sleeping simply as lost time. The quint-essential U.S. inventor Thomas Alva Edison summarized his viewpoint when he said, "Anything which tends to slow work down is a waste." He went on to explain, "We are always hearing people talk about 'loss of sleep' as a calamity. They better call it loss of time, vitality and opportunities." Edison had a solution to the problem of "unproductive" sleep time— the electric light bulb, which would banish the darkness and thus make it possible for people to work around the clock. Edison firmly believed that sleep was merely a bad habit and could be done away with quite easily.

Edison's light bulb did have the effect that he wanted, and people are regularly sleeping less now than they did before it was widely available. In North America today, for example, the typical young adult reports sleeping about 7½ hours each night. This can be compared with sleep patterns in 1910, before the modern coiled-tungsten-filament light

Stanley Coren is a Professor of Psychology at the University of British Columbia.

bulb was introduced, when the average person slept nine hours each night. Thus, Edison could claim to have added 1½ to 2 hours per day, or roughly 500–700 hours per year, of waking time to everyone's life. The problem is that this achievement may have turned out to be a bad thing for our psychological and physical health and even for our efficiency in the workplace.

Thomas Alva Edison (left) viewed the time spent asleep as unproductive and hoped that his electric light bulb would help people eliminate sleep. In 1959 disc jockey Peter Tripp (below, with nurse) learned firsthand the penalties of doing without sleep during a 200-hour sleepless marathon. During his ordeal Tripp lost the ability to concentrate and suffered bouts of hallucinations and paranoia.

(Top) Culver Pictures; (bottom) UPI/Corbis/Bettmann

MINDS WITHOUT SLEEP

People more extreme than Edison have actually suggested that sleep is not really needed at all. Some have attempted to put this claim into practice by holding sleepless marathons. One of the best known was held in 1959 by Peter Tripp, a radio disc jockey in New York City. As part of a charity fundraiser, Tripp decided to stay awake continuously for 200 hours (over eight days), during which he would continue doing his three-hour daily radio show. Although he managed to finish his ordeal, it was not without many problems. By the end of the fourth day, he could not successfully complete the simplest tests requiring focused attention. One psychologist watching him was quoted as saying, "Here is a competent New York disc jockey trying vainly to find his way through the alphabet." Bizarre behaviors also appeared; Tripp began to have hallucinations and distorted visual perceptions. At one point he became quite upset when he thought that spots on a table were bugs. He fancied that spiders were crawling around the booth and once complained that they had spun cobwebs on his shoes. Toward the end of the marathon, he became paranoid. During a physical examination on the last day, he charged that one of the doctors was an undertaker who intended to bury him alive. He then fled from the room, half-dressed and in panic, with doctors and psychologists in pursuit, all trying to calm him down.

In 1964 the world record for going without sleep was held by Randy Gardner, a 17-year-old high-school senior. In January of that year he and two friends prepared a science fair project. Gardner would stay awake for 264 hours (11 days) without sleep, with his friends alternating shifts to make sure that he stayed awake. This length of time was chosen so that if the project was successful it could be submitted to *The Guinness Book of Records*. Like Tripp, Gardner had problems. A few days into his vigil, he had difficulty focusing his eyes and had to give up watching television for the rest of the experiment. He had hallucinations and bouts of paranoia and suspiciousness. His speech became slurred and without intonation, and he had to be encouraged to talk to get him to respond at all. His attention span was very short, and his mental abilities were noticeably diminished. In a "serial sevens" test, in which he was supposed to count backward by sevens from 100, Gardner

reached 65 and then stopped. When the examiner prompted him, he replied that he had forgotten what he was doing.

DEAD TIRED

Whereas Tripp's and Gardner's experiences make it clear that going without sleep is not beneficial for a person's psychological well-being, there is evidence that it can also be physically devastating. Research on the problem has been done on laboratory animals because of the danger to human participants. For instance, in the 1980s Allan Rechtschaffen of the University of Chicago systematically deprived rats of sleep, using a device that awakened them whenever their brain waves showed that they

were falling asleep. As time wore on, the animals began to look unwell. Their fur took on a yellowish tinge, and they began to lose weight such that by the end of the experiment they had shed about 20% of their initial body weight. The loss was remarkable in that the ever-awake animals were eating two and a half times their usual food intake. After 13 days of sleep deprivation, the first rat in the group died; after 21 days all were dead.

Why did the lack of sleep cause the animals to die? The answer may have to do with the intimate link between sleep and the immune system. Research has shown that the immune system works best when animals are asleep, and depriving them of sleep reduces their

resistance to infectious disease. This link explains why college students who stay up all night cramming for finals are at increased risk of coming down with a cold. It also explains why people want to sleep more when they become sick. Sleep is the body's way of allowing a rallying call of the resources of the immune system. This relationship was demonstrated by James M. Krueger and L.A. Toth, working at the University of Tennessee at Memphis in 1995. In several studies the investigators infected rabbits with various infectious forms of bacteria. The rabbits that slept the most in response to the introduced infections turned out to be the animals most likely to survive the infections.

Students who stay up all night studying for finals are more likely to catch colds than those who get enough sleep. The immune system works best when the body is asleep; sleep deprivation reduces resistance to infectious disease.

Some marine mammals such as the killer whale (below) were once assumed not to sleep because they never stop swimming. The same was thought for the albatross (left), which can stay in the air for many days without landing. Scientists now have begun to realize that even animals in constant motion have evolved strategies for sleeping.

(Top) Carolina Biological Company/Phototake; (bottom) Amos Nachoum—Words & Pictures

In 1993 Carol Everson of the National Institute of Mental Health, Rockville, Maryland, reported that rats that died of sleep deprivation looked very much like cancer victims whose bodies had been weakened by the progress of the disease. In the final stages of their disease, cancer sufferers are often hit with secondary infections—and die from them—simply because their overtaxed immune systems can no longer fight off invaders. The same appeared to have happened in the sleep-deprived rats, which died from bacterial infections of the blood. The fatal bacteria were often strains that rats en-counter every day but that usually do not cause disease because they cannot overcome the defenses of a healthy immune system. In the sleep-deprived rats the immune system apparently had completely failed, which allowed the animals to fall prey to normally harmless microbes.

SLEEP AND EVOLUTION

Because of the physical and psychological importance of sleep, evolution has gone to some lengths to ensure that animals get enough. For instance, scientists have yet to find a species of mammal, reptile, or bird that does not sleep. Once it was believed that some marine mammals, like killer whales and certain dolphins, did not sleep because they never stopped swimming.

One example is the Indus River dolphin, which lives off Pakistan in the Arabian Sea near the delta of the Indus River. Evolution has made this species blind, presumably because vision is useless in the muddy waters that it inhabits, but, like some bats, it has a well-developed sonar system for navigating and locating prey. From the day of its birth, the Indus River dolphin never stops swimming. If it did, it would risk serious injury from dangerous currents in the region or from the debris that is carried downriver and into the sea. Although it does not lie in one place to sleep, as do most land mammals, it has not eliminated sleep.

When researchers took electrical recordings of the dolphin's brain, they found that the animal actually sleeps about seven hours a day. The trick is that it gets its sleep not in a continuous block but rather by way of many very brief naps. Since the naps range from 4 to 60 seconds long, the animal still appears to

(Opposite page, bottom) Gerry Ellis—Nature Photography

be continuously in motion. A number of animals such as the killer whale, the albatross, and some fish may also use the same strategy to get their sleep while moving.

Other animals have adopted yet more complex physical mechanisms and behaviors to get some sleep. The northern fur seal, for example, swims out to sea on fishing expeditions that may last several days. Getting sleep poses a problem for the seal, for if it stopped swimming to take a nap, it would sink and drown. Again, evolution has gone to extraordinary lengths to provide a solution. When the seal is ready to sleep, it hangs quietly in one place and slowly flaps a single flipper, enough to keep its nose above the water surface. Seals are neurologically similar to humans in some important ways, one being that the seal's brain is divided into left and right hemispheres. In both humans and seals, the right hand or right flipper is controlled by the left hemi-

sphere, while the left hand or left flipper is controlled by the right hemisphere. Thus, when the fur seal is using its right flipper to keep it afloat, the left hemisphere of the brain must be active. Electrical recordings of the seal's brain have shown that when the animal settles down, although the left hemisphere is awake enough to keep the animal afloat, the unused right hemisphere is asleep. After a nap of 20 minutes or so, the seal's brain reverses its condition, putting the rested half to work and giving the other half the chance to sleep.

Scientists know that the evolution of animal design does not tolerate excess baggage. Since vision was not needed in the Indus River dolphin, it was eliminated. The fact that sleep remains a requirement for the dolphin and the seal, even if it has to be taken in tiny fragments or half a brain at a time, suggests that it performs some vital functions for animals, although scientists are still not sure what all of those functions might be.

HOW MUCH DO WE NEED?

Modern society seems to be moving toward a 24-hour lifestyle. Electric lighting ensures that no place need close when the sun sets, while the web of modern electronic communication systems allows instantaneous, round-the-clock contact between virtually any two points on Earth, be they in daylight or darkness. Many people believe that they must be at work, available, or on call at all times if they are to succeed. The modern heroes of our culture are the ambitious, achievement-oriented individuals who display their visible fatigue like a badge of honor and value it in themselves and others

as an indicator of toughness and competitiveness.

The leaders of industry, science, and society act as if leisure time is expendable, as if sleep is merely the absence of consciousness, and as if sleep time is a resource to be tapped without concern for the consequences. In the mid-1970s, although the average workweek in the U.S., according to contract specifications, was 35

The northern fur seal manages to sleep at sea by resting one brain hemisphere at a time. Meanwhile, the active hemisphere directs the slow movement of a flipper that keeps the seal's nose above water.

Most apes and monkeys have a daily sleep and activity cycle similar to those people who still practice the siesta; *i.e.,* a long sleep at night and a mid-afternoon nap. Naps included, the rhesus monkey (bottom left) sleeps a total of 10 hours, while the gorilla (below), which is even more closely related to humans, sleeps 12 hours.

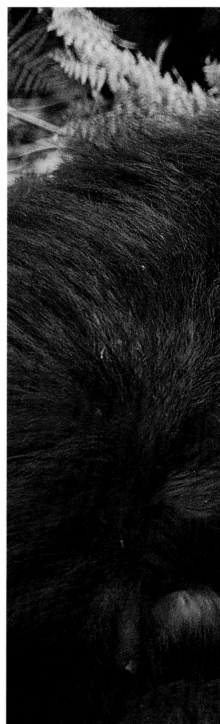

hours, actual time spent working was about 41 hours, roughly one hour extra per day. In the 1990s a person's actual work time rose to an average of 48 hours per week, or an extension of more than two hours per day. Moreover, when economic conditions worsen, although fewer people may be employed full-time, those who are still employed tend to work even longer hours. The added work time must come from somewhere, and it usually has been at the expense of sleep time. Ironically, however, as we cut down on sleep, we appear to be undermining the very gains we strive to make by staying up longer.

How much sleep is enough? David F. Dinges, a biological psychologist at the Institute of Pennsylvania Hospital in Philadelphia has said, "I can't think of a single study that hasn't found people getting less sleep than they ought to." Certainly the 7 to 7½ hours common in North America are not adequate.

One way to gain insight into the amount of sleep we need is to look at the sleep patterns of animals that are closely related to human beings. Most apes and monkeys have a 24-hour cycle of sleep and activity that is similar to that of humans who live in cultures in which the siesta is still practiced. Specifically, those animals have a long sleep at night and a shorter sleep in the mid-afternoon. When day naps, or siestas, are included, monkeys—including the baboon, rhesus monkey, and squirrel monkey—have a total daily sleep time of 10 hours. Among the great apes, our closest relatives, the chimpanzee sleeps a total of 10 hours a day, while the gorilla sleeps 12 hours.

There are other indicators that we need much more sleep than we are getting. When the pressure of work, alarm clocks, social schedules, and advanced technology is removed, people tend to sleep longer. Thus, in many less-industrialized societies total daily sleep time is still about 9–10 hours, which is also the time that people tend to sleep when they are on unstructured holidays. These numbers echo the total sleep time of North Americans before the advent of electric lights.

That our sleep needs are greater than we believe was convincingly demonstrated by Peter Suedfeld of the University of British Columbia and his associates in 1992. Suedfeld accompanied a team of researchers to a site well above the Arctic Circle during the summer, when there is continuous light around the clock. The researchers removed all watches and other timekeeping devices, and only the station's computers knew what time it was when they logged when they went to sleep and when they awakened. Although the researchers had their own scientific projects to tend, they did their research and chose

(Left) Lyn Hughes—Gamma Liaison; (right) Andrew Plumptre—Oxford Scientific Films

TYPICAL AMOUNT OF SLEEP TAKEN PER DAY BY VARIOUS MAMMALS
(rounded to nearest hour)

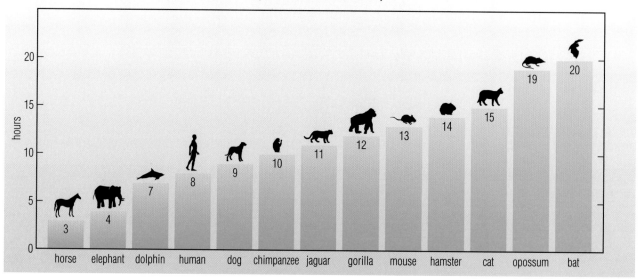

when to sleep or wake according to their "body time."

For the first days of the project, the participants tended to follow their previous sleep schedule of 7 to 7½ hours. In a short time, however, they all adopted a pattern of sleeping that was longer than their usual sleep time. By the end of the experiment, the average sleep time was 10.3 hours for each 24-hour day. All of the participants showed an increase in sleep time, with the shortest sleeper sleeping 8.8 hours a day and the longest almost 12 hours a day. In most cases the longer sleep pattern was the result of a longer single sleep per day, but on more than a third of the days, participants tended to take naps averaging one to two hours as well. This study and others suggest that our biological sleep needs might be closer to the 10 hours per day that has been found typical of monkeys and apes living in the wild and that we may actually be getting as much as three hours a night less sleep than our bodies and minds were designed to have.

SLEEP DEBT AND MICROSLEEPS

Even if society is getting too little sleep, it is reasonable to question whether this makes any measurable difference in our lives. Research has shown that when people get less sleep than they need, they build up a sleep debt, much like continued spending builds up a monetary debt. Each day without enough sleep increases the debt, and when it becomes large enough, conspicuous problems appear—not unlike the problems that people experience after skipping many hours of sleep all at once.

The problems associated with sleep debt are most likely to show themselves at certain times of the day when the press of sleep is greatest. The human body has observable cycles known as circadian rhythms, *circadian* coming from Latin words meaning "around a day." Thus, a circadian rhythm is one that varies through a roughly 24-hour cycle. For sleep and wakefulness there is a shorter, embedded cycle

around 12 hours long. The pressure to go to sleep is greatest in the wee hours of the morning, between 1 and 4 AM. A somewhat less-pronounced but still noticeable increase in sleepiness occurs 12 hours later, between 1 and 4 PM. It is this second low point that makes people sleepy after lunch, not the meal that they may have just eaten, since even if people eat exactly the same meal for breakfast, lunch, and supper, they get sleepy only after the midday meal.

If people are operating with a sleep debt, they will tend to be less efficient, particularly when their circadian cycle is at its lowest ebb. One of the most manifest results of sleep debt is the occurrence of microsleeps. A microsleep is a short period of time, perhaps only a few seconds to a minute in length, in which the brain actually goes to sleep, regardless of what the person may be doing at the time. In fact, the person often is not aware of this momentary blackout. Thus, a tired bookkeeper may sleep briefly while adding up a column of

figures and reawaken after having moved several lines lower in the column. The bookkeeper's error may be minor, but if it is caught during a tax audit, with accrued interest and penalties, it may represent a sizable loss. Similarly, a sleep-deprived medical intern, while listening to a patient explain a set of symptoms, may doze for 10 or 15 seconds—just long enough to miss the information that would have told him or her to avoid prescribing the drug being considered because it could do the patient harm. A sleepy truck driver maintaining a moderate speed of 50 kilometers (30 miles) an hour may blank out for 10 seconds, during which time the truck will travel more than the length of a football field, perhaps hitting several parked cars and an electrical pole before it stops.

In addition to encouraging microsleeps, sleep debt reduces our ability to focus attention for a prolonged time. Short-term memory deteriorates, and the brain remembers fewer items. Although mental activities involving well-practiced

routines and familiar conclusions may be unimpaired, any activity that requires a creative approach, a novel solution, or the integration of many facts will show major deficits. Microsleeps and reduced mental capacity cause sleep-deprived individuals to act both clumsier and less intelligent than they normally are—a clear invitation to accidents.

In 1996, to test whether society is as sleep deprived as it seems to be, I carried out a study of sleep loss and accident rates that made use of predictable occasions when a lot of people all lose a little sleep. More than 25 countries shift to daylight saving time (known in some countries as summer time) on a Sunday each spring and return to standard time in the fall. The spring shift results in a loss of one hour of sleep time as clock time is advanced an hour; conversely, the fall shift permits an additional hour of sleep. Although one hour's loss may seem to be a minor change in sleep patterns, if people are already sleep deprived as much as three hours

per day, that additional hour could have a noticeable effect on alertness and, hence, susceptibility to accidents. The results of the study, which looked at traffic-accident figures for Canada around the spring and fall time shifts, supported this reasoning. On the Monday after the spring shift, traffic accident rates increased about 7%. On the Monday after the fall shift, the rates fell about 7%. If one hour of sleep gained or lost on a single night can cause such a large change in traffic accident rates, we as a society may be so sleep deprived that we are teetering on the verge of disaster.

THE COSTS

The direct cost of accidents that result from sleep deprivation is probably much greater than most people imagine. For example, French researcher Damien Leger prepared a report on the cost of sleep-related accidents in the U.S. for the National Commission on Sleep Disorders Research. He found that in one year—1988—motor

vehicle accidents caused by sleepiness cost that nation $37.9 billion, with sleep-induced public-transportation accidents adding another $720 million. The cost of work-related accidents caused by sleepiness was more than $13.3 billion. Falls and other accidents in public places that were directly due to sleepiness accounted for more than $1.3 billion, while accidents around the home due to sleep deficits contributed over $2.7 billion. The grand total came to $56 billion.

Leger's report showed that the human cost is likewise staggering. In 1988 a total of 24,318 deaths in the U.S. resulted from accidents related to sleepiness. In addition, 2,474,430 disabling injuries resulted from accidents in which decreased mental efficiency and attentiveness due to sleep loss was the major underlying factor. On-the-job injuries due to sleep debt accounted for 29,250,000 lost workdays, about half due to the accident and the rest due to complications and long-term effects of

the accident within the first year. Off-the-job accidents took a toll of 23.4 million workdays lost. Thus, because of too little sleep, the U.S. workforce relinquished a total of 52,650,000 days in one year.

DISASTERS AND PUBLIC SAFETY

Some of the major disasters in recent years have been caused, in part, by sleepy people working in critical jobs. A notable one, the largest oil spill in U.S. history, occurred in 1989 when the tanker *Exxon Valdez* ran aground in Alaska's Prince William Sound. Most of the press coverage about the incident focused on reports that the captain was drunk in his cabin and, therefore, not on duty on the bridge. The real culprit, however, appears to have been a case of sleep debt due to long work shifts. The accident happened in the small hours of the morning of March 24. At 12:04 AM, near the beginning of the lowest point in the circadian cycle, the third mate, who had been working 12-hour shifts

51

and had run up a severe sleep debt, was asleep at the wheel. The ship struck a reef and spilled about 40 million liters (11 million gallons) of oil,

Numbers of traffic accidents in Canada are compared for the Monday before and two Mondays after the shifts to daylight saving time (spring) and standard time (fall) in 1991 and 1992.

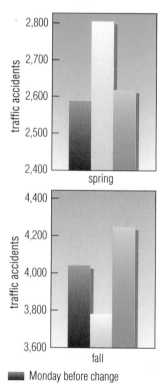

spring

fall

■ Monday before change
■ Monday after change
■ second Monday after change

which then washed up on the coast, destroying what had been called a "beautiful and pristine fjord." The full cost of the accident may never be known, but some estimates place the direct cost of the cleanup alone near $2 billion.

The explosion of the U.S. space shuttle *Challenger* in January 1986 is another sleep-deprivation-related accident, according to the report of the presidential commission appointed to investigate the disaster. In the months prior to the *Challenger* launch, NASA had been pressing to demonstrate that the space shuttle system could handle more than one flight a month. To achieve this goal, the agency extended the shifts of many employees to 10–12 hours and required them to put in stretches of 10–18 days without time off. Evidence abounds that shift workers often get insufficient sleep and sleep of poorer quality. Such schedules are wearing and cause fatigue, inefficiency, and psychological problems to the extent that many NASA workers find it impossible to continue in their jobs despite

the glamor of being associated with the space program.

The final errors that led to the disaster may well have been made in a meeting of 13 key managers the evening before the launch. According to the later statements of a number of scientists and engineers, there was adequate information available at that meeting to predict the failure of the rocket-booster O-ring seals, which was identified as the direct cause of the explosion. When the meeting started at 7 PM, most of the managers had been on duty for at least 12 hours, some longer. Two had been awake nearly 19 hours and were functioning on two or

three hours of sleep taken the previous night. For the rest, the average length of their previous sleep was around six hours. Stanford University sleep researcher William C. Dement echoed the conclusions of the investigating commission when he publicly stated, "My own speculation is that in their severely sleep-deprived condition, these managers weren't able to assess the full impact of the O-ring data they were receiving from the manufacturer." The cumulative sleep debt of many people thus appears to have contributed to the tragic and fatal decision to launch the *Challenger*. In addition to the lives lost, the monetary costs connected with the

The human body's circadian cycle of sleepiness and wakefulness is reflected in a plot of errors made by shift workers over the 24-hour day. Major disasters have occurred near the highest probability for error.

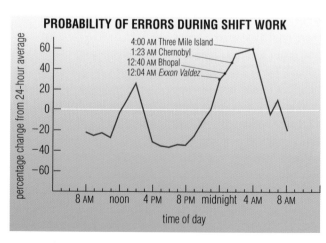

PROBABILITY OF ERRORS DURING SHIFT WORK

percentage change from 24-hour average

60
40
20
0
−20
−40
−60

4:00 AM Three Mile Island
1:23 AM Chernobyl
12:40 AM Bhopal
12:04 AM *Exxon Valdez*

8 AM   noon   4 PM   8 PM   midnight   4 AM   8 AM

time of day

Sleep debt appears implicated in the early-morning grounding of the tanker *Exxon Valdez* (inset) in Alaska's Prince William Sound. The accident resulted in the largest oil spill in U.S. history and an expenditure estimated near $2 billion for cleaning up polluted waters and coastlines (full-page photo).

Al Grillo—Saba; (inset) Michelle Barnes—Gamma Liaison

The explosion of the space shuttle *Challenger* (left) in 1986, which killed seven astronauts, was judged by the official investigating committee to be a sleep-deprivation-related accident. The 1986 Chernobyl disaster in Ukraine occurred at the low ebb time of 1:23 AM. It resulted in the destruction of a nuclear reactor (bottom left) and widespread illness from radioactive contamination (bottom right).

delays, lost contracts, new astronaut training, increased insurance, and loss of the space vehicle itself have been estimated to be in the billions of dollars.

Numerous problems concerning public safety have been traced to sleep deprivation. For example, the near disasters at the nuclear power plant on Three Mile Island, Pennsylvania, in 1979, the Davis-Besse nuclear reactor in Oak Harbor, Ohio, in 1985, and the Rancho Seco reactor near Sacramento, California, in 1985 were all, in part, attributed to sleep-deprived plant operators' having made wrong choices or having reacted too slowly. Underscoring the recognized seriousness of the problem, the U.S. Nuclear Regulatory Commission closed the Peach Bottom nuclear power plant in Pennsylvania in 1987 for six months after an inspection found operations personnel actually asleep on the job.

Fortunately, those cases were only "near misses." In April 1986, however, the world was not as lucky. At the circadian low ebb time of 1:23 AM, a reactor at the Chernobyl power station in Ukraine went out of control and exploded, spreading hot, extremely radioactive debris over more than 5,200 square kilometers (2,000 square miles). Seventeen million people, including 2.5 million children below the age of five, all suffered some degree of radioactive contamination. Dozens of people near the site of the explosion died of radioactive poisoning and burns soon after the accident. During the first five years after the catastrophe, Ukraine experienced a large drop in the live-birth rate and an increase in the death rate, while the average life span dropped from 74.5 years to 63.3 years. Again, investigations suggested that a major factor in the accident was the fact that sleep-deprived engineers and plant operators were working long shifts and being forced to operate in the small hours of the morning, when sleep pressure is greatest. Predictably, their fatigue-fogged minds were unable to process incoming information accurately about conditions in the reactor, and the result was a series of bad decisions that ultimately lead to the tragedy.

A WAKE-UP CALL

The disastrous consequences of sleep deprivation in our society often go unnoticed. Policy makers, health-care workers, and society in general need to recognize that sleep debt leads to poor mental efficiency, numerous errors, and costly wrong decisions and that it rep-

resents a danger both to individuals and to the public. As a society, we attempt to exert controls on many personal behaviors when they constitute personal health hazards or have the potential to affect the health and safety of others. Tobacco smoking, for example, is subject to many restrictions because sidestream smoke may cause disease, including cancer, in others. Society also restricts alcohol use because pub-

Is this the portrait of a wrongdoer? In the future, people who operate on too little sleep may be considered as much a menace to themselves and society as intoxicated motorists.

lic drunkenness is associated with outbreaks of violence, while drunkenness on the highway may kill other drivers. Nevertheless, at one time smoking was considered a sign of sophistication and later of toughness, while the ability to "hold one's liquor" was viewed as a mark of strength and self-control. In a similar way, the person who runs on little sleep is admired by today's society. Perhaps, as society recognizes the harm that sleep debt can do, how long we can go without sleep will no longer be accepted as an index of success. Someday, perhaps, society may label the person who comes to work or gets behind the wheel while sleepy as being reprehensible, dangerous, or even criminally negligent.

FOR ADDITIONAL READING

■ *Encyclopedia of Sleep and Dreaming,* M.A. Carskadon, ed. (Macmillan, 1993).

■ *Losing Sleep: How Your Sleeping Habits Affect Your Life,* Lydia Dotto (Morrow, 1990).

■ *Sleep, Sleepiness and Performance,* T.H. Monk, ed. (Wiley, 1991).

■ *Sleep Thieves,* Stanley Coren (Free Press, 1996).

■ *The Sleepwatchers,* William C. Dement (Stanford Alumni Association, 1992).

To Glimpse Tomorrow

Attempts to predict the future have come far since the likes of Verne and Wells. Most modern prophets count themselves within a unique and diverse intellectual community united in the belief that humankind can influence the future and has a duty to do so constructively.

by Edward Tenner

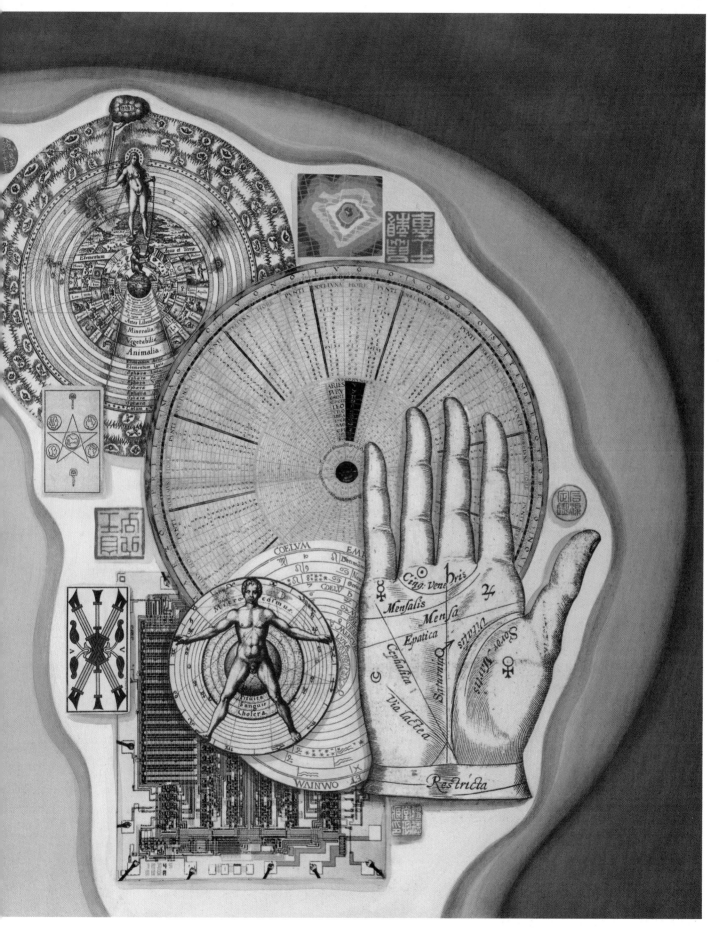

Anita Kunz

utures research is the name most often preferred for their field by the thousands of men and women who are professionally interested in long-term forecasts and in decisions intended to promote private and public well-being. Nearly all people have at least implicit views of the paths along which the world and their country are headed, and many scholars and analysts make forecasts, but those who engage in futures research give a high priority to developing and improving their methods. Although these analysts include, among others, well-known economists, sociologists, political scientists, and historians, degrees and departmental affiliations matter less to most futurists than shared questions and concerns. Wendell Bell, a U.S. sociologist who gave one of the earliest university courses in futures thinking, called the field a "transdisciplinary matrix."

Futurists, a term widely accepted by futures researchers themselves, have encountered extremes of enthusiasm and hostility from academia, the

Edward Tenner is a visiting researcher in the Department of Geosciences, Princeton University.

media, and the lay public. The stereotyped futurist is held to extrapolate naively from fads and uncertain trends into the distant future. He or she is said to substitute mystifying neologisms for rigorous analysis, to express unwarranted alarm or uncritical optimism, to serve the interests of big government and big business, to be inclined to manipulation and coercion. The futurist is accused of self-promotion and even hucksterism. Above all, the futurist is said to have a poor track record. How could it be otherwise, since even in securities analysis, with its narrower and often shorter-term goals, few practitioners consistently outperform the market? Thus, it is

not surprising that many scholars and scientists concerned with the same questions as professed futurists try to avoid the label.

Yet, despite some setbacks, futures research—also known as futurism and futurology—continues to thrive. Two leading U.S. futurists in the private sector, Joseph F. Coates and Jennifer Jarratt, have argued that practitioners share common assumptions: the existence of many alternative futures, our ability to imagine them, our capacity to influence the future, our obligation to do so positively, and the increasing importance to the future of unplanned side effects of our present-day actions. All these

contradict the stereotype. Employers and clients find the ideas and techniques of futurists valuable; otherwise, their positions would have been eliminated long ago and their firms dissolved for lack of business. Ever since the U.S. futurist Alvin Toffler's book *Future Shock* (1970) dominated the best-seller lists in the early 1970s, millions of readers have responded enthusiastically to futurists' methods of analyzing change.

A full view of the field requires four parts: its origins in the speculation of writers from the late 18th to the early 20th century, its emergence as a policy discipline in U.S. military and government circles after

58

World War II, its organizational development and expansion to the corporate and educational worlds beginning in the 1960s, and its present divisions and issues. The full story reveals an intellectual community that on the verge of the 21st century is still improvising an identity and a set of common goals, far from the rigor of the more established natural and social sciences, yet offering much of interest.

PREINDUSTRIAL BACKGROUND

Long-term thinking and ambitious, forward-looking social undertakings did not begin in the Industrial Age. The public works and urbanism of Assyria, Egypt, Rome, China, and the pre-Columbian New World empires all suggest provision for the needs of many generations beyond the ones that began them. Medieval rulers, prelates, and nobles also established towns, drained marshes, improved ports, built canals, and resettled populations on a formidable scale.

The practice of innovation and technological novelty was unmistakable in those early civilizations, yet an element was missing. The U.S. geographer and historian David Lowenthal has underscored the fear of change, even positive change, that prevailed in Christian Europe before the Renaissance. For all the instability of the world, its order was thought to be fixed and Scripture to be the source both of humankind's past and of its future. The powerful might do audacious things, but their advisers had no pretensions of creating a new society. Even enterprises on the scale of the conquest of the Americas were justified as steps in a divine plan. Genuine innovations were presented as revivals of sound practice. Even many radical heretics claimed to restore true order. It is no wonder that the first recorded meaning of *futurist* in English denotes one who believes that Scrip-

tural prophecies are yet to be fulfilled, and even this usage dates only from the early 19th century.

Futurism in the present sense was born before the word, in the ferment of the Enlightenment in the 17th and 18th centuries. Time no longer stretched out uniformly before thinkers. The progress of the arts and sciences, assured by wise government, could lead to new forms of religion as well as of administration. Political economists began to debate measures to promote long-term prosperity. The hot-air balloon,

still largely an aristocratic amusement, extended educated Europeans' temporal as well as spatial horizons with its promise of shrinking distances. The French writer Louis-Sébastien Mercier's *L'An 2440* (1770) presented a utopia of global concord among peoples, founded on improvements of the world's transportation, especially its canals. But Mercier did not try to identify the technologies that would make this world possible.

If Mercier set the pattern for optimistic futurism, a later French writer named Jean-Bap-

A woodcut from 1493 shows Christopher Columbus reaching the New World. Before the Renaissance, even such innovative enterprises as the conquest of the Americas were justified as steps in a preordained divine plan.

The newly invented hot-air balloon extended both the spatial and the temporal horizons of Enlightenment Europeans, encouraging them to think about the future as a realm of realizable possibilities.

tiste Cousin de Grainville, a former seminarian, marked the beginning of secular doomsday futurism with his novel of 1805, *Le Dernier Homme,* presenting a nature so exhausted and degraded by human abuse that the last days of human life were approaching. No doubt impressed like his contemporaries with the pessimism of the English economist Thomas Malthus, whose *Essay on Population* had appeared in 1798, Grainville portrayed a humanity multiplied beyond the ability of Earth to sustain it.

Well into the 20th century, futures thinking was an individual, speculative enterprise, often with a pronounced optimistic or cautionary message. Whereas Mercier and Grainville avoided technical details, new generations of futures writers were more directly inspired by avid reporting of invention and innovation. The telegraph, steam-powered presses, lower-cost paper, and postal services—all not only expanded coverage but also in their very success illustrated how technology could change human relations. In fact, the first speculation about an emerging society based on the rapid increase and diffusion of knowledge dates from the early 1830s. In the words of a small-town Vermont periodical, also the title of a recent scholarly

book, "Reading Is Becoming a Necessity of Life."

Speculation about the progress of technology and civilization was so widespread for most of the 19th century that it is not easy to separate futures thinkers from others with visions of things to come. The English historian of futurism I.F. Clarke has demonstrated that not only socialist prophets like the French social theorists Charles Fourier and Henri de Saint-Simon but also literary figures of the stature of Johann Wolfgang von Goethe, Alfred Tennyson, and Honoré de Balzac rejoiced in canals, railroads, and other wonders to come. In the U.S. Edward Bel-

lamy showed the converse: a more modest literary talent could become financially successful and socially influential with a utopian vision of things to come.

TECHNICAL VERSUS INTUITIVE

Nineteenth-century futurism was not yet a profession, yet writers of the era explored some of the same themes that would be pursued by the professional forecasters who followed World War II. The contrast between the French author Jules Verne (1828–1905) and his less-known but equally ingenious compatriot Albert Ro-

bida (1848–1926) is especially enlightening. Verne, as scholars have shown, borrowed widely from earlier adventure stories. Nevertheless, he also lent his stories a stunning plausibility with myriad specific technical details, even when some flaw underlay the broader concept, such as accelerating living beings into space with a giant cannon in *De la terre à la lune* (1865). For all his striking imagery, Verne preferred to extrapolate from known and tested technology rather than to imagine new principles.

Verne's opposite number, Robida was also a social and political conservative from the provinces. He did not, however, bother with the specifics of engineering or project their evolution. Robida began with an intuitive grasp of the social. The international expositions that flourished in Paris throughout the late 19th century were showcases for world fashion as well as for technology, and as editor of a satirical journal, Robida was in touch with the popular opinion that swirled around such events. Verne's heroes use technology to remove themselves from society, to soar above it or dive below it; Robida's unheroic protagonists live on the surface, surrounded by dazzling spectacle. In his vision of the

In *De la terre à la lune*, Jules Verne (above) described a trip to the Moon in a spaceship (left) that had been shot from a giant cannon. Although its main concept was flawed, the story was given plausibility by the inclusion of numerous specific technical details.

Jean-Loup Charmet; painting by Abel Faivre

Albert Robida (left) forecasted in an intuitive mode, favoring conceptual leaps over technical extrapolation.

1950s, *Le Vingtième Siècle* (1883), videophones link the continents, and a family watches on large-format, wall-mounted flat-screen television screens while correspondents on camelback report guerrilla wars from North Africa. In 1895, collaborating with the writer Octave Uzanne, Robida depicted a "phono-opera-scope," a tiny, belt-mounted recorded-music player connected to earphones that could be worn by a mountain hiker to develop mind and body at the same time.

Robida's insights derived paradoxically from his conservatism. He was a patriarchal provincial petit bourgeois at heart. Where Verne saw the extreme possibilities of existing transportation and communications, Robida anticipated (and dreaded) the demand for unfeasible ones. This contrast foreshadowed one of the main divisions among futures researchers to the present—one based on the importance of present knowledge for prediction. There is, and was, no single, correct approach; most analysts are both technical and intuitive. Robida's fears were more accurate than Verne's hopes, but Verne was probably the more successful futurist. His works inspired countless young future engineers and scientists, while Robida's delight-

ful satires were powerless against change.

Interestingly, an early Verne novel titled *Paris au XXᵉ siècle,* which was completed in 1863 but never known to his contemporaries, reveals a surprisingly intuitive bent to his early forecasting and suggests a reason for Verne's turn to technical prediction. The work's picture of a materialist, soulless, apolitical, pollution-choked city dominated by railroads, automobiles, and ubiquitous centralized media was masterly in its sense of long-term trends if not always in its technological details. Nevertheless, the editor and publisher Jules Hetzel, who eventually became Verne's great patron, rejected it as unmarketable. While the young Verne's plot and characterization were indeed crude, he could always have returned to the manuscript as a mature and recognized author and revised it for publication, but he never did. His vision of the future apparently proved too radically tragic to himself as well as to Hetzel. The manuscript remained in a locked safe until 1994, when it was opened by a descendant, and was published that year.

MILITARY FUTURES

The limits of cautionary futures studies were especially apparent in the decades before World War I, the classic age of military forecasting, when Europe was witnessing the rise of Prussia and the emergence of Imperial Germany as a great power. George Tomkyns Chesney, an English engineers officer, seized on concern over the technology that could permit rapid mobilization of German forces. His best-selling novel *The Battle of Dorking,* published anonymously in 1871, portrayed an England ruined by unpreparedness against a German surprise attack. Chesney was both a riv-

eting storyteller and a gifted tactician; visitors to the fictional battle area were struck by his knowledge of the landscape. His vision was chilling enough to have been translated by the Germans as domestic propaganda as late as 1940 under the title *What England Is Expecting!* Chesney's novel began a prolonged battle of its own, not only in the form of a series of counternarratives defending Britain's military capabilities but also with four decades of martial forecasting by general staffs and civilian writers alike. The technological dynamism and aggressive sales tactics of the late-19th-cen-

In Robida's vision of the 1950s, a reporter on camelback (opposite page, bottom) monitors the sights and sounds of a war in North Africa while home viewers hundreds of kilometers away watch the action on a wall-mounted television screen (below). In this one conceptualization, Robida in the 1880s anticipated the portable electronic camera, the flat-sceen, home-theater TV, and live video news coverage.

tury armaments industries—navies in particular were among the most capital-intensive enterprises in the world—drove speculations about the outcome of world rivalries. As an acute critic of this genre, the English antiwar writer Norman Angell, noted in *The Great Illusion* (1910), military fantasy had become a mass sport in a sedentary, urban society.

Nearly all the speculation on future wars failed to predict the central fact of the Great War: protracted sieges of entrenched positions with heavy artillery and machine guns. These technologies were well known, yet hidebound general staffs and jingoist writers alike anticipated short and decisive campaigns. As I.F. Clarke has observed, the only perceptive analyses were those of a few lay writers, notably Angell, the Polish author Ivan Bloch (whose accurate forecast of trench warfare was supported by extensive technical research), the English author Arthur Conan Doyle (whose short story "Danger" correctly foretold England's vulnerability to submarine warfare), and indeed Robida (whose 1883 article and subsequent book *La Guerre au vingtième siècle,* with its aerial bombardments, fortified trains, and chemical corps, was reprinted in 1916 under the title *Un Caricaturiste prophète*).

H.G. WELLS

The most prescient military futurist of all in the long run

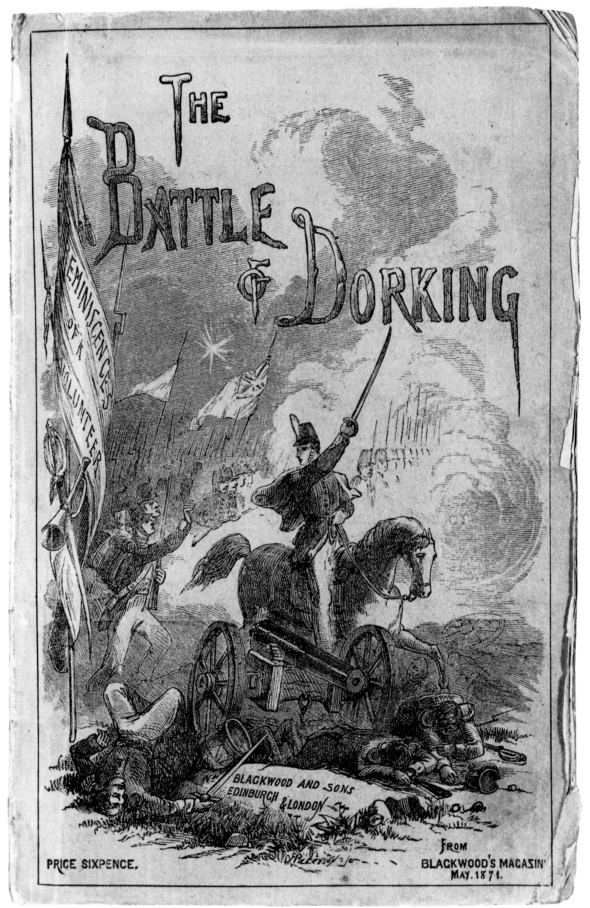

George Tomkyns Chesney's novel *The Battle of Dorking* (1871 cover, opposite page), warned of the invasion of England by a powerful German state. (Above) The extensive and protracted trench warfare characteristic of World War I failed to be anticipated in nearly all speculations on future war during the late 19th and early 20th centuries.

turned out to be the English journalist and novelist H.G. Wells, whose novel *The World Set Free* (1914) foresaw the awesome possibilities of still-uninvented nuclear weaponry allied with air power. Even earlier, however, Wells had published a series of essays around 1900 and collected them in a book called *Anticipations*. Beyond the sprightly extrapolation of Robida and the technical realism of Verne, Wells merged his retailing experience, scientific training, historical knowledge, and imagination to create a new genre: discourse on the likely effect of technological change on a global scale, ranging from patterns of settlement and commerce to

crime, punishment, and sexual morality. In a 1902 lecture to the Royal Institution of Great Britain, he even foresaw the possibility of "a systematic exploration of the future."

Wells wrote in two modes that, like the intuitive and technical strands of futures research, are present in the field even today. One explored acutely the complexity of change—for example, the way in which the defects of both the railroad and the conventional roadway might lead to wholly different configurations: wider-gauge railroads on one hand and asphalt-paved roads (with a corresponding growth of dispersed suburban living) on the other. This mode presupposed the existence of conventional representative government and market forces. The other, utopian, mode took technological efficiency as norm and promoted a society governed by a cadre of specialists and managers. Wells wrote of "the power of the scientifically educated, disciplined specialist ... the power of sanity, the power of

the thing that is provably right." The appeal of rule by experts probably reached its high-water mark with Wells's own novel *The Shape of Things to Come* (1933) and screenplay for the Alexander Korda film *Things to Come* (1935).

TOWARD MODERN FUTURISM

Until World War II, futures thinking existed in the West as literary expression and political advocacy but not as a profes-

sional pursuit. Although in the Stalinist Soviet Union and Nazi Germany future-oriented central planning was practiced, it served political objectives. In the U.S.S.R. many engineers were trained, but far from becoming the farsighted philosopher-kings of Wells's imagination, they served the state in increasingly narrow specialties.

The war changed everything. During the Battle of Britain in 1940–41, when the German air force mounted a lengthy series of intense raids against British ports and cities, groups of scientists were able to help British military commanders use a new secret weapon, radar, to deploy Royal Air Force aircraft in response to the projected courses of German bombers. Multidisciplinary teamwork, the modeling of complex pro-

In the early years of the 20th century, H.G. Wells predicted the horrific possibilities of air power coupled with still-uninvented atomic weapons. He also foresaw "a systematic exploration of the future."

The film version of Wells's novel *The Shape of Things to Come* depicts wise, almost godlike scientist-managers in charge of an efficient, happy, technologically transformed world.

cesses as systems, and the formulation of alternative strategies became essential military tools. After the war U.S. authorities sought ways to deploy those skills, which had become known as operations research, to deal with the new arms race. During the Cold War, Project RAND (later the RAND Corporation, Santa Monica, California), the Stanford Research Institute (today SRI International, Menlo Park, California), and other organizations, which came to be called think tanks, developed a new approach to the future, mixing aspects of military strategy, academic analysis, and business thinking. Moving out from their military orientation, they gradually undertook projects in health care, urban and regional planning, social policy, and environmental protection. Thanks to growing defense budgets, futurism at last had an institutional and financial base.

Many of the pioneers of modern American futures research had links to RAND. One staff member, the physicist Herman Kahn, attracted international attention with his chilling scenarios of possible thermonuclear confrontation. Kahn's account of the logic of nuclear strategy, although widely criticized at the time, promoted a great deal of informed debate on Cold War risks—a far cry from the inflammatory effect of much pre-1914 military speculation. The RAND consultant Theodore J. Gordon, an aeronautical engineer, with Olaf Helmer, a staff mathematician, founded the Institute for the Future for civilian-sector forecasting. Gordon went on to establish the Futures Group, an international consulting firm that also undertakes diverse studies of future trends. Today only a few members of the RAND staff identify themselves primarily as futures scholars.

Organized futurism grew rapidly in the 1960s and '70s. The youth movement, the Vietnam War, the energy crisis, industrial automation, and double-digit inflation all reinforced the need to consider more radical contingencies and reexamine assumptions. The environmental movement also promoted concern about population growth, resources, and the quality of life. The academic establishment began to embrace futures thinking; the American Academy of Arts and Sciences appointed a Commission on the Year 2000, headed by the Harvard University sociologist Daniel Bell, to explore alternative futures. Indeed, Bell's concept of a postindustrial society, in which information and services supplant manufacturing as sources of economic growth, became a central doctrine of business as well as academia, despite numerous challenges.

By the 1970s the institutional side of futures research had taken what remains its present shape. Futurism was a multidisciplinary domain that brought together university teachers, government officials, corporate scientists and engineers, and entrepreneurs. Unlike some other interest groups of its kind, notably the Society for the History of Technology in the United States, it never became a full-fledged academic specialty with its own Ph.D. programs. In the United States its leading organizer was not a social scientist but a journalist, Edward Cornish, who founded the World Future Society (WFS) in 1966 and was still its president 30 years later. The WFS grew from fewer than 1,000 members at the beginning to almost 60,000 in the late 1970s. Recovering from a sharp drop in membership in the early 1980s, it stood at about 30,000 in the mid-1990s, of whom about 1,200 were listed in a directory of professional futures researchers.

Internationally futures research also expanded in the 1960s and '70s. Many Western and Eastern European, Asian, and Australian futurists deplored the military and corporate basis, as they saw it, of U.S. futures research. After an initial 1967 conference in Oslo, they established the World Futures Studies Federation (WFSF) in 1973. There are dozens of other national movements and associations, notably Association Internationale Futuribles in the French-speaking world. As is discussed below, the origins of the two main societies are reflected even today in differences within the futures field.

TODAY'S DIVISIONS

The Australian scholar Richard A. Slaughter has divided the futures field into three elements: futures research commissioned by corporations and governments, generally "ana-

lytical and quantitative" and usually proprietary; futures studies, the more academic and public face of futurism, which combines consulting with teaching and popularization; and futures movements, including environmental, women's, and peace organizations that promote social innovation. Another common distinction separates normative forecasting—the development of often very complex stages of work needed to reach a goal—from the more-often-encountered exploratory forecasting. Estimating the effects of global warming on food production, population movements, and natural hazards would be exploratory; developing a 10-year international plan with specific measures for reducing the rate of increase of global warming to a certain goal would be normative.

Since futurism deals not only with the possible and the probable but with the preferable, the divisions that Slaughter uses also reflect different goals and values arising from the same widely held assumptions noted by Coates and Jarratt. Researchers working for Western corporations and governments often are helping them achieve economic, military, and political objectives that other futurists believe should be resisted. The corporate and

government futurists, in turn, may believe that the programs supported by more socially critical futures movements may harm their own goals.

Sometimes it appears that the futures field has two orientations. The "east-westers," who predominate in the WFS, concentrate on relations between the leading economic powers of Europe, North

67

America, and Asia. The "north-southers," most active in the WFSF, focus on the disparity of living standards between industrial countries and the less-developed world. Of course, this difference should not be exaggerated; most futurists of either orientation would probably agree that population growth, immigration trends, and climate change will continue to promote greater global interdependence. A number of prominent U.S. futurists participate in both the WFS and the WFSF. Furthermore, one of the most comprehensive surveys of futurist methods was prepared for the United Nations Development Programme's African Futures Project by futurists with a corporate clientele.

"GENIUS" FORECASTING

Contrary to their popular image, most futures researchers avoid a strong emphasis on their private intuition. Consequently, professional futurists in both north-south and east-west camps are cautious about the mode of analysis most familiar to the public: intuitive or "genius" forecasting, a personal view of the way present-day trends might interact, which leads to a concrete image of a future and its emergence. While a tribute to outstanding intellects like Kahn's, the phrase *genius forecasting* is also a warning that a brilliant manner is no substitute for formal methods.

The differences between intuitive and technical forecasting go back to the differences between Robida and Verne—one, the imaginative or conceptual leap; the other, the exploration of possible consequences of what is already known. How well a forecaster employs either approach does not necessarily follow from the individual's academic background or work experience. The English science-fiction writer Arthur C. Clarke, who made many acutely accurate early predictions of the potential of rocketry and satellite technology, has pointed out the many distinguished scientists who found plausible technical reasons to predict that rocketry beyond Earth's atmosphere would never come to pass. Clarke's observation that "anything that is theoretically possible will be achieved in practice, no matter what the technical difficulties, if it is desired greatly enough" could apply equally well to Robida's "phono-operascope" that became the Walkman.

Despite its poor reputation among professionals, intuitive forecasting has nonetheless helped shape the presentation of results obtained by other methods. It was Kahn who first used the theatrical term *scenario* to denote a great range of plausible, but often individually unlikely, outcomes of a collection of causal processes. By taking even remote possibilities seriously, planners can test policies more rigorously and prepare for more contingencies. Genius futurists have also influenced the style of others. Kahn popularized cornucopian futurism, the prediction of abundance through increased production. While some scholars dispute that the English author George Orwell intended *Nineteen Eighty-four* (1949) as a futurist novel, it is nonetheless the prime example of doomsday futurism. As Wendell Bell has observed, neither Kahn's nor Orwell's portrait of the future implies its inevitability; one is intended as self-fulfilling, the other as self-negating prophecy.

FORMAL TECHNIQUES

In addition to genius forecasting, one recent survey listed 15 methods of futures research; about a half dozen will show the range of possibilities. Many of the methods fall into two groups: integration of multiple opinions and analysis of quantitative data. These formal methods of futurism focus on collective phenomena, attempting to take advantage of the superiority of multiple experts' opinions or the persuasive power of quantitative relationships among data over time.

One way to list and weight contingencies, especially when data are limited, is the Delphi

Science-fiction author Arthur C. Clarke has observed that anything theoretically possible and desired greatly enough will eventually be achieved, the pessimistic forecasts of technical experts nothwithstanding.

method, which like the scenario was a RAND innovation. If assembled in a conference room and questioned, expert consultants may give personal interactions too much influence. Thus, in Delphi research a small number of experts answer questionnaires about the outcomes of events or decisions, and the investigators compare answers, asking those outside a consensus to justify their extreme opinions. In a number of rounds, the experts have a chance to revise their own views in response to the (always anonymous) judgments of their peers. The technique leads the experts either to relative consensus or to a clear divergence of opinion. Electronic networks now allow Delphi studies to be conducted more rapidly than before.

The cross-impact matrix method is often used in connection with the Delphi model. If experts agree on a set of consequences of a certain event or policy, they can also be asked to elaborate on how each consequence would affect every other one. In the case of global warming, for instance, such consequences would include higher sea levels, changed incidence of severe storms, different plant and animal distributions, new patterns of agriculture, and human migrations.

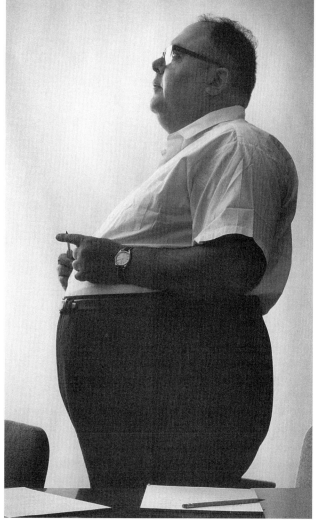

The intuitive, or "genius," forecasting mode of Herman Kahn (left) suffers from a poor reputation among professional futurists but has nevertheless influenced both their style and the formal methods that they employ.

John Loengard—LIFE Magazine © TIME Inc.

Futurists frequently investigate the consequences of an established trend. Time series analysis can be as simple as finding a trend line and fitting a projection to this curve. A well-known example of such a projection is Moore's Law, which says that the speed of the fastest microprocessors will double every 18 months. Since curves of growth may accelerate, moderate, flatten, and even decline, this form of extrapolation has limits. A more sophisticated variant is trend impact analysis, which begins with a "surprise-free" projection—or projections, because there is usually more than one way to extrapolate from present trends. Analysts then look at a variety of possible events that could affect those projections. (Trends in U.S. petroleum production, for example, might depend on the development of an economically competitive hydrogen-powered car, on international oil crises, or on other external factors.) They calculate when each such event might occur and how likely it is to occur at each of a number of dates. The resulting computer-generated curves are no better than the accuracy of the underlying estimates, but they display those estimates in concrete form for discussion.

Other methods are based not on statistical association but on construction of a system of mathematical equations that mirrors real-world phenomena. In applying these methods futurists are inspired by the success of meteorologists who have developed supercomputer-supported numerical models of long-term weather patterns. The most famous work of technical futurism in history, the Club of Rome's *The Limits to Growth* (1972), was based on the world-simulation computer model of the U.S. electrical engineer and management expert Jay W. Forrester. Equations linking population, food production, industrial output, urbanization, and pollution included feedback effects that pointed to acceleration of trends, leading to the widely criticized and ultimately inaccurate forecast of exponential population growth followed by exhaustion of non-renewable resources and economic collapse.

Gaming is a kind of simulation that adds the interaction of real people to a model. Like many other futurist methods, it began with military successes; U.S. Adm. Chester Nimitz once remarked that the Pentagon's game-room exercises had anticipated every development in World War II's Pacific theater except the kamikaze raids. In civilian life, too, gaming can not only prepare for

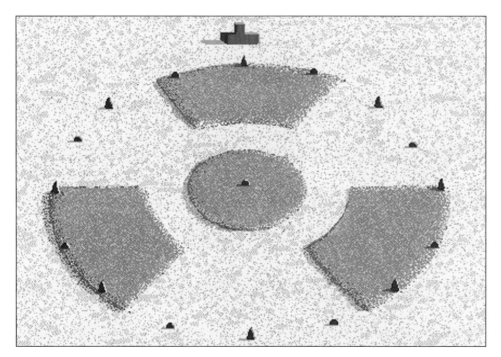

A design for marking a long-term nuclear-waste repository uses dirt, rock monoliths, and symbols to create a warning that would remain meaningful for thousands of years. It is one of several marker concepts developed using futurist techniques by a multidisciplinary panel of experts convened by Sandia National Laboratories in the U.S.

contingencies but also promote training and teamwork. For instance, an artificial "breakdown" of a company's computer network can both prepare the organization for meeting a real emergency and help it plan a more robust architecture.

Some futurists try to detect long-term trends by watching quantitative and qualitative indicators. Economic forecasters were the first to use this method, but it is also employed in environmental and social welfare studies. Content analysis of texts, for example, can detect early signs of possible shifts of opinion on particular issues. The U.S. futurist John Naisbitt's *Trend Letter* newsletters and *Megatrends* books have been the most commercially successful applications, despite severe criticism in futurist journal reviews.

APPRAISAL AND OUTLOOK

The field of futurism has come a long way since the visions of Verne and Robida and since Wells's *Anticipations* and his appeal for a new science. In particular, the atrocities of communism and national socialism in the name of social efficiency discredited Wells's call for an all-knowing cadre of trained rulers. Today's futurists are nearly all democrats; very few are would-be technocrats. Their disagreements hinge on the relative merits of markets on one hand and national and international legislation on the other. Self-promotional forecasting and uncritical embracing of new technology come almost entirely from outside the field, even though the popular press labels most prediction as "futurism." In fact, many futurists are keenly aware of ethical questions and of unintended consequences.

Futures researchers also share the willingness to present explicit scenarios, if not predictions. How valuable have these been? Most professionals in futures research do relatively technical work that is not always public or easy to evaluate. At least sometimes it has paid off for its sponsors. The Shell Oil Co., for example, was well prepared both for the energy crisis of the 1970s and for the later decline of petroleum prices. More recently futurists have participated in major revisions of the state court system of Hawaii. Others have joined field research sponsored by the U.S. Department of Energy to discover and correct potential risks in the design of long-term nuclear-waste repositories. Still others help manufacturers plan their use of new materials, techniques, and distribution centers in response to changing consumer behavior.

Of course, the history of mistaken forecasting also is quite long. The most famous has been the pessimistic results of the Club of Rome's world-simulation model, but qualitative forecasting can be just as unreliable. The U.S. historian W. Warren Wagar's *A Short History of the Future* (first edition 1989), a fictional scenario, was obsolete a few years after publication; it presupposed the Soviet Union's remaining intact as a great power well into the 21st century. On the technological side, although Wells foresaw atomic weapons, he did not, and no doubt could not, imagine the peril of radioactive fallout that checked their use after Hiroshima and Nagasaki. Some momentous innovations, notably the ubiquity of microelectronics and personal computing, seem not to have appeared even in scenarios.

The question is not whether futures research has been accurate, or even whether it has been more accurate than lay judgments. It is whether in the long run it has helped or hurt decision making. As was discussed above, some pessimistic forecasts, including *The Limits to Growth,* are supposed to galvanize people into falsifying them. Wagar's scenario was wrong, but so were the implicit and explicit scenarios of nearly all nonfuturist international relations specialists. As flawed as their record is, futurists have long considered remote contingencies ("wildcards") and side effects more seriously than have most other social scientists.

Futures research has a number of strengths, which have helped it rebound from its slump of the 1980s. While big consulting and accounting firms offer some strategic planning services that may use futurist techniques, it is the small firms, small units within large corporations, and solo practitioners that form the core of the field. Futures research is one of the few multidisciplinary endeavors to achieve and retain the patronage of government and business. Among social science fields it is one of the most international. It is also one of the few in which engineers, journalists, and novelists can exchange ideas with sociologists, economists, and philosophers. Futurists differ from many other social scientists in their confidence—once far more common in the general population—that human action can produce a better future.

The liabilities of the field are related to its assets. Despite hundreds of courses and several respected master's programs, it offers no Ph.D. degree in the United States. While leading figures like Wendell Bell and Sohail Inayatullah have worked hard to address the serious philosophical questions inevitable in the study of what does not yet exist, the base of futurism remains pragmatic: consulting and popular writing. Developing a theoretical base that will help build respect in allied disciplines and improve practice must be a high priority.

Finally, futures researchers have not always used the historical record creatively. For instance, although they are currently grappling with the unique problems that current welfare-state and health care systems will create in the next century, they have not fully tapped historical demography as a base of knowledge and insights. Historians of the economy, of technology, and of religion all might be able to help focus the attention of futurists on alternative paths that current trends could take. Whatever their other views, futures scholars are often predisposed to predicting radical change; historians' opposite bias, to search for precedents and cycles, may be a useful corrective. Historians also could help futurists analyze their successes and failures and perhaps increase their range of scenarios, if not their accuracy.

Ultimately futurism will probably flourish or decline not on its ability to predict the future but on its power to stimulate debate on questions concerning humanity. At its best it offers not a crystal ball but a kaleidoscope.

See also Feature Article: THE PERILS OF TECHNOLOGICAL FORECASTING.

A poor Philadelphia woman awaits welfare efforts to find her better housing. In projecting current welfare-state and health-care problems into the 21st century, futurists may not be making full use of historical resources.

Harvey Finkle—Impact Visuals

FOR ADDITIONAL READING

- *Encyclopedia of the Future,* 2 vol., George Thomas Kurian and Graham T.T. Molitor, eds. (Macmillan Library Reference, 1996).

- "Exploring the Future: A 200-Year Record of Expanding Competence," Joseph F. Coates and Jennifer Jarratt, *The Annals of the American Academy of Political and Social Science* (July 1992, pp. 12–24).

- "The Forfeit of the Future," David Lowenthal, *Futures* (vol. 27, no. 4, 1995, pp. 385–395).

- *Foundations of Futures Studies: Human Science for a New Era,* Wendell Bell (Transaction Publishers, 1996–   ).

- *Future Imperfect: The Mixed Blessings of Technology in America,* Howard P. Segal (University of Massachusetts Press, 1994).

- "The Methods of Futures Research," Theodore J. Gordon, *The Annals of the American Academy of Political and Social Science* (July 1992, pp. 25–35).

- *The Pattern of Expectation, 1644–2001,* I.F. Clarke (Basic Books, 1979).

- "Tomorrow and Tomorrow and Tomorrow," W. Warren Wagar, *Technology Review* (April 1993, pp. 50–59).

- *Voices Prophesying War,* 2nd ed., I.F. Clarke (Oxford University Press, 1992).

INTERNET RESOURCES

- Institute for the Future Home Page
http://www.iftf.org/index.html

- International Institute of Forecasters Home Page
http://weatherhead.cwru.edu:80/forecasting/iif.html

- World Future Society Home Page
http://www.wfs.org/wfs

- World Futures Studies Federation Home Page
http://www.fbs.qut.edu.au:80/wfsf/nfwfsf.htm

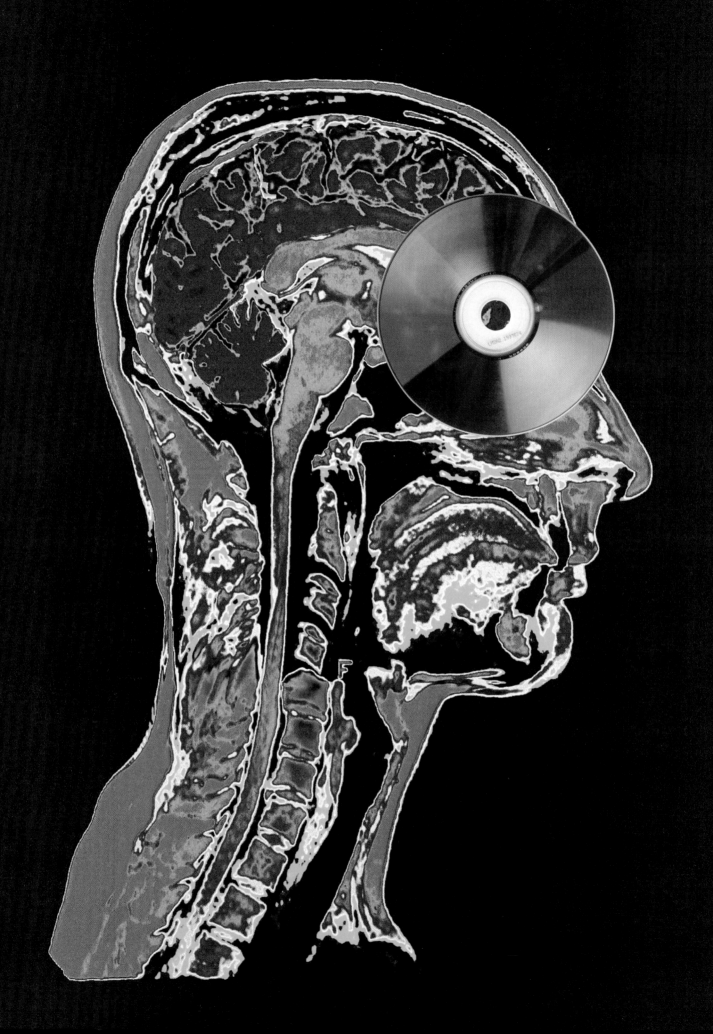

The Perils of Technological Forecasting

by Nathan Rosenberg

A review of some of our greatest technological achievements, from the steam engine to the laser, reveals that we are seldom successful at predicting the full impact of our inventions.

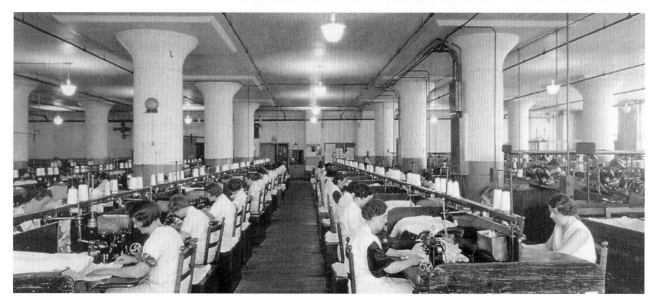

Technological innovations, old and new—how completely can their future effects be foreseen? (Opposite page) Magnetic resonance image of a human head; (inset) audio CD; (this page, clockwise from top left) optical fibers; ENIAC computer and coinventor John W. Mauchly; integrated circuit; electrified factory in 1920.

n terms of its importance for both science and society, the invention of the transistor was one of the greatest achievements of the 20th century. Consequently, one might expect to find the announcement of its invention, which happened in December 1947, displayed prominently on the front page of the *New York Times.* In fact, that announcement appeared later only as a small item buried deep in the newspaper's inside pages, in a regular weekly column titled "News of Radio." The article mentions such possible developments as improved hearing aids for the deaf, but nothing is intimated of the spectacular applications that would occur in just a few years' time.

Our failure to anticipate the full technological, economic, and social impact of a new technology is an intriguing phenomenon. After all, the main justification for the vast expenditures on science and technology in affluent industrial societies is the improvement in material well-being that is confidently expected to flow from such expenditures.

Nathan Rosenberg is Fairleigh S. Dickinson, Jr., Professor of Public Policy in the Department of Economics at Stanford University.

That confidence, however, is really an act of faith, because anticipating the specific effects of a new technology turns out to be extraordinarily difficult. Even after the technology has proved to be workable, its influence on the future often remains shrouded in uncertainty.

A doctor performs abdominal surgery using a laser and a miniature video camera. Although the laser has proved to be among the most versatile and pervasive advances of modern technology, its potential went unappreciated by the patent lawyers of the laboratory where it was invented.

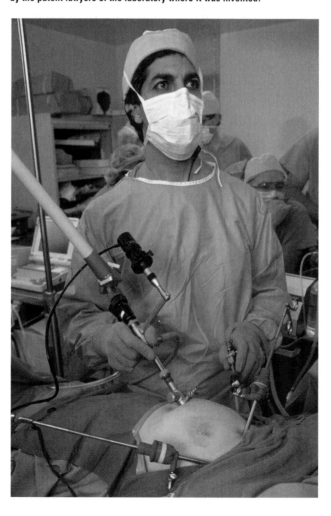

LIMITED VISIONS

Consider the laser, one of the most powerful and versatile advances in modern technology and one that is likely still on the upward arc of its trajectory of development. The truly breathtaking range of uses to which it has been put since its first demonstration in 1960 include navigation, precision measurement and alignment, communications, visual effects, industrial cutting and welding, materials analysis, and scientific research. It is essential for digital data storage on optical discs and the high-quality reproduction of music from compact discs and of printed matter and graphics from computer laser printers. It is the instrument of choice in such surgical procedures as the repair of detached retinas and the removal of gall bladders and certain types of tumors. Its myriad military applications include determining distances and guiding missiles, projectiles, and bombs to their targets.

Perhaps the most profound impact of the laser has been on telecommunications, where, in combination with fiber optics, it has been revolutionizing signal transmission. In 1966 the best transatlantic copper-wire telephone cable could carry simultaneously only 138 conversations in the form of electrical signals between Europe and North America. The first fiber-optic cable, installed in 1988, could carry nearly 40,000 simultaneous conversations on encoded laser beams, while the fiber-optic cables installed a few years later could carry nearly 1.5 million conversations. Nevertheless, the patent lawyers at Bell Laboratories, where the principle of the laser was conceived and much early work on it carried out, initially balked at applying for a patent on the laser on the grounds that it had no possible relevance to the telephone industry. In the words of the U.S. physicist Charles Townes, who shared a Nobel Prize for his pioneering research on the laser, "Bell's patent department at first refused to patent our amplifier or oscillator for optical frequencies because, it was explained, optical waves had never been of any importance to communications and hence the invention had little bearing on Bell System interests."

The telephone itself suffered a similar lack of appreciation when it was invented. Western Union telegraph company was offered the opportunity to purchase Alexander Graham Bell's 1876 telephone patent for a mere $100,000 but turned it down. In fact, as Gerald W. Brock wrote in *The Telecommunications Industry* (1981), "Western Union was willing to withdraw from the telephone field in 1879 in exchange for Bell's promise to keep out of the telegraph business." Nevertheless, if the proprietors of the old communications technology were myopic, so was the patent holder of the new tech-

(Top) Archive Photos; (bottom) Hulton Deutsch

Guglielmo Marconi (right), who invented the radio in the 1890s, believed that its main use would be in communicating between two points where wire transmission was impossible, such as between ships or between ship and shore. Many of Marconi's later experiments with radio were conducted aboard his steam yacht, *Elettra* (below), which was specially instrumented.

nology. Bell's 1876 patent did not mention a new technology at all. Rather, it bore the glaringly misleading title "Improvements in Telegraphy."

The Italian scientist Guglielmo Marconi, inventor of the radio, anticipated that it would be used primarily to communicate between two points where transmission over wire was impossible, as in ship-to-ship or ship-to-shore communication. (To this day the British call the instrument the wireless, precisely reflecting that early conceptualization.) Moreover, the radio in its early days was thought to have potential only for communication between individuals, rather like the telephone, and not at all for communicating to a large audience. Surprising as it may seem today, the inventor of the radio first saw it not as an instrument for broadcasting to the public but for "narrowcasting" to private parties. Marconi visualized its users as steamship companies, newspapers, and navies, which required directional, point-to-point communication over great distances.

The failure of social imagination to envision the radio's potential was widespread. According to James Martin in *Fu-*

ture Developments in Telecommunication (rev. ed., 1977): "When broadcasting was first proposed…a man who was later to become one of the most distinguished leaders of the industry announced that it was very difficult to see uses for public broadcasting. About the only regular use he could think of was the broadcasting of Sunday sermons, because that is the only occasion when one man regularly addresses a mass public."

The wireless telephone, when it became feasible in the second decade of the 20th century, was thought of in precisely the same terms as the wireless radio. J.J. Carty, chief engineer of the New York Telephone Co., stated in 1915: "The results of long-distance tests show clearly that the function of the wireless telephone is primarily to reach inaccessible places where wires cannot be strung. It will act mainly as an extension of the wire system and a feeder to it."

In 1949 the electronic digital computer was perceived as being of use only for rapid calculation in a few military, research, or data-processing contexts. The notion of a large potential market for the computer was rejected by no less a person than Thomas J. Watson, Sr., at the time the president of IBM. The prevailing view be-fore 1950 was that world demand could probably be satisfied by just a few computers.

The list of failures by past generations to anticipate future uses and larger markets for new technologies could be greatly extended. It is more important, however, to examine the reasons for those failures, for there is no reason to believe that today's generation will enjoy any more success.

PRIMITIVE STATE

One reason why forecasting the effects of innovations has been so difficult relates to the fact that new technologies typically come into the world in a very primitive form. Their practical applications turn upon an extended process of improvement, which vastly expands their uses. In that sense, Watson's vision of an extremely limited future market for the computer was not far off the mark if one thinks of the computer as it existed immediately after World War II. Completed in early 1946, ENIAC, the first general-purpose electronic digital computer, filled a huge

Completed in 1946, ENIAC occupied an entire room and needed 18,000 vacuum tubes. No one at the time could anticipate the course of development that would transform this primitive behemoth into the modern desktop computer.

room and relied on the simultaneous working of 18,000 vacuum tubes, which made it notoriously unreliable. The failure to predict the computer market was a failure to anticipate the demand for computers after they had been made much smaller, cheaper, and more reliable and after their performance characteristics, especially their calculating speed, had been raised by many orders of magnitude. In other words, the failure was the inability to anticipate the trajectory of future improvements and the economic consequences of those improvements.

The history of commercial aviation could be told in similar terms, as could the histories of many other innovations. It took fully a third of a century after the Wright brothers' first flight in 1903 before the airplane became commercially significant. The world's first successful commercial airliner, the Douglas DC-3, which incorporated literally many thousands of small improvements

as well as some very large ones, was introduced in 1936.

The typically primitive condition of new technologies raises a fundamental point that is insufficiently appreciated: most expenditures for research and development (R and D) are devoted to product improvement. According to annual surveys taken by the publishing company McGraw-Hill over a number of years, around 80% of R and D money is spent on bettering products that already exist rather than on the invention of new products. On reflection, this figure should not be surprising. The telephone has been around more than 100 years, but only recently has R and D work enhanced its performance significantly with facsimile transmission, cellular phones, electronic mail (E-mail), voice mail, data transfer, and various on-line services. The automobile and the airplane are each more than 90 years old, the camera is over 150 years old, and the Fourdrinier machine, the mainstay of the papermaking industry to-

day, was patented during the Napoleonic Wars.

COMPLEMENTARY TECHNOLOGIES

Whereas the developmental state of a new invention affects how people perceive its potential, so also does the developmental state of complementary inventions. For the lawyers at Bell Laboratories to have appreciated the importance of the laser for telephone communication, they would have required some sense of the technology of fiber optics and its future and the ways in which lasers and fiber optics might be combined. The laser was, in fact, of no particular use in telephone transmission without the availability of fiber optics. The revolution in telephone transmission today is due to the combined potential of these two technologies. Optical fibers did exist when the first lasers were developed, but not in a form that could accommodate the requirements of telephone transmission. It is signif-

icant that a book as recent as Brock's excellent *The Telecommunications Industry* provides no discussion whatever of fiber-optic technology. As has often been the case with other technologies, it took years for some of the attractive properties of fiber-optics technology to become apparent: resistance to electromagnetic interference, reduced energy losses, and the enormous expansion in bandwidth, or range of transmission frequencies, that fiber optics can provide.

Although the impact of invention A may depend upon some invention B, what if invention B does not yet exist? Inventions often give rise to a search for complementary inventions; that is, invention A increases the demand for invention B. For example, after the introduction of the alternating-current dynamo in the early 1880s, the declining price of electricity stimulated the search for technologies that could exploit this unique form of energy. However, the times that such complementary innovations took to develop turned out to vary considerably. The search almost instantly resulted in a burgeoning electrochemical industry, in which electrolytic techniques were employed, for example, to extract aluminum metal from its ore. On the other hand, it was well into the 20th century before the development of the alternating-current electric motor could be identified with gains in produc-

tivity. Similarly, a main reason for the modest prospects predicted for the computer in the late 1940s was that transistors had not yet been incorporated into the computers of the day. The introductions of the transistor and, later, of the integrated circuit were, of course, momentous events that transformed the computer industry. Indeed, in one of the more remarkable technological achievements of the 20th century, the computer in essence became an integrated circuit with the advent of the micro-

processor in the early 1970s. The world would be a far different place today if computers were still being made with vacuum tubes.

The need for complementary technologies may have had a great deal to do with the apparent failure of computer technology over the last couple of decades to help raise produc-

Though much improved since its invention in 1799, the Fourdrinier machine still sustains the papermaking industry. About 80% of R and D money goes to bettering products that already exist.

tivity growth in the U.S. above its rather dismal recent levels. The distinguished U.S. economist Robert Solow observed that we see computers everywhere today except in productivity statistics. Nevertheless, it appears typical of truly major new technological regimes that they take many years to replace established technologies and begin to show their effects.

The historical experience with the introduction of electricity offers parallels. If the beginning of the electric age is set at the early 1880s (the in-

Ann Ronan Picture Library/Image Select

79

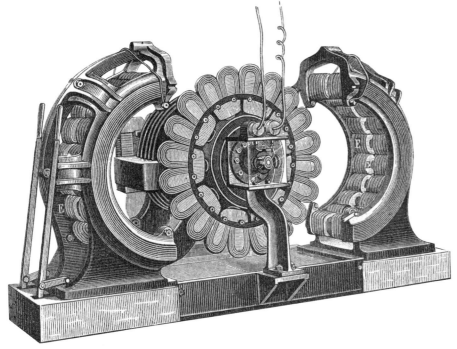

(Left) The Granger Collection, New York; (bottom) Keystone/EB Inc.

Although the invention of the alternating-current dynamo (left) gave rise almost immediately to a thriving electrochemical industry, four decades of complementary developments were needed before the electrification of factories made itself felt in the productivity statistics. (Below) Contemporaries of U.S. railroads in the early 1800s narrow-mindedly saw that technology only as a supplement to existing transportation systems.

troduction of alternating-current dynamos), fully 40 years passed before the electrification of factories began to show up as a significant measured growth in productivity. Part of the delay was due to the need to develop numerous components of a larger technological system. Switching a factory from steam or water power to electric power commonly required a complete redesign and restructuring of a factory facility. It represented, among other things, a revolution in the principles of factory organization. Factory machinery could now be laid out with far more flexibility and versatility than it could with the old power sources. Learning the best ways to exploit these new freedoms inside the plant involved decades of experimentation and education. Indeed, major technological innovations have commonly required significant organizational changes as well.

The radical new technology represented by the computer may well need the same kind of gestation period before its characteristics and opportuni-

ties are understood and can be thoroughly exploited. In 1910, about a quarter century after the dynamo's introduction, only 25% of U.S. factories used electric power, but after another 20 years the figure had risen to 75%. Yet if we date the beginning of the modern computer, a much more complex general-purpose technology than electricity, from the invention of the microprocessor, we are still only perhaps a quarter century into the computer age. It took some 40 years before electric power came to play a dominating role in manufacturing. History strongly suggests that technological revolutions are never completed overnight.

THE SYSTEM AS INNOVATION

An invention and its complementary technologies are often so interdependent that the true major innovation is the entire new technological system, comprising the whole cluster of complementary inventions. It is extremely difficult, however, to conceptualize an entirely new system at once. Thinking about a new technology is likely to be done in terms of the old technology that it will eventually replace. Time and again, contemporaries of a new technology have been handicapped by conceiving of it merely as a supplement that would offset certain inherent limitations of an existing technology. In the 1830s and 1840s, railroads in the U.S. were thought of only as feeders

into the existing canal systems, to be constructed where the terrain had rendered canals impractical—precisely the same kind of restricted vision that was later encountered in the earliest days of radio. Similarly, the telephone was originally seen primarily as a business instrument, like the telegraph, to be used to exchange very specific messages, such as the terms of a prospective contractual agreement. This limited thinking may well explain why Bell's telephone patent was titled "Improvements in Telegraphy."

Improvements that take place in only one part of a system characteristically are of limited significance unless there are concurrent improvements in other parts. Improvements in power generation can have only a limited impact on the delivered cost of electricity unless improvements are made in the transmission network and the cost of transporting electricity over long distances. This need for innovation in complementary activities is an important reason why even apparently spectacular individual breakthroughs usually produce only a slow rise in productivity. On the other hand, the cumulative effects of large numbers of improvements within a new technological system may eventually be immense.

NARROWLY DEFINED NEEDS

Another—and historically very important—reason why it has been so difficult to foresee the full impact of a new technology is that many major inventions have had their origins in the attempt to solve very specific, and often very narrowly defined, problems. Nevertheless, once a solution to such a problem was found, it commonly turned out to have significant applications in totally unanticipated contexts.

The first practical steam engines, for example, were developed by English inventors in the late 17th and early 18th centuries specifically as devices for pumping water out of flooded mines. For a long time, in fact, the steam engine was regarded exclusively as a pump. A succession of improvements later rendered it a feasible source of power for textile factories, iron mills, and an expanding array of other industrial establishments. During the early 19th century, the steam engine became a generalizable power source and had major applications in transportation—railroads, steamships, and steamboats. Later in the 19th century, it was used for a time to produce a new and even more generalizable power source—electricity—which, in

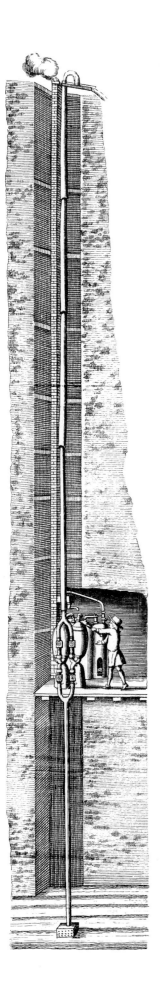

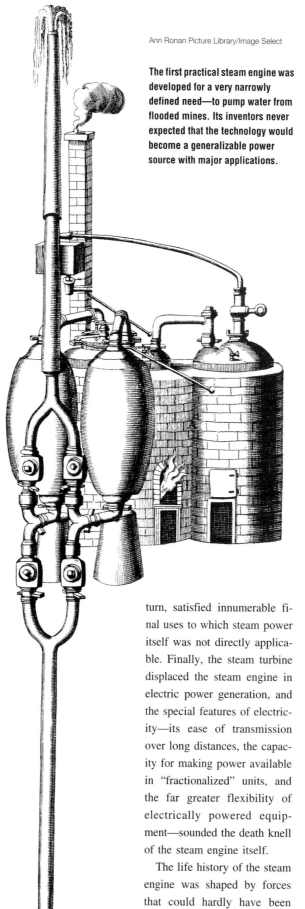

Ann Ronan Picture Library/Image Select

The first practical steam engine was developed for a very narrowly defined need—to pump water from flooded mines. Its inventors never expected that the technology would become a generalizable power source with major applications.

foreseen by its inventors. Nevertheless, its very existence, once its operating principles were thoroughly understood, served as a powerful stimulus to other inventions. Indeed, the ability to induce further innovation and economic investment functions as a reasonably good definition of a major innovation.

A SHORTAGE OF IMAGINATION

Yet one more constraint on accurate technological forecasting is rather less precise than the rest, but no less important. Prognosticating the overall impact of some new invention is more than a matter of perceiving its technical feasibility or the improved performance that it offers. It is also a matter of identifying the specific categories of human needs that it engages and how it can cater to those needs in novel or cost-effective ways. A new technology needs to pass an economic test as well as a technological one. Thus, the Concorde supersonic passenger aircraft may have been a spectacular success in terms of flight performance, but it has proved to be a financial disaster for British and French taxpayers.

Ultimately, what is often called for in technological prognostication is not just tech-

turn, satisfied innumerable final uses to which steam power itself was not directly applicable. Finally, the steam turbine displaced the steam engine in electric power generation, and the special features of electricity—its ease of transmission over long distances, the capacity for making power available in "fractionalized" units, and the far greater flexibility of electrically powered equipment—sounded the death knell of the steam engine itself.

The life history of the steam engine was shaped by forces that could hardly have been

nical expertise but an exercise of the right kind of imagination. Understanding the technical basis for wireless communication is a very different matter from anticipating the ways in which the device might be used to enlarge the human experience. Marconi had an excellent grasp of the first but nothing of the second. On the other hand, David Sarnoff, an uneducated Russian immigrant, had a lively vision of how the new technology might be used to transmit news, music, and other forms of entertainment and information into every household in the country. Sarnoff appreciated the commercial possibilities of the new technology, and his vision eventually prevailed under his leadership of RCA after World War I.

Similarly, the American mathematician Howard Aiken, who was a great pioneer in the early development of the computer throughout the 1940s, continued to think of it in the narrow context in which its early development took place—*i.e.,* purely as a device for solving esoteric scientific problems. As late as 1956 he stated: "If it should ever turn out that the basic logics of a machine designed for the numerical solution of differential equations coincide with the logics of a machine intended to

make bills for a department store, I would regard this as the most amazing coincidence that I have ever encountered." Aiken's mock prediction, of course, turned out to be absolutely accurate, but it was hardly a coincidence. A technology originally invented for one specific purpose—the numerical solution of large sets of

Predicting the overall impact of a new invention means foreseeing how well it will do both economically and technologically. Although a success in terms of flight performance, the Concorde supersonic aircraft became a financial liability for British and French taxpayers.

differential equations—did prove to be readily adaptable to solving problems in entirely different contexts, such as the making out of bills for department stores. But it was not obvious in the 1950s.

A vision of the social change or economic effect that a new technology will engender cannot be extrapolated out of a piece of hardware. A new tech-

nology is an unrealized potential that may take a very large number of eventual shapes. Many of the shapes that it actually ends up taking depends on the ability to visualize how it might be employed in new contexts. Sony's development of the Walkman personal stereo is a brilliant example of the way in which an existing tech-

nological capability, involving batteries, magnetic tape, and earphones, was recombined to create an entirely new product for providing entertainment in contexts where it previously could not be delivered—indeed, where no one previously had even thought of delivering it. To be sure, the product required much engineering redesign of existing components,

but the real breakthrough was the identification, by Sony's chairman Akio Morita, of a previously unrealized market opportunity.

Although the videocassette recorder (VCR) is commonly perceived to have been an American invention, in actuality the U.S. pioneers in the field, RCA and Ampex, gave up long before a truly usable product had been developed. The quest was carried on by the Japanese corporations Matsushita, JVC, and Sony, which, by making thousands of small improvements in design and manufacturing, were able to introduce the first relatively convenient and low-cost VCRs. A crucial step forward in that process was the realization that households represented a potential mass market for VCRs if certain performance characteristics of the product, especially storage capacity, could be sufficiently improved. Whereas the initial American conception of the VCR had been as a piece of equipment for television stations, some American participants, like the Japanese, eventually did become aware of the much larger home market possibilities. The crucial difference, however, seems to have been the confidence of the Japanese companies, based on their previous manufacturing experience, that

83

Back Forward Home Reload Images Open Print Find Stop

Netsite: http://blackhistory.eb.com/cgi-bin/switcher

timeline   1619-1863   1863-1896   1896-1929   1929-1954   1954-1997   biographies
                                                                                          audio/video
                                                                                          bibliography

King, Martin Luther, Jr.

Audio and Video Clips

(b. Jan. 15, 1929, Atlanta, Ga., U.S.--d. April 4, 1968, Memphis, Tenn.), eloquent black Baptist minister, who led the Civil Rights Movement in the United States from the mid-1950s until his death by assassination in 1968. His leadership was fundamental to that movement's success in ending the legal segregation of blacks in the South and other portions of the United States. King rose to national prominence through the organization of the Southern Christian Leadership Conference, promoting nonviolent tactics such as the massive March on Washington (1963) to achieve civil rights. He was awarded the Nobel Prize for Peace in 1964. The U.S. Congress voted to observe a national holiday in his honour, beginning in

BRITANNICA online

about this BRITANNICA feature

1954-1997

---

they could achieve the necessary cost reductions and performance improvements. The rapid transformation of the VCR into one of Japan's larg-

The true breakthrough in the development of Sony's Walkman was the identification of a new product for providing entertainment in contexts where no one previously had thought of delivering it.

est export products was, therefore, an achievement of both imagination and justified faith in its engineering capabilities.

The limited view once held by U.S. companies of the potential for the VCR bears some parallels to the disdain of the mainframe computer makers toward the personal computer as it began to emerge in the late 1970s. It was then fashionable to dismiss the personal computer as a mere "hacker's toy," with no real prospects in the business world and, therefore, no serious threat to the economic future of mainframes.

To be sure, uses for a new technology do not necessarily have to be visualized before they are realized. It may be more accurate to say that, under certain circumstances, uses simply evolve. The Internet was originally conceived by

Now a worldwide information and communication system, the Internet was originally conceived for a specific military purpose. No one ever visualized its multiplicity of uses; those uses simply evolved.

military planners in the late 1960s as a way of automatically rerouting messages around areas that had been devastated by a nuclear attack. It nevertheless evolved into a complex worldwide communication system connecting millions of computers. No one ever planned it that way or even vaguely anticipated such an outcome.

OLD VERSUS NEW

In considering the difficulties of anticipating the future trajectory of a new technology, it is necessary to acknowledge the contribution of the old technologies to those difficul-

ties. In highly competitive societies where there are strong incentives to innovation, those incentives apply to improving existing technologies as well as to inventing new ones. In fact, innovations often induce vigorous and imaginative responses from firms that find their traditional products threatened by close substitutes, and it is not at all uncommon that the competitive pressure from a new technology leads to accelerated improvement in the old technology. Some of the greatest improvements in wooden sailing ships, for instance, took place between 1850 and 1880, just after the introduction of the iron-hull steamship and the compound steam engines that were to displace sails by the beginning of the 20th century. Drastic changes in wooden-hull design allowed greater speed and more cargo in proportion to the tonnage of the ship, while the introduction of labor-saving machinery reduced crew requirements by no less than two-thirds. In the same way, the greatest improvements in gas lamps, used for interior lighting, occurred shortly after the introduction of the incandescent electric light bulb.

A major feature of the post-World War II telecommunications industry has been that research has increased the capabilities of the already installed transmission system at the same time that it has generated new, more productive technologies. Every major transmission system, be it pairs of wires, coaxial cables, microwaves, satellites, or fiber optics, has had its message-carrying capabilities substantially improved, often with only comparatively minor modification of the existing technology. For example, time-division multiplexing—continuously sampling a number of separate signals and transmitting them interleaved in time sequence—allowed an existing pair of wires to carry 24 voice channels or more where it had once carried one. Similarly, when the American Telephone and Telegraph Co. began field trials with fiber-optic cables in the mid-1970s, information was transmitted at 45 megabytes per second. By the early 1990s, the standard for new fiber-optic cables had reached 565 megabytes per second, with reliable sources predicting capacities of nearly 1,000 megabytes per second in the near future. In some cases, such gains in the productivity of existing systems led to the postponement of the introduction of new generations of transmission technologies.

Although the competitive pressure of innovations can

stimulate renewed vigor in existing technologies, it can also bring about unexpected reversals of fortune. Even a comparatively new technology that seems to warrant distinctly bullish expectations can have its life expectancy drastically shortened by another technology that proves to be a better substitute. The prospects for communications satellites declined quite unexpectedly during the 1980s with the introduction of fiber-optic cables and the huge, reliable expansion of channel capacity that accompanied them. In turn, fi-

Wooden sailing ships experienced some of their greatest technological improvements between 1850 and 1880 under competitive pressure after the iron-hull steamship was introduced.

ber optics, whose first significant application was in medical diagnostics in the early 1960s, may be approaching the end of its useful life in that field. Fiber-optic endoscopes had made possible a huge improvement in minimally invasive techniques for visualizing the gastrointestinal tract and other areas within the body. Recently, new sensors from the realm of electronics called charge-coupled devices have begun to provide medical images with a resolution and degree of detail impossible with fiber-optic instruments. Likewise, computed tomography, one of the great diagnostic breakthroughs of the late 20th century, is already giving way to an even more powerful diagnostic capability, magnetic resonance imaging.

Uncertainties of this sort impart a large element of risk to long-term investments in expensive new technologies. The competitive process that eventually resolves those uncertainties is not the traditional textbook competition between producers of a homogeneous product, each seeking to deliver the same product to market at a lower cost. Rather, it is a competition between different technologies, a process that has been appropriately described as "creative destruction." Thus, it is no paradox to say that one of the greatest uncertainties confronting new technologies is the invention of yet newer ones.

NO EASY FIX

Advances in new technology, simultaneous with the substantial upgrading of old technology, underline the pervasive uncertainty that is inescapable in a world of rapid technological change. One would have to be very optimistic and naive to think that any single intellectual paradigm can be developed to handle all the relevant variables in some neat, systematic way. On the other hand, it is not unrealistic to believe that an awareness—and a continuing analysis—of the many factors that influence the ultimate effects of a new technology can improve considerably the way we think about the future.

FOR ADDITIONAL READING

■ *Electricity in the American Economy,* Sam H. Schurr *et al.* (Greenwood Press, 1990).

■ "Factors Affecting the Diffusion of Technology," in Nathan Rosenberg, *Perspectives on Technology* (Cambridge University Press, 1976, pp. 189–210).

■ "From Shafts to Wires: Historical Perspective on Electrification," Warren D. Devine, Jr., *Journal of Economic History* (June 1983, pp. 347–372).

■ *Future Developments in Telecommunications,* James Martin (Prentice-Hall, rev. ed., 1977).

■ "The Introduction of Electric Power in American Manufacturing," Richard B. Du Boff, *Economic History Review* (December 1967, pp. 509–518).

■ *The General: David Sarnoff and the Rise of the Communications Industry,* Kenneth Bilby (Harper & Row, 1986).

■ *Inventing American Broadcasting, 1899–1922,* Susan J. Douglas (Johns Hopkins University Press, 1987).

■ *Invention & Innovation in the Radio Industry,* W. Rupert Maclaurin (Macmillan, 1949).

■ "Quantum Electronics, and Surprise in Development of Technology," Charles H. Townes, *Science* (Feb. 16, 1968, pp. 699–703).

■ *Railroads and American Economic Growth,* Robert W. Fogel (Johns Hopkins University Press, 1964).

■ *The Telecommunications Industry,* Gerald W. Brock (Harvard University Press, 1981).

■ "Toys Now, Computers Tomorrow?" John Markoff, *New York Times* (April 20, 1994, p. D1).

■ *The Twilight of Sovereignty: How the Information Revolution Is Transforming Our World,* Walter B. Wriston (Scribner, 1992).

■ "An Unforeseen Revolution: Computers and Expectations, 1935–1985," Paul E. Ceruzzi, in Joseph J. Corn (ed.), *Imagining Tomorrow: History, Technology, and the American Future* (MIT Press, 1986, pp. 188–201).

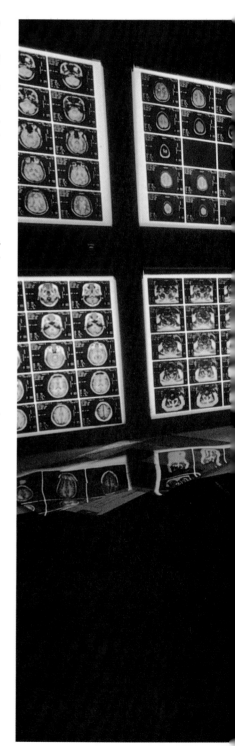

Magnetic resonance imaging (MRI) scans surround two physicians. MRI is already superseding computed tomography, one of the most important diagnostic breakthroughs of the late 20th century.

Charles Gupton--Stock, Boston

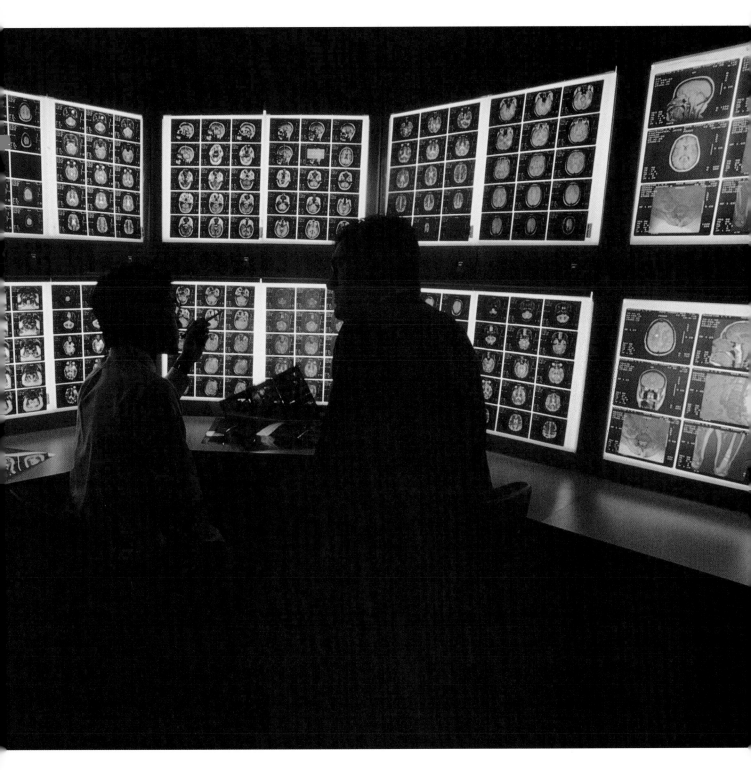

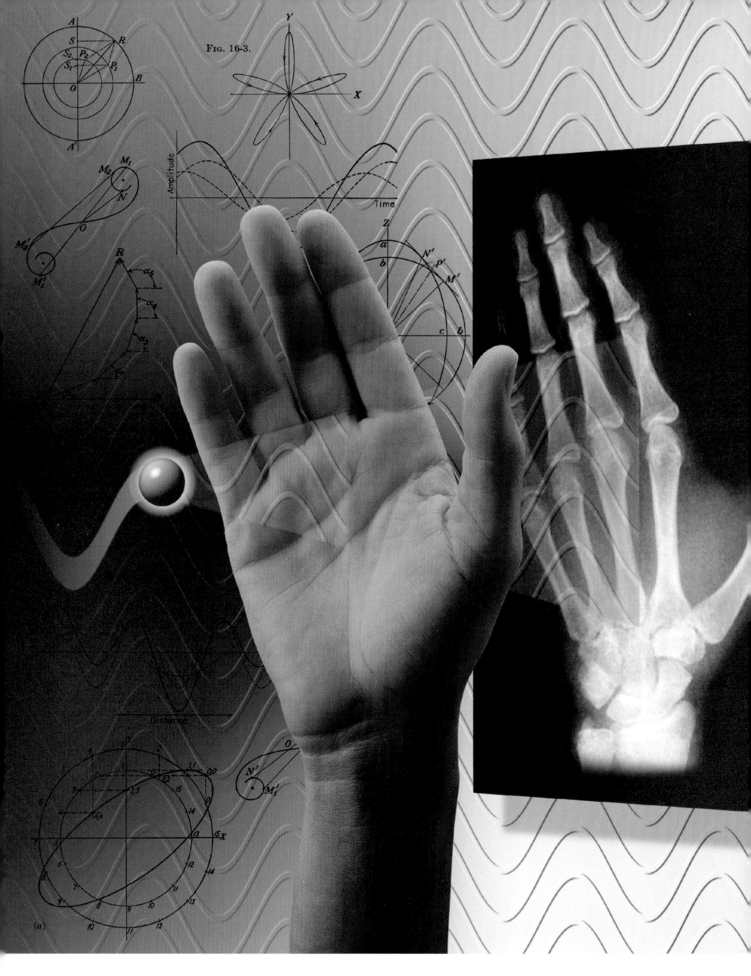

Fig. 16-3.

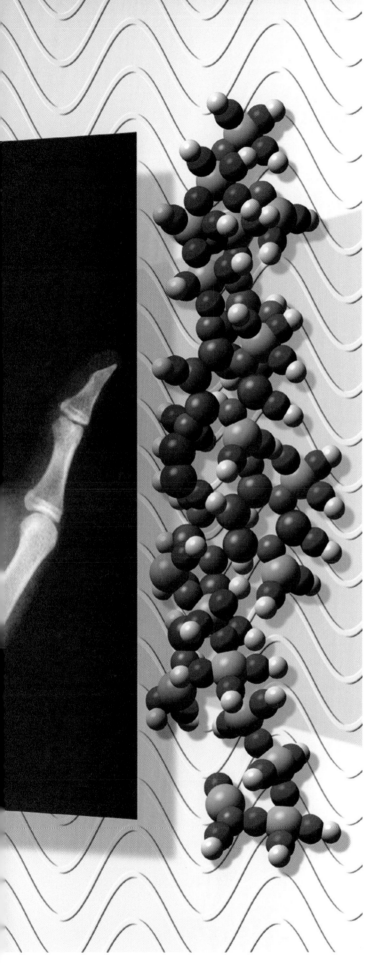

Bright New Lights for Physics

by David E. Moncton

A century after the discovery of X-rays, specially designed particle accelerators around the world are providing scientists with immensely powerful, laserlike X-ray beams for a wide variety of physical and biological research.

David E. Moncton *is Associate Laboratory Director for the Advanced Photon Source, Argonne (Illinois) National Laboratory.*

O
n Nov. 8, 1895, Wilhelm Conrad Röntgen, a physicist at the University of Würzburg, Germany, was experimenting with the recently developed cathode-ray tube when he noticed a faint glow on a piece of fluorescent material lying some distance away. Whatever was causing the material to glow when the tube was operating was something dramatically different from known forms of radiation such as ordinary light or the beta rays (streams of electrons) that so engaged physicists of the day. The new rays, or X-rays, as Röntgen called them, would penetrate substantial amounts of material depending on the material's density and would expose photographic plates. Almost immediately he realized that X-rays could be used to "see" through objects to view their internal structure— even the anatomy of the human body. Needing both of his own hands to operate his equipment, Röntgen imposed on his wife to lend her hand for what was to become the first X-ray picture of a part of the body.

Röntgen's announcement of his discovery at the beginning of 1896 took the world by storm. Within days the results had been duplicated in many laboratories in the United

Illustration by Randee Ladden

89

States and Europe, and within weeks X-ray pictures were being taken of broken limbs and gunshot wounds. In 1901 Röntgen received the first Nobel Prize for Physics, which was also the first of more than a dozen Nobel Prizes that would be awarded to various scientists for research using X-rays. That single ability of X-rays—to provide clear pictures of the detailed internal structure of all kinds of objects—has since exerted a powerful influence on science and technology and added immeasurably to the quality of human life.

Nevertheless, the X-ray beam was to have a far greater impact than physicists of that era realized. In the years following his initial discovery, Röntgen and many other physicists struggled to understand a fundamental puzzle: were X-rays particles or waves? The challenge that comprehending the nature of X-rays presented, coupled with the 1896 observation of radioactive decay and the 1897 discovery of the electron, stimulated the quantum revolution of 20th-century physics. As physicist Philip Morrison of the Massachusetts Institute of Technology said, "The discovery of the X-ray ushered in the 20th century five years early."

Scientists now know that X-rays are not particles of matter but rather a more energetic form of ordinary light. They share a common origin in the mutually interdependent oscillations of electric and magnetic fields caused by the motions of charged particles like electrons. The charged particle is the boat, and the X-rays are the waves that the particle makes as it moves. The conclusive evidence that X-rays are waves, and the first new discovery concerning X-rays since Röntgen's work, came with the demonstration in 1910 that X-rays diffract; that is, they spread as they pass the edges of obstacles, as do all kinds of waves.

Unlike the ability of X-rays to image the internal structure of opaque objects, which had virtually instant and obvious application, the ability of X-rays to diffract appeared to be a laboratory curiosity. It took more years, a few more giants like the German physicist Max von Laue and the British father and son team of William and Lawrence Bragg, and a few more Nobel Prizes to establish the basic physics of X-ray diffraction. That understanding, however, gave scientists the

Wilhelm Röntgen (above) and early X-ray images (below) appeared on the Feb. 1, 1896, cover of the French periodical *L'Illustration* three months after his discovery of X-rays. (Opposite page) The hand of Röntgen's wife, Bertha, served as the subject of the first X-ray picture of a part of the human body (left). Physicians of the day quickly adapted the penetrating power of X-rays to medical diagnosis (inset).

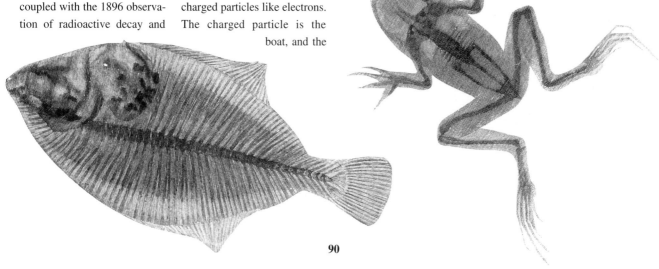

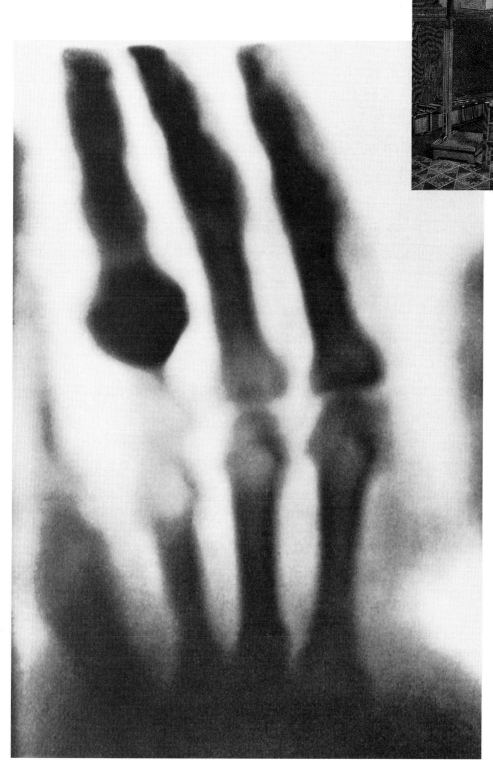

means to use X-rays to determine the precise locations of atoms in the structures of the materials that make up our world. From pure elemental solids like diamond, copper, and silicon and simple compounds like rock salt and quartz to complex biological molecules like DNA and hemoglobin, X-ray crystallography has provided detailed information on atomic positions on a scale of length that is nearly incomprehensible—10 billion times smaller than a centimeter (about 0.4 inch).

NEED FOR BRIGHTER BEAMS

Even as the most important influence of X-rays on science was unfolding, the technology of X-ray production remained essentially that of the cathode-ray tube used by Röntgen. The low intensity from these "light bulbs" was beginning to limit progress in the use of X-rays to study more complex and subtle properties of materials. The problem stemmed from the design of the cathode-ray tube itself in which X-rays are produced by bombardment of a metal target (anode), such as copper or tungsten, with a beam of electrons accelerated from the cathode of the tube (hence, the original name *cathode rays* for the electron beam) by a high applied voltage. The electron beam's strength, and thus the intensity of the X-ray beam produced, is limited by heating of the anode to the material's melting point. Although the development of water-cooled and rotating anodes resulted in modest improvements, by 1960 the X-ray intensity had increased by only a factor of 10 or so since Röntgen's time. X-ray scientists watched with envy as their colleagues who worked with visible light invented the laser and put its intense, pure-color beams of light to myriad uses. Could technology be developed that would produce laser-like beams of X-rays?

As often happens in science, the answer came from an entirely different field—high-energy accelerator physics. In the early part of the 20th century the need for beams of fast-moving charged particles to study the fundamental nature of matter and energy provided the impetus for the development of particle accelerators.

Every accelerator has three essential parts: a source of particles, an evacuated chamber in which to accelerate them, and a source of the electric fields used to push the charged particles to high kinetic energies. The first such machines were linear accelerators, or linacs, which simply accelerated particles in a straight line by means of an applied voltage. An electron accelerated across a space by a voltage of one thousand volts, for example, would have an energy of one thousand electron volts (1 keV). Subsequently, cyclic accelerators were designed in which the path of the particles is bent by the action of a magnetic field into a spiral or circular orbit. In this arrangement the particles pass many times through the accelerator, and their final energy depends not only on the applied voltages but also on

the number of times the particles cycle through the machine. In today's cyclic accelerator designs, the particles travel through a ring-shaped, evacuated pipe and are confined to a circular orbit by electromagnets, called bending magnets, placed along the length of the pipe. Electromagnetic waves in the radio-frequency range (RF waves) provide the electric fields for acceleration.

As a particle's energy is raised in an accelerator, the bending magnets must increase their field strength to keep the particle precisely in its defined orbit. To do this requires that the changing magnetic field be perfectly synchronized with the increasing accelerating forces of the applied RF field. Ac-

celerator designs that allow this synchronism, called synchrotrons, have made it possible to raise the energy of electrons and other charged particles to hundreds of millions and eventually hundreds of billions of electron volts. That accomplishment, in turn, has given physicists the ability to study high-energy particle collisions and gain a much deeper understanding of matter and energy.

Early on in the development

The first X-ray apparatus comprised a glass cathode-ray tube connected to a source of high voltage. The basic design of the tube limited subsequent improvements such that, 65 years later, X-ray intensity had increased only about 10-fold.

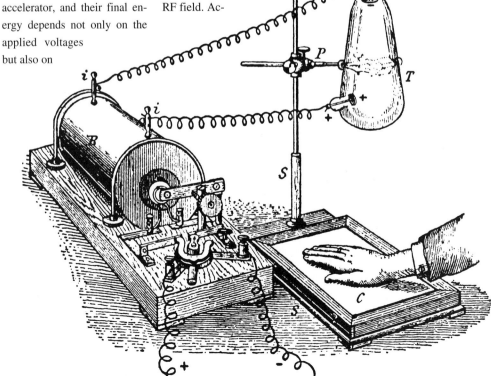

of synchrotrons, scientists realized that there was a catch. Highly energetic particles that are bent by a magnetic field radiate away energy as electromagnetic waves, similar to the way that energy is lost in the screeching of tires as a car turns a corner. The lost energy needs to be replaced before more can be added, and the higher the particle's energy, the more rapid is its radiated energy loss. This radiated energy, dubbed synchrotron radiation, became a subject of intense interest as accelerator physicists realized that it posed a barrier to achieving higher and higher energies. Efforts in the laboratory to observe this radiation finally were successful at General Electric's 70 million-electron-volt (70-MeV) synchrotron in Schenectady, New York, in 1947. Although that radiation was in the form of visible light, theory had established a clear relationship between an accelerated particle's energy and the energy of the radiation that it emitted. Thus, when larger, higher-energy synchrotrons came on line in the 1950s, they radiated brightly at higher energies in the X-ray part of the spectrum. Although high-energy physicists agonized over this energy loss, a few other creative scientists began to think about using the radiation itself.

Visible light shines from General Electric's 70-MeV synchrotron in Schenectady, New York, where synchrotron radiation was observed for the first time in 1947. The light was emitted by fast-moving electrons whose paths were bent in the accelerator's magnetic field.

EARLY GENERATIONS OF MACHINES

During the 1950s theoretical work, observations at synchrotrons in the U.S.S.R. and the U.S., and contributions by scientists familiar with the use of electromagnetic radiation to study materials led not only to a basic understanding of synchrotron radiation but also to the first concrete suggestions that it would indeed be a much improved resource for many specific X-ray applications such as crystal-structure determination. These suggestions had no immediate impact, however, because particle accelerators were extremely expensive and the diverse community of X-ray researchers had experience in neither the technology nor the fund raising required to develop and support them.

Meanwhile, high-energy physicists continued to make rapid improvements in accelerator technology. As they moved on to better machines and newer challenges, they gradually began to abandon accelerators that were strong synchrotron-radiation sources, handing them over to scientists eager to put that liability to work. In 1968 the first of these accelerators, a small 240-MeV ring at the University of Wisconsin known as Tantalus, changed its career. Although its synchrotron radiation was less energetic than X-rays—it

produced ultraviolet light—Tantalus allowed a very successful research program to be carried out in the spectroscopy of solids.

The first real opportunity for a large community of scientists to use synchrotron X-rays came in 1974 when five experimental stations were opened on the 2.5 billion-electron-volt (2.5-GeV) SPEAR storage ring at Stanford University. Because the facility was being simultaneously used for its main purpose, high-energy physics research—the source of the primary funding at the time—synchrotron-radiation work was "parasitic." Consequently, it received second priority and always suffered from less than the best operating conditions. Nevertheless, such access provided the opportunity to do real research and savor the extraordinary potential of synchrotron-radiation applications, particularly for complex crystal-structure determinations. By the late 1970s other parasitic operations were being conducted in Germany, the U.S.S.R., and France. As the decade ended, the field of synchrotron-radiation research came of age with ambitious plans around the world to build the first machines whose purpose from the outset was the optimal production of radiation. Whereas the accelerators

Exceptional among second-generation synchrotron-radiation sources has been the National Synchrotron Light Source (NSLS; right) at Brookhaven National Laboratory, Upton, New York. Its designers, Ken Green and Renate Chasman (below, left and right, respectively, pictured with design committee chairman Martin Blume), carefully considered the properties of the particle beam that would optimize the NSLS for radiation production. To help provide those properties, Green and Chasman invented a new bending-magnet arrangment that since has become the starting point for all synchrotron-radiation accelerator designs.

supporting the parasitic experiments could be considered the first generation of synchrotron-radiation facilities, these new, dedicated machines would be the second generation, and they would revolutionize X-ray research.

It is important to emphasize that the synchrotron-radiation community at that time comprised a collection of diverse researchers with no accelerator design experience. When they set out to build their own machines, they had to rely on experts who had cut their teeth on machines for high-energy physics. As a result, designs for some of the earlier second-generation facilities failed to take full advantage of the opportunity to optimize the ma-

chines for radiation production.

The clear exception was the design for the National Synchrotron Light Source (NSLS) at Brookhaven National Laboratory, Upton, New York. The machine's designers, Ken Green and Renate Chasman, asked themselves what characteristics should the particle beam have to make it the best source of radiation. The answer was twofold: the particles should be as close together as possible so that they produce a point of light, and they should be traveling as parallel as possible in their respective orbits so that their light comes out of the machine in a highly directional beam. Unfortunately, in conventional storage-ring design, those two characteristics

Photographs, Brookhaven National Laboratory

are inversely related. The more compact a beam one tries to generate, the less parallel it becomes; that is, the more divergence it has. To lower both quantities simultaneously Green and Chasman had to invent an entirely new bending-magnet arrangement, termed a lattice. Their design represented a 100-fold improvement over all first-generation and early second-generation machines. Today the Green-Chasman lattice is the starting point for all synchrotron-radiation accelerator designs.

THE THIRD GENERATION

Even as the second-generation machines were burgeoning, designers began experimenting with special magnets intended to enhance radiation production still more. The typical producer of radiation had been the bending magnets, which are an integral part of the accelerator, and their use in this way was imposing two major limitations. First, a bending magnet generates radiation from the orbiting particles in the form of a sweeping beam, similar to the sweep of a locomotive headlamp across the landscape as the engine rounds a curve. Consequently, the beam points only briefly in the direction desired. Second, to fulfill their main function of bending the particles into a precise orbit, the magnets must have a certain well-defined magnetic field strength. Thus, although physicists recognized that the intensity of synchrotron radiation at different wavelengths, or energies, could be tuned by changing the magnets' field strength, they could not put this knowledge into practice without affecting the proper operation of the accelerator.

To get around these constraints, scientists working at second-generation synchrotron facilities at the Lawrence Berkeley Laboratory, Berkeley, California, and in Novosibirsk in the Soviet Union in the 1970s began experimenting with long arrays of permanent magnets set up along the particles' path. The arrays comprised many alternating north- and south-pole magnets, which caused the particles to undergo a gentle to-and-fro bending, or undulating, motion as they passed. The undulations were strong enough to generate substantial intensities of radiation but weak enough to keep the radiation beam from sweeping out in a large fan. As a bonus, the burst of radiation created from each separate undulation interfered constructively with all the other bursts—as many as 100 or more—and resulted in sharp peaks in beam intensity at certain energies in the radiation spectrum that could be hundreds of times the average intensity. By proper design these peaks could be made to occur at precisely the X-ray energy a scientist needed for a particular application. Further-

(continued on page 97)

95

MAKING SYNCHROTRON RADIATION

When a charged particle is accelerated, it radiates electromagnetic radiation. This acceleration can consist of a change in either the speed or the direction of the particle's motion. In a conventional X-ray tube, electrons are accelerated to energies of a few hundred kilovolts and directed onto a metal target. Their sudden deceleration on striking the target—that is, their change in speed—gives rise to the X-ray radiation.

In a synchrotron-radiation facility, charged particles are accelerated by magnetic fields. Most of this acceleration comprises not a change in speed but a change in direction as the particles' paths are bent away from a straight line. A particle whose path is bent by a magnetic field perpendicular to its motion produces a fanlike pattern of synchrotron radiation. In earlier-generation facilities, which rely on the accelerator ring's electromagnetic bending magnets to generate the radiation, the fan pattern of the radiation beam is relatively broad. By contrast, in modern third-generation facilities, the radiation is produced principally by arrays of permanent undulator magnets that bend the particles' paths gently back and forth hundreds of times, resulting in a less sweeping, more directional beam.

In the traditional X-ray tube, radiation is produced uniformly in all directions. By contrast, the physics of synchrotron-radiation production leads to a collimated beam pointing ahead in the direction of the particle's motion. The degree of collimation, or, more specifically, the angle of the beam's divergence, is determined directly by the energy of the particle. This effect was directly predicted by Einstein's general theory of relativity, in which rapidly moving objects "warp" the space around them. In the case of synchrotron radiation, the warping caused by particles moving near the speed of light squeezes the radiation into a narrow beam.

METHODS OF X-RAY GENERATION

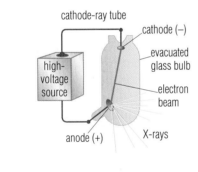

cathode-ray tube

cathode (–)

evacuated glass bulb

high-voltage source

electron beam

anode (+)   X-rays

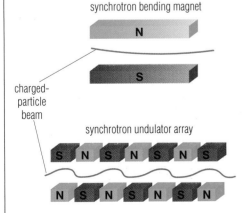

synchrotron bending magnet

N

S

charged-particle beam

synchrotron undulator array

S N S N S N S

N S N S N S N

SHAPE OF X-RAY BEAM

essentially
omnidirectional

Traditional tube sources of X-rays emit radiation in all directions. Synchrotron X-rays produced by accelerator bending magnets emerge as a fairly broad beam. By contrast, undulator magnet arrays produce a more directional beam.

(continued from page 95)

more, it was possible to develop undulator magnets whose field strength could be varied to shift the intense peak in the spectrum to any desired energy over a wide range.

Taken together, the features of undulator magnets had the potential to improve the X-ray brilliance of synchrotron-radiation machines by a factor of 100,000 over then-current performance. Unfortunately, second-generation machines were not designed with the space needed to insert these special magnets. Moreover, detailed studies showed that for best X-ray production the storage-ring energy had to be in the 6–8 GeV range, whereas the second-generation machines were in the vicinity of 3 GeV. Yet another generation of accelerators would be necessary.

By the early 1980s activities were under way in the U.S., Europe, and Japan that would lead to the third generation of synchrotron X-ray facilities—machines making use of lattice-type bending magnets and optimized for undulator magnet arrays. Such a facility represented an enormous undertaking, typically requiring a storage ring a kilometer (0.6 mile) in circumference; more than 90,000 square meters (nearly a million square feet) of building floor space; a billion dollars for design, con-

A typical undulator array comprises two opposing rows of alternating north and south magnetic pole pieces. Charged particles sent through the gap between the rows experience a gentle to-and-fro bending motion that is strong enough to generate substantial synchrotron radiation but weak enough to keep the radiation beam from fanning out.

struction, and instrumentation; and a decade from conception to completion. As of early 1997 three such facilities existed in the world: the 6-GeV European Synchrotron Radiation Facility (ESRF) in Grenoble, France (opened 1994); the 7-GeV Advanced Photon Source (APS) near Chicago (1996); and the 8-GeV Super Photon Ring (SPring-8) in Harima, Japan (1997). The three machines, each producing on the order of 50 X-ray beams simultaneously, represent the future of X-ray research for at least the next two decades.

WHEN X-RAYS MEET MATTER

Although the applications of X-rays have expanded immensely since 1895, the fundamental physics of their interactions with matter has remained rather simple. When X-ray photons, the quantum packages of energy that represent the particle nature of light, are directed at a material target, only

a few things can happen. One possibility is that a given photon passes through the material without interacting. Like the case of a person running straight through a crowded room, the probability of hitting something increases with the density of the objects making up the target—people in case of the runner, and atoms, or more precisely, the atoms' electrons, in the case of the X-ray photon. In the X-ray image of Mrs. Röntgen's hand, the photographic film was exposed

by photons that made it through without hitting anything. In this respect, X-rays act quite like particles.

A second possibility is that the X-ray photon can interact with an atomic electron in the target. In that case one of two things happens: either the photon gives up energy to the target, or it does not. In a dense target—one with many "obstacle" electrons—the most likely thing to happen is that some of the photon's energy is absorbed by an electron, which consequently is ejected from its atom. Next, the photon, which now carries less energy than when it entered the target, is likely to give up more energy to another atomic electron with similar consequences.

Nevertheless, some lower-energy photons do escape the target and bring with them a great deal of information about the identity of the atoms that make up the target, since each

element is unique in the amounts of energy that its electrons absorb. Analytical techniques based on this absorption process, generally called spectroscopy methods, are even sensitive enough to tell the type and location of atoms that neighbor the absorbing atom. Of course, photons that are completely absorbed do not die in vain, since it is their absence that creates the shadow contrast in an X-ray image.

In the second kind of interaction, the X-ray photon retains all of its energy. Like an ideal billiard ball hitting a cushion, the photon changes its direction but keeps moving with no energy loss. This process is called elastic X-ray

scattering. Some photons that contribute to a photographic X-ray image undoubtedly come from elastically scattered X-rays. Because they have spread out from their original direction, they tend to make the image less sharp, but the process is generally weak and little harm is done.

Owing to the dual, particle/wave nature of light, X-ray interactions with matter that can be explained in terms of particles also have equivalent explanations in terms of waves. Elastic X-ray scattering, for example, can be shown to correspond to the wave phenomenon of X-ray diffraction that von Laue and the Braggs first characterized early in the 20th century. When an X-ray wave passes an atom in the target, its oscillating electric field moves the atom back and forth very slightly. The motion, in turn, generates a set of circular wavelets emanating from the

atom. Because the X-ray wave passes many atoms in the target at the same time, all those atoms simultaneously radiate their own wavelets, like mooring balls in a harbor that are set to bobbing by the wave from a passing boat. If the atoms in the target are arranged periodically, as they are in crystals, their wavelets can constructively interfere—the peaks and troughs of all the wavelets falling precisely on top of each other—in certain well-defined directions in space. This generally happens for all, or at least a large fraction, of the target atoms, giving rise to a comparatively strong wave traveling in some direction relative to that of the incident wave. This new wave is just as much an X-ray wave as the original, having the same wavelength and, so, the same energy. It is, in fact, equivalent to the elastically scattered photons discussed above.

X-RAY INTERACTIONS WITH MATTER

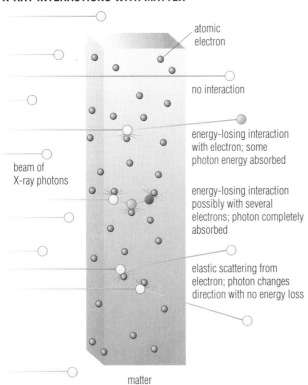

atomic electron

no interaction

energy-losing interaction with electron; some photon energy absorbed

energy-losing interaction possibly with several electrons; photon completely absorbed

beam of X-ray photons

elastic scattering from electron; photon changes direction with no energy loss

matter

When an X-ray photon is directed at a matter target, the outcome can be complete penetration with no interaction, partial or full absorption of the photon's energy, or elastic scattering of the photon with no energy loss.

With quantum theory has come scientists' understanding that this scattering process is probabilistic; each incoming X-ray photon has some small probability of being scattered in each of many different directions, all related to the position of the atoms in the target. If enough X-rays are sent in to accurately measure all these probabilities by their scattered photons, the locations of the atoms with respect to each other in the target can be determined easily and reliably.

SYNCHROTRON X-RAYS

The X-ray beams available from third-generation machines have many unique and extremely useful properties. Although intensity may seem to be the most important advantage, a related property called brilliance is even more important to scientists using the beams. Brilliance is related to the size of the source, the angle of beam divergence, and the "purity" of the radiation energy; it is higher if the source is smaller, the beam more collimated, and the radiation more concentrated at a particular energy (*i.e.*, more monoenergetic or monochromatic). Third-generation synchrotron-radiation facilities produce beams that are as much as a trillion times more

brilliant than that from Röntgen's tube.

Tunability of the beam is the next most important feature. Because the way that X-rays interact with matter is determined primarily by their energy, scientists must be able to vary the X-ray beam energy continuously in order to have the right energy for each experiment. Synchrotron-radiation sources can deliver electromagnetic radiation over a wide range of energies, from infrared radiation, through visible and ultraviolet light, to high-energy (so-called hard) X-rays. Shifting the peak energy requires changing the magnetic field strength, which for a machine equipped with undulator magnets means simply adjusting the separation of the component magnet pole pieces.

Yet another useful attribute of synchrotron X-ray beams is the fact that the radiation is produced as a series of short flashes or bursts.

Charged particles in storage rings circulate in short bunches a few centimeters long separated by many meters. A particle bunch three centimeters long gives rise to an X-ray burst that is also three centimeters long, which takes about one ten-billionth of a second to pass while traveling at the speed of light. Because each burst is separated by about a millionth of a second, researchers have time to measure what is happening in the target material before the next burst oc-

In an X-ray structural study, a beam of X-rays is diffracted by the atoms in a crystallized sample. The detected diffraction pattern is then used to compute the precise locations of the atoms in the crystal.

X-ray source

X-ray beam

crystal sample

diffracted X-rays

diffraction pattern

detector

computed image of atoms in crystal

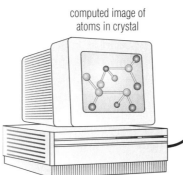

curs. The situation is analogous to photographic strobe lighting, in which the complexity of continuous motion can be reduced to a series of stop-action photos. Third-generation undulator beams have enough intensity in each burst to give good diffraction data from a complex molecule. This feature makes it possible to track molecules in motion as they execute complex physical, chemical, and biological functions.

Sources of synchrotron radiation already have added much to scientists' knowledge of the physics and structure of the materials on which nature's and our own technologies are based, and the latest generation should make even greater contributions in the next two or

three decades. Improvements in useful materials are expected to range from more efficient catalysts to stronger fibers and from better electronic devices to tougher surface coatings. Increases in the speed and resolution with which new structures can be determined should result in faster drug development and lead to drugs that interact more precisely with the body's biochemical processes. The high sensitivity afforded by synchrotron techniques promises to improve researchers' understanding of environmental chemistry and the distribution and movement of toxins and other specific molecules in the environment. Synchrotron radiation may also spur new techniques in medical

imaging and radiation treatment. A selection of examples of recent and ongoing X-ray research offers some idea of the exciting paths being paved for the future.

IMAGING

The intensity, collimation, and tunability of synchrotron radiation has allowed great advances in basic X-ray imaging. Moreover, the small size of the synchrotron beam is particularly well-suited to imaging the structure of small objects. For example, using bending-magnet radiation from the second-generation NSLS, investigators have taken simple X-ray pictures of tiny insects called thrips, some of which are con-

Instrumentation covers the main floor of Brookhaven's NSLS. The X-ray beam lines of the facility have been used for a wide variety of experiments in the physical and biological sciences.

siderably less than a millimeter (0.04 inch) long. The images have such high resolution that they easily reveal internal structural details about a micrometer (0.00004 inch) in size.

The medical imaging technique known as computed tomography (CT scanning) employs routine mathematical computations to synthesize a three-dimensional view of the body's internal structure from many two-dimensional X-ray exposures. Adapting these computations, scientists at

(continued on page 102)

ANATOMY OF THE APS

The Advanced Photon Source at Argonne (Illinois) National Laboratory is shown schematically (right) and in an aerial photo (inset).

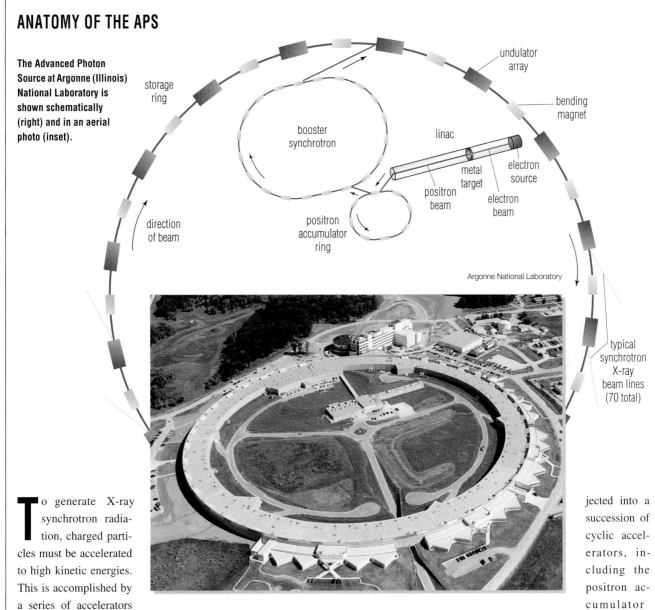

storage ring

undulator array

bending magnet

booster synchrotron

linac

metal target

electron source

positron beam

electron beam

direction of beam

positron accumulator ring

Argonne National Laboratory

typical synchrotron X-ray beam lines (70 total)

To generate X-ray synchrotron radiation, charged particles must be accelerated to high kinetic energies. This is accomplished by a series of accelerators that create, accelerate, and store the particle beams for use in the undulator magnets.

As an example of a third-generation synchrotron-radiation facility, the Advanced Photon Source (APS) at Argonne (Illinois) National Laboratory can serve to illustrate the anatomy of the various component accelerators of the total system. Electrons are first produced in the upstream end of the linear accelerator, or linac, by a filament not unlike that in an electric light bulb. A modest voltage of a few thousand volts pulls the electrons away from the filament and begins the acceleration process. The basic acceleration process is quite simple; the particles surf-ride on electromagnetic waves with frequencies in the hundreds of megahertz to gigahertz (hundreds of millions to billions of cycles per second) range, which is in the radio-wave part of the spectrum. Proper timing of the waves gives the electrons an energy boost, and soon they have obtained energies of a few hundred million electron volts.

Although most synchrotron-radiation facilities do use circulating electrons to generate the radiation, there are certain technical advantages to using positrons, the antimatter equivalent of electrons. At the APS, positrons are produced in collisions of accelerated electrons with a heavy metal target positioned a third of the way down the linac. The positrons are then accelerated the rest of the way along the linac and in-jected into a succession of cyclic accelerators, including the positron accumulator ring and the booster synchrotron, where their energy ultimately is raised to seven billion electron volts. Finally, they are injected into the storage ring. There the positrons circle for hours at a time, making 300,000 revolutions per second. On each trip they pass through the undulator magnets and the bending magnets, where they emit synchrotron radiation to feed 70 beam lines that can operate simultaneously or independently for a wide range of experiments.

(continued from page 100)

Exxon Corp. have developed synchrotron-based technologies that allow them to see micrometer-size detail in tiny samples of materials important in their business. One such material is a type of sandstone present in some oil reservoirs. Detailed understanding of the microscopic porous structure of the material can help petroleum scientists devise improved methods for extracting the oil contained in its internal voids. After researchers X-ray a submillimeter-size sandstone grain from many directions, they can use the data to create a three-dimensional computer image that is viewable from any direction—even from the perspective of being inside the object.

As researchers continue to work with third-generation machines, they look forward to significant improvements in imaging speed and resolution. They are also enthusiastic about another—in some ways more powerful—aspect of imaging that can actually be used to distinguish one chemical element from another in a sample. In addition to the concentration of electrons in a material, there is a second factor that affects X-ray absorption. When X-ray photons have an energy that exactly matches the energy needed to break an electron's bond to the atomic nucleus, their absorption rate rises markedly. Because electron binding energies are unique to each element, by making an X-ray image of a sample using different X-ray energies, researchers can locate regions with concentrations of particular elements. This element-specific imaging method has the potential to detect elements at levels of parts per billion. One exciting area of application would be in environmental science, where an urgent need exists for technology capable of detecting small amounts of toxic materials and following their movements, for example, through the soil and into plants.

DIFFRACTION

Until the development of synchrotron-radiation sources, the inherent limitations of conventional X-ray tubes had severely restricted structural studies of some very important aspects of matter. One such aspect is the surface structure of solids, and a good example is offered by the element silicon, the basis of the ubiquitous semiconductor chip. The internal, or bulk, crystal structure of silicon can be completely described very simply in terms of a pair of atoms separated by about an angstrom (a ten-billionth of a meter), that is repeated periodically in a three-dimensional cubic array called a lattice. A real piece of silicon, however, also has surfaces at which its periodic structure ends and the rest of the world begins.

An X-ray image of a tiny thrip was made with bending-magnet radiation at the NSLS. The intensity, collimation, and small size of synchrotron beams make them suited to imaging small objects.

Brookhaven NSLS

While the electronic properties that make silicon so useful are based on its bulk structure, the only way to make electrical contact with silicon is through its surface. As critical as that surface may be, its properties are confined to the first few layers of atoms. Those layers contain so few atoms compared with the atoms in the bulk crystal that they scatter only a minute fraction of an X-ray beam being used to probe the structure. The increased X-ray intensity provided by synchrotron radiation has made that weak scattering detectable and, thus, has opened the field of surface structure determination—and not only for silicon but also for many other materials. Surfaces, whether they are the surfaces of electronic contacts, chemical catalysts, or biological cells, are where the action literally takes place, and the ability to determine these structures in atomic detail is having truly revolutionary consequences.

Synchrotron-radiation studies conducted over nearly 20 years have revealed that surfaces are extremely complex, even for materials with simple bulk structures like silicon. Because some of the bonds connecting atoms to their neighbors are broken at the surface, surface atoms assume different atomic arrangements than in

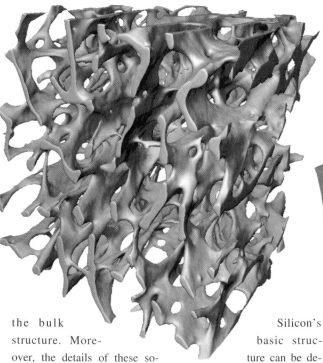

Synchrotron X-rays combined with the techniques of computed tomography produced high-resolution, three-dimensional microscopic images of the structure of a sandstone grain (below) and of a live human bone (left).

the bulk structure. Moreover, the details of these so-called reconstructed arrangements depend on the orientation of the surface with respect to the bulk lattice. Different facets of a crystal have different reconstructions, some of them requiring many different atomic positions for a complete description. When a crystal is cut along an arbitrary direction not corresponding to a facet, the surface may break up into periodic bands of alternating facets angling one way and then the other. To add complication, if the surface is in contact with a gas of other atoms, say, the atoms that exist in the atmosphere, it may absorb some of these atoms to form whole new sets of atomic arrangements. To top it off, if the complexity of silicon's surface appears formidable, it pales by comparison with that of a biological surface, such as the membrane of a living cell.

Silicon's basic structure can be described with two atoms, but such simplicity is not the case for the structure of biological molecules and multimolecular assemblies, which are often so complex that a million or more atom positions are required to determine them. To conduct diffraction studies scientists must make crystals of these molecules, although the subject of interest is not their lattice arrangement but the identities and positions of all the atoms in the molecule. It is in these studies that synchrotron radiation's high degree of collimation becomes just as important as its high intensity.

To determine the positional coordinates of all the atoms in a molecule, researchers need precise measurements of the intensity of as many diffracted beams (*i.e.*, beams of scattered photons) as there are atom coordinates. The diffracted beams are not only weak but also very closely spaced in angle with respect to one another. Conventional X-ray tubes have no intrinsic collimation—they radiate equally in all directions—and so they impose limits on how well resolved the closely spaced diffracted beams can be. Unraveling the structure of very large molecular structures absolutely requires the high collimation of synchrotron radiation.

Using the synchrotron-radiation facility at Cornell University, Ithaca, New York, researchers determined the structure of the polio virus in one of the first viral structure studies. Since the mid-1980s, the percentage of new structures determined by synchrotron methods rose steadily, so that by 1996 it represented 70% of the work.

Today the demand is growing in basic research and industry for structural determinations of biological molecules that are important in our lives. They include DNA and RNA molecules, the carriers of genetic information; specialized proteins that catalyze critical biochemical reactions or control the way that genetic information is copied and expressed in cells; signaling molecules that tell cells when to switch certain activities on and off; and receptor molecules to which the signalling molecules attach. To carry out structural determinations on potential new drugs, major pharmaceutical companies are investing millions of dollars in equipment to be installed along synchrotron-radiation beam lines.

More important than knowl-

edge of a biological molecule's basic structure is an understanding of how the structure changes when the molecule is performing its particular function. As mentioned above, a tremendous opportunity lies in the fact that synchrotron radiation is emitted in pulses. Using such light flashes, investigators can take a stop-action photographs of a molecule at various stages of change; the photos can then be combined to form a stroboscopic sequence, or even a movie, of molecular motion. Studies are just now beginning to exploit this possibility.

MEDICINE

The two major applications of X-rays that are most familiar to people, medical diagnostic imaging and radiation therapy, have remained exclusively the province of traditional X-ray sources despite the routine use of synchrotron radiation in other scientific endeavors for more than two decades. The reasons have less to do with the lack of research and opportunity than with economics—the physical size and cost of synchrotron-radiation machines would make patient-care facilities associated with them large and expensive—and the fairly long time typical of the introduction of new diagnostic

methods in medicine. Nevertheless, potential applications for synchrotron radiation do exist in both diagnosis and therapy.

The major advantage of synchrotron radiation for medical imaging resides in the intense monoenergetic beams that can be delivered, compared with the broad range of X-ray energies from conventional sources. One use being explored is in a technique for imaging the coronary arteries that avoids the need to inject an X-ray–opaque contrast agent via

a catheter that is threaded through the body to the heart. Such coronary angiograms are currently far from routine procedures. The use of catheters involves a high level of risk and generally are not administered without clear indication of cardiac disease—usually evidenced by a recent heart attack. In the synchrotron-based technique, monoenergetic beams are used in combination with atoms like iodine, which have very high absorption at certain X-ray energies. To synchrotron X-rays tuned to the

right energy, solutions of relatively low concentrations of iodine are highly opaque; they thus make excellent contrast agents even when simply injected intravenously into the bloodstream. Furthermore, the intensity of synchrotron radiation allows short-exposure stop-action pictures to be taken, avoiding blur from the heart's motion.

It is clear that synchrotron radiation can make considerably better images of the coronary arteries with less X-ray exposure to the patient. Unfor-

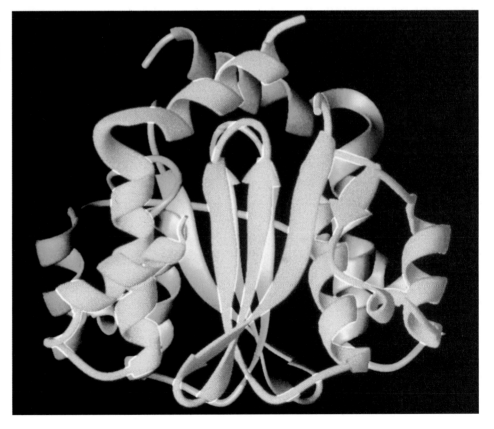

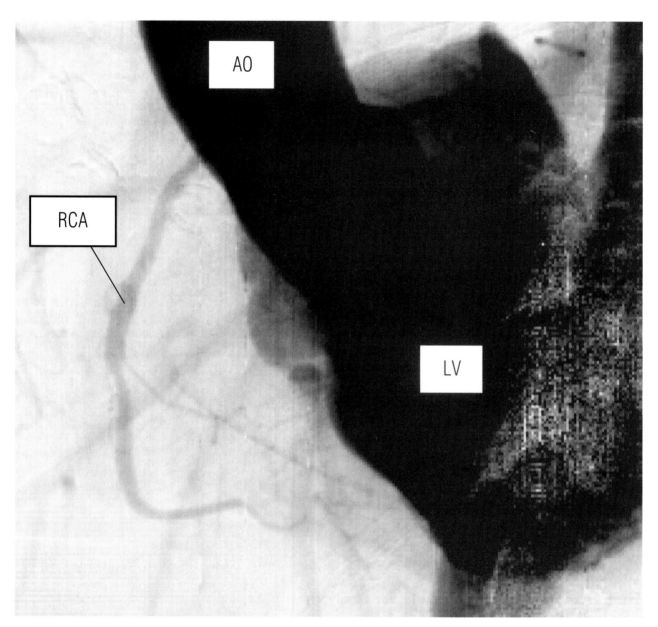

tunately, iodine requires relatively low-energy—and thus less penetrating—X-ray photons, which limit the effectiveness of the technique to patients with a relatively thin chest. Although continuing research will likely overcome the problem, the availability of the new technique ultimately will hinge on medical business decisions. Other synchrotron-based diagnostic applications being explored include brain imaging, mammography, and a lung-imaging method that uses xenon gas as a contrast agent.

A second opportunity for synchrotron radiation in the medical field is in the radiation treatment of tumors. One technique showing particular promise is called stereotactic radiosurgery. Intense, extremely thin, highly collimated X-ray beams are directed into the body from different angles such that they overlap only in the tumor tissue. At the point of overlap the radiation dose is the sum of the dose from every beam, whereas elsewhere it is only the dose from one beam. With reasonable beam separa-

tion only the tumor is destroyed; the damage done to healthy tissue is minimal and heals readily. The technique has great potential for treating tumors deep inside the brain.

TOWARD AN X-RAY LASER

Although it is risky to speculate much into the future, the history of science shows that the repercussions of a new technology are often much more profound and far-reaching than initially expected. The

An angiogram revealing the right coronary artery (RCA) of a human heart was made with synchrotron X-rays at the NSLS after intravenous injection of an iodine contrast agent into a large vein. AO is the aorta; LV is the left ventricle. To synchrotron X-rays tuned to the right energy, relatively low concentrations of iodine solution are highly opaque.

wealth of new biostructural information collected by means of synchrotron radiation, coupled with other new tools and discoveries, may well lead to a revolution in which we evolve from being spectators of nature's handiwork to being active participants in the use of molecular engineering to serve individual and societal needs.

Whether that revolution happens during the lifetime of the current generation of synchrotron-radiation sources, advances are on the horizon that will bring even more powerful tools. Over the past three decades the characteristics inherent in laser light have transformed the scientific use of the visible spectrum. Laser light consists of an intense beam of visible-light photons that are coherent; not only are all the photons moving in the same direction, but they also all have a single wavelength (to a high degree of accuracy) in which all the wave components are in step with each other. Current synchrotron-radiation sources provide scientists with X-ray beams that approach the properties of laser light. Nevertheless, certain highly useful optical techniques, such as three-dimensional holography, require a photon beam that is completely coherent. For years scientists have dreamed of using X-ray holographic imaging to see the atomic structure of single molecules, but to do so they will need a device that produces X-rays having considerably higher coherence than present sources—in other words, an X-ray laser.

X-ray scientists and accelerator physicists believe that synchrotron-radiation technology can serve as the basis for an X-ray laser. The emerging consensus is that the best way to produce a laserlike X-ray beam is to extend the length of the undulator magnet array. The longer array would not only increase the intensity of the X-ray beam but also, by means of a feedback process, increase the efficiency of the particle bunches in the beam at generating radiation of the desired wavelength. Researchers also recognize that the bending magnets in current circular synchrotrons are a hindrance to an efficient X-ray laser. To get laser action started, the lengths of the particle bunches must be reduced to about less than 0.1 millimeter (0.004 inch), but the synchrotron radiation created by the bending magnets introduces a spread of energies into the particle beam, making it difficult to reduce bunch length. It appears that the only way to circumvent the problem is to use linacs, which have no bending magnets.

As a consequence of these considerations, efforts are under way in Europe, Japan, and the U.S. to study the physics of linac-based X-ray lasers. In 15 or 20 years this work may result in new, fourth-generation X-ray sources even more powerful and coherent than today's machines. In addition to the coherence that could make atomic-resolution holography a reality, an X-ray laser beam would have a pulse length of a ten-trillionth of a second—1,000 times faster than current beam pulses—because of the short particle bunch that produces it. This brevity would make possible the study of the fastest processes that occur in molecules, such as the transfer of energy during photosynthesis or the uptake of oxygen molecules by hemoglobin in red blood cells. An X-ray laser essentially would be an almost unimaginably fast stop-action camera with atomic resolution. With such a device it would be only a matter of time before scientists compiled a detailed understanding of many of nature's most intimate secrets.

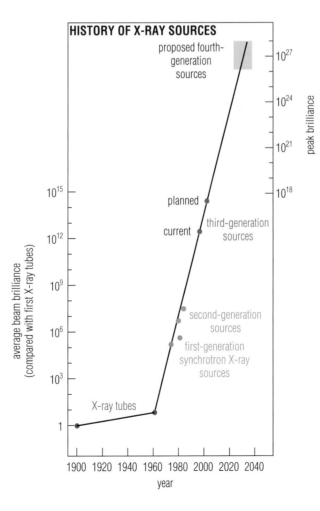

HISTORY OF X-RAY SOURCES

Unnatural Selection

by John Bickham

Environmental pollution has been linked to everything from cancer to delayed learning. Scientists now suspect that environmental contaminants may even be disrupting the course of evolution in organisms around the globe.

Raul Colon

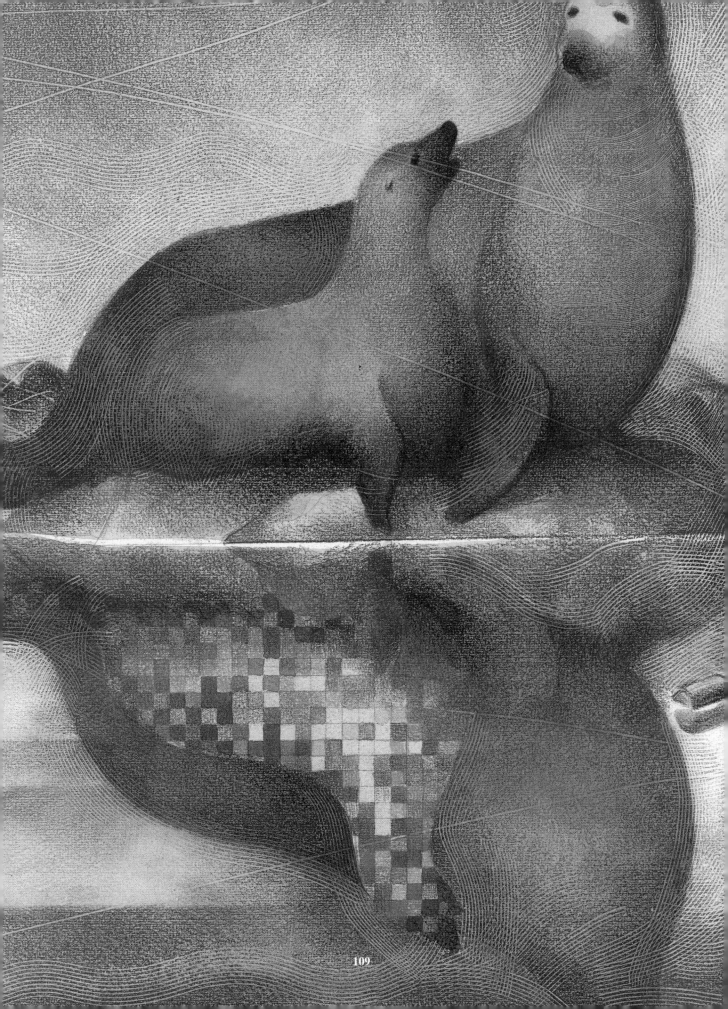

Nestled in the sleepy heart of Tennessee hill country, the Oak Ridge National Laboratory produced nuclear weapons for the U.S.'s Cold War arsenal for more than five decades. Today, with its swords beaten into plowshares, the facility has turned its attention to peace-time purposes, including research in environmental cleanup—with good reason. Some of the country's most intractable pollution lies just outside the laboratory's doorstep. Its ecological legacy includes soil and water contaminated with polychlorinated biphenyls (PCBs), radioactivity, and an estimated 100 to 300 tons of mercury.

In 1992–93 Oak Ridge researchers Chris Theodorakis and Lee Shugart investigated the effects of exposure to radioactive waste on local populations of a topminnow called the mosquito fish. The researchers selected fish from two contaminated ponds and compared them with fish from a pair of clean ponds. Using a technique called the randomly amplified polymorphic DNA

John Bickham is a Professor in the Department of Wildlife and Fisheries Sciences at Texas A&M University at College Station.

assay, the researchers examined the genetic diversity in the fish's nuclear DNA. The results were surprising. The fish in the two radioactive ponds shared more genetic similarities with each other than with fish in the uncontaminated reference ponds, even though the population in one of the polluted sites originally came from fish stocks in one of the clean ponds. Theodorakis and Shugart offered their most likely explanation for the genetic similarity between the populations at the contaminated sites: the fish were evolving certain characteristics that allowed for enhanced survival in the polluted environments and were transferring

these characteristics to their offspring. The Oak Ridge research demonstrated what scientists are just beginning to understand—that environmental contamination has the potential to alter the genetic systems, and therefore the future survival, of organisms around the globe.

Environmental contamination with the power to disrupt the natural course of evolution takes many different forms and comes from a variety of sources, including agricultural pesticides, by-products of industrial paper processing, insulation for electrical transformers, nuclear wastes, and petrochemical products. More often than not, their effects on

the environment are unknown or poorly understood. According to the authors of the 1996 book *Our Stolen Future,* for example, more than 100,000 synthetic chemicals currently crowd the shelves of the world's marketplace. Each year 1,000 new chemicals are added to their numbers; only a comparative handful have been tested for their power to cause genetic mutations and other health problems.

As a result, many researchers now project a future far more troubling than even the dire picture Rachel Carson painted in her landmark 1962 book, *Silent Spring,* about the hazards of pesticide use. During the past few decades, sci-

Before the use of DDT was severely restricted in the U.S. in 1972, the chemical was widely dispensed both in and outside of the home to control such insect pests as mosquitoes, potato beetles, and gypsy moths.

entists have learned that synthetic insecticides, industrial compounds, and radiation have serious effects on the health of animals, including humans. These agents have been linked to increased levels of cancer, physical deformities, impaired reproduction, weakened immune systems, and behavioral abnormalities, among other problems.

Now scientists are beginning to document even more alarming global trends—transgenerational changes caused by persistent toxic chemicals in the environment. Given time and the right circumstances, some of these transgenerational effects can imperil the future of an entire species.

HERE TODAY, HERE TOMORROW

Recent research has shown that long-term exposure to the barrage of potent contaminants in the environment is more troublesome than previously thought. Because many of these chemicals are human-made and do not occur naturally in the environment, organisms have never evolved defense mechanisms against them. Furthermore, each year the environment is flooded with new compounds. According to some estimates, between 1940 and 1982, billions of kilograms of human-made chemicals entered the environment as worldwide production of synthetic materials increased about 350-fold. The trend is likely to continue.

The success of these compounds in a variety of industrial and agricultural applications means that they are widely distributed. For example, it has been estimated that prior to their restricted use in the U.S. and other industrialized countries in the 1970s, enough PCBs, a family of suspected carcinogens commonly used during the 1930s and '40s as insulation for electrical equipment, were produced to poison every fish in the world's oceans.

Carried by atmospheric and ocean currents, PCBs have found their way into some of the most remote corners of the Earth. High levels of contamination, for example, have been detected in Arctic polar bears, ringed seals, and whales, far from their place of origin in the industrial cities of Europe and America. Studies of reproductive failure in seabirds on the remote Pacific Midway Islands near the western end of the Hawaiian archipelago prove that even living in the middle of the world's largest ocean is no protection. In 1996 researchers reported finding high levels of organochlorine contaminants, including PCBs, dioxins, and dibenzofurans, in the fat of two species of albatross from the Midway atoll. In fact, scientists predict that the oceans will likely serve as the ultimate repository for a majority of these long-lived contaminants, since compounds washed into rivers eventually flow into the sea.

Once in the environment, many of these pollutants degrade very slowly. Dangerously long-lived, PCBs, radionuclides from nuclear-weapons tests, industrial accidents, and nuclear waste, polycyclic aromatic hydrocarbons (PAHs) from crude oil and petrochemical products, and the synthetic insecticide DDT are expected to persist in the environment for centuries.

In the meantime, through a process known as bioaccumulation, these contaminants have become dangerously concentrated in the fatty tissues of many animals high on the food chain. When chemicals, for example, are washed or atmospherically deposited into streams, rivers, and lakes, they are ingested by microscopic life-forms. These organisms are eaten by animals progressively higher on the food chain, including small fish, larger fish, mammals, birds, and ultimately humans. Those highest on the food chain, such as gulls, otters, polar bears, and humans, are exposed to concentrated doses of these compounds when they eat food from contaminated waters. Stored in body fat, which is metabolized very slowly, these pollutants accumulate to dangerous levels in living tissue.

In a process known as bioaccumulation, animals high on the food chain, such as polar bears, concentrate dangerous levels of toxins in their fat tissues after consuming contaminated prey.

In the Great Lakes, for example, concentrations of PCBs in the water may be extremely low. A predator in the upper reaches of the food chain, however, may harbor concentrations 25 million times higher. Unlike females, which pass a large percentage of their contaminant load on to their offspring, males typically retain greater concentrations of contaminants, which are sequestered in their fat.

CONTAMINANTS AND DISEASE

The field of ecotoxicology—the study of the toxic effects of environmental contaminants—traditionally has focused on measuring the acute symptoms of chemical poisoning in humans. As a result, scientists know comparatively little about the chronic long-term effects of exposure to environmental contamination, especially on the health and survival of wildlife populations.

What they do know suggests that contaminants have severe and lasting consequences. Among the most thoroughly studied organisms are bottom-dwelling fish that live in habitats polluted by PAHs, some of which, such as benzo[a]pyrene, are highly mutagenic. Studies of these fish began in the 1970s

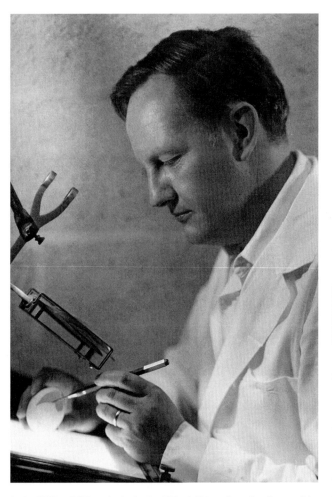

In the 1960s wildlife toxicologist David Peakall traced an alarming crash in the populations of several bird species to high levels of DDT in their tissues. The contaminated birds produced eggs with abnormally thin shells.

when Bruce B. McCain of the School of Medicine at the University of California, Davis, reported a high incidence of liver tumors in English sole from Puget Sound. Subsequent research in the 1980s and '90s focused on winter flounder from Boston Harbor, brown bullhead from the Great Lakes, and Atlantic tomcod from the Hudson River. Not surprisingly, fish found in rivers, harbors, and estuaries with PAH-contaminated sediments had high levels of PAHs in their tissues. Like McCain's work, later research also found a corresponding increase of tumors in these fish, including malignant growths on their livers.

Follow-up research has demonstrated how PAHs can cause these cancer-causing mutations. After analyzing the cells of diseased fish, scientists found that PAHs bind to the DNA found in the nucleus of the fishes' liver cells and form chemical structures known as adducts. In DNA the adduct can displace one of the normal building-block molecules, or nucleotides, along the DNA strand and cause a mismatch along the other strand or impair the normal process of DNA synthesis. The result is a mutation in which the original nucleotide, displaced by the adduct, is replaced by a different nucleotide when the DNA

strand is copied. This process is thought to be the first step in triggering the DNA mutations that lead to cancer.

CONTAMINANTS AND FUTURE GENERATIONS

In the 1960s scientists began to recognize that environmental contaminants could not only affect the health and survival of individual animals but also alter the prospects for their offspring and thereby potentially change the genetic makeup of entire populations.

Researchers were first alerted to problems in wildlife in the 1940s after the populations of eagles, falcons, and other fish-eating birds in Britain plummeted. In nest after nest the birds' eggshells were so thin that they cracked under the weight of the adults during incubation. In the 1960s David Peakall and other wildlife toxicologists demonstrated that the accumulation of very high levels of such pesticides as DDT in the birds' tissues had seriously impaired their reproductive capabilities. Some of these declines resulted in the complete disappearance of populations from large portions of their former range. In North America, for example, the eastern population of the peregrine falcon was virtually wiped out.

In the 1980s and 1990s, Sandra W. Jacobson and Joseph L. Jacobson conducted studies to determine how prenatal exposure to high levels of PCBs affected the learning and behavior of children. Researchers tested the visual-recognition memory in infants by showing the subjects photographs of other infants (right) and recording their responses on a computer (below). The researchers found that those infants whose mothers had eaten PCB-contaminated fish from Lake Michigan demonstrated poorer visual-recognition memory.

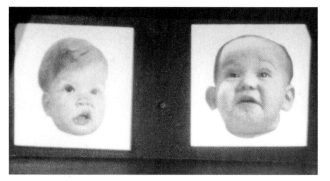

More recently, the Gulf Coast population of the brown pelican disappeared as a result of eggshell thinning thought to be caused by the organochlorine pesticides dieldrin and endrin.

Since then, researchers have provided additional evidence that environmental pollution can affect future generations. For example, exposure to high levels of PCBs has been shown to affect the learning and behavior of children. In the 1980s Sandra W. Jacobson and Joseph L. Jacobson of Wayne State University, Detroit, Michigan, studied a group of children whose mothers had eaten PCB-contaminated fish from Lake Michigan. The re-searchers found that the children's prenatal exposure to these compounds resulted in neurological anomalies at birth and developmental delays in motor function during infancy. The Jacobsons retested the children at age 11. In a 1996 report they noted that the children exhibited significantly poorer intellectual function, amounting to a 6.2-point deficit in the IQs of the most highly exposed subjects.

Contaminants also have been linked to a critical loss of genetic variability in populations of living organisms. One of the best studies of this phenomenon was published in 1994 by M.H. Murdoch and P.D.N. Hebert of the University of Guelph, Ontario. The study measured the variations in the mitochondrial DNA (mtDNA) of populations of brown bullhead catfish in the Great Lakes, comparing bullheads from pristine reference areas with bullheads living in sites heavily contaminated with such pollutants as organochlorines and petrochemicals. The two researchers used one of the most powerful tools of modern molecular population genetics—molecular analysis of DNA. By revealing differences in the specific code, *i.e.,* in the sequence of nucleotides, contained in the DNA of a particular gene, the technique can help identify and quantify genetic variety within and among populations. For their study Murdoch and Hebert examined variations in genes of the cellular mitochondria, which possess their own DNA (mtDNA) that is distinct from the DNA found in the cell nucleus. Because mitochondrial genes are not "shuffled" in the production of sperm and egg cells, as are nuclear genes, and because they are transmitted to offspring only by the mother, they are ideal for charting the relatedness and evolutionary history of species.

The researchers found that although the numbers of fish were abundant in both types of sites, the levels of genetic variability were always significantly higher in the pristine areas. The most likely explanation is that the bullhead populations in polluted waters crashed after their initial contact with contaminants, but the remaining fish were able to repopulate because a few individuals possessed rare genes that allowed them to adapt and survive. Thus, even though the bullhead populations appeared to be thriving in contaminated areas, the genetic makeup of their populations had undergone a damaging simplification, a depletion of the storehouse of adaptations that the animals can draw upon to surmount environmental challenges such as the introduction of a new disease or fluctuations in climate. Their genetic diversity potentially could be quickly increased by the influx of new genes from migrant fish, but most fish from other populations might not survive in the polluted sites long enough to contribute to the gene pool.

In some of the most alarming news since the discovery of DDT's environmental consequences, researchers have suggested that synthetic chemicals can upset the normal functioning of the endocrine system

Hormones and their receptors function as a "lock-and-key" mechanism to communicate complex chemical messages to living cells. Recent research has shown that some synthetic chemicals in the environment can wreak havoc on cellular activity by mimicking hormones. The imposters can either send the wrong message or block vital transmissions.

and mimic or block the effects of hormones on their target tissues and organs. In 1996 Theo Colborn of the World Wildlife Fund, Washington, D.C., and two colleagues, Dianne Dumanoski of the *Boston Globe* and John Peterson Myers of the W. Alton Jones Foundation, Charlottesville, Virginia, published *Our Stolen Future,* a landmark book summarizing and interpreting evidence gathered in recent years that certain chemicals, such as the organochlorines (PCBs, DDT, and others), could interfere with the delicate balance of regulatory hormones during critical stages of development. Known as endocrine mimics and disrupters, these fat-soluble chemicals are passed to offspring in the eggs of birds and reptiles or in mammals through the placenta or in the mother's milk. Wreaking havoc with the glandular system that controls such vital processes as reproduction and

metabolism, they can adversely affect many aspects of the development of the fetus or the young. Some effects are readily apparent, such as in bird chicks that appear normal at birth but starve within days owing to faulty metabolism. Problems in other organisms may take years to manifest themselves, including lowered IQs in humans, infertility, suppression of the immune system, or abnormal behavior.

SEA LION DECLINE

Recent advances in molecular biology have greatly increased scientists' ability to study the genetics of natural populations and to pinpoint changes that may be due to toxic exposure. There is evidence suggesting that the endocrine-disruptive effects of contaminants are causing long-term declines in fish and wildlife populations. Among the animals suspected

of being affected are Steller sea lions. Covering a wide area in the North Pacific Ocean, the sea lions' range can be divided into two parts: an eastern range that extends from California north to the Gulf of Alaska and a western range that encompasses the area west of the Gulf of Alaska through the Aleutian Islands chain to Kamchatka, Russia, and south through the Kuril Islands. Studies by several marine mammalogists, including Thomas R. Loughlin and Richard Merrick of the National Marine Mammal Laboratory, Seattle, Washington, and Donald G. Calkins of the Alaska Department of Fish and Game, have shown that while populations in the eastern range are stable, animals in the western rookeries have declined by more than 80% since the 1960s, falling from about 177,000 individuals to an estimated 33,600 animals in 1994. Since this region historically

ENDOCRINE MIMICS AND DISRUPTERS

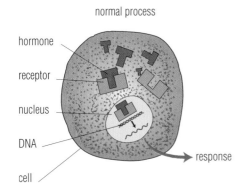

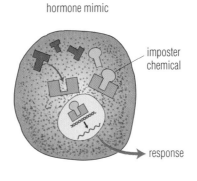

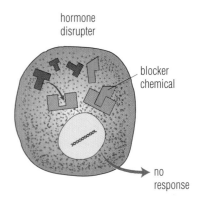

has supported the majority of the sea lion population, the decline is especially alarming.

Scientists have been unable to isolate an exact reason for the decline but suspect a combination of causes, including competition for food with the huge commercial pollock fishery (the hypothesis favored by most of the biologists studying the problem), natural boom-and-bust population cycles in Pacific fauna, and the effects of environmental contaminants. Most of the research has focused on the sea lions' competition with area commercial fishing. However, several scientists, myself included, theorize that the decline of Steller sea lions in their western range could in part be due to the presence of human-made chemicals in the environment and that this decline eventually could lead to the loss of genetic variability critical to the long-term survival of the species.

Each spring yearling sea lions and their mothers reunite with the adult males in rookeries on uninhabited islands or islets, which serve as mating grounds and a nursery for newborn pups. In the past three decades—the period during which noticeable population declines have occurred— Calkins has observed that far fewer one-year-old sea lions have returned to these remote rookeries. Some researchers have suggested that organochlorine contamination may be responsible. Although the animals live far from civilization, they are not insulated from the contamination of modern industry and agriculture. The high levels of PCBs and DDT reported in the blubber of Steller sea lions—the highest concentrations reported for a marine mammal—are likely the result of ingesting contaminants that originated in Asia and found their way into the North Pacific ecosystem by way of ocean currents.

Through the process of bio-accumulation, these contaminants have been concentrated at very high levels in the animals' blubber, or fat. Pregnant and nursing sea lions transfer much of this fat, along with the fat-soluble contaminants it contains, to their offspring. Thus, the developing fetus and the nursing young are exposed to levels of contamination much higher than the adult population. This contaminant transfer occurs at a time in the animals' development when they are most susceptible to the endocrine-disruptive effects of

Biologists approach a herd of Steller sea lions near Ketchikan, Alaska, looking for clues to the decline in their population. Some blame the overfishing of pollock; others cite exposure to environmental toxins.

116

organochlorines. For example, if the development of the nervous system is compromised, young animals may never acquire the ability to learn how to catch food and avoid predators. Other effects of organochlorine contamination could be just as lethal. Some of these chemicals have the ability to suppress the immune system and could possibly lower the resistance of young sea lions to ordinary diseases that otherwise would not be fatal.

SAVING THE SEA LION

Because of the decline in its overall numbers, in 1990 the Steller sea lion was listed as threatened under the U.S. Endangered Species Act. Supported by data gathered from studies I conducted with Loughlin, a 1996 proposal by federal wildlife biologists to protect the western sea lions as an endangered species while retaining threatened status for the eastern population is under consideration by the U.S. government. Making use of the molecular analysis of DNA to determine if genetic differences exist between the eastern and western populations, our studies focused on a particular stretch of the animal's mtDNA that evolves especially rapidly and that does not code for any

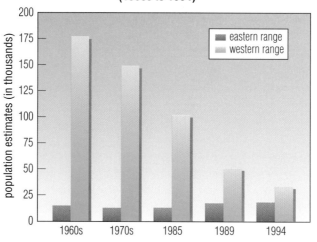

POPULATION ESTIMATES FOR STELLER SEA LIONS (1960s to 1994)

Sources: T.R. Loughlin, A.S. Perlov, and V.A. Vladimirov, 1992. Range-wide estimation of total abundance of Steller sea lions in 1989. Marine Mammal Science 8:220–239.

R.L. Merrick, T.R. Loughlin, and D.G. Calkins, 1987. Decline in abundance of the northern sea lion, *Eumetopias jubatus,* in Alaska 1956–86. Fisheries Bulletin 85:351–365.

National Marine Fisheries Service. Unpublished data.

Although the Steller sea lion population in the animals' eastern range has remained fairly stable, the number of sea lions in the western range has dropped substantially, from 177,000 individuals in the 1960s to 33,600 in 1994. Such precipitous declines may result in a dangerous loss of genetic diversity, as in the case of the northern elephant seal (below), which once was hunted to near extinction.

protein product but, rather, functions as a genetic-control region.

The good news is that despite the decline in the numbers of sea lions in the animal's western range, our study turned up numerous variants of this mtDNA control region—52 distinctly different kinds—in the Steller sea lion's combined populations. One variant was distributed throughout most of the animal's range; the distribution of other variants, however, was limited to either the western or eastern population, which led us to conclude that there are two genetically distinct stocks of Steller sea lions.

The high number of variants indicates that appreciable levels of genetic diversity still exist in this species. However, as their federally protected status indicates, Steller sea lions remain a population at risk. When numbers drop, genetic variation can be lost as rare or uncommon variants fail to be passed to the next generation, and the species is left with a less-diversified insurance portfolio for coping with change.

Conservation biologists therefore are concerned about monitoring not only the numbers of individuals in a population but also the levels of genetic variability in the species. In a recent study Calkins, Loughlin, and I examined the

Although DDT has been restricted in most industrialized countries since the 1970s, it is exported legally to less-developed countries, such as India, where it comprises a major part of the country's agrochemical arsenal.

mtDNA diversity in Steller sea lions, using archived frozen tissues collected in the Gulf of Alaska in the 1970s shortly after the beginning of the animal's decline. We then compared it with the diversity found in tissue samples taken from the same area in the 1990s. Our study results indicate that no loss of genetic variability occurred during this time. Unfortunately, on the basis of past and current rates of decline, statistical population models predict that within the next 20 years many rookeries will be reduced to only a few individuals or disappear altogether. The result will be certain loss of this valuable genetic variability. It is therefore critical that the population decline be stopped now and reversed. If current efforts to restrict sea lion hunting and pollock fishing near sea lion rookeries result in population recovery, then it is likely that no long-term harm will have been done to this species. However, if the decline is due primarily to stress resulting from heavy contaminant loads, and population recovery does not begin within the next 20 years, then surviving sea lion populations may be genetically depleted in the future.

Unlike Steller sea lions, some vertebrate species that have gone through similarly se-vere population bottlenecks did not recover in time to conserve their genetic variability. A classic example is the northern elephant seal, which lives mainly on coastal islands off California and Baja California. At the beginning of the 20th century, the seals were hunted to the verge of extinction. Although the numbers of these animals have rebounded, genetic variation is now almost nonexistent. A new pathogen or other threat could wipe out the entire population, since the herd lacks the genetic variability that would allow some individuals to survive and pass their adaptive endowments on to future generations. Regaining this critical genetic diversity through beneficial natural mutations alone could take hundreds, if not thousands, of generations.

NO COUNTRY IS AN ISLAND

The lesson that persistent toxic chemicals have taught us is that the world is a closed loop in which nutrients, as well as contaminants, ceaselessly flow. Therefore, regulating the use of toxic compounds is a matter of global concern. For example, although DDT use was severely restricted in the United States and Europe in the 1970s, many less-developed countries have stepped up their use of this troubling chemical, legally importing it and other toxic pesticides from chemical producers in the United States. In countries such as India, DDT and the chemical lindane constitute at least 60% of the country's arsenal of agricultural chemicals, and there is no slowing of their use in sight.

Environmental monitoring, regulation, and cleanup transcend national interests and should become shared issues on our global agenda. I am currently conducting studies in the vicinity of Baku, the capital city of Azerbaijan and the center of the country's oil industry, with Gilbert T. Rowe of Texas A&M University at College Station, W. James Rogers of the Battelle Memorial Institute, Columbus, Ohio, and several Azeri scientists. Bordering the Caspian Sea just north of Iran, Azerbaijan is faced with a post-Soviet legacy of environmental contamination by oil and industrial chemicals. Baku's harbor, for example, is so contaminated that the bottom is covered in oil to a depth of up to two meters (more than six feet). The levels of PAHs in the harbor sediment are possibly the highest ever recorded.

In the seaside city of Sumqayit to the north, the leakage of chemical waste into the Caspian Sea and adjacent ponds and wetlands has created areas virtually devoid of life. In other nearby places we observed such wildlife as turtles, snakes, frogs, fish, and birds living in habitats so contaminated that the fumes from the aromatic contaminants soon drove us away.

In this highly contaminated area, we found wildlife tenaciously holding on and humans, mainly refugees from the war between Azerbaijan and Armenia, catching fish in contaminated waters and growing crops on polluted land. There is much anecdotal evidence to suggest that the health of living organisms is at risk. The local cemetery, for example, has dedicated an entire section to children who have died in the past 20 years. Although corroborating statistics are unavailable, the people of

119

Sumqayit blame environmental contaminants for what they perceive as a high childhood mortality.

Places like Baku and Sumqayit remind us that contaminants recognize neither political nor biological boundaries and that the microscopic recesses of our being bear the coded messages that will determine the future of all living things on Earth.

FOR ADDITIONAL READING

■ "High Variability for Control-Region Sequences in a Marine Mammal: Implications for Conservation and Biogeography of Steller Sea Lions," J.W. Bickham, J.C. Patton, and T.R. Loughlin, *Journal of Mammalogy* (February 1996, pp. 95–108).

■ *Our Stolen Future,* Theo Colborn, Dianne Dumanoski, and John Peterson Myers (Dutton, 1996).

■ "Somatic and Heritable Effects of Environmental Genotoxins and the Emergence of Evolutionary Toxicology," J.W. Bickham and M.J. Smolen, *Environmental Health Perspectives,* Supplement 12 (December 1994, pp. 25–28).

John Spaull—Panos Pictures

Pollution is not contained by political or geographic boundaries. Contaminants from the PAH-laced harbor of Baku, Azerbaijan, are transported via air and water currents to places far from their source.

An
Appetite
for
Poison

*Scientists and engineers
are cleaning the
environment by spoon-
feeding hungry microbes
and obliging plants an
alphabet soup of toxic
pollutants.*

by Patricia J. West

In this sewage-treatment pond in
Devils Lake, North Dakota, a
technician skims over a rubber
lattice to harvest a floating mat of
duckweed. The tiny water plant is
used to absorb residual impurities
from partially treated wastewater.

The word *pollution* brings to mind many insidious images—tall stacks spewing black smoke, oil-slicked beaches, underground storage tanks that leak diesel fuel, the lurid green sheen of mining wastes floating on the surface of a tailings pond.

For thousands of years waste products were merely dumped onto the land or into the air and water under the assumption that they could be adequately absorbed by the environment. It was not until the Industrial Revolution unfolded in the late 18th century that the toll on the environment began to surface. In his 1994 book *A Brief History of Pollution,* Adam Markham, director of the World Wildlife Fund's Energy and Climate Program, Washington, D.C., pointed out that societies have long operated under the assumption that the oceans and rivers would wash away pollution, the winds would cleanse the air, and the soil could bury the rest. We now know that Earth's natural assimilative capacity is being overwhelmed by the poisonous waste we generate. As a result, these pollutants are affecting the health of living organisms

Patricia J. West is a freelance writer based in Tuscaloosa, Alabama.

and the well-being of future generations, causing a host of ailments from cancer and immune disorders to reproductive problems.

In the last several decades, researchers have developed many techniques for the cleanup of dangerous pollution, such as excavating contaminated soil for incineration or pumping polluted groundwater to the surface for treatment. However, such physical solutions have proved to be either ineffective or so prohibitively expensive that they strain the budgets of even the world's most prosperous nations. According to *The Entec Directory of Environmental Technology* (1993), cleanup expenditures in Europe alone are expected to top $1.3 trillion around the turn of the century. In the U.S. expenditures may exceed $500 billion. Estimates for remediating pollution problems in the former Soviet Union vary widely, but the price tag is predicted to be enormous.

Recent technologies that harness some very ancient processes may provide hope for a world faced with costly, intractable pollution. The rapidly emerging field of biological remediation, or bioremediation, is helping industries and governments degrade hazardous wastes in the environment through the use of living or-

ganisms. Scientists are enlisting the natural processes of bacteria, fungi, and even vascular plants to break down toxins into harmless substances such as carbon dioxide and water. Often cheaper and less disruptive than traditional cleanup methods, this natural approach to remediating hazardous wastes in the soil, water, and air is capturing the attention of government regulators, industries, landowners, and researchers interested in finding better and less expensive ways to clean up the world's toxic waste.

DOING WHAT COMES NATURALLY

That living organisms are adept at degrading toxins in the environment should come as no surprise. For more than three billion years, microorganisms have played an essential role in the world's ecosystems. Most microorganisms, such as bacteria and fungi, are decomposers; they break down, or catabolize, the organic materials produced by plants and animals and make the nutrients contained in them available to successive generations of living things. In some ways bioremediation can be viewed as nothing more than an extension of these natural processes.

Microbes regard organic

Societies once believed that natural systems could cleanse themselves of pollutants. Scientists now warn, however, that the Earth's assimilative capacity is overtaxed and that toxic buildups threaten living organisms and their offspring.

contaminants much as they do any other food source. First, such pollutants provide a source of carbon, which is the basic building block of new cells. Second, they provide electrons, which are used by the microbes in a variety of electron-transfer reactions to generate energy for growth and reproduction. In the microbial transformation of contaminants, organisms can either "eat" the toxins or break them down in the process of consuming other substances. The end products are typically carbon dioxide, water, and new microbial cells that are generally harmless to the environment.

It is their versatility and amazing catabolic abilities that make microorganisms ideal candidates for cleaning up toxic materials in the environment. Microbes are highly adaptable organisms, surviving extreme environmental conditions ranging from hot springs to Antarctic ice. (*See* Feature Article: LIFE ON THE EDGE.) They are able to break down a diversity of organic compounds and have the ability to transform many inorganic ones as well. Microorganisms also can adapt quickly to changing conditions; some forms of bacteria, for example, evolve quickly to deal with introduced contaminants. Furthermore,

their small size makes it easy for them to penetrate hard-to-reach environments such as subsoils and groundwater. Finally, because the variety of reactions that they can carry out is much greater than that found in higher life forms—microbes have a greater array of biological pathways than higher organisms—they can break down toxins better than most other organisms, including plants.

TACKLING TOUGH ASSIGNMENTS

The biological treatment of waste is not new. In 1887, for example, the first experiment in biological waste treatment was conducted in Massachusetts. Since then, municipal water-treatment plants routinely have purified sewage by using bacteria, which consume and stabilize the organic matter in the waste prior to its discharge into a body of water. Since the 1970s scientists have been investigating other biological remediation techniques, experimenting mainly with the degradation of petroleum products.

However, bioremediation really caught the attention of researchers only in 1989 when the tanker *Exxon Valdez* spilled about 40 million liters (11 million gallons) of crude oil into

Alaska's Prince William Sound. Scientists from Exxon, working closely with the U.S. Environmental Protection Agency (EPA), applied nitrogen-based fertilizers to test plots on oil-contaminated beaches in hopes of enhancing the microbial degradation already under way. The test, which remains the largest bioremediation project to date, was extremely successful. James R. Bragg of Exxon, Ronald M. Atlas of the University of Louisville, Kentucky, and other scientists and engineers concluded that the fertilizer accelerated the rate of oil removal by up to a factor of five. Indeed, the treated areas had noticeably less oil within two weeks of application. The door for further bioremediation study and application was opened.

Scientists now consider bioremediation an attractive alternative to traditional cleanup technologies, since it is less disruptive to the treated site and, in most cases, leaves no harmful traces. Traditional approaches—physical, chemical, and thermal—usually involve the removal and transport of contaminated materials for treatment by incineration, the application of chemicals, or landfilling. These treatments often emit toxic gases, leave contaminated ash and sludge,

kill organisms present at the site, or form by-products that remain more resistant to degradation than the parent chemical.

In addition, there seem to be few pollutants that are too toxic for microbial degradation. According to the EPA, some of the world's most dangerous and stubborn chemicals—petroleum, wood preservatives such as creosote, and industrial solvents—currently make up almost three-quarters of the waste undergoing microbial remediation. Microbes appear to work best on organic compounds, for example, gasoline and pesticides, that resemble the natural compounds that are part of their typical diet. Indeed, the biological treatment of petroleum hydrocarbons, as showcased at Prince William Sound, is now relatively straightforward. This is largely because petroleum is a natural product, and many species of bacteria and fungi already have evolved the capacity to degrade it.

Even some of the most recalcitrant chemicals are responding to microbial treatment. Polychlorinated biphenyls (PCBs)—toxic and possibly carcinogenic chemicals widely used as lubricants and electrical insulators until they were banned in the 1970s—once were thought to

In an experiment (bottom) following the *Exxon Valdez* oil spill, researchers found that an oil-slicked test plot (left) was noticeably cleaner (right) three weeks after fertilizers were applied to speed up the degradation of oil by microbes.

be resistant to bioremediation. However, scientists at General Electric's (GE's) Corporate Research and Development Center, Niskayuna, New York, are researching a two-step microbial degradation process that has shown some success in reducing PCB toxicity. In the more than three decades that GE manufactured capacitors at its two Hudson River plants, the company discharged PCB-laden waste into the river. For years most of the PCBs were trapped in the sediments behind a dam. The removal of the dam in 1976, however, in combination with the occurrence of a major flood soon thereafter, served to disperse the PCBs, contaminating approximately 32 kilometers (20 miles) of the upper Hudson River. While developing a system for cleaning up the PCB pollution, GE scientists discovered that the river's anaerobic bacteria—those living in its oxygen-free sediments—had naturally degraded the polychlorinated biphenyl molecules, which typically contain three to five chlorine atoms per molecule, into monochlorobiphenyls and dichlorobiphenyls, which contain one and two chlorine atoms, respectively. Aerobic, or oxygen-requiring, bacteria then can finish the job by breaking down these partially degraded molecules—known as lightly chlorinated PCBs—so that only cell mass, carbon dioxide, and water are left.

Like PCBs, polycyclic aromatic hydrocarbons—a class of carcinogenic chemicals present in wood preservatives and coal tar—were considered completely impervious to natural breakdown. In a major commercial remediation effort led by Barry Ellis of Biotreatment Limited, however, a creosote-contaminated site in Stockholm was reclaimed by means of a combination of microbe-based

Four common pathways of microbial degradation (below) demonstrate how microorganisms metabolize environmental pollutants in either the presence or absence of oxygen. Aliphatic chains of hydrocarbons, for example, are broken into less-harmful two-carbon blocks. In PCB molecules anaerobic microbes remove halogen atoms from carbon rings before aerobic organisms take over to degrade the rings. In the fused rings that make up PAH molecules, microbes cleave one ring at a time from the structure until the final ring is opened and degraded. In the breakdown of alkyl halides, halogen atoms are removed one by one until common ethylene remains.

techniques. After the site had been treated for two years, the Swedish government declared it clean enough to be developed with offices and residences.

BIOREMEDIATION TECHNIQUES

If the right mix of nutrients and environmental conditions is present, many microorganisms can perform their cleanup function naturally without intervention from humans. Intrinsic bioremediation, as this process is called, makes use of the microorganisms already present at a site and already customized by evolution to use the contaminants as a food source.

More often, in a process known as engineered bioremediation, the indigenous microorganisms receive assistance from humans. When used in combination or singly, introduced nutrients and electron acceptors—commonly oxygen, nitrate, sulfate, and iron—stimulate microbial activity so that the microbes can more quickly detoxify the chemicals of concern. Sometimes nonindigenous bacteria are introduced; these microbes are selected for their ability to degrade targeted contaminants more rapidly than the native microbial populations.

Microbial degradation of pollutants is accomplished either in situ, that is, in the place where they occur, or ex situ, a process by which the contaminants are removed for treatment. Since both strategies offer advantages as well as present limitations, they often are used in combination or in concert with more conventional forms of treatment.

In situ bioremediation is becoming increasingly popular for treating hazardous waste underground because it reduces human exposure to pollutants and eliminates the need for excavation. The major challenge of in situ remediation is getting the right mix of nutrients, water, oxygen, and sometimes additional microbes to contaminated soils or aquifers.

In this process, engineers transfer the appropriate remedial "recipe" through one or more injection wells bored horizontally or vertically into the ground. At a U.S. Department of Energy site in South Carolina, for example, researchers from Westinghouse Savannah River Co. have demonstrated the utility of horizontal wells to treat soil and groundwater contaminated with industrial solvents such as trichloroethylene (TCE). TCE, an organic degreasing solvent that also is used as a chemical in dry cleaning, has contaminated aquifers and soil in most industrialized nations.

Westinghouse scientists use the wells first to deliver nutrients (such as methane or phosphate mixed with air) to the

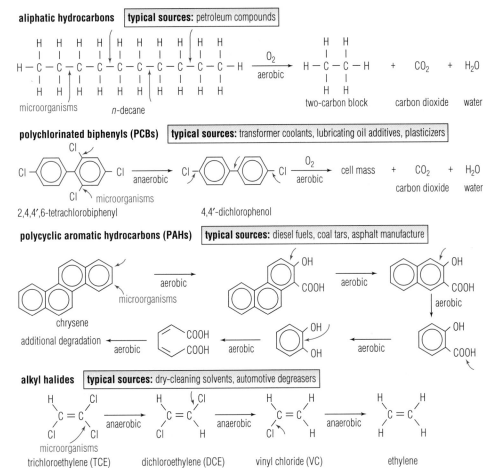

aliphatic hydrocarbons | typical sources: petroleum compounds

microorganisms n-decane O_2 aerobic   two-carbon block   carbon dioxide   water

polychlorinated biphenyls (PCBs) | typical sources: transformer coolants, lubricating oil additives, plasticizers

2,4,4',6-tetrachlorobiphenyl   anaerobic microorganisms   4,4'-dichlorophenol O_2 aerobic   cell mass + CO_2 + H_2O carbon dioxide   water

polycyclic aromatic hydrocarbons (PAHs) | typical sources: diesel fuels, coal tars, asphalt manufacture

chrysene   aerobic microorganisms   aerobic   aerobic   additional degradation   aerobic   aerobic   aerobic

alkyl halides | typical sources: dry-cleaning solvents, automotive degreasers

microorganisms   trichloroethylene (TCE)   anaerobic   dichloroethylene (DCE)   anaerobic   vinyl chloride (VC)   anaerobic   ethylene

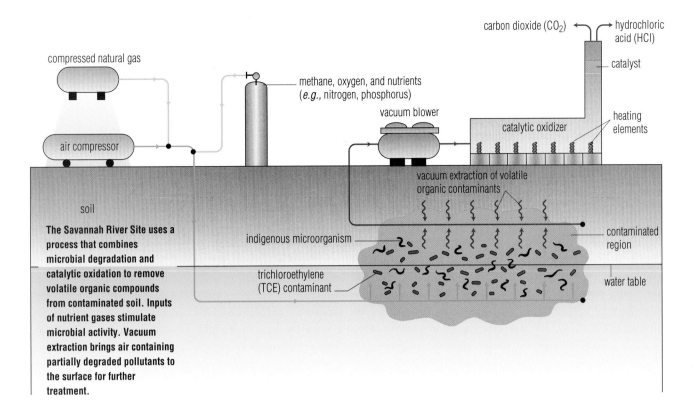

carbon dioxide (CO_2) → hydrochloric acid (HCl)

catalyst

compressed natural gas

methane, oxygen, and nutrients (*e.g.*, nitrogen, phosphorus)

vacuum blower

heating elements

catalytic oxidizer

air compressor

soil

vacuum extraction of volatile organic contaminants

The Savannah River Site uses a process that combines microbial degradation and catalytic oxidation to remove volatile organic compounds from contaminated soil. Inputs of nutrient gases stimulate microbial activity. Vacuum extraction brings air containing partially degraded pollutants to the surface for further treatment.

indigenous microorganism

contaminated region

trichloroethylene (TCE) contaminant

water table

contaminated areas below the surface. Indigenous methanotrophic bacteria, which can be increased by a factor of 10 million with the addition of methane nutrients, produce an enzyme that degrades the solvents. Then the air containing the partially degraded solvents is extracted and taken to the surface for further treatment. Horizontal wells not only offer better delivery of the nutrients and easier recovery of the gas than conventional nutrient-delivery methods such as vertical wells but also are useful for reaching contaminated areas under existing structures, such as buildings and storage tanks.

Ex situ treatment often relies on the use of aboveground biological treatment facilities constructed near the contaminated site. In this case, pollutants are removed for treatment, which often is conducted in specially designed chambers

called bioreactors. These engineered treatment facilities enable scientists to control the conditions under which the microorganisms work, allowing them to monitor the microbes' consumption rate and add nutrients or additional microbes as needed.

The type of bioreactor most frequently used for contaminated soils is a slurry-type treatment system. Contaminated soils are excavated, mixed with water to form a slurry, and then treated in a reactor that contains various types of microbes and nutrients. The slurry is agitated to promote breakup of the soil, aerate the mixture, and increase the contact between the soil and the microbes. Temperature and pH (acidity-alkalinity level) are carefully controlled, as are any resulting emissions to the atmosphere.

Bioreactor treatment generally is faster than treatment of

the same compound in situ because conditions are much more easily regulated. In the early 1990s, for example, the bioremediation firm Ecova Corp., Redmond, Washington, used a bioreactor in North Dakota to treat water and soil tainted with toxic herbicides. In 90 days the concentration of the herbicides dropped from 14,000 parts per million to only 10 parts per million.

Not all large-scale bioremediation projects can be accommodated by bioreactors. Widely used in the U.S. and Europe, landfarming is another approach to treating contaminated soils. Tractors distribute the soils on the surface of a field and then churn them while oxygen, water, and nutrients are added to accelerate degradation of contaminants by indigenous microbes. Special measures are taken to ensure that runoff and leaching from the soil will not spread the con-

tamination. Within a matter of weeks, the top layer of soil is significantly cleaner. This upper strata is bulldozed to expose the layer below. Then the churning process is repeated until all the contamination has been treated.

Joop Harmsen of the DLO Winand Staring Centre for Integrated Land, Soil and Water Research, Wageningen, The Netherlands, has investigated various landfarming techniques in treating pentachlorophenol (penta), a toxic disinfectant, fungicide, and wood preservative. In 1993 he reported that up to 90% of the contaminant in soils could be degraded through intensive landfarming treatment. After trying various treatment combinations, Harmsen concluded that the most effective and economical approach to bioremediating penta in soils was simply to use low-input landfarming for extended periods of time.

CLEANING WASTES WITH PLANTS

The environmental benefits of plants have long been recognized; they recycle carbon dioxide from the atmosphere and produce oxygen. In the past 15 years, however, new advantages have been discovered as scientists search for ways to remediate contaminated ecosystems. By means of a technology known as phytoremediation, a term coined in 1991 by Ilya Raskin of Rutgers University, New Brunswick, New Jersey, growing plants may join microorganisms in helping to restore the world's environmental quality.

Phytoremediation presents a very attractive method for large-scale toxic-waste remediation for several reasons. Plants can remove a variety of contaminants, including heavy metals, such as lead, zinc, and nickel, and organic substances, such as solvents, pesticides, and munitions wastes. In addition, the phytoremediation reduces the amount of contaminated material to be landfilled or incinerated by as much as 98%.

The technology also leaves the land relatively undisturbed; in fact, growing plants help stabilize the soil and reduce the likelihood that the contaminants will become airborne and cause additional exposure to humans. Finally, research suggests that the technology is considerably less expensive than conventional cleanup methods. For example, phytoremediation is estimated to cost about $80 per ton, compared with the excavation of soil and incineration, which costs approximately $400 per ton.

Plants used in phytoremediation mitigate pollution in a number of ways. Some of them take up toxic substances from contaminated soils and water just as they absorb nutrients, water, and essential minerals. These contaminants accumulate in the plant's tissues, where they may be evaporated, transformed to carbon dioxide and water, metabolized to various breakdown products, or harmlessly stored. Vegetation laden with some substances, such as metals, must eventually be incinerated, but the volume and toxicity of the contaminants are greatly decreased. Furthermore, these metals sometimes can be recovered from the ash and recycled.

To date, scientists have identified many types of plants that can be utilized in a variety of environmental cleanup jobs. Viet Ngo of the Lemna Corp., St. Paul, Minnesota, for example, has developed a water-treatment system that uses floating plastic grids to contain mats of duckweed. The thick layer of duckweed prevents the growth of oxygen-producing organisms and thus provides the anaerobic conditions necessary for the degradation of raw sewage. In addition to facilitating the breakdown of organic materials, the plants absorb the abundant nutrients routinely found in wastewater, including nitrogen and phosphorus, reducing the levels of these pollutants to the point where the treated effluent can be safely discharged into nearby lakes and rivers. The duckweed, which is periodically harvested by specially designed mowers, can be added to farm fields as a nutrient-rich soil amendment.

Scientists are discovering that some plants can be used to tackle more serious pollution problems. Plants known as hyperaccumulators concentrate trace elements, radionuclides, and metals at levels 100-fold or more than normal. About 400 hyperaccumulators have been identified from every continent except Antarctica, and scientists speculate that there are many more to be discovered. In particular, Indian mustard and some other members of the Brassicaceae family (the mustard, cabbage, and rape family) have proved to be excellent absorbers of heavy metals.

Field trials conducted in 1995 and 1996 at the Chernobyl nuclear reactor site in Ukraine and at a former U.S. Department of Energy uranium-processing facility in Ashtabula, Ohio, have produced impressive preliminary results. Researchers at Phytotech, Inc., Monmouth Junction, New Jersey, in collaboration with investigators from the International Institute of Cell Biology, Kiev, Ukraine, have demonstrated that sunflowers can dramatically reduce radioactive cesium and strontium levels in contaminated water in six to eight weeks.

At the University of Washington, researchers Stuart Strand, Lee Newman, and Milton Gordon are investigating the ability of poplar trees to

remove TCE. Their studies have demonstrated that poplar trees take up TCE and transpire about 90% of the contaminant through their leaves into the atmosphere, where—preliminary evidence suggests—it is degraded by sunlight into less-toxic compounds. A percentage of the TCE is oxidized into carbon dioxide in the plants' tissues. The team hopes to increase this percentage by genetically manipulating the plants.

In addition to absorbing contaminants, plants also remediate the environment by releasing enzymes (proteins that promote chemical reactions) and exudates—sugars, alcohols, and acids—directly into the soil. Laboratory and field tests conducted by Steven Mc-Cutcheon and Lee Wolfe at the EPA's laboratory in Athens, Georgia, have identified three enzymes in sediments and soils that completely degrade organic chemicals, including munitions wastes such as trinitrotoluene (TNT) and plastic explosives, both of which are common on military bases. Their research indicates that enzymes produced by common pond weeds such as parrot's feather can actually degrade TNT in water to nondetectable levels. EPA researchers have identified beneficial enzymes in several other plants as well, including poplars, Eurasian water milfoil, and algae, and currently are screening others, in particular, native plants.

Plants perform this cleanup role in the root zone, or rhizosphere, where roots support associated microbial communities. The mycorrhizae fungi that grow in concert with plant roots, for example, secrete enzymes that degrade organic compounds in ways that bacteria cannot. The roots also pump oxygen into this underground microbial habitat, which ensures the aerobic supply necessary for many chemical transformations.

Using these natural plant systems to technological advantage is still very new, but laboratory experiments suggest that plant roots and the microbial communities they sustain may offer an important treatment strategy in the future.

CHALLENGES FOR BIOREMEDIATION

Scientists warn that microbial bioremediation, in spite of its promises, is not a panacea for pollution. Still in its infancy, the technology has many limitations. For example, not all pollutants are amenable to bioremediation, although the number of organic and inorganic compounds that can be treated by means of biological systems is growing. Furthermore, the technology is considerably slower in most cases

The Lemna Corp., a U.S. company, has pioneered a phytoremedial approach to wastewater treatment using floating mats of the tiny duckweed plant (top). Some installations, such as one for the town of Gorgonzola, Italy (left), are enhanced by parklike landscaping.

Photographs, Lemna USA, Inc.

Phytotech, Inc.; photograph, Slavik Dushenkov

Plants are able to break down contaminants through chemical processes in their root zones and leaves or accumulate pollutants in their tissues, which can be harvested for further treatment. In as little as six to eight weeks, these sunflowers (left) have been shown to significantly reduce levels of radioactive cesium and strontium in a contaminated pond near the disabled Chernobyl nuclear reactor in Ukraine.

nutrients (*e.g.*, nitrogen, phosphorus, potassium)

oxygen (O_2) and water (H_2O)

contaminants collect in leaves

phytotransformation

phytoaccumulation

photosynthesis breaks down organic contaminants

contaminants collect in wood

transported to hazardous waste facility for incineration, recycling, or disposal

carbon dioxide (CO_2)

wood harvested

phytostimulation

roots secrete compounds to stimulate microbial growth

plant uses nutrients

microbes break contaminants down into nutrients and degraded wastes

degraded wastes

soil contaminants (*e.g.*, heavy metals, organic contaminants)

than physically removing the offending water or soil.

Similar concerns have been expressed for phytoremediation. For example, because of the limited depth of most plants' root systems, phytoremediation will most likely be effective only for shallow contamination. Concerns about the potential for wildlife to ingest contaminated plants and then carry toxins through the food chain are being investigated. How to dispose of metal-enriched plants once they have been harvested also remains a matter of scientific debate.

In addition, bioremediation often requires very precise environmental conditions that are difficult to maintain in the field. In order for microorganisms to break down waste, a number of important conditions must be met. The temperature of the environment must be right, as must the pH. Nutrients and electron acceptors (such as oxygen for aerobic respiration) must be present in sufficient quantities as well. One of the most difficult challenges is creating an appropriate recipe of microbes for treating a site that contains a complex mixture of contaminants. Sites often are tainted with multiple compounds that have vastly different chemical properties and thus require a highly site-specific cleanup approach.

To solve such problems, biotechnology is making it possible for scientists to fine-tune naturally occurring microbes through genetic engineering. Techniques such as gene splicing and DNA manipulation are creating new forms of microbes specially designed to degrade problematic chemicals or groups of chemicals.

"Souped-up" microbes offer some definite advantages for degrading hazardous waste. First, genetic material from several strains can be combined into a single, more powerful strain of microorganism. Engineered microbes often can be grown at much higher concentrations and at a lower cost than natural microbes. Furthermore, engineered microorganisms are created with precise molecular techniques that potentially can produce organisms more predictable than those found in nature.

However, before any of

these strains of engineered microbes can be used in large-scale applications, scientists must overcome the public's fear of microorganisms and resistance to their use in the open environment, as well as the uncertainty of many in the scientific community about what constitutes a safe release of created strains of microorganisms. To date, release of such microorganisms is tightly regulated, and few have been used outside the laboratory or in other controlled settings, such as bioreactors.

Scientists are addressing these concerns by creating microorganisms that have built-in biological control mechanisms. For example, M. Carmen Ronchel and colleagues of the Spanish Council for Scientific Research, Madrid, have constructed a bacterium that survives only in the presence of alkylbenzoates and dies when the contaminants have been consumed.

Before the effectiveness of any microbial application can be determined, however, researchers must resolve numerous regulatory questions and determine the standards that remediated environments must meet in order to receive a clean bill of health. Because regulators in the U.S. and other countries are uncertain about what constitutes acceptable risk

when it comes to toxic pollutants, there have been conflicting views about the usefulness of the technology. Clearly, consensus on performance standards must be reached and acceptable ways to ensure those standards must be put in place before bioremediation can be more widely used.

THE FUTURE

In spite of some uncertainty about its effectiveness, bioremediation has enormous potential for many of the still-unsolved contamination problems we face. Some scientists predict, for example, that bioremediation may even play a role in global problems, such as the removal of greenhouse gases from the atmosphere in order to limit global warming.

The technology also has enormous potential for mitigating pollution at its source before it creates a cleanup problem. Scientists currently are investigating ways to treat materials biologically before they are released to the environment. At the University of Lund, Sweden, scientists are using bacteria to remove up to 90% of the inorganic sulfur from coal in an attempt to decrease the amount of sulfur dioxide emitted to the atmosphere when the fuel is burned by power plants.

The wide-ranging potential of bioremediation is just now coming of age. Scientists' increased knowledge of how to use nature's inherent cleansing abilities may help lead us into the 21st century by creating the cleaner, healthier world we will all want to live in.

FOR ADDITIONAL READING

■ "Bioremediation," Ronald M. Atlas, *Chemical & Engineering News* (April 3, 1995, pp. 32–42).

■ *Bioremediation,* Katherine H. Baker and Diane S. Herson, eds. (McGraw-Hill, Inc., 1994).

■ "Bioremediation: Healing the Environment Naturally," Robert Keeler, *R&D Magazine* (July 1991, pp. 34–40).

■ *Bioremediation Engineering,* John T. Cookson, Jr. (McGraw-Hill, Inc., 1995).

■ *Handbook of Bioremediation,* Robert D. Norris *et al.* (CRC Press, Inc., 1994).

■ *Microbial Ecology: Fundamentals and Applications,* Ronald M. Atlas and Richard Bartha (Benjamin/Cummings Publishing Co., Inc., 1993).

■ "Off-the-Shelf Bugs Hungrily Gobble Our Nastiest Pollutants," James D. Snyder, *Smithsonian* (April 1993, pp. 67–76).

■ *Pollution: Ecology and Biotreatment,* Sharron McEldowney, David J. Hardman, and Stephen Waite (Longman Scientific & Technical, 1993).

■ *Practical Environmental Bioremediation,* R. Barry King (Lewis Publishers, 1992).

Plants known as hyperaccumulators can concentrate pollutants at levels 100 times that of ordinary plants. The Brassicaceae family, which includes the rape plant (below), has been shown to be especially effective in absorbing heavy metals.

The Life
and
Science
of
Neanderthals

by Karen R. Rosenberg

*For nearly 150 years Neanderthals
have captured the imagination of
scientists and the general public
alike. Despite dramatic new
revelations about their lives,
however, Neanderthals remain
in many ways as intriguing as ever.*

Details in Matt Mahurin's
illustration imaginatively trace the
course of human ancestry from apes
to modern humans. The place of
Neanderthals along this
evolutionary continuum is one of the
most hotly contested issues in
anthropology today.

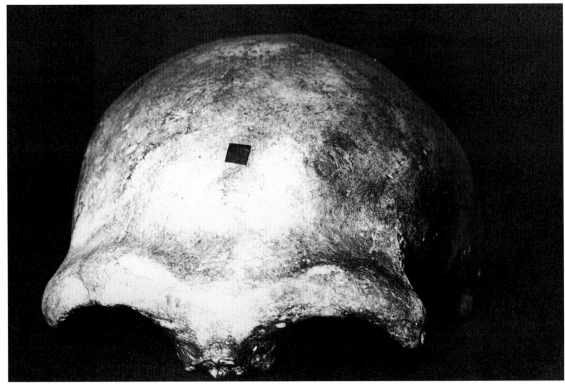

On a summer day in 1856 a group of German stone-cutters working in a quarry in the Neander Valley near Düsseldorf uncovered a skull tucked away in a hard-to-reach limestone grotto. Thinking that it belonged to an ancient cave bear, the men continued digging until they had added bones of the thigh, arm, and shoulder, a few ribs, and part

Karen R. Rosenberg is an Associate Professor in the Department of Anthropology at the University of Delaware.

of a pelvis. Although they didn't realize it at the time, the workers had stumbled on one of the most important anthropological finds in history—the bones of a Neanderthal, the first identified fossils of an extinct human ancestor.

The discovery touched off a fascination with Neanderthals that after nearly 150 years shows no sign of abating. In the 19th century the Neander Valley skull with its jutting brow and chinless jaw was used by some to support one of the most radical scientific ideas of the time—Charles Darwin's theory of evolution. Proponents

claimed that the fossil provided the "missing link" between modern humans and apes. Indeed, many early reconstructions portrayed Neanderthals as hairy, apelike half-humans with beetle brows and sloping foreheads, their postures stooped and their stance bent at the knee.

Although scientists have since demonstrated that the path of human evolution has been less straightforward than initially thought, the enthusiasm for Neanderthals has not diminished. If anything, Neanderthals have become even more familiar, if not necessar-

ily more accurately portrayed, as they have peopled popular culture in the form of cartoon cavemen like Alley Oop, Fred Flintstone, or the characters in Gary Larson's "Far Side" parodies. Neanderthals also have served as central characters in the popular fiction of such writers as Jean Auel (*The Clan of the Cave Bear*), Björn Kurtén (*Dance of the Tiger*), and William Golding (*The Inheritors*). Even the word *Neanderthal* has entered the vernacular as a pejorative term used to describe a brutish, backward-looking person who exhibits more brawn than brains.

(Opposite page) Roger-Viollet/Gamma Liaison Network; (top) American Museum of Natural History/Photo Researchers Inc.; (bottom) ©JonesFilm/Shooting Star

The discovery of the first known Neanderthal skull (opposite) in 1856 touched off a fascination with Neanderthals that continues to the present day. A 1920 mural (top) by Charles R. Knight is imbued with the romanticized primitivism of its time. The 1985 film *The Clan of the Cave Bear* (below) blends modern science with entertainment.

Neanderthals also have continued to be a source of fascination—and controversy—for scientists. In the mid-19th century discoveries of their fossils quickly spread from the Neander Valley to Gibraltar, Belgium, and then throughout Europe and the Near East. The numerous limestone caves in these regions, whose shelter and soil chemistry provided excellent conditions for the preservation of bone, yielded a wealth of material. To date, the collection of Neanderthal fossils includes several hundred individuals. Some are represented by only small fragments of bone or teeth. Because Neanderthals practiced burial of their dead, however, many fossils encompass virtually complete skeletons, allowing paleoanthropologists to examine issues of evolutionary change, sexual dimorphism (physical differences between males and females), growth and development, and regional variation in morphology (physical structure). New scientific techniques that spotlight this growing fossil database in unprecedented detail and accuracy have generated ever-changing insights into the nature of Neanderthal anatomy and behavior.

Interestingly, although our knowledge of Neanderthals has increased dramatically, many

Because Neanderthals buried their dead, the fossil record contains numerous examples of complete skeletons, including these 60,000-year-old remains of a male Neanderthal from Kebara in Israel.

present-day concerns continue to revolve around the same questions that anthropologists asked more than a century ago, namely, how similar were Neanderthals to living humans, and what is their place in modern human ancestry? Sometime around 35,000 years ago, Middle Eastern and European humans shifted from a form typical of Neanderthals to one similar to the people of these regions today. What caused this shift? Did Neanderthals

contribute to the ancestry of modern humans, or did they become extinct? These are some of the most hotly contested questions in the field of human evolution today.

WHO WERE THE NEANDERTHALS?

Neanderthals were archaic humans who lived in Europe and Western Asia approximately 35,000–130,000 years ago during the early part of the late

Pleistocene Epoch. They evolved from earlier archaic populations throughout much of their range, namely, *Homo erectus* and several intermediate forms of early archaic *Homo sapiens,* which exhibited evolutionary trends in the direction of Neanderthals. They differed from these earlier populations primarily in their larger brain cases and smaller back teeth.

Neanderthals took their name from the Neander Valley, where the first recognized fossils were found (the silent "h" in *thal*—in German, "valley"—has been dropped in modern German to reflect the pronunciation, leading to the variant spelling, Neandertal). They covered a wide geographic area ranging from the Atlantic Coast of western Europe to as far east as Uzbekistan in Central Asia and from Germany and Belgium in northern Europe to the Mediterranean. Neanderthals are by far the best-known human group from this time period, although there were other contemporaneous archaic humans living throughout the Old World.

The regions inhabited by Neanderthals included wide climatic variations ranging from temperate to cold habitats. In general, however, Neanderthals lived in a world considerably colder than today's and were subject to the dramatic climatic and ecological fluctuations that occurred near the end of the last ice age (known as the Würm Glacial Stage in Alpine Europe and the Weichsel Glacial Stage in northwestern Europe). Neanderthals often were subjected to tough climatic conditions and lived alongside now-extinct Pleistocene species of mammals.

In many important respects Neanderthal anatomy was not much different from that of modern humans. Contrary to popular wisdom, Neanderthal brains were not significantly larger than those of modern humans. The size of their posterior teeth, range of arm and leg motion, upright posture, and efficient bipedalism also exhibited no marked differences. Examination of Neanderthal pelvic anatomy reveals a fully modern mechanism of birth.

What distinguished Neanderthals most from modern humans was their skull. A receding forehead gave way to a long protruding face with jaws and teeth positioned far forward. Their front teeth were large and exhibited a characteristic wear that suggests they were used not only for eating but also for other purposes, such as a third hand for holding or gripping objects.

Many Neanderthals also lacked a defined chin. One of their most prominent—and most often caricatured—features was the large browridge, or supraorbital torus, that formed a prominent bar of bone over the eyes. At the back of the skull was a bulge known as an occipital bun to which powerful neck muscles were

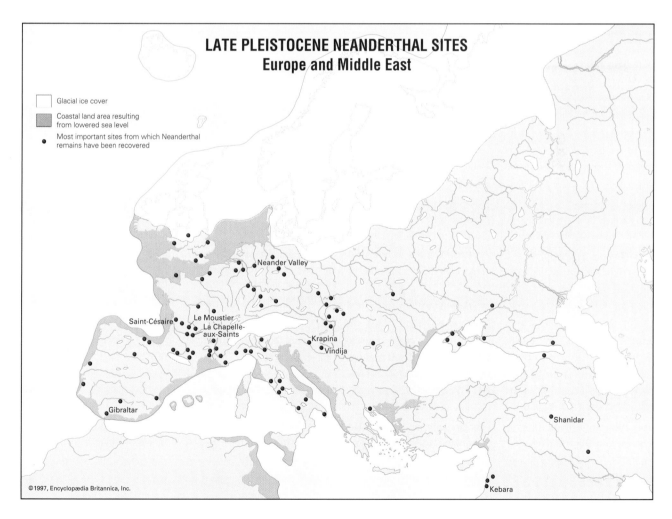

LATE PLEISTOCENE NEANDERTHAL SITES
Europe and Middle East

Glacial ice cover

Coastal land area resulting from lowered sea level

Most important sites from which Neanderthal remains have been recovered

Neander Valley

Saint-Césaire

Le Moustier

La Chapelle-aux-Saints

Krapina

Vindija

Gibraltar

Shanidar

Kebara

©1997, Encyclopædia Britannica, Inc.

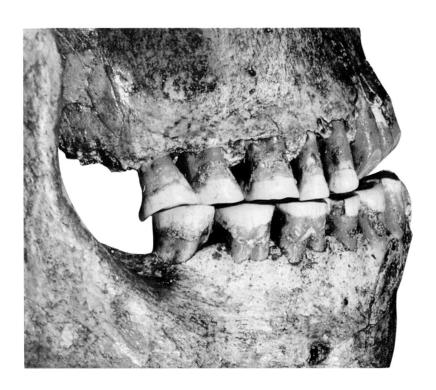

attached. According to scientists, these strong, rugged features were adapted to chewing, as well as to the tearing of animal skins and the clamping of objects.

Neanderthals exhibited this kind of robustness in other parts of their bodies as well. Although they were not very tall—estimates of European Neanderthal height average about 165 centimeters (5½ feet) for males and 156 centimeters (5 feet) for females— they were probably at the high end for muscular "hulkishness" in human evolution and weighed about 20% more than most modern humans of the same stature. Analysis of Neanderthal bone dimensions indicates that they had large joint surfaces and relatively short forearms and distal legs (below the knees). Their chests were broad and their trunks barrel-shaped.

These morphological features gave Neanderthals the greater-than-average musculoskeletal strength that their active lives demanded. In the past 20 years studies of bone cross-sections have revealed insights into the daily activities of Neanderthals. Using computed tomography scans and X-rays, researchers have measured the width and distribution of corti-

The rounded front teeth of this individual from the Shanidar site in Iraq (top) exhibit signs of wear typically associated with Neanderthals. Scientists theorize that Neanderthals used their large teeth as a third hand for holding or gripping objects, such as clamping the ends of animal skins while tearing them (right).

cal bone, the dense outer layer of bones that is built up through the stresses of repetitive activities. These studies indicate that the long-bone shafts of Neanderthals' upper and lower limbs were hypertrophied (excessively developed) compared to most modern humans, indicating that Neander-

thals would have registered at the high end of the human range of strength. Researchers also noted marked asymmetry between right and left sides, demonstrating that like modern humans Neanderthals had hand preferences. In fact, the differences in the cortical bone layers of their preferred arms

shafts and the curved long bones of the lower limbs.

The anatomy of Neanderthals also reflects several adaptations to their cold environment. Their noses were large and wide, helping to warm and humidify cold, dry air before it entered the lungs. The shape of Neanderthal bodies is consistent with the Bergmann and Allen rules, which state that cold-adapted mammals tend to be bulkier than members of the same species in warm climates and that they tend to have shorter distal-limb segments (those farthest from the trunk of the body). These physical adaptations minimize the ratio of surface (skin area) to volume (body mass) in order to conserve body heat. This can be accomplished in one of two ways: increasing body size or shortening distal limb segments and increasing the volume of body mass in the trunk. Neanderthals optimized their heat conservation by adopting both strategies. In Neanderthals the short limbs and barrel-shaped trunk reduced the percentage of body mass located far from the body core, where heat loss is highest.

TOOLS OF THE PAST

Early studies of Neanderthals tended to focus on their phylogenetic status—that is, on their

show an extreme degree of asymmetry matched in living humans only by professional tennis players.

The studies also reveal additional details about Neanderthal life. Although Neanderthals had a powerful grip, for example, these early humans probably were slightly less developed than modern humans in executing activities that required fine motor skills. Early reconstructions of Neanderthal posture and locomotion portrayed them as hunched with a shuffling gait, but new research has revealed that in their lower limbs they were efficient, fully adapted bipeds with greater reserves of strength and endurance than modern humans. The robust muscle markings on their bones, for example, showed that their muscles were capable of great force. Neanderthals also demonstrated the capacity for unusual strength in the distribution of bone seen in the cross sections of long-bone

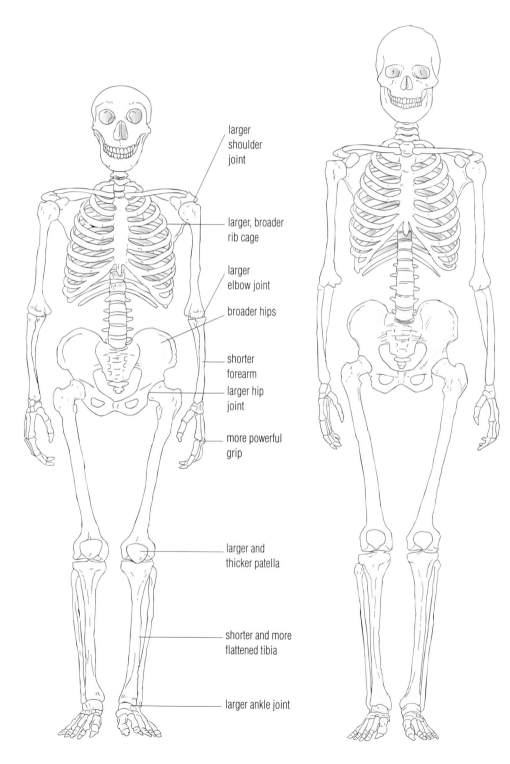

larger
shoulder
joint

larger, broader
rib cage

larger
elbow joint

broader hips

shorter
forearm

larger hip
joint

more powerful
grip

larger and
thicker patella

shorter and more
flattened tibia

larger ankle joint

evolutionary relationship to today's humans. More recent research, on the other hand, has attempted to use the archaeological record to construct a picture of Neanderthal behavior.

Evidence for behavioral theories comes from a study of both artifacts and human remains. The Neanderthals' use of tools has been particularly revealing. Neanderthal remains have been found in association with stone tools that were part of flake-tool industries known as the Middle Paleolithic or Mousterian (named after the Neanderthal site Le Moustier in France). In fact, this relationship between flake tools and Neanderthals was so well established that early scientists routinely referred to Neanderthals as "men of the Mousterian culture."

Neanderthals appear to have constructed specialized tools for different purposes. In some cases, they made tools by using a method known as the Levallois technique, in which the shape of a stone was roughed out before the flakes were struck off the surface of the core. Because the flakes were of a relatively uniform size and shape, they could be further modified into specialized tools. Generalized scrapers and denticulates (stone flakes with jagged edges) dominated Mousterian tool assemblages. Recent analysis of the wear on the edges of these implements supports the idea that Mousterian tools were used primarily in processing and manufacturing activities rather than highly specialized activities related to food procurement or processing.

Tools were generally handheld rather than hafted, or mounted on spears or handles. The stone often was procured at a considerable distance from the place where it was used. Although it has been argued that Mousterian tools were created on the spot for particular tasks and then discarded, recent evidence demonstrates that they were kept and curated for long periods of time, with tools resharpened as they became dull and reused for other purposes as they wore out.

In western Europe it appears that the transition in the fossil record from Neanderthals to anatomically modern humans coincided approximately with the shift from Mousterian to Upper Paleolithic industries, the latter of which included

more varied and specialized tools such as stone knives, scrapers, borers, and chisel-like woodworking implements. Nevertheless, the exclusive association of Neanderthals with the Mousterian culture does not always hold. The remains of a late Neanderthal from the Saint-Césaire site in France, for example, were discovered with Châtelperronian (Upper Paleolithic) tools. Neanderthals also seem to have been responsible for the Aurignacian (early Upper Paleolithic) tools found at the Vindija site in Croatia. In the Middle East skeletal remains from the Israeli sites of Skhul and Jebel Qafzeh, for example, are generally considered to be anatomically modern in morphology but were present in the same stratigraphic levels as Mousterian tools.

Despite this lack of consistent association between hominid type and tool type, many researchers continue to assume that Mousterian tools excavated in Europe must have been made by Neanderthals, even in the absence of verifying skeletal remains. In Slovenia, for example, researchers in 1995 uncovered what they believe is a musical flute made of bone. Although no human fossils were found at the site, scientists assumed the flute was made by a Neanderthal because

it was discovered beneath layers of Mousterian artifacts.

NEANDERTHAL HUNTERS

Recent research has provided new, detailed information about Neanderthal hunting patterns. Early interpretations of archaeological evidence portrayed Neanderthals as scavengers and ineffective hunters. By analyzing the taphonomy (study of processes affecting remains during fossilization) and ages of animals found at archaeological sites, researchers have been able to draw a far more precise picture of Mousterian people's hunting capabilities. Their work has al-

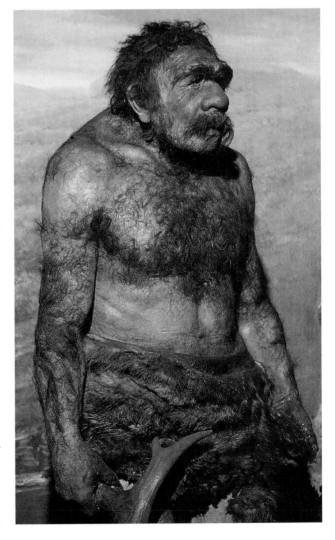

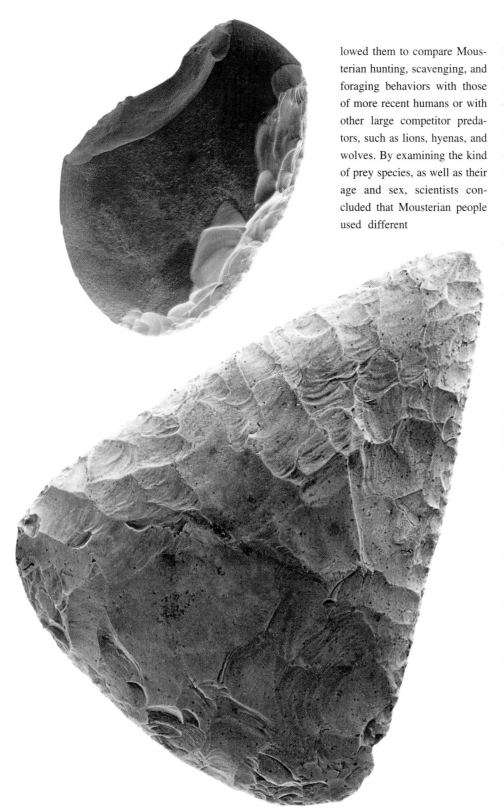

lowed them to compare Mousterian hunting, scavenging, and foraging behaviors with those of more recent humans or with other large competitor predators, such as lions, hyenas, and wolves. By examining the kind of prey species, as well as their age and sex, scientists concluded that Mousterian people used different

hunting strategies than other predators. Furthermore, hunting patterns appear to have changed over the course of the Mousterian period. Initially Neanderthals were probably opportunists who took advantage of weak individuals or salvaged the remains of animals that died of natural causes. By about 50,000 years ago, however, Mousterian people killed adult prey in the prime of life using strategies that involved organization, planning, and cooperation, such as surrounding and distracting prey or taking advantage of various landscape features to pursue and kill prey more easily.

NEANDERTHAL LIFE AND DEATH

Because the database of Neanderthal fossils contains a large sample of infants and children, scientists have been able to assess Neanderthal growth and development in considerable detail. A number of theories over the years have suggested that Neanderthals exhibited differences from modern humans at all stages in the life cycle, including lengthier gestations, accelerated fetal growth rates, larger brain sizes in newborns, and accelerated growth and development during the childhood years. To date, however, there is no

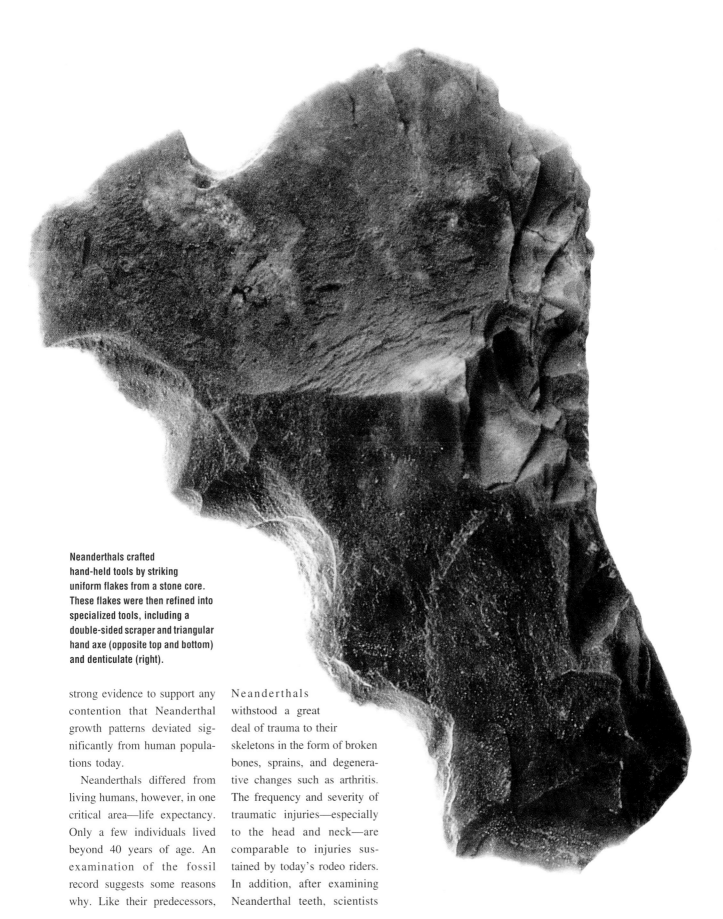

Neanderthals crafted
hand-held tools by striking
uniform flakes from a stone core.
These flakes were then refined into
specialized tools, including a
double-sided scraper and triangular
hand axe (opposite top and bottom)
and denticulate (right).

strong evidence to support any contention that Neanderthal growth patterns deviated significantly from human populations today.

Neanderthals differed from living humans, however, in one critical area—life expectancy. Only a few individuals lived beyond 40 years of age. An examination of the fossil record suggests some reasons why. Like their predecessors, Neanderthals withstood a great deal of trauma to their skeletons in the form of broken bones, sprains, and degenerative changes such as arthritis. The frequency and severity of traumatic injuries—especially to the head and neck—are comparable to injuries sustained by today's rodeo riders. In addition, after examining Neanderthal teeth, scientists observed abnormally thin enamel layers and numerous cases of hypoplasia (defects in the tooth enamel), which suggests that Neanderthals suffered major growth disruptions owing to nutritional deficiencies or other stresses. Such injuries and abnormalities attest to the harsh existence that Neanderthals led, which must have contributed considerably to their shortened lives.

Interestingly, several Neanderthal specimens demonstrate that even some severely injured individuals survived for long periods. For example, one individual from Shanidar Cave in Iraq sustained multiple healed injuries, including a skull fracture that may have blinded one eye, a severed lower arm, severe arthritis, and numerous healed fractures throughout the body. Such evidence suggests that disabled members of the group were cared for by relatives and friends and indicates a sense of compassion and strong affective bonds among members of the social group.

These emotional attachments also are evidenced in the care Neanderthals extended to their own dead. Early in the 20th

Early studies of Neanderthals focused on their evolutionary relationship to modern humans. More recently researchers have consulted the fossil record for a better understanding of Neanderthal behavior. A potentially important clue is this carved bone fragment, discovered in 1995 in a cave in Slovenia, which some researchers believe is a Neanderthal flute.

century scientists noted intentional burial among Neanderthals. Since many early digs, however, did not use modern archaeological techniques, intentional mortuary practices could not be scientifically verified. Recent excavations that have been carried out using more rigorous standards demonstrate that Neanderthals provided formal ritual treatment of the dead. The Kebara site in Israel, for example, clearly shows the construction of a burial pit. Although controversy surrounds the question of whether grave goods were included with the body, the act of burial is a ritual treatment of the dead that goes beyond the merely functional need for corpse disposal.

The presence of a grave alone provides proof that Neanderthals were capable of symbolic acts, which indicates the development of an ideological or belief system. In a more ambiguous instance, pollen discovered in the soil surrounding human remains at Shanidar has led some researchers to suggest that Neanderthals even may have gone so far as to have marked the grave with an offering of flowers.

Recent analysis of Neanderthal burial has added to the ambiguity. In sites such as Krapina in Croatia, anthropologists have noted certain patterns of breaking and preserving human bones along with tool cut marks on human bones that are identical to those found on the bones of animal prey. The results of scanning-electron-microscopy analysis and taphonomic studies of the cut marks on human bones suggest two possibilities. Neanderthals may have practiced secondary burial, in which human remains are buried after death and then ceremonially disinterred at a later date so that remaining soft tissue can be removed from the bones as part of a ritual (as is done in some cultures today). They also may have practiced cannibalism for ritual purposes or subsistence in times of severe food shortages.

ART AND LANGUAGE

Researchers have discovered evidence of other kinds of symbolic behavior among Neanderthals. Although the extraordinary explosion of cave art in Europe occurred well after the arrival of modern humans, Neanderthals nonetheless left behind limited evidence of art. Modified animal bones, sometimes incised or drilled, seem to have been used as a form of body adornment.

Scientists also have found indirect physical evidence for Neanderthal speech. Because language is a uniquely human form of symbolic communication based on arbitrary association between words and meaning, a great deal of interest has centered on the question of language in Neanderthals. The ability to speak requires the vocal apparatus to make the necessary sounds as well as the neurological structures to process those sounds. Judging from the size and the surface details of the Neanderthal brain and the morphology of the mandible as well as from the results of recent studies focusing on the base of the cranium and the hyoid bone (located at the base of the throat), there is no convincing evidence that Neanderthals were any less capable linguistically than modern humans.

In the early 1980s scientists carried out a new reconstruction of the base of the cranium of a Neanderthal found at the La Chapelle-aux-Saints site in France. Contrary to the findings of an earlier study of the specimen, which suggested limited linguistic capabilities in Neanderthals, the later work demonstrated that the shape of the Neanderthal vocal tract as seen in the cranial base closely resembled that of modern humans. Researchers received a more direct piece of Neanderthal vocal-tract anatomy to study with the 1983 discovery of a beautifully preserved hyoid bone from Kebara. The hyoid bone in modern humans, situated at the base of the tongue, makes articulated speech possible by anchoring the tongue muscles and serving as a kind of fixed hinge for the muscles of the lower jaw and neck. Although slightly larger, the Neanderthal bone turned out to resemble the structure of the modern human hyoid in every detail.

The weight of current evidence counters the theory among some scientists that Neanderthals went extinct because they were outcompeted by modern humans who were better adapted to speech and language. Furthermore, the possession of a large brain and modern vocal tract suggests that Neanderthals derived some significant advantages from them since these features also present a number of serious evolutionary liabilities. Large brains, for example, consume a large share of the body's energy and are obstetrically dangerous to both mothers and infants, while vocal tracts

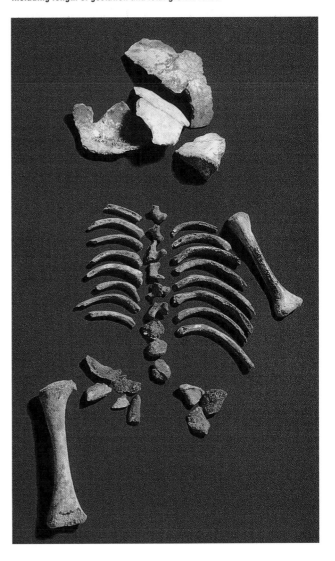

Analysis of the remains of Neanderthal children, such as this skeleton of an infant from La Ferrassie in France, suggests that Neanderthal growth patterns were not significantly different from those of children today, including length of gestation and fetal growth rates.

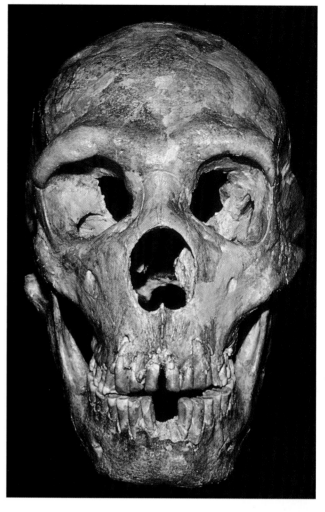

This skeleton from Shanidar shows evidence of recovery from severe trauma, which suggests that Neanderthals nursed disabled individuals. While the arm bones (below) both exhibit healed fractures, the withered bone on the left indicates possible amputation below the elbow. The ankle and big toe (below right) show signs of injury-induced arthritis. A skull fracture (right) likely blinded the Neanderthal's left eye.

increase the possibility of choking to death. The selective advantage offsetting these risks most likely was language and the benefits of the complex social structure that results from its development.

WHAT HAPPENED TO NEANDERTHALS?

As recently as the mid-1970s anthropologists' knowledge of late Pleistocene chronology suggested a simple model in which Neanderthals preceded anatomically modern forms of humans in both Europe and the Near East. This was consistent with the two leading hypotheses about the fate of Neanderthals, namely, that they evolved into or were replaced by anatomically modern humans. Since then the evolutionary picture has grown considerably more complicated.

As discoveries about early humans accumulated in the 20th century, many paleoanthropologists came to regard Neanderthals as an extinct side branch in human evolution and not the immediate predecessors of modern humans. Proponents of this view subscribed to the "out of Africa" hypothesis for the origin of modern humans, which maintains that modern humans are descendants of early people who migrated

from Africa some 40,000–100,000 years ago. As they spread throughout the Old World, these newcomers pushed indigenous populations, including Neanderthals, into extinction.

On the other hand, other experts looking at the same evidence took a more decentralized approach, claiming that modern humans evolved from a network of numerous indigenous populations, including Neanderthals, scattered across a broad geographical range. According to this "multiregional evolution" hypothesis, new anatomical features and behaviors arose in many separate regions and were spread through genetic and cultural exchanges as these human ancestors encountered one another. In this "melting-pot" scenario Neanderthals did not go extinct but would have contributed to the ancestry of today's Europeans and Middle Easterners.

The out-of-Africa theory seemed to receive support in the 1980s from a team of biochemists at the University of California, Berkeley, who compared the mitochondrial DNA (mtDNA) of 147 individuals from around the world. Based on the small amount of variation in mtDNA, the scientists concluded that all humans on Earth, regardless of their physical differences, could trace their origin to a common ancestral population and a "mitochondrial Eve," since mitochondrial DNA is inherited from the mother. This population lived in Africa about 200,000 years ago. Between 100,000 and 50,000 years ago, Eve's descendants spread out of Africa and replaced the indigenous populations of Europe and Asia without interbreeding. As further support

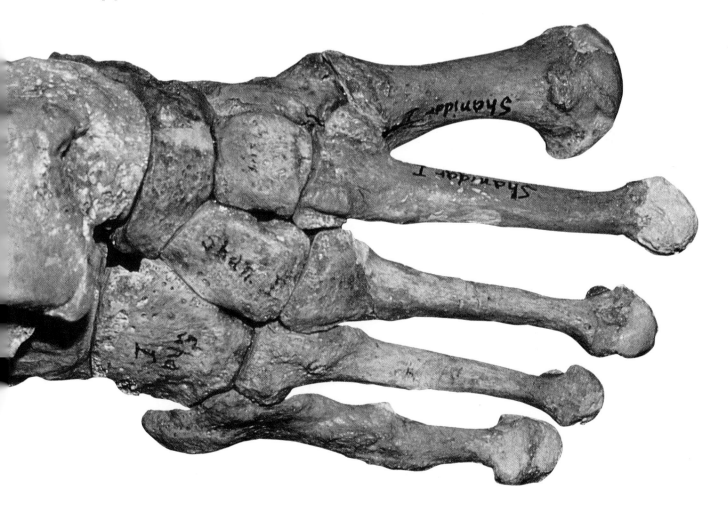

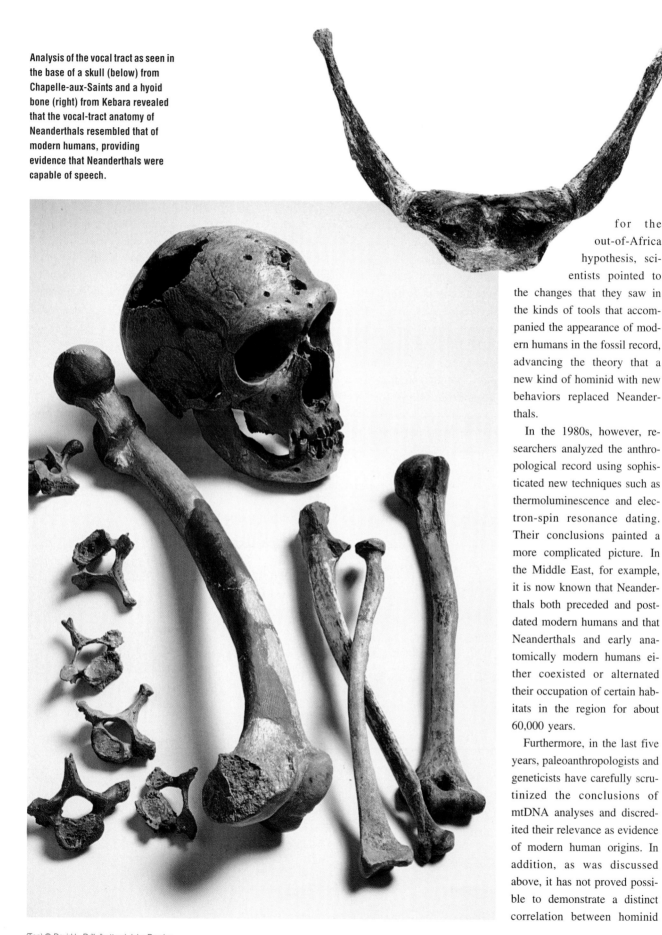

Analysis of the vocal tract as seen in the base of a skull (below) from Chapelle-aux-Saints and a hyoid bone (right) from Kebara revealed that the vocal-tract anatomy of Neanderthals resembled that of modern humans, providing evidence that Neanderthals were capable of speech.

for the out-of-Africa hypothesis, scientists pointed to the changes that they saw in the kinds of tools that accompanied the appearance of modern humans in the fossil record, advancing the theory that a new kind of hominid with new behaviors replaced Neanderthals.

In the 1980s, however, researchers analyzed the anthropological record using sophisticated new techniques such as thermoluminescence and electron-spin resonance dating. Their conclusions painted a more complicated picture. In the Middle East, for example, it is now known that Neanderthals both preceded and postdated modern humans and that Neanderthals and early anatomically modern humans either coexisted or alternated their occupation of certain habitats in the region for about 60,000 years.

Furthermore, in the last five years, paleoanthropologists and geneticists have carefully scrutinized the conclusions of mtDNA analyses and discredited their relevance as evidence of modern human origins. In addition, as was discussed above, it has not proved possible to demonstrate a distinct correlation between hominid type and industry. Tools of modern humans, for example, have been discovered with Neanderthal remains at numerous sites and vice versa. Since there is no evidence of a correlation between biology (type of human) and culture (type of tools and other evidence of behavior), the simple model of population replacement does not work.

The dating of flints taken from the Jebel Qafzeh site in Israel suggests that Neanderthals and modern humans either shared or alternated their occupation of the Levant region for about 60,000 years.

Supporters of the multi-regional theory maintain that Neanderthals did not become extinct but evolved into modern humans. The best evidence for morphological continuity between Neanderthals and early anatomically modern humans comes from well-dated sites in Central Europe. Studies of the human remains from these sites demonstrate a gradual, chronologically well-ordered transition in many physical traits characteristic of late Neanderthals, such as dimensions of the teeth and cranial robustness, both of which de-

crease in size from Neanderthals to modern humans.

While recent decades have seen dramatic advances in our understanding of the anatomy, lifestyle, and behaviors of Neanderthals and their successors, the Neanderthal story is far from over. The period around 30,000–40,000 years ago will provide material for lively debates for a good time to come.

FOR ADDITIONAL READING

■ *In Search of the Neanderthals,* Christopher Stringer and Clive Gamble (Thames and Hudson, 1993).

■ "Neandertals," Rick Gore, *National Geographic* (January 1996, pp. 2–35).

■ *The Neandertals,* Erik Trinkaus and Pat Shipman (Alfred A. Knopf, 1993).

■ *The Neanderthal Legacy,* Paul Mellars (Princeton University Press, 1996).

■ "The Neanderthal Peace," James Shreeve, *Discover* (September 1995, pp. 70–81).

■ *Race and Human Evolution,* Milford Wolpoff and Rachel Caspari (Simon & Schuster, 1997).

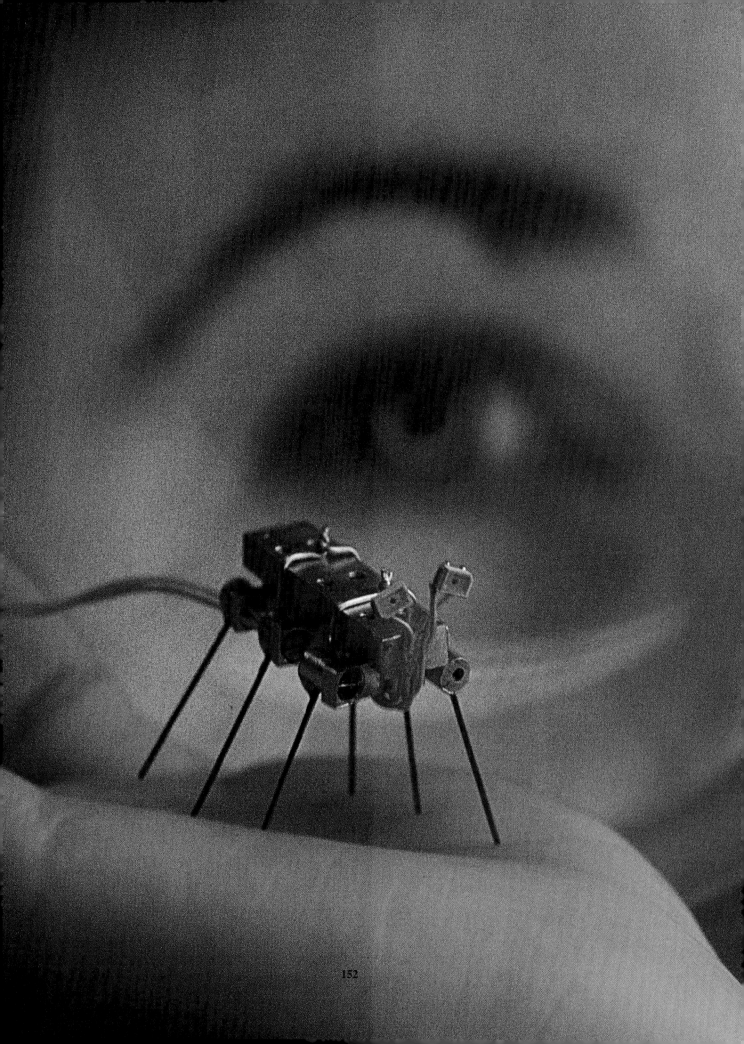

Robots on the Move

From exploring Mars to cleaning up nuclear dump sites, scientists hope that robots can someday navigate worlds too dangerous for humans. First, however, these machines must learn to think and move more like living organisms.

by Gary Taubes

The tiny Gnat, designed by scientist Anita Flynn, points to the future of robot technology. Mechanical bugs like this one someday could be programmed to perform tasks in tight, hard-to-reach places, such as repairing underground electrical cables or performing surgery within the human body.

© Peter Menzeleter Menzel

n January 1993 the robot Dante stood on the summit of Antarctica's Mt. Erebus poised for its first descent into the volcano. Stretching to a height of two meters (six feet) and resembling an enormous mechanical spider, the eight-legged Dante tentatively rose to its feet and scanned the steep slope before stepping confidently into the crater's maw. Eight and a half meters (28 feet) into the robot's descent, the Erebus mission came to an abrupt and embarrassing end when the cable that Dante used as a combination rappelling rope and communications tether snapped. The immobilized robot was unceremoniously dragged out of the crater on a piece of plywood, and its creators returned to their drawing boards at Carnegie Mellon University, Pittsburgh, Pennsylvania.

A year and a half later, Dante II followed in the ambitious steps of its predecessor, this time successfully descending into the volcanic crater of Mt. Spurr in Alaska. While climbing back to the surface, however, Dante II lost its balance about 125 meters (410 feet) from the rim. Stranded helplessly on its back, the sec-

Gary Taubes is a correspondent for Science *and a contributing editor of* Discover *magazine.*

ond-generation robot had to be airlifted by helicopter, but not before Dante II had demonstrated that deploying an autonomous robot explorer was a difficult but not hopeless task.

The two Dantes are among the first working prototypes of an autonomous robot technology that researchers hope can someday be used to explore the surface of Mars, track pollution beneath the ocean, or clean up toxic wastes. For now, however, the most heavily funded goal of the United States, the

world leader in robotic research, followed closely by Japan, is to develop machines that will dismantle nuclear weapons. The U.S. Department of Energy, for example, recently invested $33 million in a new Robotic Manufacturing Science and Engineering Laboratory (RMSEL) located at Sandia National Laboratories, Albuquerque, New Mexico. In time, officials hope to transfer some of the laboratory's military technologies to civilian uses, including the develop-

Using computerized simulators (right), researchers at Sandia National Laboratories are able to test robot motions before trying them out on actual robots. Scientists hope to adapt Sandia technology, such as this microrobot (top), to civilian uses.

ment of microrobotics for activities ranging from eye surgery to searching out survivors in earthquake rubble. "Intelligent machines will terraform Mars; that is, they will be used in altering the planet's surface to support life. They will make able the disabled, safeguard the peace, swim in the veins of our children's children performing molecular analysis and surgery as needed, and using their sensors and communications capabilities, they will carry us to foreign and hostile environments without our leaving

Dante II illustrated the perils and the possibilities of autonomous robot technology after stumbling before it nearly completed an exploration of the volcanic crater of Mt. Spurr in Alaska.

home," said RMSEL director Pat Eicker.

Yet robotic technology is far from being able to deliver on such heady promises. As the disillusioned writer of a recent article in *The Economist* pointed out, "The problem with robotics is not so much with the technology itself, but with the expectations that it has raised."

The complexity involved in programming and designing independent machines that can execute functions that humans carry out effortlessly has stretched—and stumped—the technological imagination. Even such a seemingly simple task as navigating through a furnished room in a reasonable amount of time requires a robot

The dream that robots could someday serve humans as surrogate babysitters (below) or teatime companions (bottom) is not even close to becoming reality. Scientists are far from creating an automated creature that thinks or moves like a human.

capable of state-of-the-art performance in perception, reasoning, and locomotion.

After three decades of research, robotic scientists have not even come close to creating an automated creature that thinks or even moves like a human. Indeed, many researchers have given up for now on the idea of creating machines capable of emulating human thought, including reasoning, learning, and symbolic processing.

This initial disappointment, however, has been replaced by renewed interest in robotic technology. Following a near collapse in the 1980s, robotics research and development are enjoying a resurgence. Instead of focusing on building a complex, pricey, and technologically intensive robot—what some have called a "gazillion-dollar thinking machine" with a centralized, richly preprogrammed command-and-control system—many researchers now are working from the bottom up. Endowed with decentralized "nervous systems," some of these new generations of robots go about their jobs entirely by reflex. Others function under the direction of robotic software programs that have evolved on their own from simple programmed survival and exploration mechanisms to higher-level activity.

Regardless of their technological approach, however, most researchers agree that the immediate benchmark task is to build a robot that can successfully navigate and maneuver its way through a realistic environment.

EARLY STEPS TOWARD AUTONOMY

Some of the first attempts to create independent robots serve to illustrate the huge gap between robotic reality and technological expectations. In the late 1960s, for instance, Marvin Minsky of the Massachusetts Institute of Technology (MIT) set out to create a robot that would view a stack of building blocks and then attempt to duplicate the stack. While this seemed like a simple objective, Minsky aborted the project in 1971. His robot could not image the blocks properly, nor did it have the dexterity to place them where it wanted them. The device also showed a dismaying tendency to try to erect stacks from the top down, rather than from the bottom up. Minsky and his colleagues responded by writing more lines of computer software, but the robot's performance was little enhanced. Minsky later explained that the project had failed be-

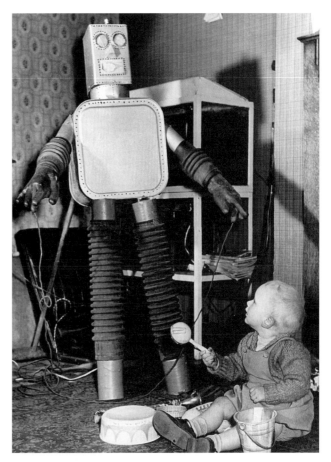

cause they had tried to create a robot that would utilize a single method to achieve a particular task, unlike the human brain, which might use a dozen different mechanisms or strategies to accomplish the same goal, shifting instantaneously from one to another as the exigencies of the task required it.

In 1969 Nils Nilsson of Stanford University created a robot that incorporated greater programming complexity as well as mobility. Known as Shakey, the 1.5-meter (5-foot)-tall mobile robot devoured so much computing power that it required an outboard computer for its processing. Even with these added technological resources, Shakey could move across a nearly vacant room only at the rate of one meter (3.28 feet) every 15 minutes.

Despite its limitations, Shakey became the conceptual template for generations of robots. Like Shakey, these machines rely on vision as the source of the sensory information used to guide their maneuvers. Computer programs allow the robots to analyze the sensory input, plot a course of action, and execute the necessary steps. All of this "thinking" is done from a central processing computer that constitutes the robot's brain.

Key to the scheme is a symbolic representation of the en-

vironment that the robot generates and uses as a map. For instance, after processing a visual image of a room, the robot might then inventory the objects in it. By comparing this catalog with its own internal, preprogrammed representations of the objects, the robot is able to identify them as chairs, tables, or other objects. It could then chart a course of movement around these obstacles, using the symbolic map that it has now created for itself. According to science writer David Freedman, author of *Brainmakers: How Scientists Are Moving Beyond Computers to Create a Rival to the Human Brain,* "The ability to recognize obstacles and follow internal maps has always been considered the starting points for mobile robots, the minimum qualifications for navigational intelligence."

Nevertheless, even such a simple problem as interpreting an image by using a machine-vision algorithm (a program that allows a machine to pick up visual stimuli from its environment and respond to it) can bring the most ambitious robots to a less-than-elegant halt. The problem is that the real world is an unstructured environment subject to continual change. One of the roboticist's greatest challenges is to create a machine that can recognize

and react to a constant stream of shifting images, not just a single static picture. Consider, for example, a project in the 1980s funded by the U.S. Department of Defense's Advanced Research Projects Agency to create a robot truck known as the Autonomous Land Vehicle (ALV). Designed to navigate down a paved road without human guidance, the ALV relied on a video camera that relayed images of the road to the vehicle's computer. By looking for lines that were comparatively straight and converged as they moved

higher up in the image, the computer could identify the sides of the road. Unfortunately, the computer occasionally would home in on a tree by the side of the road, identify its trunk as having straight lines that converged higher up in the image, and aim the vehicle toward the tree. Even un-

One of the earliest experiments in autonomous robot design was Shakey, created in 1969. Despite the enormous computing power devoted to operating the robot, Shakey could do little more than traverse an empty room at a snail's pace.

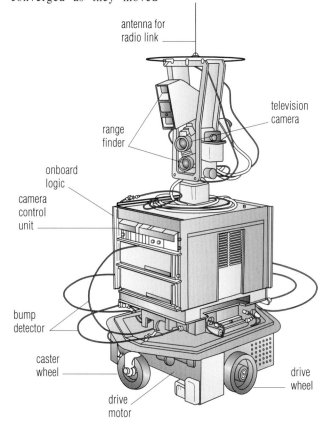

antenna for radio link

range finder

television camera

onboard logic

camera control unit

bump detector

caster wheel

drive motor

drive wheel

Adapted from information obtained from Tom Logsdon

der ideal conditions, such as a straight, barrier-free road, the computer prevented the vehicle from traveling faster than eight kilometers (five miles) per hour. Any hope that someday such a vehicle would be able to pilot itself through the jungles of a foreign nation in wartime receded into the far future.

TWO WAYS TO GO

The knowledge-representational approach used in the design of Shakey and the ALV has met with greater success in

Dante and his robotic descendants. Built by a team at Carnegie Mellon University led by William ("Red") Whittaker, Dante plots out its moves in advance like a human chess player. Each step of its eight legs is the equivalent of the move of a single piece on a chessboard. The rules are determined by the obstacles in Dante's path, the reach of its legs, and its ability to keep its balance. Dante creates an internal map of the terrain by using stereo cameras and then tries to recognize rocks, holes,

The unmanned Autonomous Land Vehicle designed by the U.S. Department of Defense is equipped to drive itself down a paved road. Video cameras mounted on the vehicle's exterior (above) relay images of the road to the interior navigational computers (top) that plot the vehicle's course.

157

or other impediments. Rather than plotting each step in piecemeal fashion, Dante, like a good chess player, will put together a strategy of moves, such as determining the foot placements that will maximize its forward progress. If it puts a foot down on what looks like solid ground only to find that the surface will not support its weight, it will pull back, and its central planning program will reassess the sequence of planned moves.

Mimicking higher intelligence by means of the representational view of the universe is not the only technique for producing successful mobility in robots. On the other end of the robotics spectrum from Dante are the creations of Rodney Brooks and his colleagues at MIT's Artificial Intelligence Laboratory. Since the mid-1980s Brooks's laboratory has created more than two dozen small, insectlike robots that are capable of little more than reflexive actions.

Creator of the concept of "subsumption architecture" (a program approach that organizes and prioritizes the robot's functions or behaviors), Brooks has suggested that the most efficient way to create an autonomous robot is by limiting its processing to simple questions, such as whether to move a leg sideways to walk around an

obstacle or lift the leg to climb over it. Brooks has challenged the orthodoxy—and the patience—of his fellow roboticists by claiming in articles with titles such as "Elephants Don't Play Chess" and "Intelligence Without Reason" that the creation of elaborate apparatuses for apprehending and processing sensory data is not only computationally inefficient but a waste of time and effort. He asserts that his robots have been far more successful—and at a fraction of the processing power needed by robots that take a representational approach. In other words, they deliver a bigger bang for their computational buck.

Brooks has staked his reputation and his research on the idea that all a robot needs to know before maneuvering through the world is what lies directly in front of it and under

it. Brooks's most advanced cockroachlike robot, Attila, is both technologically complex and logically simple. The 1.6-kilogram (3.6-pound) device has 6 legs, 23 motors, 10 microprocessors, and some 150 separate sensors. Unlike such robots as Dante, however, it lacks a central processor that makes the decisions on what each leg should do next. Its apparently complex, seemingly intelligent behavior arises from simple straightforward reflexes that are built into its parts. The sensors, processors, and actuators are all tightly coupled so that the robot responds to stimuli with immediate and correct behavior. If the robot is commanded to walk through a room, for instance, the legs will be sent a simple "walk" signal. Each leg has its own processor and programs that respond to the walk signal and begin moving the leg forward.

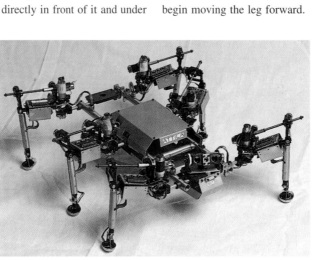

If an obstacle is placed in Attila's path, its front sensors, functionally akin to the whiskers on a cat, will detect the obstacle and respond by triggering a series of steps to either climb over it or walk around it. Meanwhile, the walking behavior of the back legs will be temporarily "subsumed," or put on hold, while Attila's front legs deal with the higher priority of overcoming the obstacle.

The processor in one of the front legs might signal it to lift higher. If the leg makes it to the top of the object, then Attila will climb over it and continue. If the obstacle is insurmountable, the robot will try to walk around it.

As a way to simplify the robot's needs even more, Attila actually "learns" to walk each time it is turned on, which eliminates the requirement for a built-in walking program. When Attila's switch is thrown, its legs flail about chaotically. As it begins to move across the floor, however, sensors communicate the information to the processors in the legs, which take favorable note of the type of motions and timing that lead to forward progress. In little more than a minute, the individual legs learn to repeat desirable behavior, *i.e.,* walking forward, and Attila begins moving at a respectable insectlike gait.

The result is what scientists refer to as emergent behavior—complex behavior that emerges from the operation of simple parts. Over the years researchers known as complexity theorists have tried to interpret various human characteristics—for instance, consciousness, abstract reasoning, or object recognition— as behavior that somehow emerges naturally from the interaction of many relatively simple parts, in particular, nerve cells. In the case of Attila, the emergent behavior is in direct response to the environment; *i.e.,* its programming evolves naturally as it tries to deal with changes in the real world. It avoids what Brooks and his collaborators see as the

(Above) Rick Friedman—Black Star;
(opposite) Peter Menzel—Stock Boston

bête noire of the knowledge-representational approach—the requirement that the robot somehow continuously recreate and maintain its internal representation of the external world even while that external world is constantly changing, both on its own and in response to each movement of the robot. These machines, they charge, are of necessity big and require a lot of computing power; furthermore, they maintain that the robots' lackluster performance does not justify their exorbitant costs.

Jim Bellingham of MIT's Sea Grant laboratory has adapted Brooks's approach in his design for an autonomous underwater vehicle (AUV) named Sea Squirt. Bellingham's goal was to create a light, compact, and inexpensive machine that could navigate the ocean without colliding with boats or undersea rocks. Instead of relying on a costly and cumbersome centralized brain that determines the vehicle's course by continually updating a map of the world, Sea Squirt's moves are governed by a hierarchy of independent behaviors. In this scheme the simplest behaviors, such as self-preservation, are given the highest priority. For

example, if the robot's sonar detects a possible collision, the obstacle-avoidance control subsumes all other commands.

Since Sea Squirt's creation in 1988, Bellingham's group has developed a far more powerful and sophisticated mariner robot known as Odyssey IIB. On its first voyage in 1995, the AUV dived 65 meters (213 feet)—within two meters of the ocean floor—to collect video and acoustic data in a study of marine habitats at Stellwagen Bank off the Massachusetts coast. In the future, AUVs like Odyssey could be used to collect oceanographic data, map the seafloor, or even neutralize underwater mine fields.

BUILDING BRAINS FOR BODIES

While Brooks has dreams of unleashing swarms of his kilo-gram-sized robots to explore Mars or nuclear-reactor test sites, his colleagues in robotics research have vigorously criticized his methodology. His achievements, and those of his robots, have been disparaged as trivial, and he has been accused of avoiding the one endowment that could make robots seem more like humans and therefore more effective human substitutes—an ability for abstract reasoning.

Brooks has countered his critics by initiating research on his most ambitious robot to date. Named Cog, shorthand for "cognitive reasoning," the robot is a realization of an idea promoted by Alan Turing, the British mathematician and computer pioneer who suggested that true intelligence in a machine cannot be programmed from without but must emerge out of the machine's "body" and its perceptual and sensory experience of the real world.

An exercise in basic research rather than an explanation of practical applications, Cog is expected to take more than a decade to reach full fruition. At that time, Brooks predicts, it will possess the cognitive abilities of a six-month-old infant. Like an infant's, its mobility also will be limited. Brooks and his colleagues see locomotion as being too challenging and counterproductive for their purposes and prefer to focus all their attention instead on facilitating the emergence of abstract reasoning ability. Although Cog has hips that

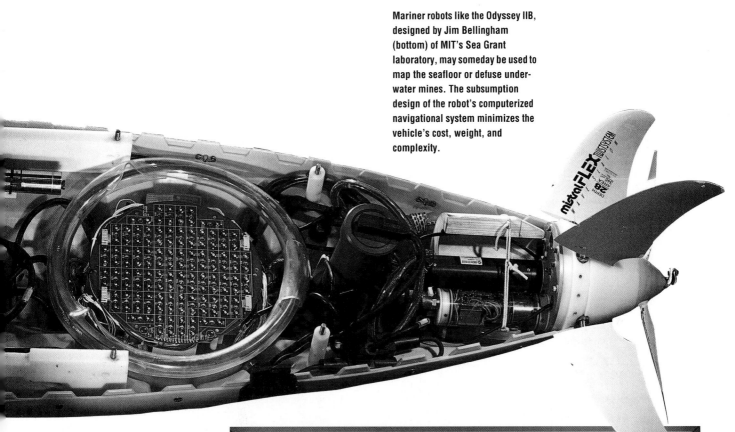

Mariner robots like the Odyssey IIB, designed by Jim Bellingham (bottom) of MIT's Sea Grant laboratory, may someday be used to map the seafloor or defuse underwater mines. The subsumption design of the robot's computerized navigational system minimizes the vehicle's cost, weight, and complexity.

swivel like a human's, its torso is bolted to an immobile base. Eventually the robot will have microphones for ears, video cameras for eyes, and two arms, each ending in a rigid thumb and three flexible fingers. Although it will have enormous computing power—comparable to 64 computer workstations—its brain will be located not in its head but in another room.

Cog's brain will work on the principle of parallel processing; *i.e.*, its various motor functions will be distributed among different processors that all "think" simultaneously while communicating with each other. Separate processors will serve as visual and auditory cortexes and as a cerebellum,

According to its creators, Cog (opposite) will be able to develop the mental capacity of a six-month-old infant. Equipping it with a pair of mechanical arms, microphones for ears, and video cameras for eyes, researchers expect that Cog's "intelligence" will emerge from its sensory experience. To the right, the world through Cog's eyes.

which controls motor function. Although Cog's brain will be simple compared with a human's, its creators hope that it will be able to "evolve" the mental activity of an infant. To facilitate this development, Cog will be programmed with learning techniques to build cognitive channels known as neural networks, which are modeled after the networks of nerve cells in the human brain. Within these networks connections that are used frequently will strengthen as seldom-used connections weaken. Brooks and his colleagues hope that Cog, like a newborn infant, will evolve its own model of reality and its own natural intelligence on the basis of interactions with its environment.

Cog will begin by physically mimicking the behavior of human infants, including stretching and learning to control its arms and then moving on to more complex behaviors, such as coordinating visual input with motion and reaching for a moving object. Cog also will have the programmed ability to recognize a "mother" and to respond with "bonding" behavior to smiles and other physical

gestures. By following a parallel to the learning path of human babies, Cog's creators hope to provide the machine with the circumstances in which humanlike intelligence can emerge.

While Brooks and his colleagues hope that Cog will develop the ability to learn and even show signs of basic intelligence, their critics are less sanguine. They maintain that scientists know so little about the development of consciousness and cognitive behavior that to attempt to program their emergence in a robot is foolish at best. In a 1994 issue of *Science,* Steven Pinker, a linguistics expert in the cognitive science department at MIT, has dismissed the Cog experiment, saying, "There's so little known about the early stages of cognition that it's kind of silly to spend hundreds of thousands a year to simulate what we don't know."

Brooks is undeterred. A

1993 laboratory memo, for instance, coauthored by him and colleague Lynn Andrea Stein, described the Cog development project in heroic terms as "Building Brains for Bodies." The two MIT researchers claimed that Cog would learn to "think" by integrating its physical experiences into thought processes that eventually would accomplish abstract tasks.

Cog also will indirectly test a common, albeit controversial, belief among robot designers that any robot whose cognitive abilities are truly complex—including qualities such as creativity, sociability, and humor—will be too difficult to design up front. This is a corollary of the belief among cognitive psychologists that if the human brain were simple enough to understand, it would not provide humans with enough intelligence to try to understand it. As a result, roboticists are finding ways to let

evolution and natural selection do the design job for them. Rather than engaging in the time-consuming task of writing ever-more-complex computer programs, roboticists are hoping to start with simple codes and then let natural selection do the rest. In this bottom-up approach, programmers write in only the most rudimentary instructions, leaving it up to the robot to learn by trial and error. Robot designers have taken to modeling their programs after the neural networks in the human brain or even the genetic code of DNA in order to provide the plasticity needed for the robots to evolve and grow.

In another example of the bottom-up approach, the Evolutionary Robotics Group at the University of Sussex, Brighton, England, has created a robot whose sole ambition in life is to learn to differentiate a white triangle from a white square. The machine is not programmed to actually find the triangle. Instead the robot uses a programming strategy that its creators have modeled after the genetic code, in which strings of computer codes are treated as the equivalent of chromosomes. Certain elementary codes allow it to move and see in rudimentary ways. Other codes, specifying more sophisticated levels of mobility and visual programming, are generated randomly. The Sussex researchers then observe how closely each set of codes brings the robot to the triangle. The codes that best accomplish the goal—"the fittest," so to speak—are "bred" together to

produce a new set of codes that combine features of the "parent" codes.

Researchers conducted trial runs in which 30 sets of random codes were taken through 30 "generations." In only two days the process of computerized natural selection produced a robot with the ability to home in on the triangle quickly and effortlessly. The researchers then went on to provide a more challenging environment, adding blinking lights, for instance, to the environment to see if the robot could further evolve to handle an ever-changing environment.

A similar approach is being used at the University of California, Los Angeles (UCLA), where researchers have explored the idea of breeding robotic software programs on a "farm" as though they were livestock. Their goal is to develop low-cost software for

Roboticist Maja Mataric is testing the idea that robot intelligence can evolve out of cooperative interactions with other robots. In a puck-gathering exercise (opposite), issues of interference, cooperation, and individuality are tested by comparing actions of behaviorally identical and diverse robots.

Members of the Evolutionary Robotics Group at the University of Sussex used the principle of natural selection, treating strings of computer codes as chromosomes, to design a program that enabled their robot to distinguish the difference between a white triangle and a white square.

fleets of microsatellites in a global communications network. Prohibitively expensive to control from Earth, the satellites could be managed instead by robotic satellite computers orbiting the Earth.

The researchers set 20 small wheeled robots to work on a simple task such as grasping table-tennis balls. The actions of the robots—such as opening and closing pincers or moving toward or away from the balls—are directed by randomly generated codes that in some combinations might actually succeed. The robots that come closest to picking up and

gathering the balls are allowed to "breed"; *i.e.,* their instruction codes are intermingled with those of other successful robots. Those that fail have their programming erased. The new combinations then are fed into the microprocessors of those robots whose programming has been wiped clean. Like the process of mutation in natural selection, some of the newly programmed robots perform worse than their parents, and their codes once again are "killed off." Those codes that perform better than their parent codes are bred again. Researchers hope to use this process of natural selection to refine the codes that someday can be used to control an armada of microsatellites.

The amount of time and number of robot generations it will take to accomplish this goal are uncertain. To hasten the evolutionary process, the UCLA researchers may turn to a commonly used technique—computer simulations in which virtual robots are used to speed through thousands or millions of generations. The evolved codes will then be tested on real robots to ensure that the world of cyberspace corresponds to reality. This simulated approach allows researchers to avoid the hardware and software costs of building generations of robots to produce succeeding generations of software. At NASA's Ames Research Center, Mountain View, California, researchers are taking this technology one step farther. They are designing a simulated environment that connects virtual and actual worlds at the touch of a keystroke. Simulated robot tasks can be tested on a computer before programs are downloaded to direct the motions of actual robots.

Other researchers are exploring the concept that robot intelligence, like that of humans, must evolve in cooperation with other members of its spe-

EXPERIMENTAL SETUP FOR COLLECTION OF SCATTERED PUCKS

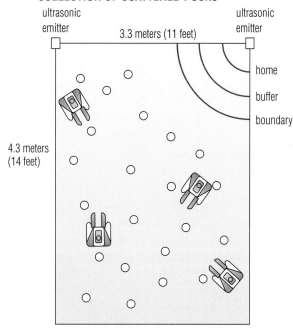

COLLECTION OF SCATTERED PUCKS

cies. At Brandeis University, Waltham, Massachusetts, for instance, researchers have created about two dozen small wheeled robots, each equipped with pincers and a two-way radio, which is used for communication and for triangulating the robot's position. The machines are programmed with a minimal set of instructions that allow them to accomplish a goal within a social context, such as homing in on a particular target while avoiding collisions with other robots.

The Brandeis robots also are programmed to learn as they go. The researchers have built in a scoring system by which the robots accrue positive scores for correct actions related to their goal and negative scores for incorrect ones. They are also programmed to share, in that they all get positive scores whenever any individual robot performs well. The robots are then set to maximize their scores as they pursue their goal. As a result, the robots quickly learn to display apparently altruistic behavior, as well as behavior that is socially responsible. In time the researchers hope to breed more complex social behaviors into their robots.

James McLurkin, a researcher at MIT's Artificial Intelligence Laboratory, has pursued similar research with a community of 12 robots modeled after a colony of social insects. McLurkin's thumb-sized robotic "ants" forage as a group, signaling each other when one of the members has located "food"—*i.e.,* a brass ball the size of a pea. The U.S. Department of Defense, the project's principal funder, is especially interested in McLurkin's foraging research. Robotic ants, for example, someday could be used to retrieve fragments of cluster bombs from bomb-strewn fields.

MAKING THE MIND-BODY CONNECTION

Researchers have looked to insects and other lower life forms not only to glean strategies for the cognitive design of robots but also to find prototypes for physical mobility, an approach that has become an entire sub-field of robotics research known in the trade as "animat."

For negotiating flat surfaces, wheeled robots are sufficient. When it comes to climbing rocky slopes or stepping into holes, however, robots require a more stable and flexible means of locomotion. Roboti-

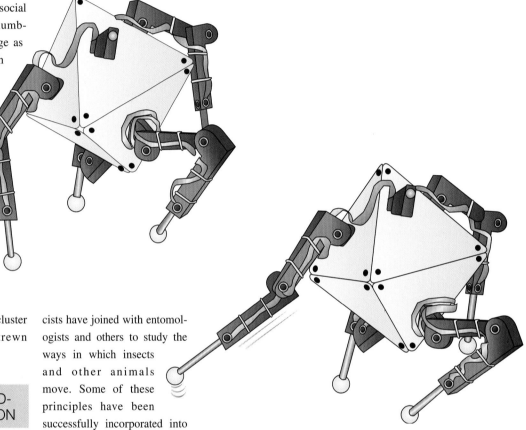

cists have joined with entomologists and others to study the ways in which insects and other animals move. Some of these principles have been successfully incorporated into the programming of robots. Researchers at MIT's Leg Laboratory, for instance, have studied the locomotive abilities of everything from cockroaches to kangaroos and applied their findings to robots. One of the laboratory's first creations, in 1982, was a one-legged robot whose hopping locomotion was modeled after a pogo stick. To date, the MIT researchers have created robots that can run up to 21 kilometers (13 miles) per hour, climb chairs, and perform simple

gymnastic exercises.

In the early 1970s researchers at the Tokyo Institute of Technology responded to the challenge of robot mobility by using the snake as a model. The advantage of snakes is that they have little trouble with balance and can easily insinuate themselves into tight spaces. On the other hand, snakes present a mechanical and programming challenge in their sinuous concatenation of joints and actuators. While the

Tokyo researchers were able to create a snake that could slink across the floor and even wrap itself around an object and tug it home, the programming complexity needed to control all of its joints made the robot slow and clumsy. In the late 1980s roboticists at the California Institute of Technology (Caltech) began to solve that problem. Avoiding the reductionist approach—looking at the snake's progress as the sum of all its simplest motions—

166

researchers instead preprogrammed a combination of coordinated bends, stretches, and contractions. By combining these intermediate motions, their metallic snake, which measures 6 meters (19.6 feet) long and weighs 50 kilograms (110 pounds), can imitate a range of snake locomotion from worm wriggles to sidewinder ripples and do it with impressive speed. In the future the Caltech researchers hope to miniaturize the snake to a size at which it could be used to perform surgery or carry out surveillance within a human body.

To solve the physical problems of robot mobility, Dinesh K. Pai of the University of British Columbia has looked not to the biology of living forms but to the mathematics of geometric shapes. His four-legged, octahedral-shaped robots known as Platonic beasts avoid the kind of robot design that stranded Dante II on its back in the crater of Mt. Spurr. Instead of being created with a front and a back or a top and a bottom, Platonic beasts are spherically symmetrical. They move in a kind of slow-motion somersault, in which three legs support the crystal-shaped body at any given time while the fourth swings over the top of the machine to plant the next step. The result is a machine that can unfailingly recover from the tumbles that immobilize other robots.

The future of robotics seems unlimited. While few researchers expect to see any kind of consciousness or intellect rivaling that of a human's manifested in an autonomous robot in the near future, they are expecting to see robots that span the realm of human imagination—from robots the size of gnats produced by integrated-circuitry technology and robotic fish that roam the ocean depths to machine astronauts that inexpensively and safely investigate the solar system. Whittaker, the creator of Dante and the leader of the Carnegie Mellon robotics program, has predicted that in his lifetime he will witness the successful fruits of robotics research in all walks of life. "I'll see these things out in the world, plowing fields, entertaining kids at theme parks, restoring nuclear sites, exploring

Platonic beasts, designed by Dinesh K. Pai of the University of British Columbia (top), take their cues from geometry to resolve the problem of robot mobility. Moving in a kind of slow-motion somersault, the spherically symmetrical robots recover easily from the kinds of missteps that can strand other robots.

Adapted from information obtained from D.K. Pai and R.A. Barman. Photograph (top), University of British Columbia

the planets," he said. "Not just a few, but whole families of robots—millions of individuals."

FOR ADDITIONAL READING

■ "Birth of a Human Robot," Roger Lewin, *New Scientist* (May 14, 1994, pp. 26–30).

■ *Brainmakers: How Scientists Are Moving Beyond Computers to Create a Rival to the Human Brain,* David Freedman (Simon & Schuster, 1994).

■ "Building a Baby Brain in a Robot," John Travis, *Science* (May 20, 1994, pp. 1080–82).

■ *Designing Autonomous Agents: Theory and Practice from Biology to Engineering and Back,* Pattie Maes, ed. (MIT Press, 1990).

■ *In Our Own Image: Building an Artificial Person,* Maureen Caudill (Oxford University Press, 1992).

■ "Look to the Insect…," Kurt Kleiner, *New Scientist* (Nov. 12, 1994, pp. 27–29).

■ "The Mathematical Springs in Insect Steps," Jim Collins and Ian Stewart, *New Scientist* (Oct. 8, 1994, pp. 36–40).

■ *Mind Children: The Future of Robot and Human Intelligence,* Hans P. Moravec (Harvard University Press, 1988).

■ "Platonic Beasts," Gregory T. Pope, *Popular Mechanics* (October 1995, pp. 38–40).

■ "Robot Ant-ics," Stephanie V. Grepo, *Technology Review* (February/March 1996, p. 13).

■ "Robots: The Next Generation," Clive Davidson, *New Scientist* (Jan. 14, 1995, pp. 32–34).

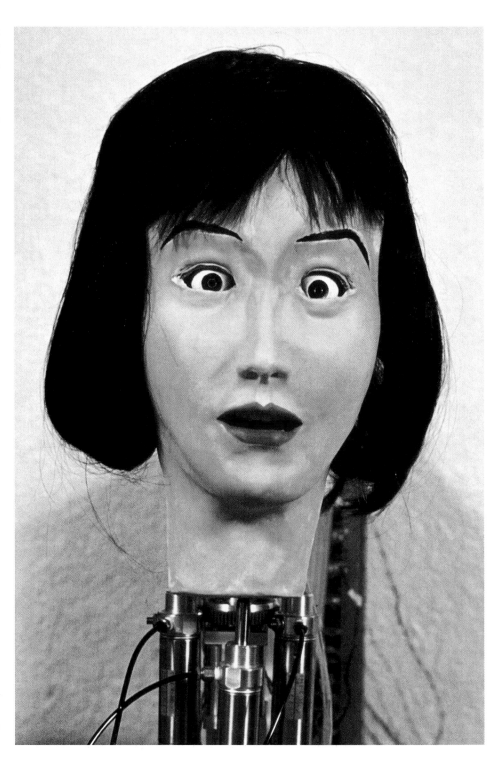

■ *Robots: The Quest for Living Machines,* Geoff Simons (Cassell, 1992).

■ "Send in the Robots," Vincent Kiernan, *New Scientist* (Sept. 23, 1995, pp. 34–37).

■ "The Sharebots," Carl Zimmer, *Discover* (September 1995, p. 37).

■ "A Thousand Diving Robots," Robert Kunzig, *Discover* (April 1996, pp. 60–71).

■ "Where No Robot Has Gone Before," Rosie Mestel, *New Scientist* (April 30, 1994, p. 9).

Fumio Hara of the Science University of Toyko developed robots that interact emotionally with users (opposite). Beneath the robot's silicon face is an apparatus (left) that imitates a wide range of feelings.

Rice
to Feed
the
Hungry

by Robert D. Huggan

Planting rice is never fun
Bent from morn till set of sun
Cannot stand and cannot sit
Cannot rest for a little bit.

—From an old Filipino
folk song

Robert D. Huggan is Head of the Information Center, International Rice Research Institute, Los Baños, the Philippines.

At the close of the 1950s, the specter of mass famine loomed over the Asian world. Population growth, spurred by a greater availability of medicines and improvements in health care, threatened to outstrip the ability of farmers to supply the people of Asia with their dietary staple—rice. While populations surged, increases in global rice production remained sluggish. With several hundred million people already suffering from malnutrition in Asia, it was clear that drastic action had to be taken to avoid the human misery of further food shortages, not to mention the resulting social, political, and economic turmoil of widespread famine. One of the first organizations to respond was the Ford Foundation. In 1959 Forrest F. Hill, then foundation vice president, delivered this dire warning to Ford trustees: "At best, the world food outlook for the decades ahead is grave; at worst, it is frightening."

In 1958 the Ford and Rockefeller foundations joined forces to develop a rice re-

Ninety-one percent of the world's rice is grown and consumed in Asia, where the grain accounts for 80% of the total calories consumed. Here, Vietnamese farmers spread the harvested crop in the sun to dry.

170

The International Rice Research Institute helped avert famine in rice-dependent nations in the 1970s. The new millennium, however, may present institute researchers with even greater challenges.

search center near the Los Baños campus of the University of the Philippines. On Feb. 7, 1962, the International Rice Research Institute (IRRI) was formally dedicated, providing the world with the first international research and training center devoted to increasing food production from rice-based farming systems.

Since its founding the institute has revolutionized agriculture in many less-developed nations and helped avert the calamity of widespread hunger. Despite its phenomenal achievements over the last 35 years, however, the IRRI's greatest challenges may lie ahead. Recent trends in rice production once again have raised serious doubts about Asia's ability to meet its growing demand for rice. Although there is an increasing dependence on rice in Africa and Latin America, 91% of the world's rice is cultivated and eaten in Asia, where rice provides 80% of the total calories consumed. In many of these countries, current rice yields are beginning to lag behind population growth, with pressures intensifying on dwindling agricultural resources. The numbers are staggering. From 1985 to 1995, for example, annual rice production grew at an anemic 1.6%, compared with 3.2% in 1975–85 and 3% in

1965–75. These modest increases come at a time when each year Asia must feed an additional 50 million–55 million people annually. In its 1996 publication *A 2020 Vision,* the Washington, D.C.-based International Food Policy Research Institute estimated that Asia's annual unmilled rice production must increase by nearly 60% over the next three decades just to keep pace with population growth and increased consumption due to rising income levels. By the year 2025 rice yields in irrigated areas of Asia must increase substantially from a current level of 5 tons per hectare to 8 tons per hectare; yields in rain-fed lands must swell from 1.9 tons per hectare to 3.8 tons per hectare. (A hectare is about 2.5 acres.)

At the same time, there is a growing competition for land as prime rice-growing fields increasingly are losing scarce water resources and land area to urban and industrial expansion. As a result, resource-poor farmers and landless rural people are being forced to migrate to urban areas in search of work (which fuels the cycle of destructive urbanization) or to till highly erodible and mar-

ginal lands, a practice that exchanges short-term benefits for long-term environmental degradation. Satisfying the growing need for rice now must be done on less land and with less water and fewer rural workers. To meet these unprecedented challenges, IRRI researchers are bringing to bear a host of strategies ranging from maintaining an international gene bank of rice and testing genetically engineered seeds and new methods of sustainable agriculture to developing new rice stocks whose potential yields outstrip the productivity of existing strains.

Among those presiding over the formal dedication of the International Rice Research Institute in 1962 were John D. Rockefeller III (far left) and Pres. Diosdado Macapagal of the Philippines (second from right).

MODERN RICE BREEDING

When the Rockefeller Foundation agreed to support a rice research center in the late 1950s, the organization could point to prior success in similar agricultural ventures. In 1943, for example, the foundation embarked on a cooperative research program with the government of Mexico to boost the country's wheat yields, which were well below the world average. Known as the Cooperative Mexican Agricultural Program, the initiative proved that an intensive, problem-oriented research and training center could transform a nation of food deficits into one of surplus in little more than a decade.

By 1956 Mexico's yields of wheat had doubled. The difference was due to changes in agricultural practices and resources, including the use of fertilizers and irrigation, as well as newly developed varieties of wheat that could be sown in the fall instead of the spring. Programs patterned after the Mexican model were established in Colombia (1950), Chile (1955), and India (1956). These centers emphasized research on basic indigenous food crops and livestock as well as the training of promising young scientists. In each

As a scientist with the Rockefeller Foundation's Cooperative Mexican Agricultural Program from 1944 to 1960, Norman Ernest Borlaug created new strains of wheat that dramatically boosted yields in Mexico. Encouraged by his success, the foundation established the IRRI to focus on rice research.

program U.S. scientists worked side by side with their local counterparts with the aim of developing strong national leadership and building enduring research and educational institutions.

The IRRI shared the goals of many of these agricultural centers. Its researchers focused on boosting yields by developing improved varieties of rice for the tropics and subtropics, the regions most utilized for rice growing. Since IRRI researchers were not the first to engage in modern rice breeding, they could draw upon several superior varieties of rice already de-

veloped by scientists in Japan and Taiwan. This early work focused on two time-honored strains of *Oryza sativa* known as japonica and indica. The differences between the two rice varieties—which are due to both geography and culture—developed over thousands of years after some farmers moved to new land at higher elevations while others established lowland rice fields in dry land, seasonally flooded ground, or tidal swamp areas. Over time, cultural and socio-religious traditions guided the farmers' plant selections for grain size, shape, and color.

Today there are thousands of varieties of japonica and indica rice grown in more than 100 countries.

Modern rice breeding began in the 1930s when the Japanese developed a series of rice varieties of the japonica type. These plants incorporated such characteristics as stiff straws (stems) that prevented the plants from falling over and upright leaves that could absorb and utilize solar energy more efficiently. These varieties had many other advantages. They were fast-growing, tolerant of low temperatures, and responsive to fertilizers, a feature that increased their yield potential. They also appealed to Japanese consumers, who preferred the short wide grains that, when cooked, were stickier and glossier than those of the indica varieties grown in the tropics.

During the 1930s and 1940s, the Japanese market for rice outstripped domestic production. To meet the demand, Japanese and Chinese plant breeders in Taiwan sought to extend the growing range of japonica varieties by developing plants with a tolerance for the higher temperatures and shorter days of the tropics. The varieties were widely grown in Taiwan and formed the bulk of the country's rice exports to Japan.

After World War II the Taiwan government mounted a sizable rice-breeding program to improve the local indica varieties. Out of this effort emerged a variety known as Taichung Native 1, a rice that combined short stature and high yield potential. Taichung Native 1 was first released in 1956; by 1960 it was widely grown by Taiwanese farmers, often yielding relatively high returns of six to eight tons per hectare.

In the 1950s researchers at the Central Rice Research Institute in Cuttack, India, in cooperation with the Food and Agriculture Organization of the United Nations, initiated a project to hybridize indica and japonica varieties. The progeny from these crosses were distributed to several cooperating countries for trial and selection, which resulted in several superior varieties of rice with higher yield potential.

DEVELOPMENT OF MIRACLE RICE

Although Japan, China, and India had established successful rice-breeding initiatives, many poorer nations lacked national rice programs that took into account the specific conditions of climate, soil, farming practices, and consumer tastes found in their countries. When the IRRI embarked on its massive rice-breeding program in the early 1960s, it sought to address the rice-growing needs of as many countries as possible.

As their starting point, IRRI researchers drew on the established portfolio of improved varieties of japonica and indica rice developed by the Japanese and Chinese breeders. In late 1962 they produced 38 crossbreeds. In 11 of these hybrids, one parent came from a Taiwanese variety selected for its short stature. The other parents were drawn mainly from tall indicas adapted to the tropics.

The hybrids were planted in greenhouse pots, and the harvested seeds were sown in the field, generating about 10,000 plants. All tall, late-maturing plants were discarded in favor of plants that matured more quickly (a characteristic that allows farmers to harvest more than one rice crop during the growing season). Seeds from the remaining plants were sown in a nursery and exposed to rice blast, a common fungal disease. Highly susceptible individuals were then culled. From that generation, 298 of the best plants were selected, and seed from each was subjected to another round in the blast disease nursery.

In row 288, plant 3 (the eighth cross among the 38 hy-

IR8, the "miracle rice," shown here with its parent plants, was the product of a massive rice-breeding program in the 1960s designed to help avert rice shortages in Asia.

brids developed by the IRRI; hence its name, IR8-288-3), researchers pinpointed the plant that later became hailed by agriculturalists as "miracle rice." The plant was a semidwarf cross between Peta—a tall Indonesian variety widely grown in the Philippines and known for its vigor and resistance to several insects and diseases—and Dee-geo-woo-gen—a short variety from Taiwan known as a heavy-tillered (multiple-stalked) plant with a potential for high yields.

The plant's seeds were harvested and sown through several generations in order to amass sufficient seed stock for cooperative trials in the Philippines, Malaysia, Thailand, and Taiwan at the beginning of the wet season in late June 1965. The results were analyzed not only for yields but also for such characteristics as maturation times, number of stalks and flower clusters (the greater the number of stalks and flowers, the higher the yield), degree of lodging (falling over), incidence of disease, milled rice yields, and the gelatinization temperature and amylose content of the starch (determinants of the rice's texture and consistency when cooked). When all factors were considered, the researchers judged that IR8-288-3 (later shortened to IR8) showed the greater

promise over traditional varieties of rice. Consequently, in 1966 they decided to test it broadly and at the same time to multiply the seed as rapidly as possible.

By early 1966 IRRI scientists had compiled a group of 303 varieties (including IR8) and genetic lines that showed promise in trials either as stock to be planted or as parent plants to be used in crossbreeding with local varieties. Their goal was to develop rice stocks adapted to the cultural and environmental circumstances of many different countries. To be sure that this collection received proper attention, it was sent only to research facilities in countries where a Rockefeller or Ford Foundation representative was in residence: Colombia, India, East Pakistan (now Bangladesh), Malaysia, and Thailand. In addition, 300 breeding lines were sent to rice scientists in Mexico, Costa Rica, the Dominican Republic, Taiwan, and the United States. Upon request, sets with a more limited selection of breeding materials were supplied to agricultural experiment stations around the world. In total, 6,000 seed packets of IRRI breeding lines were sent out.

In the 1966 international yield trials, IR8 performed even more spectacularly than it had in the more limited trials

IR8, one of the technological advances that helped inaugurate the Green Revolution, contributed to a doubling in the world's supply of rice. By the 1980s many countries dependent on rice imports, including India, became self-sufficient rice producers for the first time in their history.

of 1965. Not only did it outproduce all other existing rice varieties by a factor of two, but IR8 also matured in 130 days, unlike the 160–170 days required by previous varieties.

THE GREEN REVOLUTION

The institute's development of IR8 was a landmark in the history of agriculture, helping to spark what is now known as the Green Revolution. In the 1960s and 1970s, organizations and countries throughout the world had mobilized the financial and scientific resources to underwrite research that would increase the productivity of major crops in less-developed

countries through the use of higher-yielding seed stocks, chemical fertilizers, and pesticides. The result was large gains in wheat production as well as a doubling in the supply of rice. Eighty percent of this increase in rice production was attributed to improved productivity as well as the development of IR8 and numerous new semidwarf varieties that featured faster growth rates, greater resistance to diseases and insects, and a greater responsiveness to fertilizers than existing strains. The revolution was so successful that in the 1980s several countries saddled with chronic food shortages and dependent on imported rice, such as India,

175

Indonesia, the Philippines, and Vietnam, became self-sufficient in rice production for the first time in their history.

Critics of the Green Revolution, however, maintain that this productivity came at a price—namely, a dependence on costly inputs of pesticides and other chemicals that degraded soils and polluted waterways. A concern for protecting the environment and sustaining natural resources soon made its way to the top of the institute's agenda. By the early 1970s, for example, resistance to insects and disease was being incorporated into new rice varieties. Since the development of IR8, researchers at the IRRI, in cooperation with many national rice-breeding programs in Asia, have released more than 400 high-yield varieties that have better grain quality and higher resistance to insect pests and diseases than previous rice hybrids. As a result, these new varieties have enabled farmers to more than double their pro-

(Right) International Rice Research Institute; photograph, R. Cabrera; (opposite) Heldur Netocny—Panos Pictures

A magnet for rice researchers from around the world, the IRRI's complex near Manila (above) includes laboratories, classrooms, offices, and an international gene bank for rice. At the institute's 252-hectare experimental farm (opposite), researchers test new and traditional approaches to growing rice.

duction from the same number of hectares while lessening their dependence on pesticides.

The new varieties also have boosted yields by reducing the rice-growing season from more than 150 days to about 100. This has allowed more than one rice crop—and sometimes up to three crops in select areas—to be cultivated in a single year. This shorter growth cycle has also freed up land that could be used for growing other crops between the rice seasons. Without the increased productivity, many farmers would have been forced to expand their rice fields by plowing up fragile, marginal lands—such as the uplands—causing erosion, siltation of streams, and loss of wildlife

habitat. Increased productivity benefited rice consumers as well; there was as much as a 30% decline in the cost of rice from the late 1960s to the present.

THE IRRI TODAY

The IRRI's $30 million annual core budget now is supported by the Consultative Group on International Agricultural Research (CGIAR), an association of governments, foundations, and development agencies that funds 16 international agricultural research centers. Among the CGIAR donors, Japan is the largest contributor.

Today, as in the past, most of the institute's research and training is done in cooperation with national and international agricultural research and development institutions as well as farming communities. Under the supervision of the IRRI's 60 core researchers, graduate students and visiting scientists learn new and traditional approaches to growing rice on the

institute's 252-hectare experimental farm 65 kilometers (40 miles) south of Manila. Each year about 200 trainees, most of them from less-developed countries, update their rice-research skills to address their nations' agricultural needs. The institute's research divisions are Agricultural Engineering; Agronomy, Plant Physiology and Agroecology; Biometrics; Entomology and Plant Pathology; Plant Breeding, Genetics, and Biochemistry; Soil and Water Sciences; and Social Sciences. Researchers concentrate on four different rice-growing ecosystems: irrigated, rain-fed lowland, upland, and flood-prone. A fifth area of study—cross ecosystems—is devoted to investigating ecosystems' interrelationships.

Of the institute's seven research divisions, Plant Breeding, Genetics, and Biochemistry probably has had the greatest impact on Asian rice farming to date. Under the 30-year leadership of Gurdev S. Khush, head of the division and the institute's principal plant breeder, more than 300 new rice-breeding lines were developed and released as varieties by national rice-improvement programs throughout the world. As a result, more than 60% of the world's rice fields now are planted with varieties whose origins can be

Sixty percent of the world's
rice fields are planted with
varieties developed by IRRI's
Gurdev S. Khush, shown here
with a close-up of his new
plant type (NPT) rice.

traced to Khush's program. During the 1980s one of those varieties, IR36, was planted to 11 million hectares; no other single variety of rice—or indeed any other food crop—has ever been planted that widely. For their work on the development of improved strains of rice, Khush and Henry M. Beachell, who played a major role in the development of IR8, were awarded the Japan Prize in 1987 and the World Food Prize in 1996. These prestigious international awards rec-

ognize the achievements of individuals who advance human development by improving the quality, quantity, and availability of food around the world.

Developing improved strains of rice remains an IRRI priority. Researchers hope to release a new variety yielding 25% more grain per hectare than existing types by the turn of the century. Hailed as a "super rice" in *Time* magazine's roundup of best environmental stories of 1994, the rice is being developed by a team led by

Khush. Researchers hope that this new plant type (NPT) will not only increase yields but also address environmental concerns and consumer preferences in less-developed countries. In 1995–96 numerous advanced-generation breeding lines of NPT were evaluated, and new crosses were made to improve grain quality and resistance to insects as well as bacterial blight and rice blast. Preliminary testing shows that NPT lines also can be grown with greater water efficiency.

All of these benefits can be delivered without sacrificing consumer tastes. In the initial rounds, prototype lines of the NPT had short, round grains, but now a number of new lines have produced the long, slender grains preferred by people in the tropics and subtropics.

GENE BANKING

While the IRRI focuses on the development of new high-yield varieties of rice, it preserves the genetic resources of exist-

With some 80,000 samples of rice from more than 110 countries, the IRRI's gene bank contains the largest and most varied collection of rice seeds in the world. By the year 2000 the IRRI hopes to complete its collection with representative samples of most of the world's cultivated and wild rices.

ing strains through its International Rice Genebank. The largest and most diverse collection of rice seeds in the world, the institute's gene bank contains some 80,000 registered samples from more than 110 countries. The collection includes modern crossbred varieties as well as traditional varieties nurtured by farmers for generations, obsolete strains, and wild species. These seeds are multiplied, dried to a low moisture content, and then stored at −20° C (−4° F), a process that preserves their viability for decades, if not longer.

The IRRI's seed collection by no means represents all the rices in the world. For several countries—including Sri Lanka, Cambodia, Laos, and the Philippines—the germ plasm conserved in the institute's gene bank represents a complete duplicate of the national collection stored in that country. For other countries, such as India and China, only a portion of their national collections is duplicated at the IRRI. To fill in the gaps in its collection, the IRRI is currently coordinating a project involving farmers in 14 countries in Asia, Africa, and South America. Enlisting the help of local farmers in identifying different varieties has been extremely successful. In 1995, for

example, more than 2,000 samples of *O. sativa* were collected in six months in southern regions of Laos. The program's goal is to collect samples of most of the world's cultivated and wild rices by the year 2000.

This genetic storehouse can help donating nations as well as rice researchers. During a series of recent conflicts in Cambodia, for example, many of the country's traditional rice varieties were lost when 80% of the rice fields were destroyed through warfare or abandoned after their owners were killed or driven out, and the seeds in its gene bank, which had held more than 1,000 indigenous rice varieties, were consumed by hungry war refugees. Fortunately, Cambodia's national genetic resources could be restored, using seeds collected and preserved by the IRRI's gene bank. Similar restorations have been made in other countries whose national collections have been lost or have deteriorated over time.

BIOLOGICAL PEST CONTROL

The IRRI focuses on developing new varieties of rice not only to increase yields but also to reduce the inputs, costs, and crop losses of farming. Rice growing in upland areas, for

example, is an important area of IRRI research, since many of the world's poorest farmers cultivate crops on steep mountainous slopes. More than 17 million hectares of upland rice are grown worldwide, and about 60% are in Asia. Weeds are the most serious biological constraint in upland rice production. Because herbicide use is uncommon, controlling weeds is a time-consuming task. IRRI scientists now are pursuing biological strategies to manage invasive vegetation with less labor.

One approach is to identify rice varieties that exhibit a characteristic called allelopathy. Allelopathic plants can prevent the growth of nearby plants by releasing into the soil biological compounds that are toxic to these plants. According to Maria Olofsdotter, IRRI affiliate scientist, "We are currently looking for allelopathic rices that inhibit the growth of weeds detrimental to rice production. If we are successful, we might be able—through breeding—to develop rice cultivars that control weeds themselves and thus help reduce one of the rice farmer's most time-consuming chores."

In field experiments during the 1995 wet and dry seasons, Olofsdotter found several rice varieties that can reduce the annual weedy grass *Echi-*

nochloa crus-galli by more than 50%. In laboratory tests the varieties proved to be such powerful inhibitors that they also reduced root length of germinating weed seedlings by 50%. Researchers hope to incorporate these allelopathic traits into existing high-yield varieties to improve their weed-repellant properties.

IRRI researchers also are helping upland farmers implement other kinds of biological pest control. Parasitic nematodes, tiny soil-dwelling worms that invade the roots of rice plants, are omnipresent in upland rice fields. Because the nematodes are nearly microscopic, most infestations remain unnoticed by upland farmers—even if the pests are causing substantial crop losses. Jean-Claude Prot, a visiting French nematologist at the IRRI, found that problem nematodes can be controlled by implementing crop-rotation systems that alternate plantings of nematode-resistant strains of rice with nonhost crops.

For example, Prot recently identified goatweed (*Ageratum conyzoides*) as a harborer of root-knot nematode (*Meloidogyne graminicola*), a particularly troublesome agricultural parasite in Indonesia, Thailand, and Laos. Keith Fahrney, upland agronomist with the Lao-IRRI Project, currently is

working on a crop-rotation scheme with a farmer in the Laotian uplands to control an infestation of root-knot nematodes in his rice fields. In the past, rice fields that were allowed to go fallow between plantings became overrun with worm-infested *A. conyzoides*. On the basis of research demonstrating that rotations of different plants, such as corn (maize) and peanut, can help control nematode populations, the farmer will plant these non-rice crops on his land between rice plantings.

WATER QUALITY

Farmers in South and Southeast Asia grow approximately 10 million hectares of rice on flood-prone lands, nearly 88% of all such rice grown in the world. There are three major kinds of flood-prone rice: deepwater, which tolerates water depths of 50–100 centimeters (20–40 inches); floating, which can be found in water up to 400 centimeters (160 inches) deep; and tidal wetland, which can survive submergence, sometimes in salty water, for short periods.

Because water is used so extensively in flood-prone rice fields, contaminated runoff is an environmental concern, especially during the wet season. The soils of coastal lowlands

and deltas naturally contain high concentrations of acid sulfate. The high acidity releases the aluminum (Al) in the soil's mineral content, so the metal becomes highly soluble. Because farmers commonly use rain and irrigation water to flush the acidity from their fields, the runoff, which is contaminated with toxic aluminum, washes into drainage ditches, where it pollutes the network of canals that lines rice fields. If the concentration of aluminum is high enough, plants and aquatic animals are killed, and the water becomes unfit for drinking.

Scientists from the University of Can Tho, Vietnam, the Agricultural University, Wageningen, The Netherlands, and the IRRI are working to solve this dilemma in Vietnam, where about 2.5 million hectares are used to grow flood-prone rice. Researchers studying soils during the dry season have discovered that evaporation brings high levels of soluble aluminum from deep soil layers into the topsoil (the upper 20 cm [8 in] of earth), where it can readily be washed away.

They have found that several land-management techniques can reduce the levels of aluminum accumulation in acid sulfate soils. Mulching with straw and early plowing, for exam-

ple, decrease evaporation, which reduces the aluminum transported to the soil surface. Over time, mulching also increases the organic matter in the soil, which can bind the free aluminum in structures called organic matter-Al complexes.

By studying several other land-management practices, scientists from Can Tho and the IRRI also are working on curbing the leaching of acid sulfate from flood-prone rice fields. Farmers in the Mekong Delta of Vietnam, for example, typically construct raised beds for upland crops to avoid the ravages of annual flooding. Depending on the frequency with which these soils are tilled, however, the practice can contribute significantly to the leaching of acid into the environment. Researchers found a direct correlation between the amount of acid leached by rain from these planting beds and the gaps (pores) between chunks of soil. Frequent tillage and the uprooting of crops increase the number and size of the pores, as well as the channels for conducting water. For instance, scientists measured greater levels of acid leached from the soil in raised beds planted with yams, in which the earth is tilled annually and plants uprooted, compared with beds

planted with pineapples, where plants and soils are left undisturbed for two years. On the basis of their findings, researchers recommended that farmers utilize land-management techniques that limit the amount of soil disturbance.

International Rice Research Institute;
photograph, Ariel Javellana

CROSSING BOUNDARIES

One of the newest directions in IRRI rice research is the cross-ecosystems approach. Scientists not only study the biological and chemical interactions within the confines of the rice fields but also examine the plants' complex relationships to the larger landscape. In this interdisciplinary approach, researchers draw on the knowledge and tools of many different scientific disciplines. For instance, in an effort to develop more stable integrated pest-management strategies in irrigated and rain-fed rice fields, entomologists are moving beyond cultivated land to study its interactions with surrounding nonrice habitats. Scientists

Water that drains from the rice fields of coastal lowlands (below) often contains toxic concentrations of aluminum flushed from the soil. IRRI researchers are investigating how changes in land-management techniques, such as mulching with straw and early plowing, can help reduce aluminum accumulations.

have discovered that many plants in adjacent areas—weed-covered embankments or fields of banana and corn—harbor numerous beneficial insects. According to K.L. Heong, IRRI entomologist and coordinator of the Rice Integrated Pest Management Network, scientists are learning how to help farmers plant and maintain surrounding areas so that an available pool of beneficial insects is ready for migration into a rice field as soon as a crop has been planted.

Among the habitats currently under scrutiny are those dominated by *Paspalum conjugatum,* a common perennial grass known as sourgrass, which is home to two cricket species, *Anaxipha longipennis* and *Metioche vittaticollis.* These crickets are efficient predators of planthopper nymphs and lepidopteran eggs, whose larvae together with the planthopper nymphs are among the most common pests of rice crops. Farmers routinely use herbicides to clear the foliage surrounding their rice fields and thereby diminish cricket populations. IRRI researchers hope to educate farmers about the importance of these adjacent habitats and also encourage them to diversify their monocrop planting schemes with vegetated havens for insect predators.

SCIENCE AND CULTURE

To establish a connection between rice research and agricultural practices in the field, IRRI researchers often study cultural attitudes as much as they do scientific findings. For example, rice farmers often eliminate the weeds on their canal embankments with herbicides—primarily for cosmetic purposes. As a result, they may be missing a critical opportunity to use the beneficial insects that thrive in these environments to kill the pests that plague their rice fields. In 1992 IRRI researchers adopted several novel, inexpensive approaches to introducing Vietnamese farmers to integrated pest-management strategies.

IRRI research, for example, demonstrated that spraying rice crops with insecticides to control leaf folders (larvae of certain moths species) within the first 40 days after sowing resulted in no appreciable differences in the insects' numbers. However, in Vietnam, as Heong has pointed out, "farmers are only convinced of a technology if they see it for themselves." So in cooperation with the University of Can Tho and the Ministry of Agriculture and Rural Development (MARD), the institute invited groups of farmers in Can Tho,

An Giang, and Tien Giang provinces to conduct spraying experiments of their own and prove to themselves the futility of early-season spraying. This participatory approach was very effective in communicating simple pest-management concepts to farmers.

To expand the scope of their message and speed its delivery, in 1994 IRRI researchers and the MARD mounted a media campaign in Long An province in the Mekong Delta publicizing their simple pest-management message. Posters were placed in village markets and stores, leaflets were delivered to homes, dramas were broadcast on provincial radio stations, and billboards were erected at major intersections. The advertisements encouraged thousands of rice farmers in the region to apply the results of the IRRI's insecticide research to their own fields.

The media blitz was successful. At least 60% of the 12,500 farmers in the province stopped early-season spraying in their autumn-winter crop of 1994. By February 1995, 88% of the farmers in Long An had said they were aware of the campaign. By May 1995 officials in six other Mekong Delta provinces had used similar campaigns of their own to promote participatory research. Provincial agriculture depart-

ments throughout the Mekong Delta continued the farmer experiments and media campaign into 1996 in an effort to expand the message to the region's more than 2.2 million farmer households.

BIOTECHNOLOGY

Although it is one of the IRRI's most controversial areas of rice research, biotechnology is considered an important tool for attaining higher yields through sustainable agriculture. Among the most contentious is the recent development of a transgenic rice known as Bt rice, which has been genetically modified to

An IRRI scientist uses a particle gun to introduce beneficial genes into the cells of a host plant. Although it is highly controversial, genetic research is a major part of the institute's research agenda.

International Rice Research Institute; photograph, R. Cabrera

An IRRI researcher examines a sprig of rice whose biological makeup has been altered with genes from the soil bacterium *Bacillus thuringiensis* (Bt). The change gives the plant added resistance to stem borers, a common pest.

control stem borers, chronic pests in all rice-growing Asian countries. Since the 1970s moderate resistance to the insect has been incorporated into many modern rice varieties through traditional breeding techniques. In 1995, however, IRRI researchers introduced genes from the soil bacterium *Bacillus thuringiensis* (Bt) to provide much higher levels of resistance to stem borers. Bt genes produce proteins that accumulate in the leaves and other green tissues of rice

plants without affecting the grain. Although they are highly toxic to select insect groups, these proteins are harmless to humans and other animals.

According to critics, releasing Bt rice for widespread use increases the risk that stem borers will quickly evolve a resistance to the toxic effects of Bt proteins and leave blighted fields and starving people in their wake. In response to these concerns, Michael Cohen, IRRI specialist in insect–host-plant resistance, and his institute colleagues are evaluating various approaches to slowing the evolution of Bt resistance in stem borers, including creating a Bt rice with multiple genetically engineered toxins. Cohen also has suggested the

establishment of "refuges" of non-Bt plants in areas where Bt rice is being grown. Refuges will maintain a supply of stem borers that are susceptible to Bt toxins. Research has shown that when these insects mate with Bt-resistant borers, the offspring generally will be Bt-susceptible.

FOOD: THE FIRST STEP

The less-developed world and its highly industrialized benefactors usually cite population control, industrial development, and environmental protection as the only routes to national prosperity and security. The IRRI cautions that food production must remain

the first priority of poor nations. If the demand for food is not met, other growth cannot be assured.

Research can make major contributions to this national prosperity and peace by increasing crop yields and reducing the inputs, costs, and losses of growing rice. To do so will require coordinated national and international efforts and, above all, strong political will, government determination, and major investments in rice research. As it has demonstrated for the last 37 years, the IRRI will remain at the forefront of this effort.

See also *1996 Yearbook of Science and the Future* Feature Article: THE GODDESS AND THE GREEN REVOLUTION.

Kjell B. Sandved: Wonders on the Wing

To some it might seem a cliché to speak of the endless marvels of nature, but for one man at least, the phrase still has great resonance. Kjell B. Sandved, the Norwegian-born photographer, moviemaker, lecturer, and sometime encyclopedist, has devoted almost four decades of a career with the National Museum of Natural History (a branch of the Smithsonian Institution, Washington, D.C.) to revealing the beauties and amazements of natural and scientific objects.

Sandved has trained his lenses on many large-scale phenomena—coral reefs, herds of elephants, ancient burial grounds—but his most ingenious and memorable work concerns the miniature, especially the intricate wing designs of butterflies and moths. Somewhere between a vocation and an avocation lies Sandved's "Butterfly Alphabet," a complete set of letters and numbers he has photographed over the years on the wings of his lepidopteran subjects. The project was an instant hit when it appeared in 1996 as an eye-catching book and poster (*see* pages 190–91).

This small sampling from the myriad images that Sandved has made, often using unusual methods and special apparatus rigged up to overcome tough technical problems or to shoot in awkward locations, is intended not only to give the flavor of the work of one of the world's leading na-

ture photographers, but once again to remind us—cliché or not—of nature's never-ending capability to astonish.

Inquiries about Sandved's "Butterfly Alphabet" poster may be made to a U.S. toll-free telephone number, 1-800-ABC-WING.

Faces imaginary and real appear on a totemlike bud from a European ash (top left) and a Hawaii gecko (top right). Antarctic emperor penguins (center) pause on the way to the ocean to feed. Kjell Sandved (above) poses amid his subjects in the Amazonian rain forest. Edible fruits (opposite page) belong to the akee tree, native to West Africa.

A pyralid moth rests on the back of an arctiid, or tiger, moth in Malaysia.

A newly emerged silkworm moth in New Guinea dries out its antennae.

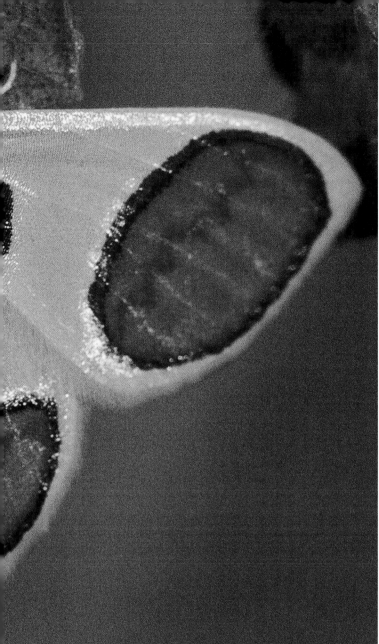

A strikingly colored geometrid moth (left)
of Malaysia assumes a resting pose.

A brush-footed butterfly of Peru displays a wing design resembling numbers.

A sphinx moth of New Guinea mimics a dead leaf.

Sandved's "Butterfly Alphabet" (opposite page and this page) culminates nearly a quarter century's search for a complete set of letters and numerals on the wings of butterflies and moths. All of the insects were photographed without being caught or killed. (Top right) An iridescent-winged morpho butterfly is from Peru.

A magnificent cone stands atop a cycad in South Africa.

Radially arranged floral head (above left) belongs to a *Bulbophyllum makoyanum* orchid from Malaysia. (Opposite page) The fruiting bodies of a Malaysian fungus form delicate umbrellas.

Reflections shimmer in the water-filled leaf cup of a Brazilian bromeliad.

African elephants, the largest living land animals, roam the plains.

An East African leopard reclines in the sun.

East Africa also is home to Grevy's zebra, one of three living zebra species.

Amphibious hippopotamuses bask on an African riverbank.

The back of a moth becomes an imaginary masklike face.

Seeds and floral parts of a common four-o'clock take on an impudent cast.

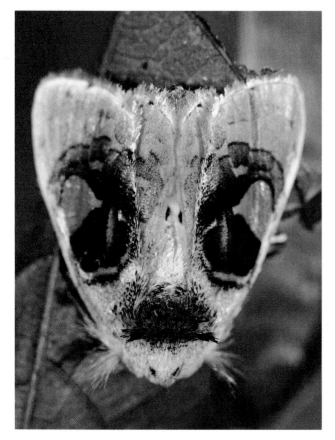

Another fanciful visage glares from the wings and body of a moth.

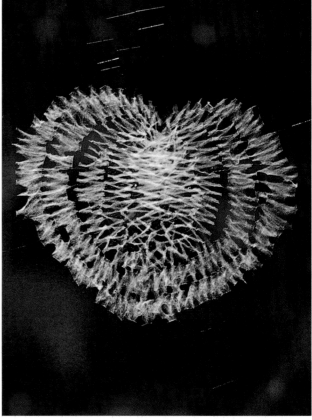

A heart-shaped web was woven by an *Argiope* spider of West Africa.

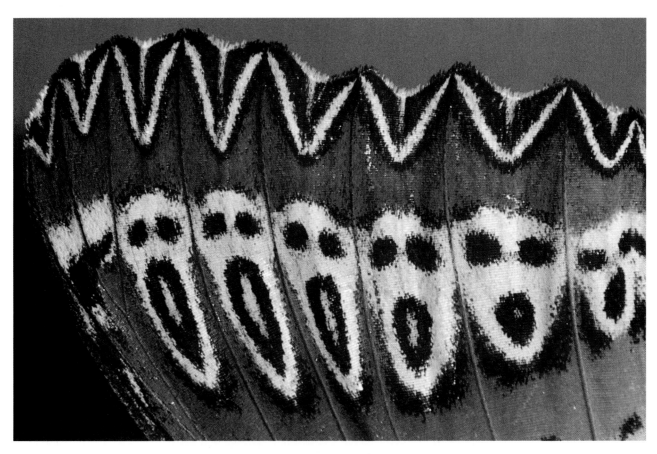

A choir frozen in song is one interpretation of a pattern found on the wing of a nymphalid butterfly from Thailand.

The seed of a sweet gum tree in Washington, D.C., shows a definite personality.

Animal eyes, such as the eye of an iguanid lizard (above) and the square-pupiled eye of a king penguin (opposite page), are intriguing subjects in themselves.

Eyes like globes of glass adorn the head of a shrimp from Puerto Rico.

A goat's eye displays its unusual rod-shaped pupil.

ENCYCLOPÆDIA BRITANNICA SCIENCE

update

Major Revisions from the 1997 *Macropædia*

The purpose of this section is to introduce to continuing *Yearbook of Science and the Future* subscribers selected *Macropædia* articles or portions of them that have been revised or written anew. It is intended to update the *Macropædia* in ways that cannot be accomplished fully by reviewing the year's events or by revising statistics annually, because the *Macropædia* texts themselves—written from a longer perspective than any yearly revision—supply authoritative interpretation and analysis as well as narrative and description.

Sections from a major article, the 95-page The BIO-SPHERE and Concepts of Ecology, have been chosen. They appear in the 1997 printing of the *Macropædia* and are also available to *Britannica Online*™ subscribers. Each is the work of distinguished scholars, and each represents the continuing dedication of the *Encyclopædia Britannica* to bringing such articles to the general reader.

The Biosphere and Concepts of Ecology

Before the coming of life, the Earth was a bleak place, a rocky globe with shallow seas and a thin band of gases—largely carbon dioxide, carbon monoxide, molecular nitrogen, hydrogen sulfide, and water vapour. It was a hostile and barren planet. This strictly inorganic state of the Earth is called the geosphere; it consists of the lithosphere (the rock and soil), the hydrosphere (the water), and the atmosphere (the air). Energy from the Sun relentlessly bombarded the surface of the primitive Earth, and in time—millions of years—chemical and physical actions produced the first evidence of life: formless, jellylike blobs that could collect energy from the environment and produce more of their own kind. This generation of life in the thin outer layer of the geosphere established what is called the biosphere, the "zone of life," an energy-diverting skin that uses the matter of the Earth to make living substance.

The biosphere is a system characterized by the continuous cycling of matter and an accompanying flow of solar energy in which certain large molecules and cells are self-reproducing. Water is a major predisposing factor, for all life depends on it. The elements carbon, hydrogen, nitrogen, oxygen, phosphorus, and sulfur, when combined as proteins, lipids, carbohydrates, and nucleic acids, provide the building blocks, the fuel, and the direction for the creation of life. Energy flow is required to maintain the structure of organisms by the formation and splitting of phosphate bonds. Organisms are cellular in nature and always contain some sort of enclosing membrane structure, and all have nucleic acids that store and transmit genetic information.

All life on Earth depends ultimately upon green plants, as well as upon water. Plants utilize sunlight in a process called photosynthesis to produce the food upon which animals feed and to provide, as a by-product, oxygen, which most animals require for respiration. At first, the oceans and the lands were teeming with large numbers of a few kinds of simple single-celled organisms, but slowly plants and animals of increasing complexity evolved. Interrelationships developed so that certain plants grew in association with certain other plants, and animals associated with the plants and with one another to form communities of organisms, including those of forests, grasslands, deserts, dunes, bogs, rivers, and lakes. Living (biotic) communities and their nonliving (abiotic) environment are inseparably interrelated and constantly interact upon each other. For convenience, any segment of the landscape that includes the biotic and abiotic components is called an ecosystem. A lake is an ecosystem when it is considered in totality as not just water but also nutrients, climate, and all of the life contained within it. A given forest, meadow, or river is likewise an ecosystem. One ecosystem grades into another along zones termed ecotones, where a mixture of plant and animal species from the two ecosystems occurs. A forest considered as an ecosystem is not simply a stand of trees but is a complex of soil, air, and water, of climate and minerals, of bacteria, viruses, fungi, grasses, herbs, and trees, of insects, reptiles, amphibians, birds, and mammals.

Stated another way, the abiotic, or nonliving, portion of each ecosystem in the biosphere includes the flow of energy, nutrients, water, and gases and the concentrations of organic and inorganic substances in the environment. The biotic, or living, portion includes three general categories of organisms based on their methods of acquiring energy: the primary producers, largely green plants; the consumers, which include all the animals; and the decomposers, which include the microorganisms that break down the remains of plants and animals into simpler components for recycling in the biosphere. Aquatic ecosystems are those involving marine environments and freshwater environments on the land. Terrestrial ecosystems are those based on major vegetational types, such as forest, grassland, desert, and tundra. Particular kinds of animals are associated with each such plant province.

Ecosystems may be further subdivided into smaller biotic units called communities. Examples of communities include the organisms in a stand of pine trees, on a coral reef, and in a cave, a valley, a lake, or a stream. The major consideration in the community is the living component, the organisms; the abiotic factors of the environment are excluded.

A community is a collection of species populations. In a stand of pines, there may be many species of insects, of birds, of mammals, each a separate breeding unit but each dependent on the others for its continued existence. A species, furthermore, is composed of individuals, single functioning units identifiable as organisms. Beyond this level, the units of the biosphere are those of the organism: organ systems composed of organs, organs of tissues, tissues of cells, cells of molecules, and molecules of atomic elements and energy. The progression, therefore, proceeding upward from atoms and energy, is toward fewer units, larger and more complex in pattern, at each successive level.

This article focuses on the makeup of the biosphere and examines the relationships between its principal components, including man. The characteristics and dynamics of biological populations and communities are dealt with, as are the interactions that constitute the primary stabilizing links among the constituent organisms. Due attention is also given to the distribution patterns of these biotic units and to the processes that produced such patterns. The major aquatic and terrestrial ecosystems of the Earth are treated in some detail. Other points include energy transformations and transfers within the biosphere and the cyclic flow of materials needed for life.

(David M. Gates)

THE ORGANISM AND THE ENVIRONMENT

The diversity of life

The biosphere supports between 3 and 30 million species of plants, animals, fungi, single-celled prokaryotes such as bacteria, and single-celled eukaryotes such as protozoans (Figure 1). Of this total, only about 1.4 million species have been named so far, and fewer than 1 percent have been studied for their ecological relationships and their role in ecosystems. A little more than half the named species are insects, which dominate terrestrial and freshwater communities worldwide; the laboratories of systematists are filled with insect species yet to be named and described. Hence, the relationships of organisms to their environments and the roles that species play in the biosphere are only beginning to be understood.

THE ORGANIZATION OF THE BIOSPHERE

Natural groupings. This tremendous diversity of life is organized into natural ecological groupings. As life has evolved, populations of organisms have become separated into different species that are reproductively isolated from one another. These species are organized through their interrelationships into complex biological communities. The interactions in these communities affect, and are affected by, the physical environments in which they occur, thereby forming ecosystems through which the energy and nutrients necessary for life flow and cycle. The mix of species and physical environments vary across the globe, creating ecological communities, or biomes, such as the boreal forests of North America and Eurasia and the rainforests of the tropics. The sum total of the richness of these biomes is the biosphere.

Processes of evolution. This hierarchical organization of life has come about through the major processes of evolution—natural selection (the differential success of the reproduction of hereditary variations resulting from the interaction of organisms with their environment), gene flow (the movement of genes among different populations of a species), and random genetic drift (the genetic change that occurs in small populations owing to chance). (See EVOLUTION, THE THEORY OF: *The process of evolution.*) Natural selection operates on the expressed characteristics of genetic variants found within populations, winnowing members of the population who are less well suited to their environment from those better suited to it. In this manner, populations become adapted to their local ecosystems, which include both the physical environment and the other species with which they interact in order to survive and reproduce.

The genetic variation that is necessary for a species to adapt to the physical environment and to other organisms arises from new mutations within populations, the recombination of genes during sexual reproduction, and the migration of and interbreeding with individuals from other populations. In very small populations, however, some of that variation is lost by chance alone through

Speciation

random genetic drift. The combined result of these evolutionary processes is that after many generations populations of the same species have widely divergent characteristics. Some of these populations eventually become so genetically different that their members cannot successfully interbreed, resulting in the evolution of a separate species (speciation).

The diversification of life through local adaptation of populations and speciation has created the tremendous biodiversity found on the Earth. In most regions a square kilometre (0.4 square mile) will harbour hundreds—in some places even thousands—of species. The interactions between these species create intricate webs of relationships as the organisms reciprocally evolve, adapting to one another and becoming specialized for their interactions (coevolution; see below *Community ecology: The coevolutionary process*). Natural communities of species reflect the sum of these species' interactions and the ongoing complex selection pressures they constantly endure that drive their evolution. The many ecological and evolutionary processes that affect the relationships among

Coevolution

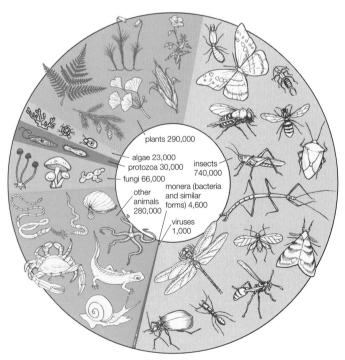

Figure 1: Estimated number of known living species. The majority of species are still unknown—*i.e.,* yet to be described by taxonomists.
Encyclopædia Britannica, Inc.

species and their environments render ecology one of the most intricate of the sciences. The answers to the major questions in ecology require an understanding of the relative effects of many variables acting simultaneously.

THE IMPORTANCE OF THE BIOSPHERE

The continued functioning of the biosphere is dependent not only on the maintainance of the intimate interactions among the myriad species within local communities but also on the looser yet crucial interactions of all species and communities around the globe. The Earth is blanketed with so many species and so many different kinds of biological communities because populations have been able to adapt to almost any kind of environment on Earth through natural selection. Life-forms have evolved that are able to survive in the ocean depths, the frigid conditions of Antarctica, and the near-boiling temperatures of geysers. The great richness of adaptations found among different populations and species of living organisms is the Earth's greatest resource. It is a richness that has evolved over millions of years and is irreplaceable.

It is therefore startling to realize that our inventory of the Earth's diversity is still so incomplete that the total number of living species cannot be estimated more closely than between 3 and 30 million species. Decades of continuous research must be carried out by systematists, ecologists, and geneticists before the inventory of biodiversity provides a more accurate count. The research has been slow. Only recently, as the extinction rate of species has been increasing rapidly, have societies begun to realize the interdependence of species. To sustain life on Earth, more than the few animal and plant species used by humans must be preserved. The flow of energy and the cycling of nutrients through ecosystems, the regulation of populations, and the stability of biological communities, all of which support the continued maintenance of life, rely on the diversity of species, their adaptations to local physical conditions, and their coevolved relationships.

Despite the limited scientific knowledge of most species, ecological studies during the 20th century have made great headway in unraveling the mechanisms by which organisms coevolve with one another and adapt to their physical environment, thereby shaping the biosphere. Each new decade has produced a steady stream of studies showing that the biological and physical elements of the Earth are more interconnected than had been previously thought. Those studies also have shown that often the most seemingly insignificant species are crucial to the stability of communities and ecosystems. Many seemingly obscure species are at risk worldwide of being dismissed as unimportant. The effect that the loss of species will have on ecosystems is appreciated only by understanding the relationships between organisms and their environments and by studying the ecological and evolutionary processes operating within ecosystems.

The impact of species extinction

The need to understand how the biosphere functions has never been greater. When human population levels were low and technological abilities crude, societies' impact on the biosphere was relatively small. The increase in human population levels and the harvesting of more of the Earth's natural resources has altered this situation, especially in recent decades. Human activities are causing major alterations to the patterns of energy flow and nutrient cycling through ecosystems, and these activities are eliminating populations and species that have not even been described but which might have been of central importance to the maintenance of ecosystems.

The biologist Edward O. Wilson, who coined the term "biodiversity," estimated conservatively that in the late 20th century at least 27,000 species are becoming extinct each year. The majority of these are small tropical organisms. The impact that this freshet of extinctions would have on the biosphere is akin to receiving a box of engine parts and discarding a portion of them before reading the directions, assuming that their absence will have no negative repercussions on the running of the engine. The following sections describe how many of the biological and physical parts fit together to make the engine of the biosphere run and why many seemingly obscure species are important to the long-term functioning of the biosphere.

(John N. Thompson)

COMMUNITY ECOLOGY

As populations of species interact with one another, they form biological communities. The number of interacting species in these communities and the complexity of their relationships exemplify what is meant by the term "biodiversity." Structures arise within communities as species interact, and food chains, food webs, guilds, and other interactive webs are created. These relationships change over evolutionary time as species reciprocally adapt to one another through the process of coevolution. The overall structure of biological communities, the organization of interspecific interactions, and the effects the coevolutionary process has on the biological community are described below.

Biotic elements of communities

TROPHIC PYRAMIDS AND THE FLOW OF ENERGY

Autotrophs and heterotrophs. All biological communities have a basic structure of interaction that forms a trophic pyramid. The trophic pyramid is made up of trophic levels, and food energy is passed from one level to the next along the food chain (see below *Food chains and food webs*). The base of the pyramid is composed of species called autotrophs, the primary producers of the ecosystem. They do not obtain energy and nutrients by eating other organisms. Instead, they harness solar energy by photosynthesis (photoautotrophs) or, more rarely, chemical energy by oxidation (chemoautotrophs) to make organic substances from inorganic ones. All other organisms in the ecosystem are consumers called heterotrophs, which either directly or indirectly depend on the producers for food energy.

Producers and consumers

Within all biological communities, energy at each trophic level is lost in the form of heat (as much as 80 to 90 percent), as organisms expend energy for metabolic processes such as staying warm and digesting food (Figure 13; see above *The organism and the environment: Resources of the biosphere: The flow of energy*). The higher the organism is on the trophic pyramid, the less energy is available to it; herbivores and detritivores (primary consumers) have less available energy than plants, and the carnivores that feed on herbivores and detritivores (secondary consumers) and those that eat other carnivores (tertiary consumers) have the least amount of available energy.

The pyramid structure of communities. The organisms that make up the base level of the pyramid vary from community to community. In terrestrial communities, multicellular plants generally form the base of the pyramid, whereas in freshwater lakes a combination of multicellular plants and single-celled algae constitute the first trophic level. The trophic structure of the ocean is built on the plankton known as krill. There are some exceptions to this general plan. Many freshwater streams have detritus rather than living plants as their energy base. Detritus is composed of leaves and other plant parts that fall into the water from surrounding terrestrial communities. It is broken down by microorganisms, and the microorganism-rich detritus is eaten by aquatic invertebrates, which are in turn eaten by vertebrates.

The most unusual biological communities of all are those surrounding hydrothermal vents on the ocean floor. These vents result from volcanic activity and the movement of continental plates that create cracks in the sea-

Communities surrounding hydrothermal vents

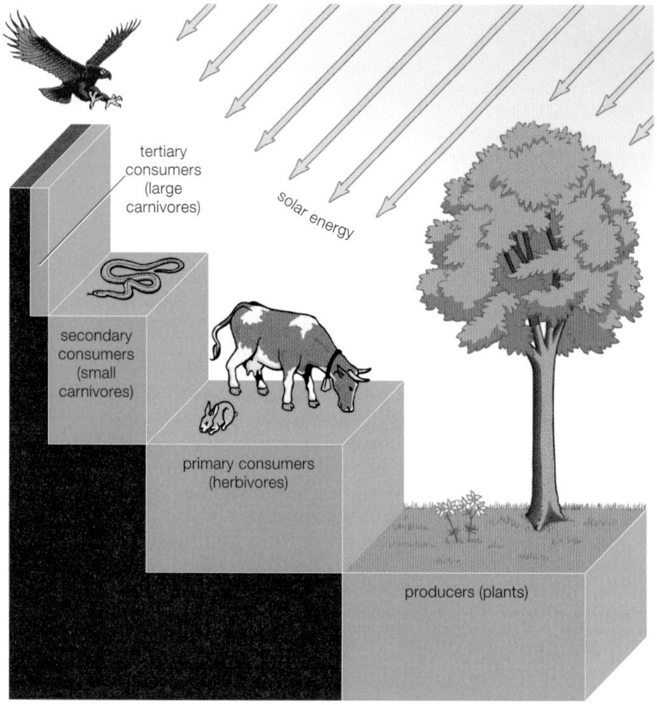

Figure 13: Transfer of energy through an ecosystem. At each trophic level only a small proportion of energy (approximately 10 percent) is transferred to the next level.

Encyclopædia Britannica, Inc.

floor. Water seeps into the cracks, is heated by magma within the Earth's mantle, becomes laden with hydrogen sulfide, and then rises back to the ocean floor. Sulfur-oxidizing bacteria (chemoautotrophs) thrive in the warm, sulfur-rich water surrounding these cracks. The bacteria use reduced sulfur as an energy source for the fixation of carbon dioxide. Unlike all other known biological communities on Earth, the energy that forms the base of these deep-sea communities comes from chemosynthesis rather than from photosynthesis; the ecosystem is thus supported by geothermal rather than solar energy.

Some species surrounding these vents feed on these bacteria, but other species have formed long-term, reciprocally beneficial relationships (mutualistic symbioses) with sulfur bacteria. These species harbour the chemoautotrophic bacteria within their bodies and derive nutrition directly from them. The biological communities surrounding these vents are so different from those in the rest of the ocean that since the 1980s, when biological research of these vents began, about 200 new species have been described, and there are many more that remain undescribed—*i.e.,* not formally described and given scientific names. Among the described species there are at least 75 new genera, 15 new families, one new order, one new class, and even one new phylum.

FOOD CHAINS AND FOOD WEBS

Because all species are specialized in their diets, each trophic pyramid is made up of a series of interconnected feeding relationships called food chains. Most food chains consist of three or four trophic levels. A typical sequence may be plant, herbivore, carnivore, top carnivore; another sequence is plant, herbivore, parasite of the herbivore, and parasite of the parasite. Many herbivores, detritivores, carnivores, and parasites, however, eat more than one species, and a large number of animal species eat different foods at different stages of their life histories. In addition, many species eat both plants and animals and therefore feed at more than one trophic level. Consequently, food chains combine into highly complex food webs (Figure 14). Even a simplified food web can show a complicated network of trophic relationships.

KEYSTONE SPECIES

Even a fully constructed food web, however, can provide only a superficial and static view of the structure of biological communities. Not all the relationships between species are of equal importance in the dynamics and evolution of populations and the organization of communities. Food webs include both strong and weak interactions between species, and these differences in interaction strength influence the organization of communities. Some species, called keystone species, have a disproportionately large effect on the communities in which they occur. They help to maintain local diversity within a community either by controlling populations of species that would otherwise dominate the community or by providing critical resources for a wide range of species.

The starfish *Pisaster ochraceus* is a keystone species in the rocky marine intertidal communities off the northwest coast of North America. This predatory starfish feeds on the mussel *Mytilus californianus* and is responsible for maintaining much of the local diversity of species within certain communities. When the starfish have been removed experimentally, the mussel populations have expanded rapidly and covered the rocky intertidal shores so exclusively that other species cannot establish themselves. Consequently, the interaction between *Pisaster* and *Mytilus* supports the structure and species diversity of these communities. In other communities in which *Pisaster* occurs, however, the starfish has little overall effect on the structure of the community. Therefore, a species can be a keystone species in some communities but not in others.

In some forest communities in tropical America, figs and a few other plants act as keystone species but in a very different manner from the starfish *Pisaster*. Figs bear fruit year-round in some of these forest communities, and a large number of birds and mammals rely heavily on this small group of plant species during the times of the year when other food resources are scarce. Without figs, many species would disappear from the community.

GUILDS AND INTERACTION WEBS

Most communities contain groups of species known as guilds, which exploit the same kinds of resources in comparable ways. The name "guild" emphasizes the fact that these groups are like associations of craftsmen who employ similar techniques in plying their trade. Guilds may consist of different insect species that collect nectar in similar ways, various bird species that employ corresponding insect-foraging techniques, or diverse plant species that have evolved comparable floral shapes with which they attract the same group of pollinators.

Guilds often are composed of groups of closely related species that all arose from a common ancestor. They exploit resources in similar ways as a result of their shared ancestry. Hence, several species within a single genus may constitute a guild within a community. A less common but not unknown occurrence is for unrelated species to make up a guild.

Because members of a guild engage in similar activities, it is not surprising that they are often competitors for the resources they share, especially when those resources are scarce. This competition among guilds emphasizes the fact that, in addition to food webs, the structure of the community is built on other types of interaction. Species not only eat one another; they compete for resources, forging a variety of interspecific interactions. Many species also interact cooperatively to search for food or avoid predators. These and other nontrophic relationships between species are as important as food chains and food webs in shaping the organization of biological communities (see below *Interspecific interactions and the organization of communities*).

Nontrophic interactions

Patterns of community structure

ECOLOGICAL SUCCESSION

The structure of communities is constantly changing. All communities are subject to periodic disturbances, ranging from events that have only localized effects, such as the

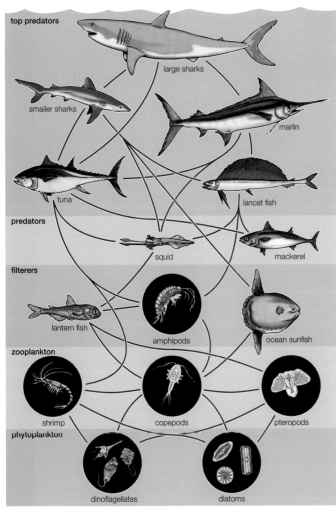

top predators

large sharks

smaller sharks

marlin

tuna

lancet fish

predators

squid

mackerel

filterers

lantern fish

amphipods

ocean sunfish

zooplankton

shrimp

copepods

pteropods

phytoplankton

dinoflagellates

diatoms

Figure 14: Generalized aquatic food web. Parasites, among the most diverse species in the food web, are not shown.
Encyclopædia Britannica, Inc.

loss of a tree that creates a gap in the canopy of a forest, to those that have catastrophic consequences, which include wildfires that sweep across vast landscapes or storms that pound immense stretches of shoreline. Each new disturbance within a landscape creates an opportunity for a new species to colonize that region. New species also alter the character of the community, creating an environment that is suitable to even newer species. By this process, known as ecological succession, the structure of the community evolves over time.

Types of succession. Two different types of succession, primary and secondary, have been distinguished. Primary succession occurs in essentially lifeless areas—regions in which the soil is incapable of sustaining life as a result of such factors as lava flows, newly formed sand dunes, or rocks left from a retreating glacier. Secondary succession occurs in areas where a community that previously existed has been removed; it is typified by smaller-scale disturbances that do not eliminate all life and nutrients from the environment. Events such as a fire that sweeps across a grassland or a storm that uproots trees within a forest create patches of habitat that are colonized by early successional species. Depending on the extent of the disturbance, some species may survive, other species may be recolonized from nearby habitats, and others may actually be released from a dormant condition by the disturbance. For example, many plant species in fire-prone environments have seeds that remain dormant within the soil until the heat of a fire stimulates them to germinate.

The process of succession. Primary and secondary succession both create a continually changing mix of species within communities as disturbances of different intensi-

*Distur-
bance
and the
changing
structure of
communi-
ties*

ties, sizes, and frequencies alter the landscape. The sequential progression of species during succession, however, is not random. At every stage certain species have evolved life histories to exploit the particular conditions of the community. This situation imposes a partially predictable sequence of change in the species composition of communities during succession. Initially only a small number of species from surrounding habitats are capable of thriving in a disturbed habitat. As new plant species take hold, they modify the habitat by altering such things as the amount of shade on the ground or the mineral composition of the soil. These changes allow other species that are better suited to this modified habitat to succeed the old species. These newer species are superseded, in turn, by still newer species. A similar succession of animal species occurs, and interactions between plants, animals, and environment influence the pattern and rate of successional change.

STRATIFICATION AND GRADATION

Community structure can become stratified both vertically and horizontally during the process of succession as species become adapted to their habitat. Gradations in environmental factors such as light, temperature, or water are responsible for this fractionation. The vertical stratification that occurs within forests results from the varying degrees of light that the different strata receive: the taller the plant and the more foliage it produces, the more light it can intercept. Three or more vertical strata of plants—an herb layer, a shrub layer, a small tree layer, and a canopy tree layer—often are found in a forest. Animals are affected by this stratification of plant life. Although they can move from one layer to another quite easily, they often adhere closely to a specific layer for foraging, breeding, or other activities.

*Vertical
and
horizontal
patterns*

Horizontal patterns among species also can emerge from gradients in the physical environment. Differences in the amount of water or nutrients over a region can affect the distribution of animal and plant species (see below *Major biogeographic regions of the world*). On a mountain, plant and animal species vary at different elevations as well as among the north, south, east, and west slopes. Drastic differences in certain factors over a very short distance can create sharp boundaries between communities, whereas gradual differences can produce a more integrated flow of species. These gradients help to maintain regional biodiversity.

ECOTONES

Ecosystems are almost always a patchwork of communities that exist at different successional stages. The sizes, frequencies, and intensities of disturbances differ among ecosystems, creating differences in what is called the patch dynamics of communities. Along the edges of each of the patches are areas called ecotones. These junction zones often contain species of each of the overlapping communities as well as some species that have become adapted specifically for living in these zones. In many cases, the number of species and the population density are greater within the ecotone than in the surrounding communities, a phenomenon known as the edge effect.

*The edge
effect*

In North America the parasitism of bird nests by brown-headed cowbirds (*Molothrus ater*) is particularly frequent in ecotones between mature forests and earlier successional patches. Cowbirds lay their eggs in the nests of other birds and are active mainly in early successional patches. Forest birds whose nests are deep within the interior of mature forests are less likely to be attacked than those within ecotones. The cutting of mature forests has increased the extent of ecotones, concomitantly increasing the rate of cowbird parasitism across North America.

ECOLOGICAL NICHES

An ecological niche encompasses the habits of a species. Essentially it refers to the way a species relates to, or fits in with, its environment. As a species adapts to the physical parameters and biota within the community, natural selection favours the development of specialized features that allow the species to uniquely exploit the surrounding resources. Physical conditions of the region—such as temperature, terrain, or nutrient availability—help to mold the niche, and biological constraints such as predation, competition, or lack of resources limit the ways in which a species exploits its environment. For example, plant species differ in their requirements for light, nutrients, and microorganisms, as well as in their ability to fend off competitors and herbivores. Herbivore species can eat only a subset of the plants available within a community, and predators can capture only some of the many potential prey species. Thus the species "carves out" a niche for itself in the community (see below *Interspecific interactions and the organization of communities: Competition: The effects of competition*).

An example of one such niche is that of the endangered Kirtland's warbler (*Dendroica kirtlandii*) found in North America. It nests only among young jack pines (*Pinus banksiana*) that are 2 to 4 metres (6.5 to 13 feet) tall and grow in homogenous stands. These trees are exposed to periodic fires, necessary for germination of the jack pine seeds. These fires also continuously provide extensive new regions of young trees, allowing the warblers to shift their nesting sites over the years to remain within stands of jack pine that are of the preferred height.

The niche of a species evolves as physical and biological factors in the community change—provided that such changes are slow enough to allow species to adapt to them. The main constraint on this evolution is that no two species in a community can have the same niche. Specialized modes of existence thus provide a selective advantage to coexistent species, offsetting direct competition for available resources.

BIODIVERSITY AND THE STABILITY OF COMMUNITIES

As species adapt to one another and to their communities, they form niches and guilds. The development of more complex structures allows a greater number of species to coexist with one another. The increase in species richness and complexity acts to buffer the community from environmental stresses and disasters, rendering it more stable.

Community equilibrium and species diversity. In some environments, succession reaches a climax, producing a stable community dominated by a small number of prominent species. This state of equilibrium, called the climax community, is thought to result when the web of biotic interactions becomes so intricate that no other species can be admitted. In other environments, continual small-scale disturbances produce communities that are a diverse mix of species, and any species may become dominant. This nonequilibrial dynamic highlights the effects that unpredictable disturbances can have in the development of community structure and composition. Some species-rich tropical forests contain hundreds of tree species within a square kilometre. When a tree dies and falls to the ground, the resultant space is up for grabs. Similarly, some coral reefs harbour hundreds of fish species, and whichever species colonizes a new disturbance patch will be the victor. With each small disturbance, the bid for supremacy begins anew.

Diverse communities are healthy communities. Long-term ecological studies have shown that species-rich communities are able to recover faster from disturbances than species-poor communities. Species-rich grasslands in the Midwestern United States maintain higher primary productivity than species-poor grasslands. Each additional species lost from these grasslands has a progressively greater effect on the drought-resistance of the community. Similarly, more diverse plant communities in Yellowstone National Park show greater stability in species composition during severe drought than less diverse communities. And, in the Serengeti grassland of Africa, the more diverse communities show greater stability of biomass through the seasons and greater ability to recover after grazing.

The relationship between species diversity and community stability highlights the need to maintain the greatest richness possible within biological communities. A field of weeds containing species only recently introduced to

The climax community

the community is quite different from a rich interactive web of indigenous species that have had the time to adapt to one another. Undisturbed species-rich communities have the resilience to sustain a functioning ecosystem upon which life depends. These communities also are better able to absorb the effects of foreign species, which may be innocently introduced but which can wreak much ecological and economic havoc in less stable communities. The tight web of interactions that make up natural biological communities sustains both biodiversity and community stability.

Biogeographic aspects of diversity. Biogeography is the study of species distribution in an area (see below *Major biogeographic regions of the world: General features*). Because islands provide a controlled area for study, they have been used to observe the factors that affect species diversity. Three variables that determine the rate of colonization of an island are the size of the island, the distance between the island and other islands or the mainland, and the number of species inhabiting the surrounding lands. The theory of island biogeography is based on this information, which can help predict the number of species that will occur on a given island. It also can be used to explain the species diversity of "islands" on land, such as mountaintops, lakes, and forest fragments left after an area has been logged. Where immigration and extinction rates are equal, the theory of island biogeography states that the number of species is proportional to the size of the island and inversely proportional to the distance of the island from the mainland.

Six months after the eruption of a volcano on the island of Surtsey off the coast of Iceland in 1963, the island had been colonized by a few bacteria, molds, insects, and birds. Within about a year of the eruption of a volcano on the island of Krakatoa in the tropical Pacific in 1883, a few grass species, insects, and vertebrates had taken hold. On both Surtsey and Krakatoa, only a few decades had elapsed before hundreds of species reached the islands. Not all species are able to take hold and become permanently established, but eventually the island communities stabilize into a dynamic equilibrium.

The theory of island biogeography

Interspecific interactions and the organization of communities

The interactive relationships that arise between populations of different species form the interactive web of communities. These interactions range from antagonistic to cooperative and have either positive, negative, or neutral effects on the species involved. In antagonistic relationships the interaction is detrimental to individuals of either one or both species; in commensal relationships (commensalism) one species benefits while the other remains unaffected; and in mutualistic relationships (mutualism) both species benefit. The organization and stability of biological communities results from the mix of these different kinds of interaction.

These relationships between species are not static; they evolve as natural selection continually shapes and reshapes them. The defenses and counterdefenses seen in the relationships between hosts and parasites, or between prey and predators, are snapshots of one point in time during the ongoing process of the evolution of interactions. As interactions between species evolve, relationships may shift from antagonism to commensalism to mutualism. As a result, the organization of biological communities is no more fixed than are the characteristics of the species or their environments. Charles Darwin called this ever-changing mix of species and their interactions the "entangled bank" and stressed its importance in the evolutionary process.

The "entangled bank"

MUTUALISM

In attempting to unravel Darwin's entangled bank and understand how these interactions form the basic structure of communities, many popular accounts of community ecology focus on extravagant antagonistic displays between species. Although aggressive behaviours are important interspecific interactions, the amount of attention that is focused on them may create the incorrect impression that they are more important than other types of interaction. Mutualistic interactions between species are just as integral to the organization of biological communities as antagonistic relationships, with some mutualistic interactions forming the most basic elements of many communities.

In many mutualistic relationships, one species acts as the host, and the other plays the role of visitor or resident. Plants are hosts for insects that pollinate them or eat their fruit and for microorganisms that attach themselves to their roots. In other mutualisms, such as flocks of birds that include a mixture of species, no species acts as host. Mutualisms also vary in the benefits the participants derive from the interaction. An individual may gain food, protection from enemies, a nesting site, or a combination of benefits. These benefits may vary from one population to another, thereby causing mutualistic relationships that exist between the same species to evolve in different directions in different populations.

The pervasiveness of mutualism. Some mutualistic relationships are so pervasive that they affect almost all life-forms. The root systems of most terrestrial plant species form complex associations with the soil microorganisms. These mycorrhizal associations aid the plant in taking up nutrients. In some environments, many plants cannot become established without the aid of associated mycorrhizae. In another relationship, legumes rely on nodule-forming associations between their roots and microorganisms to fix nitrogen, and these nitrogen-fixing plants are in turn crucial to the process of succession in biological communities.

Mutualistic associations between animals and microorganisms are equally important to the structure of communities. Most animals rely on the microorganisms in their gut to properly digest and metabolize food. Termites require cellulose-digesting microorganisms in their gut to obtain all possible nourishment that their diet of wood can provide.

At an even more fundamental level, the very origin of eukaryotic cells (those cells having a well-defined nucleus and of which higher plants and animals, protozoa, fungi, and most algae consist) appears to have resulted from an association with various single-celled species: the mitochondria and chloroplasts that occur in eukaryotic cells are thought to have originated as separate organisms that took up residence inside other cells. Eventually neither organism was able to survive without the other—a situation called obligative symbiosis.

In many terrestrial environments, mutualisms between animals and plants are central to the organization of biological communities. In some tropical communities, animals pollinate the flowers and disperse the seeds of almost every woody plant. In turn, a large proportion of animals rely on flowers or fruits for at least part of their diet. Leaf-cutting ants, an important species in neotropical forest communities, prepare cut leaves as a substrate on which to grow the specialized fungus gardens on which they feed. Thousands of plant species produce extrafloral nectaries on their leaves or petioles to attract many kinds of ants, which feed on the nectar and kill insect herbivores that they encounter on the plants.

The evolution of mutualism. Although mutualisms benefit all species involved in a relationship, they are built on the same genetically selfish principles as antagonistic interactions. In fact, many mutualisms appear to have evolved from antagonistic interactions. No species behaves altruistically to promote the good of another species. Mutualisms evolve as species that come in contact manipulate each other for their own benefit. Plants evolve particular mixtures and concentrations of nectar to tempt pollinators to behave in ways that maximize pollination. Purely for their own advantage, pollinators visit plants and navigate among them to harvest nectar or pollen in the most efficient way possible. Their concern is not with how well they function as pollinators for the plants but rather with what they can extract from the plants. Mutualism results whenever the selfish activities of species happen to benefit each of them. Natural selection continues

Obligative symbiosis

to reshape these relationships as each species evolves its ability to exploit the other.

Mutualism and cheaters. Because mutualisms develop through the manipulation of other species, they are always susceptible to invasion by "cheaters," those organisms that can exploit an existing relationship without reciprocating an advantage. Theft of a resource is one type of crime a cheater engages in. Some plants, for example, have coevolved with particular pollinators. The flowers of these plants have deep corollas (inner sets of leaves of the flower constituting an inner chamber) with nectar at the bottom that is accessible only to their pollinators that have long tongues or bills specialized for this purpose. Some short-tongued bees and short-billed hummingbirds, however, have developed their own adaptations—they extract nectar by piercing the base of these long corollas. Another form of cheating involves mimicking the appearance of one species in order to subvert an existing mutualistic association. This subversion has occurred between cleaner fish and their hosts. Cleaner fish are highly specialized fish that pick parasites off the skin of other fish. Host fish arrive at specific sites where they present themselves to the cleaner fish that groom them. Other fish have evolved to resemble the cleaner fish, but, rather than search for parasites, these imposters take a bite out of the host fish.

Theft and deception

Other cheaters use different deceptive devices to exploit mutualistic interactions. Crab spiders, phymatid bugs, and some praying mantids use flowers as places to wait for prey: they have evolved a camouflage that allows them to hide from the pollinating insects they feed on. Rather than construct a web or search through the vegetation to capture prey, this type of predator merely remains frozen on a flower until an unsuspecting pollinator stumbles into its clutches.

As cheaters evolve to exploit a mutualism, they can cause the symbiotic relationship itself to break down unless new ways of thwarting the pretenders evolve within the host population.

Community structure and the spread of mutualism. As mutualisms spread within biological communities over evolutionary time, they make possible new lifestyles that rely on the availability of a number of mutualistic species. Once fleshy fruits had evolved in many plant species and had begun to occur together within communities, bird species evolved that were specialized physiologically to feed on fruits year-round rather than as a short-term seasonal addition to their diet. Resplendent quetzals (*Pharomachrus mocinno*) and oilbirds (*Steatornis caripensis*) have evolved in tropical American forests that have a succession of fruit species throughout the year. These highly specialized birds feed almost exclusively on fruits, supplying fruit even to their nestlings, and hence are called frugivores. To maintain this year-round diet of fruit, resplendent quetzals consume at least 43 fruit species from 17 plant families, and oilbirds eat at least 36 fruit species from 10 plant families. Similarly, hummingbirds, social bees such as honeybees, and other species that feed on nectar (nectarivores) and have life spans longer than the flowering time of one plant species have mutualistic relationships with a succession of pollinating species in order to survive.

Frugivores and nectarivores

This reliance on a succession of species by some frugivores and nectarivores is one reason that the piecemeal extinction of one plant species from biological communities, so common in recent decades, has such potentially disastrous consequences. The mutualisms between nectarivores and flowers, and between frugivores and fruits, are not just extraneous additions to the organization of biological communities. They are central relationships, because they ensure that the next generation of plants is produced and distributed throughout the landscape. The local extinction of a seemingly obscure plant, however, could easily lead to the local extinction of frugivores and nectarivores if these animals rely on that plant during times of scarcity of alternative plants. The importance of the seasonal succession of flowering and fruiting plant species and their associated nectarivores and frugivores to maintaining the normal functioning of terrestrial communities is only beginning to be appreciated.

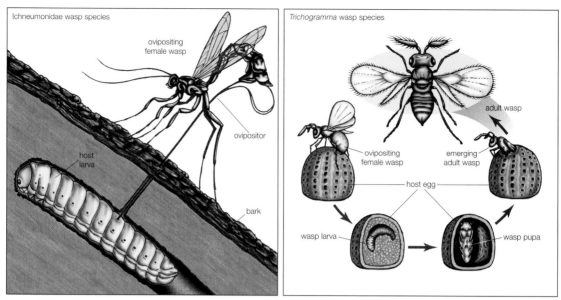

Figure 15: Parasitoids, which parasitize other arthropods by depositing eggs in the pupae, larvae, or eggs of their hosts. (Left) A female Ichneumonidae wasp lays her eggs in the host larvae by means of her ovipositor. (Right) A *Trichogramma* wasp develops within a host egg and emerges as an adult.
Encyclopædia Britannica, Inc.

ANTAGONISM

Although mutualisms are common in all biological communities, they occur side by side with a wide array of antagonistic interactions. As life has evolved, natural selection has favoured organisms that are able to efficiently extract energy and nutrients from their environment. Because organisms are concentrated packages of energy and nutrients in themselves, they can become the objects of antagonistic interactions. Moreover, because resources often are limited, natural selection also has favoured the ability of organisms to compete against one another for them. The result has been the evolution of a great diversity of lifestyles. This diversity can be categorized in any number of ways, but the edges of all the categories blend with one another. Evolution continues to mix all the different kinds of interspecific interactions into novel ways of life.

One way of understanding the diversity of antagonistic interactions is through the kinds of hosts or prey that species attack. Carnivores attack animals, herbivores attack plants, and fungivores attack fungi. Other species are omnivorous, attacking a wide range of plants, animals, and fungi. Regardless of the kinds of foods they eat, however, there are some general patterns in which species interact. Parasitism, grazing, and predation are the three major ways in which species feed on one another. The parasite lives on and feeds off its host, usually decreasing the host's ability to survive but not killing it outright. Grazing species are not as closely tied to their food source as parasites and often vary their diet between two or more species without directly killing them. Predators, however, capture and kill members of other species for food.

Parasitism. *Types of parasites.* Parasitism is thought to be the most common way of life, and parasitic organisms may account for as many as half of all living species. Examples include pathogenic fungi and bacteria, plants that tap into the stems or roots of other plants, insects that as larvae feed on a single plant, and parasitic wasps. Parasites live in or on a single host throughout either a stage in their lives or their entire life span, thereby decreasing the survival or reproduction of their hosts. This lifestyle has arisen many times throughout evolution. The most species-rich groups of organisms are parasites, which, in becoming specialized to live off their hosts alone, eventually become genetically distinct from their species, sometimes to the degree that they are considered a new species (speciation).

One common type of parasite is the parasitoid, an insect whose larvae feed and develop within or on the bodies of other arthropods. Each parasitoid larva develops on a single individual and eventually kills that host. Most parasitoids are wasps (Figure 15), but some flies and a small number of beetles, moths, lacewings, and even one caddisfly species have evolved to be parasitoids. Parasitoids alone number about 68,000 named species, and most parasitoids have yet to be named and described. Realistic estimates of the total number of described and undescribed parasitoid species are about 800,000.

The number of species of insects that develop as nymphs or larvae on a single plant host may outnumber the parasitoids. There is currently a great deal of debate concerning the number of species worldwide, and this debate centres on the number of plant-feeding insect species, many of which inhabit the canopies of tropical trees. These species have been almost impossible to collect until recently when techniques allowing access to the canopies have been adapted from mountain-climbing methods. All ecologists and systematists working on these estimates agree that there are at least a few million plant-feeding insect species, but the estimates range from 2 to 30 million.

Estimates of the number of pathogenic fungi, parasitic nematodes, and other parasitic groups also have increased as ecological and molecular studies are revealing many previously unrecognized species. Continued work on biodiversity worldwide will allow better estimates to be made of the Earth's inventory of species, which is a major prerequisite for understanding the role of parasites in the organization of communities and in the conservation of diversity.

Specialization in parasites. It is now evident that the parasitic lifestyle often favours extreme specialization to a single host or a small group of hosts. Living for a long period of time on a single host, a parasite must remain attached within or on its host, avoid the defenses of its host, and obtain all its nutrition from that host. Unlike grazers or predators, parasites cannot move from host to host, supplementing their diet with a variety of foods.

Estimates of the number of species worldwide have risen sharply in recent decades owing to research revealing parasitic species to be much more specific to one host species than previously realized. What once may have been considered a single parasitic species attacking many different host species has often turned out to be a group of very similar, yet distinct, parasitic species, each specialized to its own host. This speciation occurs because different parasitic populations become adapted to living on different hosts and coping with the defenses of these hosts. Over

Carnivory, herbivory, and fungivory

Parasitoids

The most common way of life

time, many of these different parasite populations evolve into genetically distinct species. It is through the specialization of individuals of a species onto different hosts, ultimately resulting in speciation, that parasitism appears to have become the most common way of life on Earth.

For example, swallowtail butterflies (*Papilio*) include more than 500 species worldwide. In most species an adult female lays her eggs on a host plant, and, after they hatch, the caterpillars complete their development by feeding parasitically on that plant. In North America there are two groups of these butterflies that have evolved to use different hosts: the tiger swallowtail group and the Old World swallowtail group (*Papilio machaon*). In the Old World swallowtail group are several species that feed on plants in the carrot family Apiaceae (also called Umbelliferae), with different populations feeding on different plant species. However, one species within this group, the Oregon swallowtail (*Papilio oregonius*), has become specialized to feed on tarragon sagebrush (*Artemisia dracunculus*), which is in the plant family Asteracaea (Compositae of some sources). Among the tiger swallowtail group, various members have become specialized to different plant hosts. The eastern tiger swallowtail (*Papilio glaucus*) has a long list of recorded hosts, but it is now known that the northern and southern populations are adapted to different plant species, and these populations cannot develop on the others' hosts.

Alternation among hosts. Although many parasitic species complete all developmental stages on a single host individual, thousands of other parasitic species alternate between two or more host species, specializing on a different host species at each developmental stage. Many parasites, from a diverse array of species such as certain viruses, flatworms, nematodes, and aphids, specialize on different host species at different stages of development. Among aphids alone at least 2,700 species alternate among hosts.

The evolution of alternating hosts

Parasites have evolved by three major evolutionary routes to alternate among two or more hosts. Some parasite species have evolved to alternate between their final host and an intermediate host, or vector, that transfers the parasite from one final host to another: the malarial parasite *Plasmodium falciparum* alternates between a final human host and an intermediate mosquito host by which the parasite is transferred from one person to another. The parasite uses the mosquito as a mobile hypodermic syringe. Examples of a similar kind of transmission between a final host and an intermediate host with piercing mouthparts occur in many other species. Viruses, rickettsias, protozoa, and nematodes all have species that are transmitted between vertebrates through biting flies. Some viruses and other parasites are similarly transmitted between plant species by aphids, whose piercing mouthparts transmit the parasites directly into plant tissues while the aphids are feeding.

Other parasites alternate between a host and the predator that eats it. These parasites have turned an evolutionary problem (being killed along with their host) into an evolutionary opportunity (being transferred to the predator and continuing to feed). As it develops, the parasite attacks hosts higher in the food chain, alternating between herbivore and predator or between an intermediate and a top predator in the food chain. Many parasites alternate between snails or other invertebrates and vertebrate predators that feed upon these invertebrates; others alternate among vertebrate species. The pork tapeworm (*Taenia solium*), for example, alternates between pigs and humans in societies in which improperly cooked pork is eaten.

Still other parasites employ wings, wind, or water to alternate between hosts. Many aphid species alternate between a summer host and a winter host by producing winged individuals that fly to the new host. Rust fungi such as wheat stem rust can be carried between hosts by wind currents, and the parasite *Schistosoma mansoni*, which causes the disease schistosomiasis, alternates between *Biomphalaria* snails and humans by moving through water.

The different ways by which host species are linked by parasites contribute to the complex web of interactions that shape the structure of communities. The effect of parasitism on the dynamics of populations and the organization of communities is still one of the most underexplored topics in ecology.

Grazing. *The strategy of grazing.* The word "grazing" conjures up images of large mammals moving through seas of grass. Grazing, however, is a form of interspecific interaction that has been adopted by a number of other groups as well. A grazer is defined as any species that moves from one victim to another, feeding on part of each victim without actually killing it outright. The "victim" is to the grazer as prey is to the predator. Hence, grasshoppers that jump from plant to plant, chewing a portion of the leaves of each one they visit, are grazers, as are caterpillars that crawl from one plant to another during development rather than remain as parasites on an individual plant. The grazing lifestyle differs from the parasitic lifestyle in a few important ways. Individuals can vary their diets with different foods, and, by not remaining attached to a single individual for long periods of time, their victims do not have time to develop induced specialized defenses, such as an immune response that a host can develop against a parasite.

Plants as victims

Grazing is more commonly perpetrated on plants than animals because plants have a modular structure that allows a part of them to be lost without the whole individual being destroyed. In contrast, most animals that lose a part of the body to an antagonist die immediately or soon afterward, rendering the interaction an act of predation rather than grazing. An exception to this rule occurs in species that can disconnect body parts—some lizards and salamanders are able to detach their tails if they are attacked by a predator.

Specialization in grazing. On most continents, reciprocal evolutionary changes, or coevolution, between grasses and large grazing mammals have taken place over periods of millions of years. Many grass species have evolved the ability to tolerate high levels of grazing, which is evident to anyone who regularly mows a lawn. Simultaneously, they have evolved other defenses, such as high silica content, which reduces their palatability to some grazers. A number of herbivorous mammals have responded to these defenses by evolving the ability to specialize on grasses with high silica content and low nutritional value. Many large grazing mammals such as elephants have high-crowned (hypsodont) teeth that are constantly replaced by growth from below as the crowns are worn down by the silica in their food. Many of these species also have complicated digestive systems with a gut full of microflora and microfauna capable of extracting many of the nutrients from the plants.

Not all grasslands, however, are adapted to grazing by large mammals. In North America, although the grasslands of the Great Plains coevolved with large herds of bison, the grasslands of the upper Intermontane West (which roughly includes eastern Washington and Oregon) have never supported these large grazing herds. The Great Plains had grasses that formed sods and could withstand trampling by large-hooved mammals. These sods were so tightly interwoven that early European settlers cut them to use as roofs for their houses. The grasses of the Intermontane West, however, were tuft grasses that did not form sods and quickly died when trampled. Consequently, when cows replaced bison as the large, grazing mammal of North America, the grasslands of the Great Plains sustained the grazing pressure, whereas those of the Intermontane West rapidly eroded. Similar problems have arisen in other parts of the world where cattle have been introduced into grasslands that did not have a history of coevolution with large grazing mammals.

Plants have evolved more than 10,000 chemical compounds that are not involved in primary metabolism, and most of these compounds are thought to have evolved as defenses against herbivores and pathogens. Some of these chemical compounds are defenses against grazers, whereas others are defenses against parasites. Most of the chemical compounds that make herbs so flavourful and useful in cooking probably evolved as defenses against

Figure 16: *Predatory behaviour.*
D'Orbigny's round-eared bat (*Tonatia sylvicola*) capturing a
katydid in flight.
© Merlin D. Tuttle, Bat Conservation International—Photo Researchers, Inc.

Allelo-
chemicals

enemies. These compounds, called allelochemicals, are found in almost all plant species, and their great diversity suggests that chemical defense against herbivores and pathogens has always been an important part of plant evolution.

Predation. Predation differs from both parasitism and grazing in that the victims are killed immediately. Predators therefore differ from parasites and grazers in their effects on the dynamics of populations and the organization of communities. As with parasitism and grazing, predation is an interaction that has arisen many times in many taxonomic groups worldwide. Bats that capture insects in flight (Figure 16), starfish that attack marine invertebrates, flies that attack other insects, and adult beetles that scavenge the ground for seeds are all examples of the predatory lifestyle. Cannibalism, in which individuals of the same species prey on one another, also has arisen many times and is common in some animal species. Some salamanders and toads have tadpoles that occur in two forms, one of which has a specialized head that allows it to cannibalize other tadpoles of the same species.

Canni-
balism

Because predators kill their prey immediately, natural selection favours the development of a variety of quick defenses against predators. In contrast, the hosts of parasites and the victims of grazers can respond in other ways. A parasitized host can induce defenses over a longer period of time as the parasite develops within it, and a plant population subjected to grazing can evolve traits that minimize the effects of losing leaves, branches, or flowers. Therefore, the evolution of interactions between parasites and hosts, grazers and victims, and predators and prey all differ from one another as a result of the ways in which the interaction affects the victim.

Specialization in predation. Most predators attack more than one prey species. Nevertheless, there are some ecological conditions that have permitted the evolution of highly specialized predators that attack only a few prey species. The evolution of specialization in predators (and in grazers) requires that the prey species be predictably available year after year as well as easy to find and abundant throughout the year or during the periods of time when other foods are scarce. In addition, the prey must require some form of specialization of the predator to be captured, handled, and digested successfully as the major part of a diet. The most specialized predators attack prey that fulfill these ecological conditions. Examples include anteaters (Figure 17), aardwolves, and numbats that eat only ants or termites, which are among the most abundant insects in many terrestrial communities. Among birds, snail kites (*Rostrhamus sociabilis*) are perhaps the most specialized predators. They feed almost exclusively

on snails of the genus *Pomacea,* using their highly hooked bills to extract these abundant snails from their shells.

Seed
predation

Some seed predators are also highly specialized to attack the seeds of only one or a few plant species. (Seed consumption is considered predation because the entire living embryo of a plant is destroyed.) Crossbills exhibit one of the most extreme examples of specialization. These birds have beaks that allow them to pry open the closed cones of conifers to extract the seeds. The exact shape of their bills varies among populations and species in both North America and Europe. Experiments on red crossbills (*Loxia curvirostra*) have shown that different populations of these birds have bill sizes and shapes that have been adapted to harvest efficiently only one conifer species. Hence, red crossbills are a complex of populations, each adapted to different conifer species.

Effect on community structure. Predators can greatly affect the structure of communities. For example, seed predators commonly scour the ground for each year's seed crop, eating most of the seeds produced by many different species each year. To defend against these predators, certain plants are thought to resort to mast seeding, which is the production of many seeds by the plant every two or more years in regional synchrony with other plants of the same species. Mast seeding is an effective defense because the seed predators become satiated before all the seeds have been consumed. The consequence of mast seeding for the organization of communities is that, instead of a few new seedlings establishing themselves every year, major pulses occur over time during which new plants become established and old plants die. Many conifers in boreal forests exhibit mast seeding as do other species such as bamboos. Some bamboo species grow for 100 years or more before producing seeds. Then all at once the bamboo plants over a large geographic region will set seed and die in the same year.

COMPETITION

Competition is a powerful form of interaction in the organization of communities, but it differs from other forms of antagonistic and mutualistic relationships in that no species benefits from the interaction. In competitive interactions, species evolve either to avoid each other, to tolerate the presence of the other, or to aggressively exclude the other.

Types of competition. Species compete for almost every conceivable kind of resource, and the same two spe-

Gunter Ziesler/Bruce Coleman Ltd.

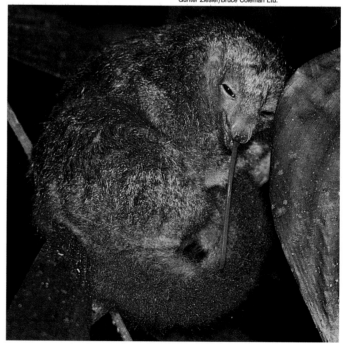

Figure 17: *Anatomical adaptation favourable to a predator.*
Silky anteater (*Cyclopes didactylus*) extending its long, narrow
tongue, which it uses to capture and ingest prey.

cies may compete for different resources in different environments. Hole-nesting birds compete for tree holes, plant species compete for pollinators and seed dispersers, and male birds compete for preferred sites to defend as territories for attracting females. Species may compete for many resources simultaneously, but often one resource, called the limiting resource because it limits the population growth of each species, is the focus of competition. Moreover, the ways in which species compete vary with the resources. In some cases, species compete by capturing resources faster than their competitors (exploitation competition). Some plant species, for example, are able to extract water and nutrients from the soil faster than surrounding species. In other cases, the two species physically interfere with one another (interference competition) by aggressively attempting to exclude one another from particular habitats.

The effects of competition. Over evolutionary time, the effects of competition on species can vary. In some environments, the effects may be highly asymmetrical, and, at the extreme called amensalism, the survival or growth of one species may be inhibited and the other(s) not affected. The weaker competitor will either go extinct locally, diverge from the other species in its use of resources, or evolve an increased competitive ability. All three outcomes have been observed in natural and experimental populations studied by ecologists.

Species diverge from one another through competition, with the result that they fill different niches within the community. The great differences in bill size and shape that some of Darwin's finches in the Galapagos have evolved have resulted from competition. This process, called character displacement, results as natural selection favours those individuals in each species that compete least with individuals of the other species. Experimental studies of coexisting seed-feeding rodents in the deserts of North America have shown that these species have evolved differences in size and other characteristics to minimize competition.

By evolving in response to one another, many competitors may be able to coexist regionally over the long term but not locally. Within any local area, one species may generally be driven to extinction by the other. Which species wins locally will depend on the physical environment, the genetic makeup of each of the competing species, and their interactions with other species in the community. Even subtle changes in the environment can affect which species wins. Experiments with species of flies (*Drosophila*) have shown that, when all other factors are held constant, small variations in temperature or in the percentage of ethanol in the larval environment can determine which species outcompetes the other. Hence, the continued coexistence of some competing species may depend critically on multiple populations of both or all species being distributed over a number of environments throughout a region (see above *Population ecology: Regulation of populations: Metapopulations*).

COMMENSALISM AND OTHER TYPES OF INTERACTION

In commensal interactions, one species benefits and the other is unaffected. The commensal organism may depend on its host for food, shelter, support, transport, or a combination of these.

One example of commensalism involves a small crab that lives inside an oyster's shell. The crab enters the shell as a larva and receives shelter while it grows. Once fully grown, however, it is unable to exit through the narrow opening of the two valves, and so it remains within the shell, snatching particles of food from the oyster but not harming its unwitting benefactor. Another form of commensalism occurs between small plants called epiphytes and the large tree branches on which they grow. Epiphytes depend on their hosts for structural support but do not derive nourishment from them or harm them in any way.

Many other kinds of interaction, however, range from antagonism to commensalism to mutualism, depending on the ecological circumstances. For example, plant-feeding insects may have large detrimental effects on plant survival or reproduction if they attack small or nonvigor-

ous plants but may have little or no effect on large or vigorous plants of the same species. Some human diseases may cause only temporary discomfort or be life-threatening, depending on the age and physical condition of the person.

No interaction between species fits neatly into the categories of antagonism, commensalism, or mutualism. The interaction depends on the genetic makeup of both species and the age, size, and physical condition of the individuals. Interactions may even depend on the composition of the community in which the interaction takes place. For example, the moth *Greya politella* pollinates the flowers of a small herb called the prairie star (*Lithophragma parviflorum*). The female moth pollinates while she lays eggs (oviposits) in the corolla of the flower. As she pushes her abdomen down into a flower, pollen adheres to her. She flies on to the next flower to lay more eggs, where some of the pollen rubs off onto the stigma of the flower, causing pollination to occur. Although this unusual pollination mechanism is very effective in some local populations, in other communities different pollinators such as bee flies and bees are so common that their visits to the flowers swamp the pollination efforts of the moths. As a result, pollination by the moths makes up a very tiny proportion of all the pollinator visits that occur within that community and probably has little effect on plant reproduction or natural selection. This moth, therefore, is a commensal in some populations and a mutualist in others, depending on the local assemblage of pollinator species.

The coevolutionary process

As pairs or groups of species interact, they evolve in response to each other. These reciprocal evolutionary changes in interacting species are called coevolutionary processes, one of the primary methods by which biological communities are organized. Through coevolution local populations of interacting species become adapted to one another, sometimes even evolving into new species.

THE STUDY OF COEVOLUTION

To understand how coevolution shapes interactions within communities, researchers must distinguish between traits that have coevolved and those that were already present in ancestors before the interspecific interaction began. For example, hummingbirds use their wings and bills to reach the nectar within flowers. A hummingbird with a long bill may have evolved its bill as a result of coevolution with a particular species of flower; however, its wings are not the result of coevolution. Wings were already present in birds before hummingbirds evolved. Therefore, both the evolutionary ecology and the history (phylogeny) of the interacting species must be studied. The phylogeny indicates when each species arose within a lineage and when each new trait made its first appearance. The ecological studies can then show how each of those traits has been shaped by and used under different ecological conditions.

The study of the coevolution between moths of the family Prodoxidae and their host plants illustrates the interplay of phylogeny and ecology. Prodoxid moths include some species that have become major pollinators of plants. These pollinators include yucca moths (of the genera *Tegeticula* and *Parategeticula*) and *Greya* moths (see above *Interspecific interactions and the organization of communities: Commensalism and other types of interaction*). *Greya* moths inadvertently, or passively, pollinate the flowers they visit, but their close relatives the yucca moths purposely, or actively, perform this function. Female yucca moths collect and carry pollen on specialized appendages attached to their mouthparts. They visit yucca flowers to lay their eggs in the floral ovary, and their offspring feed on the developing seeds (Figure 18). While visiting each flower, a female moth takes some of the pollen she is carrying and places it directly on the stigma of the flower. Her offspring are therefore guaranteed developing seeds on which to feed. The yuccas have evolved to depend solely on these moths for pollination.

Exploitation and interference competition

Character displacement

Evolutionary ecology and phylogeny

 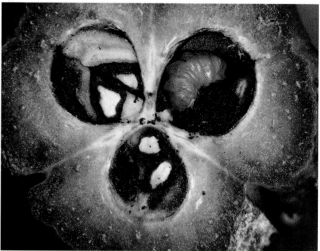

Figure 18: *Coevolution between the yucca moth and the yucca plant.*
(Left) A female yucca moth (*Tegeticula yuccasella*) pushing pollen into the stigma tube of the
yucca flower while visiting the flower to deposit her eggs. (Right) Yucca moth larvae
feeding on seeds in the yucca fruit.
Photographs, © Robert and Linda Mitchell

Unlike many other plant species, they do not produce nectar or any other reward for pollinators and so do not waste energy to attract pollinators. They lose some of their seeds to the yucca moth larvae, but this is the cost of coevolution with this highly efficient pollinator.

Phylogenetic studies have shown that the loss of nectar production in yuccas and the evolution of active pollination in yucca moths are novel traits that have arisen through coevolution, as the relatives of yuccas produce nectar, and the relatives of yucca moths, the *Greya* moths, do not actively pollinate their host plants. Some other aspects of the interaction make use of traits that did not coevolve between yuccas and yucca moths. Instead, the traits were present in ancestors. Laying eggs in flowers and local specialization to one plant species are two traits that are common to all the close relatives of yucca moths, regardless of the plants on which they feed.

Therefore, by combining ecological and phylogenetic studies, researchers can piece together the history of coevolution between these species. The coevolved mutualism between yuccas and yucca moths began when their ancestors inadvertently became more successful at survival and reproduction as a result of their interactions. Yuccas that did not waste energy on nectar production to attract other pollinators achieved an advantage over those plants that did; yucca moths that ensured the availability of developing seeds for their offspring by actively pollinating the flowers in which they laid their eggs also gained an advantage over populations that did not do so. The process undoubtedly involved many other twists and turns along the way, but the combination of evolutionary ecological and phylogenetic studies allows at least part of the coevolutionary process to be reconstructed.

All coevolved interactions are similar to those between yuccas and yucca moths in that natural selection operates on traits that are already present within species, molding them in new ways by favouring new mutations that fine-tune the relationship. Tinkering rather than engineering is how the biologist François Jacob described the process of evolution, and his analogy certainly extends to the coevolutionary process. Coevolved interactions are not designed from scratch for maximum efficiency. Instead, evolution fiddles with existing structures and behaviours and adapts them to perform new functions—in effect, jury-rigging them. Consequently, the organization of biological communities reflects this makeshift nature of adaptation and coevolution.

The makeshift nature of coevolution

THE COEVOLUTIONARY "ARMS RACE" VERSUS REDUCED ANTAGONISM

Nothing is absolutely predictable about the direction of coevolution. How an interaction coevolves depends not only on the current genetic makeup of the species involved but also on new mutations that arise, the population characteristics of each species, and the community context in which the interaction takes places. Under some ecological conditions, an antagonistic interaction between two species can coevolve to enhance the antagonism; the species "build up" methods of defense and attack, much like an evolutionary arms race. Under other ecological conditions, however, the antagonism may be lessened, resulting in reduced antagonism.

Predator-prey interactions. In an evolutionary arms race, natural selection progressively escalates the defenses and counterdefenses of the species. The thick calcareous shells of many marine mollusks and the powerful drilling appendages and musculature of their predators are thought to have coevolved through this process of escalation. A similar example of coevolution has occurred in the endemic mollusks and crabs in Lake Tanganyika. The mollusks in this lake have much thicker shells than other freshwater mollusks, and the endemic crab that feeds on them has much larger chelae (pincerlike claws) than other freshwater crabs. Differences between these mollusks and crabs and the freshwater species throughout the world to which they are related appear to be due to coevolution rather than any unique nutrient or mineral conditions in this lake.

Parasite-host interactions. Parasites and their hosts engage in a similar evolutionary arms race, although in the past parasitologists believed this not to be the case. Instead, parasites were thought to evolve gradually toward reduced antagonism—having a less detrimental effect on their hosts. The degree of virulence was sometimes regarded as an indicator of the age of the relationship: a very virulent relationship, which resulted in the swift demise of the host, was considered new. Research in population biology and evolutionary ecology, however, provided evidence that contradicts this view. Parasite-host interactions are now understood to evolve toward either increased or decreased antagonism, depending on several important ecological factors.

The density of the host population and the transmission rate of the parasite are two of the most important of these ecological factors. The density of the host species determines how often the opportunity arises for a parasite to move from one host to another; the transmission rate of the parasite determines how easily a parasite can move between hosts when the opportunity does arise. Only some parasites are transmitted easily between hosts. If the host occurs at a high density and the transmission rate of the parasite is also high, then natural selection favours increased virulence in the parasite. Being easily transmissible and having many host individuals to infect, the par-

Increased virulence

asite can multiply quickly and escape to new hosts before it kills its current host and dies along with it. Some forms (genotypes) of the parasite will already contain or will develop mutations that increase the speed and proficiency of this process. By producing more organisms that survive, the mutated form of the parasite will outcompete those parasites with the original genotype that are not able to maximize the opportunity to infect the greatest number of hosts. After several generations, many more parasites with enhanced virulence will exist, and this genotype can be said to be favoured by natural selection. If host population density remains high, the parasite genotype that confers the most virulence will become the only form of the parasite in that population.

At the other extreme, if the host population density is low and the transmission rate of the parasite is also low, natural selection will favour less virulent forms of the parasite. The highly virulent forms that quickly kill their host will often die along with their host without having spread to other hosts, leaving only the less virulent parasites to propagate the species.

In many natural environments, host populations fluctuate between high and low density. Consequently, the parasite population will fluctuate as well, sometimes containing more highly virulent forms, sometimes less virulent forms. Depending on the rate at which host density fluctuates, the host population will vary in the degree and mix of virulent forms that it harbours.

Intermediate virulence

The evolution of myxoma virus in rabbits in Australia shows how quickly coevolution of parasites and hosts can proceed to a new outcome, in this case intermediate virulence. European rabbits were introduced into Australia in the 1800s. In the absence of parasites and predators that had kept their numbers in check in their European habitat, they multiplied and disseminated rapidly, causing widespread destruction of the native vegetation. When the myxoma virus was introduced into Australia in 1950 to control rabbit populations, it was highly virulent and caused death in almost all infected rabbits within two weeks. Since then, however, coevolution of the virus and rabbit populations has occurred, resulting in an interaction less immediately lethal to the rabbits. As population levels of the rabbits decreased, mutant strains of the virus that allowed a rabbit host to live longer were favoured, thereby increasing the opportunity for the virus to spread to another rabbit before its current host died. Most infected rabbits still die from the infection, but death is not as relentless and most infected individuals survive for two and a half to four weeks after infection.

COEVOLUTION AND THE ORGANIZATION OF COMMUNITIES

The importance of interspecific interactions. The coevolution of the myxoma virus and rabbit species described above illustrates how this process operates to maintain the organization of biological communities, averting the havoc that might ensue without the proper checks and balances that the process ensures. Unfortunately the importance of interspecific interactions may become apparent only after the balance of a community has been disrupted, often by human hands and often with serious reverberations. If the rabbit species had not been introduced into a community in which none of its natural predators were found, its potential for devastation would not be fully appreciated. Interspecies interactions are necessary to maintain population levels of moderate size, and they function in most biological communities in much the same way that the rabbit population was controlled by myxoma virus.

Human disruption. As biological communities are dismantled through human activities, coevolutionary processes and their effects on the organization of communities are disrupted. Changes in population density and the introduction of new species can cause the extinction of other species. In the process, the way natural selection acts on the remaining species within those communities is altered. Increased population densities of some species, for example, are likely to favour the evolution of more virulent genotypes of some parasites (see above *The coevolutionary "arms race" versus reduced antagonism*).

Low population levels of other species can cause the chance loss of genes important to the ongoing coevolution of other interactions. It will seldom be possible to predict how these changes in coevolution will affect the organization of communities, because of the intricate interdependencies among all organisms of the biosphere.

GENE-FOR-GENE COEVOLUTION

In some interactions between parasites and hosts, coevolution can take a specific form called gene-for-gene coevolution or matching-gene coevolution. It is a form of reciprocal evolutionary change based on the idea that, if one member of a coevolving relationship has a gene that affects the relationship, the other member has a gene to counter this effect. These genes evolve reciprocally and provide the genetic basis for certain types of coevolution. This relationship has been demonstrated between plants and a number of their parasites, including rust fungi, nematodes, bacteria, viruses, and one insect species. Its principles also form the basis of many plant breeding programs designed to increase resistance against pathogens.

The process of gene-for-gene coevolution begins when a parasite population encounters a new plant host. Most host individuals will not be able to detect the presence of the parasite. Certain host individuals, however, may have a mutated gene, dubbed the resistance gene in this scenario, that allows them to detect a substance the parasite emits, encoded by a so-called avirulence gene. After being alerted to the threat of the parasite, the host responds to prevent the parasite from invading. The resistance gene will confer an advantage to plants that carry it, allowing individuals to survive and pass on their genotype to future generations. Individuals that do not possess this gene will not be able to resist invasion by the parasite and will die, unable to pass on their genotype. Thus, the new resistance gene will spread through the plant population. At this point the parasite might seem to be outwitted, but actually it may be able to circumvent this genetic evasion by the host with a genetic trick of its own. If a mutation arises in the gene that codes for the product that the host recognizes, the gene product will be altered and the host will no longer be able to resist the parasite. The spread of this mutant gene in the parasite population will be favoured by natural selection. A genetic Ping-Pong match between the two species can then ensue, as the host develops another mutation in any gene that allows it to detect the parasite, and the parasite responds to this defensive maneuver with a genetic alteration to avoid detection. The host and parasite populations therefore coevolve by the accumulation of these matching genes.

The mechanism of gene-for-gene coevolution

In agriculture, gene-for-gene relationships are maintained by introducing new resistance genes into all plants that cover a large area. In natural populations, each new resistance gene appears as a mutant in a single individual and then spreads by natural selection throughout the population in subsequent generations. Demonstrating a gene-for-gene relationship in natural populations is a difficult and time-consuming process because it demands detailed genetic and ecological studies of the plants and their pathogens that take many years.

The best-studied example is that of wild flax (*Linum marginale*) and flax rust (*Melampsora lini*) in Australia. Local populations of flax plants and flax rust harbour multiple matching genes for resistance and avirulence. The number of genes and their frequency within local populations fluctuate greatly over time as coevolution continues. In small populations, the resistance genes can be lost by chance alone through the process of genetic drift (see above *The organism and the environment: The diversity of life*). New genes in the host and parasite populations can appear through either mutation or the influx of genes from other populations. Consequently, the long-term dynamics of the gene-for-gene coevolution between flax and flax rust depend on the rate at which new genes appear within local populations of the parasite and host, the intensity with which natural selection acts on these genes (which, in turn, depends on the virulence of the particular parasite genotype), the population sizes of both host and parasite, and the rate that genes are transferred among populations.

Not all interactions between plants and parasites coevolve in a gene-for-gene manner. Resistance in a plant host is often determined by many genes rather than by a single gene. Examples of gene-for-gene coevolution, however, are slowly accumulating, and these are providing a powerful tool in breeding crop plants that are resistant to pathogens and parasites. As other forms of coevolution are studied in natural populations, the results will help determine still other ways of selecting for more durable resistance in crop plants. Such studies, however, require that intact biological communities are preserved as precious natural laboratories for understanding the coevolutionary process.

Biological communities as natural laboratories

THE GEOGRAPHIC MOSAIC THEORY OF COEVOLUTION

The study of evolving interactions in natural biological communities has indicated that the long-term dynamics of coevolution may occur over large geographic ranges rather than within local populations. This view is called the geographic mosaic theory of coevolution. It is based on the observation that a species may adapt and become specialized to another species differently in separate regions. A species that is involved in an interspecific interaction in one geographic area may not even be present in another geographic area. This geographic mosaic in evolving interactions provides the raw material for the overall direction of coevolution, which proceeds as genes that are favoured in local interactions spread out into other populations.

Some local populations may contribute little to the overall direction of coevolution between two or more species, whereas other populations may be crucial to the process. A highly virulent form of a parasite that recently has been introduced into a local population may cause the extinction of its host population, thereby causing its own extinction. In another population the evolution of a powerful host resistance gene may cause the local extinction of the parasite population. In still other populations the two species may continue to coexist but coevolve in different ways. Over a long period some adaptations in these populations will spread to other populations and influence the overall direction of coevolution between the parasite and host species. Similar geographic differences in interactions are known to occur between predators and prey and between competitors and mutualists.

For some forms of coevolution to occur at a geographic level, many populations of the interacting species must be maintained on a local scale (metapopulations) as well as across broader geographic ranges. Should a species be reduced to a few populations, the geographic mosaic of diverse adaptations that fuels the coevolutionary process is diminished.

Coevolution of one species with several species. In the process called coevolutionary alternation, one species coevolves with several other species by shifting among the species with which it interacts over many generations. European cuckoos (*Cuculus canorus*) provide an example of this type of coevolution. The cuckoos behave as brood parasites, laying their eggs in the nests of other avian species and depending on these hosts to raise their young (Figure 19). The four major host species for cuckoos in Britain are meadow pipits (*Anthus pratensis*), reed warblers (*Acrocephalus scirpaceus;* see photograph), pied wagtails (*Motacilla alba yarrellii*), and dunnocks (*Prunella modularis*).

Coevolutionary alternation

Cuckoo populations have evolved many adaptations that enable them to trick their hosts into rearing their young, the most impressive of which is the production of eggs that resemble those of their host. Cuckoos can produce eggs that are very similar in colour to the eggs of meadow pipits, reed warblers, or pied wagtails. Three different cuckoo genotypes are responsible for the production of these three different egg colours, and thus cuckoos are said to be polymorphic with respect to egg colour. These genotypes are maintained in cuckoo populations because natural selection is continually changing which genotype is favoured. This occurs because after many generations

Figure 19: *Coevolution of one species with many species.* (Top) European cuckoo (*Cuculus canorus*) egg (at left) in the nest of a reed warbler (*Acrocephalus scirpaceus*). (Bottom) Fledgling cuckoo, having kicked the young reed warbler chicks from the nest, being fed by an adult reed warbler, which accepts the chick as her own.
Photographs, John Markham/Bruce Coleman Ltd.

the host species can develop defenses against the cuckoo, such as the ability to discriminate between eggs and eject those that have only minute differences from their own. (That this ability to reject eggs is evolved is evidenced by the fact that in Iceland, where cuckoos are not indigenous, pied wagtails and meadow pipits will accept cuckoo eggs placed in their nests by researchers.) As the gene for this defensive maneuver spreads throughout the host population, cuckoos with genotypes that allow them to produce eggs mimicking the egg colour of a new host are favoured.

By alternating among hosts, cuckoos are coevolving with a number of bird species in Britain. Some of their current hosts, including dunnocks, have few defenses against cuckoos and do not reject cuckoo eggs, which may indicate that these hosts have been targeted by cuckoos relatively recently. Some other potential hosts that cuckoos do not currently colonize will strongly reject any eggs that are not exactly like their own, suggesting that these bird species may have been hosts in the recent past but were abandoned by cuckoos after defenses against them evolved. Over many generations, these former hosts will probably lose their defenses because the evolutionary pressure to retain them has been relaxed—they are no longer being attacked by cuckoos. In Britain the loss of these kinds of defenses makes the birds once again targets for attack by cuckoos, thereby continuing the process of coevolutionary alternation among hosts.

Coevolution among groups of species. Coevolution often involves even larger numbers of species, but many of these coevolving interactions are much more difficult to study than paired or alternating relationships. Examples of these larger groups of coevolving species include many butterflies that have coevolved with plants that produce showy flowers to attract them and fruit-eating birds that have coevolved with plants that produce small, fleshy fruits to disperse their seeds. Many of these interactions may have begun with a relationship between only a few species of animals and plants, but other species have evolved convergently, developing similar characteristics to exploit the existing relationships.

Convergence. Unrelated species living in similar physical environments often are shaped by natural selection to have comparable morphological, physiological, or life history characteristics; they are said to evolve convergently. Convergence is a common feature of evolution and has major effects on the organization of biological communities. Interactions as well as characteristics can converge. Once an interaction evolves between two species, other species within the community may develop traits akin to

those integral to the interaction, whereby the new species enters into the interaction. This type of convergence of species has occurred commonly in the evolution of mutualistic interactions, including those between pollinators and plants and those between vertebrates and fruits: some of the species drawn into the interaction become comutualists, contributing as well as benefiting from the relationship, whereas others become cheaters that only exploit the relationship (see above *Interspecific interactions and the organization of communities: Mutualism: Mutualism and cheaters*). Either way, these additional species may influence the future evolution of the interaction.

A clear example of this kind of convergence of species is that between flowers and hawkmoths. In the tropical dry forest of Cañas in northwestern Costa Rica, there are 65 hawkmoth species and 31 native plant species adapted for hawkmoth pollination. The hawkmoth species are all members of one moth family called the Sphingidae. They have diverged into many species from a common moth ancestor, and it is therefore not surprising that they share the same basic hawkmoth body plan. The plants adapted for hawkmoth pollination, however, are distributed

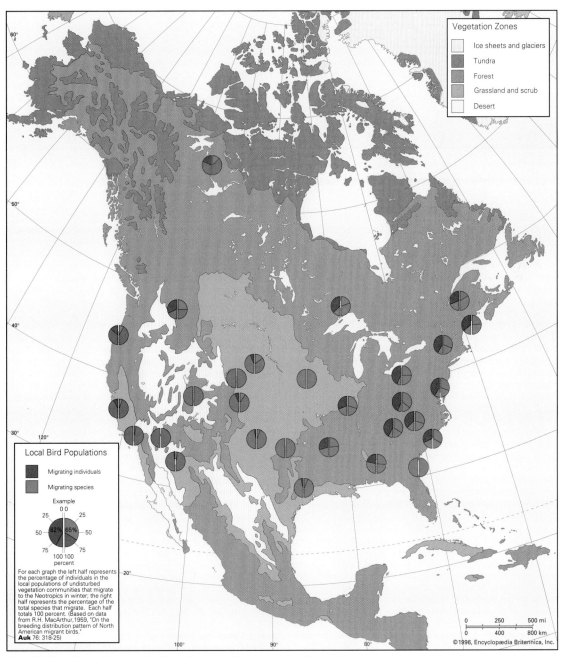

Figure 20: Proportions of breeding birds in North America that migrate to the Neotropics.

throughout 14 plant families. These species have evolved convergently from different ancestors to have floral shapes that attract hawkmoths.

Mimicry complexes. A different kind of convergence has occurred in the evolution of mimetic butterflies and other insects. Mimicry occurs when two or more species evolve to resemble and sometimes behave in ways similar to another species (see also MIMICRY). The most famous examples of mimicry are found among insects, and they take two forms: Müllerian mimicry, in which two species evolve convergently to have a similar appearance, and Batesian mimicry, in which one species evolves to resemble another. These different forms of mimicry are named after their 19th-century discoverers, the naturalists Fritz Müller and Henry Walter Bates. In the several decades following the publication of Charles Darwin's *On the Origin of Species* in 1859, mimicry was the major example used to show how evolution occurs through the mechanism of natural selection.

Müllerian mimicry can occur between two species that are distasteful to the same predators. Their predators learn to recognize and avoid distasteful prey by signals such as the colour patterns of wings. If two distasteful species develop the same colour pattern, the predator has to learn only one pattern to avoid, speeding up the learning process and providing an advantage to the convergent prey species. One of the distasteful species may initially model itself on the other, but, if they are almost equal in abundance, the species may coevolve and converge on some intermediate pattern. *Heliconius* butterflies in Central and South America form mimicry complexes of two or more species, and the colour patterns that result from this convergence vary geographically.

In Batesian mimicry a palatable species models itself on an unpalatable species to fool predators into believing that they are not tasty. Many flies have evolved to mimic bees, and some palatable butterflies have evolved to mimic unpalatable butterflies. If the mimic is uncommon, the convergence may not affect the unpalatable model, because it will be less likely that predators will consume many mimics by mistake and uncover the fraud. If the mimic, however, is abundant, its predators may eventually learn to dissociate its colour pattern with distastefulness because enough mimics would be inadvertently consumed and found palatable. Natural selection eventually would favour the evolution of a new colour pattern in the model species.

Coevolution among many species. Coevolution between birds and fruit-bearing plant species is even more complicated than that between flowers and pollinators or between models and mimics, because so many plant species have evolved fleshy fruits for dispersal by birds and so many bird species have become adapted to eat fruits as part of their diets. Almost half of the 281 known terrestrial families of flowering plants include some species with fleshy fruits. About one-third of the 135 terrestrial bird families and one-fifth of the 107 terrestrial mammal families include some partly or wholly frugivorous species. Moreover, the evolution of these interactions is not limited to relationships between species within local communities. Many frugivorous birds migrate thousands of miles every year (Figure 20), and the ripening of the fruits of many plant species in temperate regions appears to be timed to the peak of bird migrations in the autumn. Consequently, the evolution of interactions between birds and fruits occurs over very broad geographic ranges. These interactions link more species in more communities than any other form of relationship among species. They show that the conservation of species demands a geographic, even global, perspective on how interactions between species are maintained within biological communities.

(John N. Thompson)

The coevolution of birds and fruit-bearing plants

MAJOR ECOSYSTEMS OF THE WORLD

Aquatic ecosystems

MARINE WATERS

Marine waters cover two-thirds of the surface of the Earth. In some places the ocean is deeper than Mount Everest is high; for example, the Mariana Trench and the Tonga Trench in the western part of the Pacific Ocean reach depths in excess of 10,000 metres (32,800 feet). Within this ocean habitat live a wide variety of organisms that have evolved in response to various features of their environs.

Origins of marine life. The Earth formed approximately 4.6 billion years ago. As it cooled, water in the atmosphere condensed and the Earth was pummeled with torrential rains, which filled its great basins, forming seas. The primeval atmosphere and waters harboured the inorganic components hydrogen, methane, ammonia, and water. These substances are thought to have combined to form the first organic compounds when sparked by electrical discharges of lightning. Some of the earliest known organisms are cyanobacteria (formerly referred to as blue-green algae). Evidence of these early photosynthetic prokaryotes has been found in Australia in Precambrian marine sediments called stromatolites that are approximately 3 billion years old (see above *Evolution of the biosphere: Geologic history and early life-forms: Conditions prior to the emergence of life*). Although the diversity of life-forms observed in modern oceans did not appear until much later, during the Precambrian (3.8 billion to 540 million years ago) many kinds of bacteria, algae, protozoa, and primitive metazoa evolved to exploit the early marine habitats of the world. During the Cambrian Period (540 to 505 million years ago) a major radiation of life occurred in the oceans. Fossils of familiar organisms such as cnidaria (*e.g.,* jellyfish), echinoderms (*e.g.,* feather stars), precursors of the fishes (*e.g.,* the protochordate *Pikaia* from the Burgess Shale of Canada), and other vertebrates are found in marine sediments of this age. The first fossil fishes are found in sediments from the Ordovician Period (505 to 438 million years ago). Changes in the physical conditions of the ocean that are thought to have occurred in the Precambrian—an increase in the concentration of oxygen in seawater and a build-up of the ozone layer that reduced dangerous ultraviolet radiation—may have facilitated the increase and dispersal of living things.

The marine environment. *Geography, oceanography, and topography.* The shape of the oceans and seas of the world has changed significantly throughout the past 600 million years. According to the theory of plate tectonics, the crust of the Earth is made up of many dynamic plates (see PLATE TECTONICS; and EARTH: *The surface of the Earth as a mosaic of plates*). There are two types of plates—oceanic and continental—which float on the surface of the Earth's mantle, diverging, converging, or sliding against one another. When two plates diverge, magma from the mantle wells up and cools, forming new crust; when convergence occurs, one plate descends—*i.e.,* is subducted—below the other and crust is resorbed into the mantle. Examples of both processes are observed in the marine environment. Oceanic crust is created along oceanic ridges or rift areas, which are vast undersea mountain ranges such as the Mid-Atlantic Ridge. Excess crust is reabsorbed along subduction zones, which usually are marked by deep-sea trenches such as the Kuril Trench off the coast of Japan.

The shape of the ocean also is altered as sea levels change. During ice ages a higher proportion of the waters of the Earth is bound in the polar ice caps, resulting in a relatively low sea level. When the polar ice caps melt during interglacial periods, the sea level rises. These changes in sea level cause great changes in the distribution of marine environments such as coral reefs. For example, during the last Pleistocene Ice Age the Great Barrier Reef did not exist as it does today; the continental shelf on which the reef now is found was above the high-tide mark.

Marine organisms are not distributed evenly throughout the oceans. Variations in characteristics of the marine

Variations in the marine environment

environment create different habitats and influence what types of organisms will inhabit them. The availability of light, water depth, proximity to land, and topographic complexity all affect marine habitats. The availability of light affects which organisms can inhabit a certain area of a marine ecosystem. The greater the depth of the water, the less light can penetrate until below a certain depth there is no light whatsoever. This area of inky darkness, which occupies the great bulk of the ocean, is called the aphotic zone (Figure 29). The illuminated region above it is called the photic zone, within which are distinguished the euphotic and disphotic zones. The euphotic zone is the layer closer to the surface that receives enough light for photosynthesis to occur. Beneath lies the disphotic zone, which is illuminated but so poorly that rates of respiration exceed those of photosynthesis. The actual depth of these zones depends on local conditions of cloud cover, water turbidity, and ocean surface. In general, the euphotic zone can extend to depths of 80 to 100 metres and the disphotic zone to depths of 80 to 700 metres. Marine organisms are particularly abundant in the photic zone, especially the euphotic portion; however, many organisms inhabit the aphotic zone and migrate vertically to the photic zone every night. Other organisms, such as the tripod fish and some species of sea cucumbers and brittle stars, remain in darkness all their lives.

Pelagic and benthic environments

Marine environments can be characterized broadly as a water, or pelagic, environment and a bottom, or benthic, environment (Figure 29). Within the pelagic environment the waters are divided into the neritic province, which includes the water above the continental shelf, and the oceanic province, which includes all the open waters beyond the continental shelf. The high nutrient levels of the neritic province—resulting from dissolved materials in riverine runoff—distinguish this province from the oceanic. The upper portion of both the neritic and oceanic waters—the epipelagic zone—is where photosynthesis occurs; it is roughly equivalent to the photic zone. Below this zone lie the mesopelagic, ranging between 200 and 1,000 metres, the bathypelagic, from 1,000 to 4,000 metres, and the abyssalpelagic, which encompasses the deepest parts of the oceans from 4,000 metres to the recesses of the deep-sea trenches. The benthic environment also is divided into different zones (Figure 29). The supralittoral is above the high-tide mark and is usually not under water. The intertidal, or littoral, zone ranges from the high-tide mark (the maximum elevation of the tide) to the shallow, offshore waters. The sublittoral is the environment beyond the low-tide mark and is often used to refer to substrata of the continental shelf, which reaches depths of between 150 and 300 metres. Sediments of the continental shelf that influence marine organisms generally originate from the land, particularly in the form of riverine runoff, and include clay, silt, and sand. Beyond the continental shelf is the bathyal zone, which occurs at depths of 150 to 4,000 metres and includes the descending continental slope and rise. The abyssal zone (between 4,000 and 6,000 metres) represents a substantial portion of the oceans. The deepest region of the oceans (greater than 6,000 metres) is the hadal zone of the deep-sea trenches. Sediments of the deep sea primarily originate from a rain of dead marine organisms and their wastes.

Physical and chemical properties of seawater. The physical and chemical properties of seawater vary according to latitude, depth, nearness to land, and input of fresh water. Approximately 3.5 percent of seawater is composed of dissolved compounds, while the other 96.5 percent is pure water. The chemical composition of seawater reflects such processes as erosion of rock and sediments, volcanic activity, gas exchange with the atmosphere, the metabolic and breakdown products of organisms, and rain. (For a list of the principal constituents of seawater see OCEANS: *Composition of seawater.*) In addition to carbon, the nutrients essential for living organisms include nitrogen and phosphorus, which are minor constituents of seawater and thus are often limiting factors in organic cycles of the ocean. Concentrations of phosphorus and nitrogen are generally low in the photic zone because they are rapidly

taken up by marine organisms. The highest concentrations of these nutrients generally are found below 500 metres, a result of the decay of organisms. Other important elements include silicon (used in the skeletons of radiolarians and diatoms; see Figure 30) and calcium (essential in the skeletons of many organisms such as fish and corals).

The chemical composition of the atmosphere also affects that of the ocean. For example, carbon dioxide is absorbed by the ocean and oxygen is released to the atmosphere through the activities of marine plants. The dumping of pollutants into the sea also can affect the chemical makeup of the ocean, contrary to earlier assumptions that, for example, toxins could be safely disposed of there.

The physical and chemical properties of seawater have a great effect on organisms, varying especially with the size of the creature. As an example, seawater is viscous to very small animals (less than 1 millimetre [0.039 inch] long) such as ciliates but not to large marine creatures such as tuna.

Marine organisms have evolved a wide variety of unique physiological and morphological features that allow them to live in the sea. Notothenid fishes in Antarctica are able to inhabit waters as cold as $-2°$ C ($28°$ F) because of proteins in their blood that act as antifreeze. Many organisms are able to achieve neutral buoyancy by secreting gas into internal chambers, as cephalopods do, or into swim bladders, as some fish do; other organisms use lipids, which are less dense than water, to achieve this effect. Some animals, especially those in the aphotic zone, generate light to attract prey. Animals in the disphotic zone such as hatchetfish produce light by means of organs called photophores to break up the silhouette of their bodies and avoid visual detection by predators. Many marine animals can detect vibrations or sound in the water over great distances by means of specialized organs. Certain fishes have lateral-line systems, which they use to detect prey, and whales have a sound-producing organ called a melon with which they communicate. Tolerance to differences in salinity varies greatly: stenohaline organisms have a low tolerance to salinity changes, whereas euryhaline organisms, which are found in areas where river and sea meet (estuaries), are very tolerant of large changes in salinity. Euryhaline organisms are also very tolerant of changes in temperature. Animals that migrate between fresh water and salt water, such as salmon or eels, are capable of controlling their osmotic environment by active pumping or the retention of salts (see above *The organism and the environment: Environmental conditions: Salinity*). Body architecture varies greatly in marine waters. The body shape of the cnidarian by-the-wind-sailor (*Velella velella*)—an animal that lives on the surface of the water (pleuston) and sails with the assistance of a

Adaptations to life in the sea

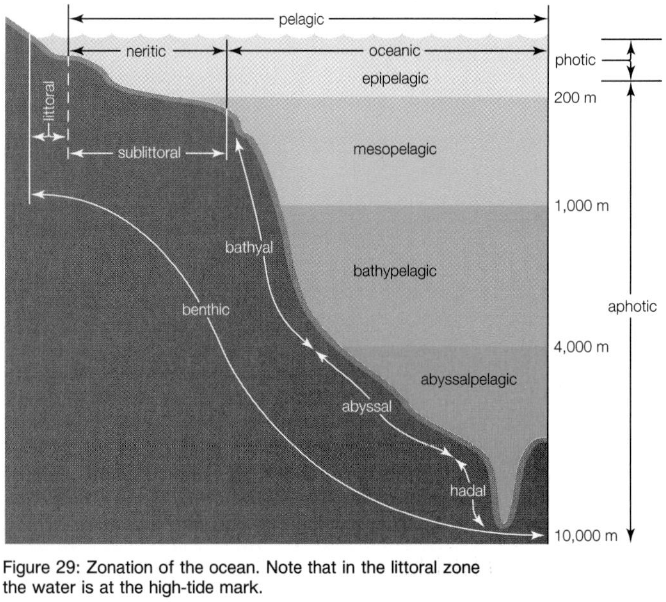

Figure 29: Zonation of the ocean. Note that in the littoral zone the water is at the high-tide mark.

modified flotation chamber—contrasts sharply with the sleek, elongated shape of the barracuda.

Ocean currents. The movements of ocean waters are influenced by numerous factors, including the rotation of the Earth (which is responsible for the Coriolis effect), atmospheric circulation patterns that influence surface waters, and temperature and salinity gradients between the tropics and the polar regions (thermohaline circulation). For a detailed discussion of ocean circulation see OCEANS: *Circulation of the ocean waters.* The resultant patterns of circulation range from those that cover great areas, such as the North Subtropical Gyre, which follows a path thousands of kilometres long, to small-scale turbulences of less than one metre.

Marine organisms of all sizes are influenced by these patterns, which can determine the range of a species. For example, krill (*Euphausia superba*) are restricted to the Antarctic Circumpolar Current. Distribution patterns of both large and small pelagic organisms are affected as well. Mainstream currents such as the Gulf Stream and East Australian Current transport larvae great distances. As a result cold temperate coral reefs receive a tropical infusion when fish and invertebrate larvae from the tropics are relocated to high latitudes by these currents. The successful recruitment of eels to Europe depends on the strength of the Gulf Stream to transport them from spawning sites in the Caribbean. Areas where the ocean is affected by nearshore features, such as estuaries, or areas in which there is a vertical salinity gradient (halocline) often exhibit intense biological activity. In these environments, small organisms can become concentrated, providing a rich supply of food for other animals.

Marine biota. Marine biota can be classified broadly into those organisms living in either the pelagic environment (plankton and nekton) or the benthic environment (benthos). Some organisms, however, are benthic in one stage of life and pelagic in another. Producers that synthesize organic molecules exist in both environments. Single-celled or multicelled plankton with photosynthetic pigments are the producers of the photic zone in the pelagic environment. Typical benthic producers are microalgae (*e.g.,* diatoms), macroalgae (*e.g.,* the kelp *Macrocystis pyrifera*), or sea grass (*e.g., Zostera*).

Plankton. Plankton are the numerous, primarily micro-scopic inhabitants of the pelagic environment (Figure 31). They are critical components of food chains in all marine environments (Figure 14) because they provide nutrition for the nekton (*e.g.,* crustaceans, fish, and squid) and benthos (*e.g.,* sea squirts and sponges). They also exert a global effect on the biosphere because the balance of components of the Earth's atmosphere depends to a great extent on the photosynthetic activities of some plankton.

The term "plankton" is derived from the Greek *planktos,* meaning wandering or drifting, an apt description of the way most plankton spend their existence, floating with the ocean's currents. Not all plankton, however, are unable to control their movements, and many forms depend on self-directed motions for their survival.

Plankton range in size from tiny microbes (1 micrometre [0.000039 inch] or less) to jellyfish whose gelatinous bell can reach up to 2 metres in width and whose tentacles can extend over 15 metres. However, most planktonic organisms, called plankters, are less than 1 millimetre (0.039 inch) long. These microbes thrive on nutrients in seawater and are often photosynthetic. The plankton include a wide variety of organisms such as algae, bacteria, protozoans, the larvae of some animals, and crustaceans. A large proportion of the plankton are protists—*i.e.,* eukaryotic, predominantly single-celled organisms. Plankton can be broadly divided into phytoplankton, which are plants or plantlike protists; zooplankton, which are animals or animal-like protists; and microbes such as bacteria. Phytoplankton carry out photosynthesis and are the producers of the marine community; zooplankton are the heterotrophic consumers.

Diatoms and dinoflagellates (approximate range between 15 and 1,000 micrometres in length) are two highly diverse groups of photosynthetic protists that are important components of the plankton (Figure 31). Diatoms are the most abundant phytoplankton. While many dinoflagellates carry out photosynthesis, some also consume bacteria or algae. Other important groups of protists include flagellates, foraminiferans, radiolarians, acantharians, and ciliates (Figure 31). Many of these protists are important consumers and a food source for zooplankton.

Zooplankton, which are greater than 0.05 millimetre in size, are divided into two general categories: meroplankton, which spend only a part of their life cycle—usually

Encyclopædia Britannica, Inc.

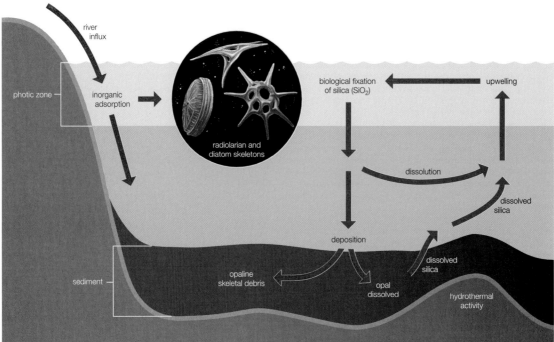

Figure 30: Cycling of silica in the marine environment. Silicon commonly occurs in nature as silicon dioxide (SiO_2), also called silica. It cycles through the marine environment, entering primarily through riverine runoff. Silica is removed from the ocean by organisms such as diatoms and radiolarians that use an amorphous form of silica in their cell walls. After they die, their skeletons settle through the water column and the silica redissolves. A small number reach the ocean floor where they either remain, forming a silaceous ooze, or dissolve and are returned to the photic zone by upwelling.

the larval or juvenile stage—as plankton, and holoplankton, which exist as plankton all their lives. Many larval meroplankton in coastal, oceanic, and even freshwater environments (including sea urchins, intertidal snails, and crabs, lobsters, and fish) bear little or no resemblance to their adult forms. These larvae may exhibit features unique to the larval stage, such as the spectacular spiny armour on the larvae of certain crustaceans (*e.g., Squilla*), probably used to ward off predators.

Important holoplanktonic animals include such lobsterlike crustaceans as the copepods, cladocerans, and euphausids (krill), which are important components of the

Encyclopædia Britannica, Inc.

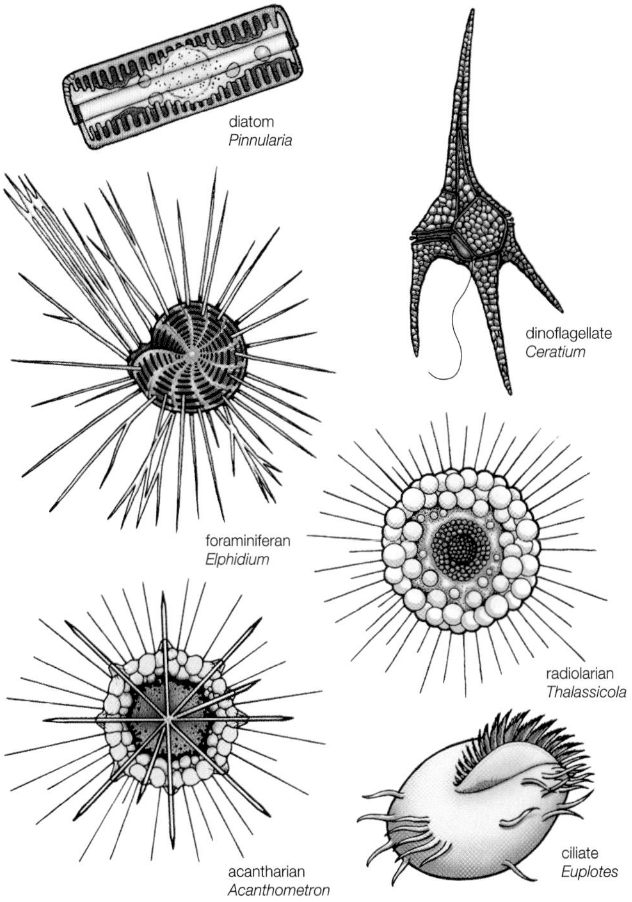

diatom
Pinnularia

dinoflagellate
Ceratium

foraminiferan
Elphidium

radiolarian
Thalassicola

acantharian
Acanthometron

ciliate
Euplotes

Figure 31: Representative plankton.

marine environment because they serve as food sources for fish and marine mammals (Figure 14). Gelatinous forms such as larvaceans, salps, and siphonophores graze on phytoplankton or other zooplankton. Some omnivorous zooplankton such as euphausids and some copepods consume both phytoplankton and zooplankton; their feeding behaviour changes according to the availability and type of prey. The grazing and predatory activity of some zooplankton can be so intense that measurable reductions in phytoplankton or zooplankton abundance (or biomass) occur. For example, when jellyfish occur in high concentration in enclosed seas, they may consume such large numbers of fish larvae as to greatly reduce fish populations.

The jellylike plankton are numerous and predatory. They secure their prey with stinging cells (nematocysts) or sticky cells (colloblasts of comb jellies). Large numbers of the Portuguese man-of-war (*Physalia*), with its conspicuous gas bladder, the by-the-wind-sailor (*Velella velella*), and the small blue disk-shaped *Porpita porpita* are propelled along the surface by the wind, and after strong onshore winds they may be found strewn on the beach. Beneath the surface, comb jellies often abound, as do siphonophores, salps, and scyphomedusae.

The pelagic environment was once thought to present few distinct habitats, in contrast to the array of niches

within the benthic environment. Because of its apparent uniformity, the pelagic realm was understood to be distinguished simply by plankton of different sizes. Small-scale variations in the pelagic environment, however, have been discovered that affect biotic distributions. Living and dead matter form organic aggregates called marine snow to which members of the plankton community may adhere, producing patchiness in biotic distributions. Marine snow includes structures such as aggregates of cells and mucus as well as drifting macroalgae and other flotsam that range in size from 0.5 millimetre to 1 centimetre (although these aggregates can be as small as 0.05 millimetre and as large as 100 centimetres). Many types of microbes, phytoplankton, and zooplankton stick to marine snow, and some grazing copepods and predators will feed from the surface of these structures. Marine snow is extremely abundant at times, particularly after plankton blooms. Significant quantities of organic material from upper layers of the ocean may sink to the ocean floor as marine snow, providing an important source of food for bottom dwellers. Other structures that plankton respond to in the marine environment include aggregates of phytoplankton cells that form large rafts in tropical and temperate waters of the world (*e.g.,* cells of *Oscillatoria* [*Trichodesmium*] *erthraeus*) and various types of seaweed (*e.g., Sargassum, Phyllospora, Macrocystis*) that detach from the sea floor and drift.

Marine snow

Nekton. Nekton are the active swimmers of the oceans and are often the best-known organisms of marine waters. Nekton are the top predators in most marine food chains (Figure 14). The distinction between nekton and plankton is not always sharp. As mentioned above, many large marine animals, such as marlin and tuna, spend the larval stage of their lives as plankton and their adult stage as large and active members of the nekton. Other organisms such as krill are referred to as both micronekton and macrozooplankton.

The vast majority of nekton are vertebrates (*e.g.,* fishes, reptiles, and mammals), mollusks, and crustaceans. The most numerous group of nekton are the fishes, with approximately 16,000 species. Nekton are found at all depths and latitudes of marine waters. Whales, penguins, seals, and icefish abound in polar waters. Lantern fish (family Myctophidae) are common in the aphotic zone along with gulpers (*Saccopharynx*), whalefish (family Cetomimidae), seven-gilled sharks, and others. Nekton diversity is greatest in tropical waters, where in particular there are large numbers of fish species.

Types of necton

The largest animals on the Earth, the blue whales (*Balaenoptera musculus*), which grow to 25 to 30 metres long, are members of the nekton. These huge mammals and other baleen whales (order Mysticeti), which are distinguished by fine filtering plates in their mouths, feed on plankton and micronekton as do whale sharks (*Rhinocodon typus*), the largest fish in the world (usually 12 to 14 metres long, with some reaching 17 metres). The largest carnivores that consume large prey include the toothed whales (order Odontoceti—for example, the killer whales, *Orcinus orca*), great white sharks (*Carcharodon carcharias*), tiger sharks (*Galeocerdo cuvieri*), black marlin (*Makaira indica*), bluefin tuna (*Thunnus thynnus*), and giant groupers (*Epinephelus lanceolatus*).

Nekton form the basis of important fisheries around the world. Vast schools of small anchovies, herring, and sardines generally account for one-quarter to one-third of the annual harvest from the ocean. Squid are also economically valuable nekton. Halibut, sole, and cod are demersal (*i.e.,* bottom-dwelling) fish that are commercially important as food for humans. They are generally caught in continental shelf waters. Because pelagic nekton often abound in areas of upwelling where the waters are nutrient-rich, these regions also are major fishing areas (see below *Biological productivity: Upwelling*).

Benthos. Organisms are abundant in surface sediments of the continental shelf and in deeper waters, with a great diversity found in or on sediments. In shallow waters, beds of seagrass provide a rich habitat for polychaete worms, crustaceans (*e.g.,* amphipods), and fishes. On the surface of and within intertidal sediments most animal

Classification of the benthos

activities are influenced strongly by the state of the tide. On many sediments in the photic zone, however, the only photosynthetic organisms are microscopic benthic diatoms.

Benthic organisms can be classified according to size. The macrobenthos are those organisms larger than 1 millimetre. Those that eat organic material in sediments are called deposit feeders (*e.g.*, holothurians, echinoids, gastropods), those that feed on the plankton above are the suspension feeders (*e.g.*, bivalves, ophiuroids, crinoids), and those that consume other fauna in the benthic assemblage are predators (*e.g.*, starfish, gastropods). Organisms between 0.1 and 1 millimetre constitute the meiobenthos. These larger microbes, which include foraminiferans, turbellarians, and polychaetes, frequently dominate benthic food chains, filling the roles of nutrient recycler, decomposer, primary producer, and predator. The microbenthos are those organisms smaller than 1 millimetre; they include diatoms, bacteria, and ciliates.

Organic matter is decomposed aerobically by bacteria near the surface of the sediment where oxygen is abundant. The consumption of oxygen at this level, however, deprives deeper layers of oxygen, and marine sediments below the surface layer are anaerobic. The thickness of the oxygenated layer varies according to grain size, which determines how permeable the sediment is to oxygen and the amount of organic matter it contains. As oxygen concentration diminishes, anaerobic processes come to dominate. The transition layer between oxygen-rich and oxygen-poor layers is called the redox discontinuity layer and appears as a gray layer above the black anaerobic layers.

Adaptations to lack of oxygen

Organisms have evolved various ways of coping with the lack of oxygen. Some anaerobes release hydrogen sulfide, ammonia, and other toxic reduced ions through metabolic processes. The thiobiota, made up primarily of microorganisms, metabolize sulfur. Most organisms that live below the redox layer, however, have to create an aerobic environment for themselves. Burrowing animals generate a respiratory current along their burrow systems to oxygenate their dwelling places; the influx of oxygen must be constantly maintained because the surrounding anoxic layer quickly depletes the burrow of oxygen. Many bivalves (*e.g., Mya arenaria*) extend long siphons upward into oxygenated waters near the surface so that they can respire and feed while remaining sheltered from predation deep in the sediment. Many large mollusks use a muscular "foot" to dig with, and in some cases they use it to propel themselves away from predators such as starfish. The consequent "irrigation" of burrow systems can create oxygen and nutrient fluxes that stimulate the production of benthic producers (*e.g.,* diatoms).

Not all benthic organisms live within the sediment; certain benthic assemblages live on a rocky substrate. Various phyla of algae—Rhodophyta (red), Chlorophyta (green), and Phaeophyta (brown)—are abundant and diverse in the photic zone on rocky substrata and are important producers. In intertidal regions algae are most abundant and largest near the low-tide mark. Ephemeral algae such as *Ulva, Enteromorpha,* and coralline algae cover a broad range of the intertidal. The mix of algae species found in any particular locale is dependent on latitude and also varies greatly according to wave exposure and the activity of grazers. For example, *Ascophyllum* spores cannot attach to rock in even a gentle ocean surge; as a result this plant is largely restricted to sheltered shores. The fastest-growing plant—adding as much as 1 metre per day to its length—is the giant kelp, *Macrocystis pyrifera,* which is found on subtidal rocky reefs. These plants, which may exceed 30 metres in length, characterize benthic habitats on many temperate reefs. Large laminarian and fucoid algae are also common on temperate rocky reefs, along with the encrusting (*e.g., Lithothamnion*) or short tufting forms (*e.g., Pterocladia*). Many algae on rocky reefs are harvested for food, fertilizer, and pharmaceuticals. Macroalgae are relatively rare on tropical reefs where corals abound, but *Sargassum* and a diverse assemblage of short filamentous and tufting algae are found, especially at the reef crest. Sessile and slow-moving invertebrates are common on reefs. In the inter-

tidal and subtidal regions herbivorous gastropods and urchins abound and can have a great influence on the distribution of algae. Barnacles are common sessile animals in the intertidal. In the subtidal regions, sponges, ascidians, urchins, and anemones are particularly common where light levels drop and current speeds are high. Sessile assemblages of animals are often rich and diverse in caves and under boulders.

Reef-building corals

Reef-building coral polyps (Scleractinia) are organisms of the phylum Cnidaria that create a calcareous substrate upon which a diverse array of organisms live. Approximately 700 species of corals are found in the Pacific and Indian oceans and belong to genera such as *Porites, Acropora,* and *Montipora.* Some of the world's most complex ecosystems are found on coral reefs. Zooxanthellae are the photosynthetic, single-celled algae that live symbiotically within the tissue of corals and help to build the solid calcium carbonate matrix of the reef. Reef-building corals are found only in waters warmer than 18° C; warm temperatures are necessary, along with high light intensity, for the coral-algae complex to secrete calcium carbonate. Many tropical islands are composed entirely of hundreds of metres of coral built atop volcanic rock.

Links between the pelagic environments and the benthos. Considering the pelagic and benthic environments in isolation from each other should be done cautiously because the two are interlinked in many ways. For example, pelagic plankton are an important source of food for animals on soft or rocky bottoms. Suspension feeders such as anemones and barnacles filter living and dead particles from the surrounding water while detritus feeders graze on the accumulation of particulate material raining from the water column above. The molts of crustaceans, plankton feces, dead plankton, and marine snow all contribute to this rain of fallout from the pelagic environment to the ocean bottom. This fallout can be so intense in certain weather patterns—such as the El Niño condition—that benthic animals on soft bottoms are smothered and die. There also is variation in the rate of fallout of the plankton according to seasonal cycles of production. This variation can create seasonality in the abiotic zone where there is little or no variation in temperature or light. Plankton form marine sediments, and many types of fossilized protistan plankton, such as foraminiferans and coccoliths, are used to determine the age and origin of rocks.

Organisms of the deep-sea vents. Producers were discovered in the aphotic zone when exploration of the deep sea by submarine became common in the 1970s. Deep-sea hydrothermal vents now are known to be relatively common in areas of tectonic activity (*e.g.,* spreading ridges). The vents are a nonphotosynthetic source of organic carbon available to organisms. A diversity of deep-sea organisms including mussels, large bivalve clams, and vestimentiferan worms are supported by bacteria that oxidize sulfur (sulfide) and derive chemical energy from the reaction. These organisms are referred to as chemoautotrophic, or chemosynthetic, as opposed to photosynthetic, organisms. Many of the species in the vent fauna have developed symbiotic relationships with chemoautotrophic bacteria, and as a consequence the megafauna are principally responsible for the primary production in the vent assemblage. The situation is analogous to that found on coral reefs where individual coral polyps have symbiotic relationships with zooxanthellae (see above). In addition to symbiotic bacteria there is a rich assemblage of free-living bacteria around vents. For example, *Beggiatoas*-like bacteria often form conspicuous weblike mats on any hard surface; these mats have been shown to have chemoautotrophic metabolism. Large numbers of brachyuran (*e.g., Bythograea*) and galatheid crabs, large sea anemones (*e.g., Actinostola callasi*), copepods, other plankton, and some fish—especially the eelpout *Thermarces cerberus*—are found in association with vents.

The producers in deep-sea vents: chemoautotrophs

Patterns and processes influencing the structure of marine assemblages. *Distribution and dispersal.* The distribution patterns of marine organisms are influenced by physical and biological processes in both ecological time (tens of years) and geologic time (hundreds to millions of years). The shapes of the Earth's oceans have been influenced by plate tectonics, and as a consequence the distributions of fossil and extant marine organisms also have been affected. Vicariance theory argues that plate tectonics has a major role in determining biogeographic patterns (see above *Major biogeographic regions of the world: General features: The concept of biogeography: Dispersalist and vicariance biogeography*). For example, Australia was once—90 million years ago—close to the South Pole and had few coral reefs. Since then Australia has been moving a few millimetres each year closer to the Equator. As a result of this movement and local oceanographic conditions, coral reef environments are extending ever so slowly southward. Dispersal may also have an important role in biogeographic patterns of abundance. The importance of dispersal varies greatly with local oceanographic features, such as the direction and intensity of currents and the biology of the organisms. Humans can also have an impact on patterns of distribution and the extinction of marine organisms. For example, fishing intensity in the Irish Sea was based on catch limits set for cod with no regard for the biology of other species. One consequence of this practice was that the local skate, which had a slow reproductive rate, was quickly fished to extinction.

Dispersal at the larval stage A characteristic of many marine organisms is a bipartite life cycle, which can affect the dispersal of an organism. Most animals found on soft and hard substrata, such as lobsters (Figure 32), crabs, barnacles, fish, polychaete worms, and sea urchins, spend their larval phase in the plankton, and in this phase are dispersed most widely (see above *Marine biota: Plankton*). The length of the larval phase, which can vary from a few minutes to hundreds of days, has a major influence on dispersal. For example, wrasses of the genus *Thalassoma* have a long larval life, compared with many other types of reef fish, and populations of these fish are well dispersed to the reefs of isolated volcanic islands around the Pacific. The bipartite life cycle of algae also affects their dispersal, which occurs through algal spores. Although in general, spores disperse only a short distance from adult plants, limited swimming abilities—*Macrocystis* spores have flagella—and storms can disperse spores over greater distances.

Migrations of marine organisms. The migrations of plankton and nekton throughout the water column in many parts of the world are well described. Diurnal vertical migrations are common. For example, some types of plankton, fish, and squid remain beneath the photic zone during the day, moving toward the surface after dusk and returning to the depths before dawn. It is generally argued that marine organisms migrate in response to light levels. This behaviour may be advantageous because by spending the daylight hours in the dim light or darkness beneath the photic zone plankton can avoid predators that locate their prey visually. After the Sun has set, plankton can rise to the surface waters where food is more abundant and where they can feed safely under the cover of darkness.

Larval forms can facilitate their horizontal transport along different currents by migrating vertically. This is possible because currents can differ in direction according to depth (*e.g.,* above and below haloclines and thermoclines), as is the case in estuaries.

In coastal waters many larger invertebrates (*e.g.,* mysids, amphipods, and polychaete worms) leave the cover of algae and sediments to migrate into the water column at night. It is thought that these animals disperse to different habitats or find mates by swimming when visual predators find it hard to see them. In some cases only one sex will emerge at night, and often that sex is morphologically better suited for swimming.

Migration of fish Horizontal migrations of fish that span distances of hundreds of metres to tens of kilometres are common and generally related to patterns of feeding or reproduction. Tropical coral trout (*Plectropomus* species) remain dispersed over a reef for most of the year, but adults will aggregate at certain locations at the time of spawning. Transoceanic migrations (greater than 1,000 kilometres) are observed in a number of marine vertebrates, and these movements often relate to requirements of feeding and reproduction. Bluefin tuna (*Thunnus thynnus*) traverse the Atlantic Ocean in a single year; they spawn in the Caribbean, then swim to high latitudes of the Atlantic to feed on the rich supply of fish. Turtles and sharks also migrate great distances.

Fish that spend their lives in both marine and freshwater systems (diadromous animals) exhibit some of the most spectacular migratory behaviour. Anadromous fishes (those that spend most of their lives in the sea but migrate to fresh water to spawn) such as Atlantic salmon (*Salmo salar*) also have unique migratory patterns. After spawning, the adults die. Newly hatched fish (alevin) emerge from spawned eggs and develop into young fry that move down rivers toward the sea. Juveniles (parr) grow into larger fish (smolt) that convene near the ocean. When the adult fish are ready to spawn, they return to the river in which they were born (natal river), using a variety of environmental cues, including the Earth's magnetic field, the Sun, and water chemistry. It is believed

Encyclopædia Britannica, Inc.

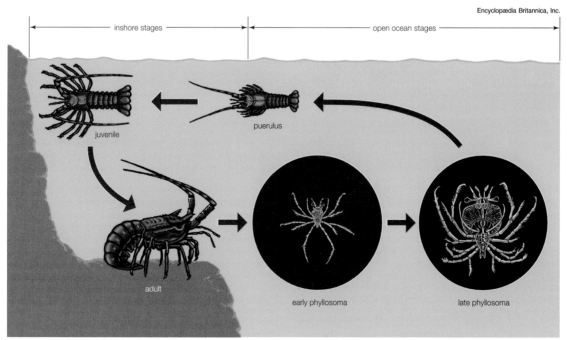

inshore stages · · · open ocean stages

puerulus

juvenile

adult

early phyllosoma

late phyllosoma

Figure 32: Life cycle of a palinurid lobster.

that the thyroid gland has a role in imprinting the water chemistry of the natal river on the fish. Freshwater eels such as the European eel (*Anguilla anguilla*) undertake great migrations from fresh water to spawn in the marine waters of the Sargasso Sea (catadromous migrations), where they die. Eel larvae, called leptocephalus larvae, drift back to Europe in the Gulf Stream.

Dynamics of populations and assemblages. A wide variety of processes influence the dynamics of marine populations of individual species and the composition of assemblages (*e.g.,* collections of populations of different species that live in the same area). With the exception of marine mammals such as whales, fish that bear live young (*e.g.,* embiotocid fish), and brooders (*i.e.,* fauna that incubate their offspring until they emerge as larvae or juveniles), most marine organisms produce a large number of offspring of which few survive. Processes that affect the plankton can have a great influence on the numbers of young that survive to be recruited, or relocated, into adult populations. The survival of larvae may depend on the abundance of food at various times and in various places, the number of predators, and oceanographic features that retain larvae near suitable nursery areas. The number of organisms recruited to benthic and pelagic systems may ultimately determine the size of adult populations and therefore the relative abundance of species in marine assemblages. However, many processes can affect the survival of organisms after recruitment. Predators eat recruits, and mortality rates in prey species can vary with time and space, thus changing original population patterns established in recruitment.

Patterns of colonization and succession can have a significant impact on benthic assemblages. For example, when intertidal reefs are cleared experimentally, the assemblage of organisms that colonize the bare area often reflects the types of larvae available in local waters at the time. Tube worms may dominate if they establish themselves first; if they fail to do so, algal spores may colonize the shore first and inhibit the settlement of these worms. Competition between organisms may also play a role. Long-term data gathered over periods of more than 25 years from coral reefs have demonstrated that some corals (*e.g., Acropora cytherea*) competitively overgrow neighbouring corals. Physical disturbance from hurricanes destroys many corals, and during regrowth competitively inferior species can coexist with normally dominant species on the reef. Chemical defenses of sessile organisms also can deter the growth or cause increased mortality of organisms that settle on them. Ascidian larvae (*e.g., Podoclavella*) often avoid settling on sponges (*e.g., Mycale*); when this does occur, the larvae rarely reach adulthood.

Although the processes that determine species assemblages may be understood, variations occur in the composition of the plankton that make it difficult to predict patterns of colonization with great accuracy.

Biological productivity. Primary productivity is the rate at which energy is converted by photosynthetic and chemosynthetic autotrophs to organic substances. The total amount of productivity in a region or system is gross primary productivity. A certain amount of organic material is used to sustain the life of producers; what remains is net productivity. Net marine primary productivity is the amount of organic material available to support the consumers (herbivores and carnivores) of the sea. The standing crop is the total biomass (weight) of vegetation. Most primary productivity is carried out by pelagic phytoplankton, not benthic plants.

Most primary producers require nitrogen and phosphorus, which are available in the ocean as nitrate, nitrite, ammonia, and phosphorus. The abundances of these molecules and the intensity and quality of light exert a major influence on rates of production. The two principal categories of producers (autotrophs) in the sea are pelagic phytoplankton and benthic microalgae and macroalgae. Benthic plants grow only on the fringe of the world's oceans and are estimated to produce only 5 to 10 percent of the total marine plant material in a year. Chemoautotrophs are the producers of the deep-sea vents.

Primary productivity is usually determined by measuring the uptake of carbon dioxide or the output of oxygen. Production rates are usually expressed as grams of organic carbon per unit area per unit time. The productivity of the entire ocean is estimated to be approximately 16×10^{10} tons of carbon per year, which is about eight times that of the land.

The pelagic food chain. Food chains in coastal waters of the world are generally regulated by nutrient concentrations. These concentrations determine the abundance of phytoplankton, which in turn provide food for the primary consumers, such as protozoa and zooplankton, that the higher-level consumers—fish, squid, and marine mammals—prey upon. It had been thought that phytoplankton in the 5- to 100-micrometre size range were responsible for most of the primary production in the sea and that grazers such as copepods controlled the numbers of phytoplankton. Data gathered since 1975, however, indicate that the system is much more complex than this. It is now thought that most primary production in marine waters of the world is accomplished by single-celled 0.5- to 10-micrometre phototrophs (bacteria and protists). Moreover, heterotrophic protists (phagotrophic protists) are now viewed as the dominant controllers of both bacteria and primary production in the sea. Current models of pelagic marine food chains picture complex interactions within a microbial food web. Larger metazoans are supported by the production of autotrophic and heterotrophic cells.

Upwelling. The most productive waters of the world are in regions of upwelling. Upwelling in coastal waters brings nutrients toward the surface. Phytoplankton reproduce rapidly in these conditions, and grazing zooplankton also multiply and provide abundant food supplies for nekton. Some of the world's richest fisheries are found in regions of upwelling—for example, the temperate waters off Peru and California. If upwelling fails, the effects on animals that depend on it can be disastrous. Fisheries also suffer at these times, as evidenced by the collapse of the Peruvian anchovy industry in the 1970s. The intensity and location of upwelling are influenced by changes in atmospheric circulation, as exemplified by the influence of El Niño conditions.

Seasonal cycles of production. Cycles of plankton production vary at different latitudes because seasonal patterns of light and temperature vary dramatically with latitude. In the extreme conditions at the poles, plankton populations crash during the constant darkness of winter and bloom in summer with long hours of light and the retreat of the ice field. In tropical waters, variation in sunlight and temperature is slight, nutrients are present in low concentrations, and planktonic assemblages do not undergo large fluctuations in abundance. There are, however, rapid cycles of reproduction and high rates of grazing and predation that result in a rapid turnover of plankton and a low standing crop. In temperate regions plankton abundance peaks in spring as temperature and the length and intensity of daylight increase. Moreover, seasonal winter storms usually mix the water column, creating a more even distribution of the nutrients, which facilitates the growth of phytoplankton. Peak zooplankton production generally lags behind that of phytoplankton, while the consumption of phytoplankton by zooplankton and phagotrophic protists is thought to reduce phytoplankton abundance. Secondary peaks in abundance occur in autumn. Seasonal peaks of some plankton are very conspicuous, and the composition of the plankton varies considerably. In spring and early summer many fish and invertebrates spawn and release eggs and larvae into the plankton, and, as a result, the meroplanktonic component of the plankton is higher at these times. General patterns of plankton abundance may be further influenced by local conditions. Heavy rainfall in coastal regions (especially areas in which monsoons prevail) can result in nutrient-rich turbid plumes (*i.e.,* estuarine or riverine plumes) that extend into waters of the continental shelf. Changes in production, therefore, may depend on the season, the proximity to fresh water, and the timing and location of upwelling, currents, and patterns of reproduction. (Michael John Kingsford)

Margin notes (left column):

Patterns of colonization and succession in benthic assemblages

Primary producers of the marine ecosystem

Krill (*Euphausia superba*), holoplanktonic omnivorous zooplankton that live only in the Antarctic Circumpolar Current.

Diatoms and radiolarians, microscopic members of the plankton and integral components of the marine food chain.

The flotation chamber of the by-the-wind sailor (*Velella*), which allows it to float on the water's surface. It also acts as a sail, transporting *Velella* great distances.

The rootlike holdfast of oarweed (*Laminaria digitata*) attached to a rocky substrate that is encrusted with *Lithothamnion*, a species of reef-building algae.

Bottle-nosed dolphins, marine mammals that are among the free-swimming animals of the open seas known as nekton.

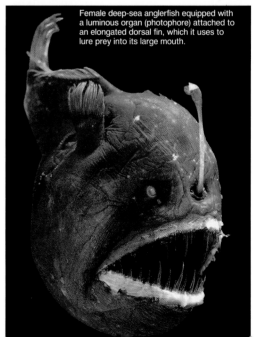

Female deep-sea anglerfish equipped with a luminous organ (photophore) attached to an elongated dorsal fin, which it uses to lure prey into its large mouth.

Blue damselfish (*Chromis*) swimming in the Caribbean above brain coral from which it obtains both food and shelter.

Plate 1: (Top left, centre right) Flip Nicklin—Minden Pictures; (centre top left, top right) © Peter Parks/Oxford Scientific Films; (centre bottom left) © Fredrik Ehrenstrom/Oxford Scientific Films; (bottom left, bottom right) © Norbert Wu

Terrestrial ecosystems

TROPICAL RAINFORESTS AND
TROPICAL DECIDUOUS FORESTS

Rainforests are vegetation types dominated by broad-leaved trees that form a dense upper canopy (layer of foliage). The trees may be either evergreen or, in seasonally dry parts of the tropics, deciduous. Rainforests contain a diverse array of vegetation at both tropical and temperate latitudes. Contrary to common thinking, not all rainforests occur in places with high, constant rainfall; for example, in the so-called "dry rainforests" of northeastern Australia the climate is punctuated by a dry season, which reduces the annual precipitation. Nor are all forests in areas that receive large amounts of rainfall true rainforests; the conifer-dominated forests in the extremely wet coastal areas of the American Pacific Northwest are temperate evergreen forest ecosystems. Therefore, to avoid conveying misleading climatic information, the term "rainforest" is now preferred over "rain forest."

This section covers only the richest of rainforests—the tropical rainforests of the ever-wet tropics—and the related tropical deciduous forests that grow in hot but only seasonally wet climates.

Origin. Tropical rainforests represent the oldest major vegetation type still present on the terrestrial Earth. Like all vegetation, however, that of the rainforest continues to evolve and change, so that modern tropical rainforests are not identical with rainforests of the geologic past.

Tropical rainforests grow mainly in three regions: the Malesian botanical subkingdom, which extends from Myanmar (Burma) to Fiji and includes the whole of Thailand, Malaysia, Indonesia, the Philippines, Papua New Guinea, the Solomon Islands, and Vanuatu and parts of Indochina and tropical Australia; tropical South and Central America, especially the Amazon basin; and West and Central Africa (see above *Major biogeographic regions of the world: Flora*). Smaller areas of tropical rainforest occur elsewhere in the tropics wherever climate is suitable. The principal areas of tropical deciduous forest are in India, the Myanmar-Vietnam-southern coastal China region, and eastern Brazil, with smaller areas in South and Central America north of the Equator, the West Indies, southeastern Africa, and northern Australia (Figure 40).

The flowering plants (angiosperms) first evolved and diversified during the Cretaceous Period about 100 million years ago, during which time global climatic conditions were warmer and wetter than those of the present. The vegetation types that evolved were the first tropical rainforests, which blanketed most of the Earth's land surfaces at that time. Only later—during the middle of the Cenozoic Era, about 40 million years ago—did cooler, drier climates develop, leading to the development across large areas of other vegetation types.

It is no surprise, therefore, to find the greatest diversity of flowering plants today in the tropical rainforests where they first evolved. Of particular interest is the fact that the majority of flowering plants displaying the most primitive characteristics are found in rainforests (especially tropical rainforests) in parts of the Southern Hemisphere, particularly South America, northern Australia and adjacent regions of Southeast Asia, and some larger South Pacific Islands. Of the 13 angiosperm families generally recognized as the most primitive, all but two—Magnoliaceae and Winteraceae—are overwhelmingly tropical in their present distribution. Three families—Illiciaceae, Magnoliaceae, and Schisandraceae—are found predominantly in Northern Hemisphere rainforests. Five families—Amborellaceae, Austrobaileyaceae, Degeneriaceae, Eupomatiaceae, and Himantandraceae—are restricted to rainforests in the tropical Australasian region. Members of the Winteraceae are shared between this latter region and South America, those of the Lactoridaceae grow only on the southeast Pacific islands of Juan Fernández, members of the Canellaceae are shared between South America and Africa, and two families—Annonaceae and Myristicaceae—generally occur in tropical regions. This has led some authorities to suggest that the original cradle of angiosperm evolution might lie in Gondwanaland, a supercontinent of the Southern Hemisphere thought to have existed in the Mesozoic Era (245 to 66.4 million years ago) that consisted of Africa, South America, Australia, peninsular India, and Antarctica. An alternative explanation for this geographic pattern is that in the Southern Hemisphere, especially on islands, there are more refugia—*i.e.,* isolated areas whose climates remained unaltered while those of the surrounding areas changed, enabling archaic life-forms to persist.

The first angiosperms are thought to have been massive, woody plants, appropriate for a rainforest habitat. Most of the smaller, more delicate plants that are so widespread in the world today evolved later, ultimately from tropical rainforest ancestors. While it is possible that even earlier forms existed that await discovery, the oldest angiosperm fossils—leaves, wood, fruits, and flowers derived from

The earliest vegetation types

Refugia

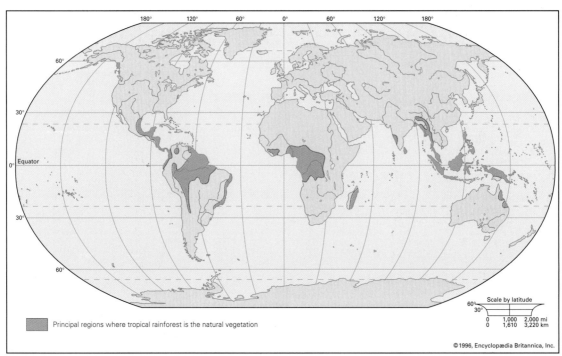

Principal regions where tropical rainforest is the natural vegetation

Scale by latitude

0   1,000   2,000 mi
0   1,610   3,220 km

©1996, Encyclopædia Britannica, Inc.

Figure 40: Worldwide distribution of tropical rainforests.

trees—support the view that the earliest angiosperms were rainforest trees. Further evidence comes from the growth forms of the most primitive surviving angiosperms: all 13 of the most primitive angiosperm families consist of woody plants, most of which are large trees.

As the world climate cooled in the middle of the Cenozoic, it also became drier. This is because cooler temperatures led to a reduction in the rate of evaporation of water from, in particular, the surface of the oceans, which led in turn to less cloud formation and less precipitation. The entire hydrologic cycle slowed, and tropical rainforests—which depend on both warmth and consistently high rainfall—became increasingly restricted to equatorial latitudes. Within those regions rainforests were limited further to coastal and hilly areas where abundant rain still fell at all seasons. In the middle latitudes of both hemispheres, belts of atmospheric high pressure developed. Within these belts, especially in continental interiors, deserts formed (see below *Deserts: Origin*). In regions lying between the wet tropics and the deserts, climatic zones developed in which rainfall adequate for luxuriant plant growth was experienced for only a part of the year. In these areas new plant forms evolved from tropical rainforest ancestors to cope with seasonally dry weather, forming tropical deciduous forests. In the drier and more fire-prone places, savannas and tropical grasslands developed.

Retreat of the rainforests
Retreat of the rainforests was particularly rapid during the late Cenozoic (5 million years ago to the present), which is the period leading up to and including the Pleistocene Ice Ages, or glacial intervals, that occurred between 1,600,000 and 10,000 years ago. Climates fluctuated throughout this time, forcing vegetation in all parts of the world to repeatedly migrate, by seed dispersal, to reach areas of suitable climate. Not all plants were able to do this equally well because some had less effective means of seed dispersal than others. Many extinctions resulted. During the most extreme periods (the glacial maxima, when climates were at their coldest and, in most places, also driest), the range of tropical rainforests shrank to its smallest extent, becoming restricted to relatively small refugia. Alternating intervals of climatic amelioration led to repeated range expansion, most recently from the close of the last glacial period about 10,000 years ago. Today large areas of tropical rainforest, such as Amazonia, have developed as a result of this relatively recent expansion. Within them it is possible to recognize "hot spots" of plant and animal diversity that have been interpreted as glacial refugia.

Tropical rainforests today represent a treasure trove of biological heritage. They not only retain many primitive plant and animal species, they also are communities that exhibit unparalleled biodiversity and a great variety of ecological interactions. The tropical rainforest of Africa was the habitat in which the ancestors of humans evolved, and it is where the nearest surviving human relatives—chimpanzees and gorillas—live still. Tropical rainforests supplied a rich variety of food and other resources to indigenous peoples, who, for the most part, exploited this bounty without degrading the vegetation or reducing its range to any significant degree. However, in some regions a long history of forest burning by the inhabitants is thought to have caused extensive replacement of tropical rainforest and tropical deciduous forest with savanna.

Destruction of tropical rainforests
Not until the past century, however, has widespread destruction of tropical forests occurred. Regrettably, tropical rainforests and tropical deciduous forests are now being destroyed at a rapid rate in order to provide resources such as timber and to create land that can be used for other purposes, such as cattle grazing. Today, tropical forests, more than any other ecosystem, are experiencing habitat alteration and species extinction on a greater scale and at a more rapid pace than at any time in their history—at least since the major extinction event at the end of the Cretaceous Period some 66.4 million years ago.

Environment. The equatorial latitude of tropical rainforests and tropical deciduous forests keeps day length and mean temperature fairly constant throughout the year. The sun rises daily to a near-vertical position at noon, ensuring a high level of incoming radiant energy at all seasons. Although there is no cold season during which plants experience unfavourable temperatures that prohibit growth, there are many local variations in climate that result from topography, and these variations influence and restrict rainforest distribution within the tropics.

Tropical rainforests occur in regions of the tropics where temperatures are always high and where rainfall exceeds about 1,800 to 2,500 millimetres (about 70 to 100 inches) annually and occurs fairly evenly throughout the year. Similar hot climates in which annual rainfall lies between about 800 and 1,800 millimetres and in which a pronounced season of low rainfall occurs typically support tropical deciduous forests—*i.e.,* rainforests in which up to about three-quarters of the trees lose their leaves in the dry season. The principal determining climatic factor for the distribution of rainforests in lowland regions of the tropics, therefore, is rainfall, both the total amount and the seasonal variation. Soil, human disturbance, and other factors also can be important controlling influences.

Areas experiencing seasonal rainfall
The climate is always hot and wet in most parts of the equatorial belt, but in regions to its north and south seasonal rainfall is experienced. During the summer months of the Northern Hemisphere—June to August—weather systems shift northward, bringing rain to regions in the northern parts of the tropics, as do the monsoon rains of India and Myanmar. Conversely, during the Southern Hemisphere's summer, weather systems move southward, bringing rain from December to February to places such as northern Australia. In these hot, seasonally wet areas grow tropical deciduous forests, such as the teak forests of Myanmar and Thailand. In other locations where conditions are similar but rainfall is not so reliable or burning has been a factor, savannas are found.

Topographic factors influence rainfall and consequently affect rainforest distribution within a region. For example, coastal regions where prevailing winds blow onshore are likely to have a wetter climate than coasts that experience primarily offshore winds. The west coasts of tropical Australia and South America south of the Equator experience offshore winds, and these dry regions can support rainforests only in very small areas. This contrasts with the more extensively rainforest-clad, east-facing coasts of these same continents at the same latitudes. The same phenomenon is apparent on a smaller scale where the orientation of coastlines is parallel to, rather than perpendicular to, wind direction. For example, in the Townsville area of northeastern Australia and in Benin in West Africa, gaps in otherwise fairly continuous tracts of tropical rainforest occur where the prevailing winds blow along the coast rather than across it.

Mean temperatures in tropical rainforest regions are between 20° and 29° C (68° and 84° F), and in no month is the mean temperature below 18° C (64° F). Temperatures become critical with increasing altitude; in the wet tropics temperatures fall by about 0.5° C (0.9° F) for every 100 metres (328 feet) climbed. Vegetation change across altitudinal gradients tends to be gradual and variable and is interpreted variously by different authorities. For example, in Uganda tropical rainforest grows to an altitude of 1,100 to 1,300 metres and has been described as giving way, via a transition forest zone, to montane rainforest above 1,650 to 1,750 metres, which continues to 2,300 to 3,400 metres. In New Guinea, lowland tropical rainforest reaches 1,000 to 1,200 metres, above which montane rainforests extend, with altitudinal variation, to 3,900 metres. In Peru, lowland rainforest extends upward to 1,200 to 1,500 metres, with transitional forest giving way to montane rainforest above 1,800 to 2,000 metres, which continues to 3,400 to 4,000 metres. These limits are comparable and reflect the similarities of climate in all regions where tropical rainforests occur. Plant species, however, are often quite different among regions.

Temperature modification by cloud cover
Although the climate supporting tropical rainforests is perpetually hot, temperatures never reach the high values regularly recorded in drier places to the north and south of the equatorial belt. This is partly due to high levels of cloud cover, which limit the mean number of sunshine

hours per day to between four and six. In hilly areas where air masses rise and cool because of the topography, the hours of sunlight may be even fewer. Nevertheless, the heat may seem extreme owing to the high levels of atmospheric humidity, which usually exceed 50 percent by day and approach 100 percent at night. Exacerbating the discomfort is the fact that winds are usually light; mean wind speeds are generally less than 10 kilometres (6.2 miles) per hour and less than 5 kilometres per hour in many areas. Devastating hurricanes (cyclones and typhoons) occur periodically in some coastal regions toward the margins of the equatorial belt, such as in the West Indies and in parts of the western Pacific region. Although relatively infrequent, such storms have an important effect on forest structure and regeneration.

The climate within any vegetation (microclimate) is moderated by the presence of plant parts that reduce incoming solar radiation and circulation of air. This is particularly true in tropical rainforests, which are structurally more dense and complex than other vegetation. Within the forest, temperature range and wind speed are reduced and humidity is increased relative to the climate above the tree canopy or in nearby clearings. The amount of rain reaching the ground is also reduced—by as much as 90 percent in some cases—as rainwater is absorbed by epiphytes (plants that grow on the surface of other plants but that derive nutrients and water from the air) and by tree bark or is caught by foliage and evaporates directly back to the atmosphere.

Soil fertility

Soils in tropical rainforests are typically deep but not very fertile, partly because large proportions of some mineral nutrients are bound up at any one time within the vegetation itself rather than free in the soil. The moist, hot climatic conditions lead to deep weathering of rock and the development of deep, typically reddish soil profiles rich in insoluble sesquioxides of iron and aluminum, commonly referred to as tropical red earths. Because precipitation in tropical rainforest regions exceeds evapotranspiration at almost all times, a nearly permanent surplus of water exists in the soil and moves downward through the soil into streams and rivers in valley floors. Through this process nutrients are leached out of the soil, leaving it relatively infertile. Most roots, including those of trees, are concentrated in the uppermost soil layers where nutrients become available from the decomposition of fallen dead leaves and other organic litter. Sandy soils, particularly, become thoroughly leached of nutrients and support stunted rainforests of peculiar composition. A high proportion of plants in this environment have small leaves that contain high levels of toxic or unpalatable substances. A variant of the tropical rainforest, the mangrove forest, is found along estuaries and on sheltered sea coasts in tidally inundated, muddy soils (see above *Boundary ecosystems: Boundary systems between water and land: Coastal systems*).

Even within the same area, however, there are likely to be significant variations in soil related to topographic position and to bedrock differences, and these variations are reflected in forest composition and structure. For example, as altitude increases—even within the same area and on the same bedrock—soil depth decreases markedly and its organic content increases in association with changes in forest composition and structure.

Biota.   Only a minority of plant and animal species in tropical rainforests and tropical deciduous forests have been described formally and named. Therefore, only a rough estimate can be given of the total number of species contained in these ecosystems, as well as the number

The most biodiverse of ecosystems

that are becoming extinct as a result of forest clearance. Nevertheless, it is quite clear that these vegetation types are the most diverse of all, containing more species than any other ecosystem. This is particularly so in regions in which tropical rainforests are not only widespread but also are separated into many small areas by geographic barriers, as in the island-studded Indonesian region (see above *Major biogeographic regions of the world: The distribution boundaries of flora and fauna*). In this area different but related species often are found throughout various groups of islands, adding to the total regional

diversity. Exceptionally large numbers of species also occur in areas of diverse habitat, such as in topographically or geologically complex regions and in places that are believed to have acted as refugia throughout the climatic fluctuations of the past few million years. According to some informed estimates, more than a hundred species of rainforest fauna and flora become extinct every week as a result of widespread clearing of forests by humans. Insects are believed to constitute the greatest percentage of disappearing species.

Flora.   All major groups of terrestrial organisms are represented abundantly in tropical rainforests. Among the higher plants, angiosperms are particularly diverse and include many primitive forms and many families not found in the vegetation of other ecosystem types. Many flowering plants are large trees, of which there is an unparalleled diversity. For example, in one area of 23 hectares (57 acres) in Malaysia, 375 different tree species with trunk diameters greater than 91 centimetres (35.8 inches) have been recorded, and in a 50-hectare area in Panama, 7,614 trees belonging to 186 species had trunk diameters greater than 20 centimetres. New species of plants—even those as conspicuously large as trees—are found every year. Relatively few gymnosperms (conifers and their relatives), however, are found in rainforests; instead, they occur more frequently at the drier and cooler extremes of the range of climates in which tropical rainforests grow. Some plant families, such as Arecaceae (palms), are typically abundant in all tropical rainforest regions, although different species occur from region to region. Other families are more restricted geographically. The family Dipterocarpaceae (dipterocarps) includes many massive trees that are among the most abundant and valuable species in the majority of tropical rainforests in western Malesia (see above *Origin*); the family, however, is uncommon in New Guinea and Africa and absent from South and Central America and Australia. The Bromeliaceae (bromeliads), a large family consisting mainly of rainforest epiphytes and to which the pineapple belongs, is entirely restricted to the New World.

Tropical rainforests, which contain many different types of trees, seldom are dominated by a single species. A species can predominate, however, if particular soil conditions favour this occurrence or minimal disturbance occurs for several tree generations. Tropical deciduous forests are less diverse and often are dominated by only one or two tree species. The extensive deciduous forests of Myanmar, for example, cover wide areas and are dominated by only one or two tree species—teak (*Tectona grandis*) and the smaller leguminous tree *Xylia xylocarpa*. In Thailand and Indochina deciduous forests are dominated by members of the Dipterocarpaceae family, *Dipterocarpus tuberculatus, Pentacme suavis,* and *Shorea obtusa*.

Dominant species

Ferns, mosses, liverworts, lichens, and algae are also abundant and diverse, although not as well studied and cataloged as the higher plants. Many are epiphytic and are found attached to the stems and sometimes the leaves of larger plants, especially in the wettest and most humid places. Fungi and other saprophytic plants (vegetation growing on dead or decaying matter) are similarly diverse. Some perform a vital role in decomposing dead organic matter on the forest floor, thereby releasing mineral nutrients, which then become available to roots in the surface layers of the soil. Other fungi enter into symbiotic relationships with tree roots (mycorrhizae).

Fauna.   Interacting with and dependent upon this vast array of plants are similarly numerous animals. Like the plants, most animal species are limited to only one or a few types of tropical rainforest within an area, with the result that the overall number of species is substantially greater than it is in a single forest type. For example, a study of insects in the canopy of four different types of tropical rainforest in Brazil revealed 1,080 species of beetle, of which 83 percent were found in only one forest type, 14 percent in two, and only 3 percent in three or four types. While the larger, more conspicuous vertebrates (mammals, birds, and to a lesser degree amphibians and reptiles) are well known, only a small minority of

A plethora of insects

the far more diverse invertebrates (particularly insects) have ever been collected, let alone described and named.

As with the plants, some animal groups occur in all tropical rainforest regions. A variety of fruit-eating parrots, pigeons, and seed-eating weevil beetles, for example, can be expected to occur in any tropical rainforest. Other groups are more restricted. Monkeys, while typical of tropical rainforests in both the New and the Old Worlds, are entirely absent from New Guinea and areas to its east and south. Tree kangaroos inhabit tropical rainforest canopies only in Australia and New Guinea, and birds of paradise are restricted to the same areas.

To a large extent these geographic variations in tropical rainforest biota reflect the long-term geologic histories of these ancient ecosystems. This is most clearly demonstrated in the Malesian phytogeographic subkingdom, which has existed as a single entity only since continental movements brought Australia and New Guinea northward into juxtaposition with Southeast Asia about 15 million years ago. Before that time the two parts were separated by a wide expanse of ocean and experienced separate evolution of their biota. Only a relatively small sea gap lies between them today; Java, Bali, and Borneo are on one side, and Timor and New Guinea are on the other, with islands like Celebes and the Moluccas forming an intermediate region between. The gap is marked by a change in flora and, especially, fauna and is known as Wallace's Line (see above *Major biogeographic regions of the world: Fauna: Wallacea*). The contrast is particularly stark with respect to mammals. To the west, the rainforests are populated—or were populated until recently—by monkeys, deer, pigs, cats, elephants, and rhinoceroses, while those to the east have marsupial mammals including opossums, cuscuses, dasyurids, tree kangaroos, and bandicoots. Only a few groups such as bats and rodents have migrated across the line to become common in both areas. Similar contrasts, albeit less pronounced, can be seen in many other animal and plant groups across the same divide.

Population and community development and structure. Tropical rainforests are distinguished not only by a remarkable richness of biota but also by the complexity of the interrelationships of all the plant and animal inhabitants that have been evolving together throughout many millions of years. As in all ecosystems, but particularly in the complex tropical rainforest community, the removal of one species threatens the survival of others with which it interacts. Some interactions are mentioned below, but many have yet to be revealed.

General structure of the rainforest. Plants with similar stature and life-form can be grouped into categories called synusiae, which make up distinct layers of vegetation. In tropical rainforests the synusiae are more numerous than in other ecosystem types. They include not only mechanically independent forms, whose stems are self-supporting, and saprophytic plants but also mechanically dependent synusiae such as climbers, stranglers, epiphytes, and parasitic plants. An unusual mix of trees of different sizes is found in the tropical rainforest, and those trees form several canopies below the uppermost layer, although they are not always recognizably separate layers. The upper canopy of the tropical rainforest is typically greater than 40 metres above ground.

Synusiae

The tropical rainforest is structurally very complex (Figure 41). Its varied vegetation illustrates the intense competition for light that goes on in this environment in which other climatic factors are not limiting at any time of year, allowing the vegetation to achieve an unequaled luxuriance and biomass. The amount of sunlight filtering through the many layers of foliage in a tropical rainforest is small; only about 1 percent of the light received at the top of the canopy reaches the ground. Most plants depend on light for their energy requirements, converting it into chemical energy in the form of carbohydrates by the process of photosynthesis in their chlorophyll-containing green tissues. Few plants can persist in the gloomy environment at ground level, and the surface is marked by a layer of rapidly decomposing dead leaves rather than of small herbaceous plants. Mosses grow on tree butts and

Figure 41: Vegetation profile of a tropical rainforest.
Encyclopædia Britannica, Inc.

there are a few forbs such as ferns and gingers, but generally the ground is bare of living plants, and even shrubs are rare. However, tree seedlings and saplings are abundant, their straight stems reaching toward the light but receiving too little energy to grow more than very slowly once food reserves from their seeds are exhausted. Their chance to grow into maturity only comes if overhanging vegetation is at least partially removed through tree death or damage by wind. Such an occurrence permits more solar radiation to reach their level and initiates rapid growth and competition among saplings as to which will become a part of the well-lit canopy.

Gaps in the canopy

Gaps in the canopy of a tropical rainforest provide temporarily well-illuminated places at ground level and are vital to the regeneration of most of the forest's constituent plants. Few plants in the forest can successfully regenerate in the deep shade of an unbroken canopy; many tree species are represented there only as a population of slender, slow-growing seedlings or saplings that have no chance of growing to the well-lit canopy unless a gap forms. Other species are present, invisibly, as dormant seeds in the soil. When a gap is created, seedlings and saplings accelerate their growth in the increased light and are joined by new seedlings sprouting from seeds stored in the soil that have been stimulated to germinate by light or by temperature fluctuations resulting from the sun shining directly on the soil surface. Other seeds arrive by various seed dispersal processes (see below). A thicket of regrowth rapidly develops, with the fastest-growing shrubs and trees quickly shading out opportunistic, light-demanding, low-growing herbaceous plants and becoming festooned with lianas. Through it all slower-growing, more shade-tolerant but longer-lived trees eventually emerge and restore the full forest canopy. The trees that initially fill in the gap in the canopy live approximately one century, whereas the slower-growing trees that ultimately replace them may live for 200 to 500 years or, in extreme cases, even longer. Detailed mapping of the trees in a tropical rainforest can reveal the locations of previous gaps through identification of clumps of the quicker-growing, more light-demanding species, which have yet to be replaced by trees in the final stage of successional recovery. Local, natural disturbances of this sort are vital to the maintenance of the full biotic diversity of the tropical rainforest.

Plate 4 Biosphere   **Terrestrial Ecosystems: Tropical Rainforests**

Lombi tree (*Dalbergia glandulosa*), Ituri Forest, Zaire, supported by buttresses that evolved in response to the lack of nutrients deep down in rainforest soils.

Enormous eyes and padded digits are adaptations that evolved in the tarsier (*Tarsius*), a nocturnal, arboreal primate of the rainforests of Southeast Asia.

Leaf-cutting ants (*Atta*) carrying leaves to underground nests. The leaves will be used as mulch to grow fungi on which these rainforest insects live.

Fungi growing on a fallen leaf in an Amazon rainforest. These saprophytic organisms decompose dead organic matter, releasing nutrients to be taken up by other plants.

Cauliflory on a tree trunk in a rainforest in Ecuador. Flowers borne directly on stems of understory plants are made available to pollinating and seed-dispersing animals that inhabit only the regions beneath the canopy.

Plate 4: (Top left, bottom left, bottom right) © Alan Watson/Forest Light; (top right) Frans Lanting—Minden Pictures; (centre left) Michael and Patricia Fogden

Compe-
tition for
nutrients

Just as tropical rainforest plants compete intensely for light above ground, below ground they vie for mineral nutrients. The process of decomposition of dead materials is of crucial importance to the continued health of the forest because plants depend on rapid recycling of mineral nutrients. Bacteria and fungi are primarily responsible for this process. Some saprophytic flowering plants that occur in tropical rainforests rely on decomposing material for their energy requirements and in the process use and later release minerals. Some animals are important in the decomposition process; for example, in Malaysia termites have been shown to be responsible for the decomposition of as much as 16 percent of all litter, particularly wood. Most trees in the tropical rainforest form symbiotic mycorrhizal associations with fungi that grow in intimate contact with their roots; the fungi obtain energy from the tree and in turn provide the tree with phosphorus and other nutrients, which they absorb from the soil very efficiently. A mat of plant roots explores the humus beneath the rapidly decomposing surface layer of dead leaves and twigs, and even rotting logs are invaded by roots from below. Because nutrients are typically scarce at depth but, along with moisture, are readily available in surface layers, few roots penetrate very deeply into the soil. This shallow rooting pattern increases the likelihood of tree falls during storms, despite the support that many trees receive from flangelike plank buttresses growing radially outward from their trunk bases. When large trees fall, they may take with them other trees against which they collapse or to which they are tied by a web of lianas, thereby creating gaps in the canopy.

Tree growth requires substantial energy investment in trunk development, which some plants avoid by depending on the stems of other plants for support. Perhaps the most obvious adaptation of this sort is seen in plants that climb from the ground to the uppermost canopy along other plants using devices that resemble grapnellike hooks. Lianas are climbers that are abundant and diverse in tropical rainforests; they are massive woody plants whose mature stems often loop through hundreds of metres of forest, sending shoots into new tree crowns as successive supporting trees die and decay (see photograph). Climbing palms or rattans (*Calamus*) are prominent lianas in Asian rainforests, where the stems, which are used to make cane furniture, provide a valuable economic resource.

Epiphytes are particularly diverse and include large plants such as orchids, aroids, bromeliads, and ferns in addition to smaller plants such as algae, mosses, and lichens. In tropical rainforests epiphytes are often so abundant that their weight fells trees. Epiphytes that grow near the upper canopy of the forest have access to bright sunlight but must survive without root contact with the soil. They depend on rain washing over them to provide water and mineral nutrients. During periods of drought, epiphytes undergo stress as water stored within their tissues becomes depleted. The diversity of epiphytes in tropical deciduous forests is much less than that of tropical rainforests because of the annual dry season.

Parasitic flowering plants also occur. Hemiparasitic mistletoes attached to tree branches extract water and minerals from their hosts but carry out their own photosynthesis. Plants that are completely parasitic also are found in tropical rainforests. *Rafflesia,* in Southeast Asia, parasitizes the roots of certain lianas and produces no aboveground parts until it flowers; its large orange and yellow blooms, nearly one metre in diameter, are the largest flowers of any plant.

The
pattern of
develop-
ment of a
fig forest

Stranglers make up a type of synusia virtually restricted to tropical rainforests. In this group are figs (*Ficus*), which begin life as epiphytes, growing from seeds left on high tree branches by birds or fruit bats. As they grow, they develop long roots that descend along the trunk of the host tree, eventually reaching the ground and entering the soil. Several roots usually do this, and they become grafted together as they crisscross each other to form a lattice, ultimately creating a nearly complete sheath around the trunk. The host tree's canopy becomes shaded by the thick fig foliage, its trunk constricted by the sur-

rounding root sheath, and its own root system forced to compete with that of the strangling fig. The host tree is also much older than the strangler and eventually dies and rots away, leaving a giant fig "tree" whose apparent "trunk" is actually a cylinder of roots, full of large hollows that provide shelter and breeding sites for bats, birds, and other animals. Stranglers may also develop roots from their branches, which, when they touch the ground, grow into the soil, thicken, and become additional "trunks." In this way stranglers grow outward to become large patches of fig forest that consist of a single plant with many interconnected trunks.

Relationships among the flora and fauna. Some of the tallest trees and lianas, and the epiphytes they support, bear flowers and fruits at the top of the rainforest canopy where the air moves unfettered by vegetation. They are able to depend on the wind for dispersal of pollen from flower to flower, as well as for the spreading of fruits and seeds away from the immediate environment of the parent plant. Ferns, mosses, and other lower plants also exploit the wind to carry their minute spores. However, a great many flowering plants, including many that grow in the nearly windless environment of the understory, depend on animals to perform these functions. They are as dependent on animals for reproductive success as the animals are on them for food—one example of the mutual dependence between plants and animals.

Mutualistic
relation-
ships
between
plants and
animals

Many rainforest trees have sizable seeds from which large seedlings emerge and thrust their way through the thick mat of dead leaves on the dark forest floor. They develop tall stems using food reserves in the seed without having to rely on sunlight, which is usually too dim, to meet their energy requirements. Because large seeds cannot be dispersed by the wind, these plants depend on a variety of animals to perform this function and have evolved many adaptations to encourage them to do so. Fruit bats are attracted by fragrant, sweet fruits typically borne conspicuously and conveniently on the outer parts of the tree canopy; the mango (*Mangifera indica*), native to the rainforests of India, provides a good example. The bats not only feed on fruits as they hang from the trees, but they also may carry a fruit away to another perch where they eat the flesh and drop the seed. Smaller fruits may be swallowed whole, the seeds passing through the gut intact and being voided at a distance. The ground beneath trees used by fruit bats as a roost is commonly thick with seedlings of fleshy, fruit-bearing trees.

A variety of birds eat fleshy fruits also, voiding or regurgitating the unharmed seeds. Birds of different sizes are typically attracted to similarly scaled fruits, which are carried on stems of appropriate thickness and strength. For example, large pigeons in New Guinea feed preferentially on larger fruits borne on thicker stems that can bear not only the weight of the fruit but also the weight of the large bird; smaller pigeons tend to feed on smaller fruits borne on thinner twigs. In such a manner, the diverse plant community is matched by a similarly diverse animal community in interdependence.

Terrestrial mammals also help to disperse seeds. In many cases this has favoured the positioning of flowers and fruits beneath the canopy on the trunks of trees accessible to animals unable to climb or fly, an adaptation called cauliflory. In some cases fruits are grown in the canopy but drop as they ripen, opening only after they fall to attract ground-dwelling animals that will carry them away from the parent tree. The durian fruit *Durio zibethinus* of Southeast Asian rainforests is an example; its fruits are eaten and its seeds dispersed by a range of mammals including pigs, elephants, and even tigers.

Cauliflory

Many other animals, from ants to apes, are involved in seed dispersal. In the Amazon basin of Brazil, where large areas of tropical rainforest are seasonally flooded, many trees produce fruit attractive to fish, which swallow them whole and void the seeds. Squirrels are also important seed dispersers in parts of South America. In the tropical rainforests of northeastern Australia, cassowaries are responsible for generating mixed clumps of tree seedlings of several species that grow from their dung sites.

It is important for seeds to be spread away from parent

plants, both to allow seedlings to escape competition with the parent and to expand the range of the species. Another capacity important to seed survival, particularly in the diverse tropical rainforest community, involves the evasion of seed predators. Many different beetles and other insects are specialized to feed on particular types of seed. Seeds concentrated beneath a parent plant are easy for seed predators to locate. Seeds that are carried away to areas occupied by different plant species—and different seed predators—are more likely to survive.

Pollination   In addition to dispersing seeds, animals are vital to tropical rainforest reproduction through flower pollination. Many insects such as bees, moths, flies, and beetles as well as birds and bats carry out this activity. Birds such as the hummingbirds of South and Central America and the flower-peckers of Asia have adaptations that allow them to sip nectar from flowers. In the process they inadvertently become dusted with pollen, which they subsequently transport to other flowers, pollinating them. The plants involved also show special adaptations in flower structure and colour. Most flowers pollinated by birds are red, a colour highly visible to these animals, whereas flowers pollinated by night-flying moths are white or pink, and those pollinated by insects that fly during the day are often yellow or orange. Bats are important pollinators of certain pale, fragrant flowers that open in the evening in Asian rainforests.

Biological productivity. Of all vegetation types, tropical rainforests grow in climatic conditions that are least limiting to plant growth. It is to be expected that the growth and productivity (total amount of organic matter produced per unit area per unit time) of tropical rainforests would be higher than that of other vegetation, provided that other factors such as soil fertility or consumption by herbivorous animals are not extremely low or high.

Various methods are employed to assess productivity. Gross primary productivity is the amount of carbon fixed during photosynthesis by all producers in the ecosystem. However, a large part of the harnessed energy is used up by the metabolic processes of the producers (respiration). The amount of fixed carbon not used by plants is called net primary productivity, and it is this remainder that is available to various consumers in the ecosystem—*e.g.,* the herbivores, decomposers, and carnivores. Of course, in any stable ecosystem there is neither an accumulation

nor a diminution in the total amount of organic matter present, so that overall there is a balance between the gross primary productivity and the total consumption. The amount of organic matter in the system at any point in time, the total mass of all the organisms present, is called the biomass. (For further discussion of productivity see above *The organism and the environment: Resources of the biosphere.*)

The biomass of tropical rainforests is larger than that of other vegetation. It is not an easy quantity to measure, involving the destructive sampling of all the plants in an area (including their underground parts), with estimates made of the mass of other organisms belonging to the ecosystem such as animals. Measurements show that tropical rainforests typically have biomass values on the order of 400 to 700 metric tons per hectare, greater than most temperate forests and substantially more than other vegetation with fewer or no trees. A measurement of biomass in a tropical deciduous forest in Thailand yielded a value of about 340 metric tons per hectare.

Increase in biomass over the period of a year at one rainforest site in Malaysia was estimated at 7 metric tons per hectare, while total litter fall was 14 metric tons, estimated mass of sloughed roots was 4 metric tons, and total live plant matter eaten by herbivorous animals (both invertebrate and vertebrate) was about 5 metric tons per hectare per year. These values add up to a total net production of 30 metric tons per hectare per year. Respiration by the vegetation itself was estimated at 50 metric tons, so that gross primary productivity was about 80 metric tons per hectare per year. Compared with temperate forests, these values are approximately 2.5 times higher for net productivity and 4 times higher for gross productivity, the difference being that the respiration rate at the tropical site was 5 times that of temperate forests.

Despite the overall high rates of productivity and biomass in tropical rainforests, the growth rates of their timber trees are not unusually fast; in fact, some temperate trees and many smaller herbaceous plants grow more rapidly. The high productivity of tropical rainforests instead results in their high biomass and year-round growth. They also have particularly high levels of consumption by herbivores, litter production, and especially plant respiration.   (Jeremy M.B. Smith)

SCIENCE
year in review

contents

THE YEAR IN SCIENCE:
AN OVERVIEW

by Robert P. Crease

Science is so integral to human experience that each year numerous scientific developments have widespread social and political consequences. In 1996 scientific procedures and analyses routinely played a role in many events that appeared on the nightly news, including plane crashes, bombing investigations, criminal trials, food and drug tests, medical screening procedures, international relations, and political platforms.

The year was exceptional, however, in the number of significant scientific advances and the degree of cultural and political visibility given to scientific research. For the first time since the AIDS epidemic began in 1981, AIDS-related deaths declined substantially, particularly in the U.S. and France. To mark this extraordinary development, the prestigious journal *Science* chose new HIV treatments as its Breakthrough of the Year, while *Time* magazine singled out AIDS researcher David Ho of the Aaron Diamond AIDS Research Center, New York City, as its Man of the Year, making him the first scientist to receive the honor since 1960. Other important developments included the discovery that three species of human beings may have coexisted as recently as 30,000 years ago, the revelation that the Earth's solid-iron inner core spins independently of and at a different rate from the rest of the planet, and the long-awaited sale of the first mass-produced electric automobile in the U.S., known as the EV1, by General Motors Corp.

Robert P. Crease is a Professor of Philosophy at the State University of New York at Stony Brook and Historian at the Brookhaven National Laboratory, Upton, N.Y.

Martian fossils and mad cows

The year's most dramatic single discovery was the revelation of lifelike structures in a meteorite that some scientists said confirmed the existence of life on Mars. A team of researchers led by David S. McKay of NASA's Lyndon B. Johnson Space Center, Houston, Texas, spent months studying peculiar wormlike structures in a potato-sized meteorite found in Antarctica but thought to have originated on Mars. In August the team announced its conclusion that the structures in the fragment known as ALH84001 were fossilized microbes.

The team's revelation made headlines around the world and set off an instantaneous firestorm of controversy in professional science circles. Critics, citing the dismal record of previous claims for evidence of life on Mars, maintained that the structures were inorganic in origin. Other less-skeptical scientists took a wait-and-see approach. If the discovery of life on other planets were confirmed, however, it would be, as U.S. Pres. Bill Clinton rightly remarked, "one of the most stunning insights into our universe that science has ever uncovered."

Despite the scientific inconclusiveness about the origin of the meteorite's lifelike structures, the NASA announcement revived professional and popular interest in extraterrestrial life. "Is Anybody Out There?" *Science News* asked on the cover of its September 7 issue. Encouraged by politicians, NASA launched two Mars-bound spacecraft during the year, the Mars Global Surveyor and Mars Pathfinder, and drew up plans to spend an additional $1 million studying meteorites believed to have come from Mars. The agency also began to rethink its launch schedule to see whether it could accelerate its visits to the planet (five missions over the next decade at a cost of $1 billion), seeking, in particular, to hasten a launch planned for early in the next century to retrieve rocks from the Martian surface.

Program detractors described the missions as media-driven science and warned of their inherent dangers, including the

AIDS researcher David Ho appeared on the cover of *Time* magazine as its 1996 Man of the Year, the first scientist so honored since 1960.

LET'S HOPE LIFE ON MARS IS MORE INTELLIGENT THAN LIFE ON EARTH.

munities. The British journal *Nature* reported that the episode "plunged Europe into one of its biggest economic and political crises since the Second World War" and underscored "the continued need for responsible ways of handling scientific uncertainty."

Meanwhile, a case of food poisoning reached epidemic proportions in central Japan, affecting nearly 10,000 schoolchildren and causing 8 deaths in one of the largest outbreaks ever recorded of a bacterium known as *Escherichia coli* 0157:H7. The Japanese health and welfare minister's announcement that white radish sprouts might have been the *E. coli* carrier instigated widespread dietary changes throughout the country. Critics charged that not only was the pronouncement based on weak and premature scientific information, but it also appeared to be politically motivated. They claimed that the Health and Welfare Ministry used the occasion to appear decisive and proactive on public health issues in the wake of disclosures earlier in the year that revealed its faulty monitoring of the nation's blood supply. Thousands of Japanese hemophiliacs were infected with the AIDS virus as a result.

Capitol Hill scorecards and witch-hunts

In 1996 science-related controversies in the U.S. continued to make headlines on Capitol Hill. In September Science Watch, a science-policy group based in Washington, D.C., stirred up concern and criticism when it published its first edition of *Science Scorecard,* an annual report that assessed the voting records of members of the U.S. House of Representatives on science and technology issues.

siphoning of money from more scientifically relevant projects to support popular but potentially unsound research.

Mars mania was not the only instance in which controversial scientific evidence had a major social impact. Scantier evidence resulted in even starker consequences in the case of the disease bovine spongiform encephalopathy (BSE), popularly known as "mad cow" disease. During the 1980s, a BSE epidemic afflicted British cattle, but the nature and epidemiology of the illness remained unclear. Was the disease caused by a virus or a protein agent called a prion? Could it spread to human beings who had eaten infected beef? In March one scientific study suggested a possible link between consumption of beef from cattle infected with BSE and a new variant of a rare but fatal human brain disease called Creutzfeldt-Jakob disease that had struck 10 people in the U.K. Despite the fact that the reliability of the research was challenged and the nature of the disease remained inconclusive, the economic consequences of the study were immense. The European Union (EU) banned exports of beef from the U.K. and destroyed hundreds of thousands of cattle there and in other countries. Not only did the controversy cost the EU almost $3 billion, but the poor handling of the crisis also helped to severely erode public confidence in the government and scientific and medical com-

The year also witnessed what may be the final episode in a decade-long drama dubbed the "Baltimore case." The controversy started in 1986 when Nobel laureate David Baltimore and immunologist Thereza Imanishi-Kari, then a researcher at the Massachusetts Institute of Technology, coauthored a paper in the journal *Cell.* Questions began to be raised about Imanishi-Kari's work after a postdoctoral student in her laboratory could not repeat her results. The case achieved national prominence beginning in 1988 when Rep. John Dingell called in the Secret Service to investigate the study as part of a series of aggressive and highly politicized fraud-hunting hearings. In 1991 publicity surrounding the hearings forced Baltimore's resignation from the presidency of Rockefeller University, New York City, and in 1994 the Office of Research Integrity (ORI) of the National Institutes of Health lodged charges against Imanishi-Kari, barring her from receiving federal funds for 10 years. Shortly after, she was stripped of her faculty position at Tufts University, Medford, Mass.

In June 1996 the appeals board of the U.S. Department of Health and Human Services delivered its judgment on the case, citing the *Cell* paper as "rife with errors" but clearing Imanishi-Kari of all alleged criminal misconduct. The appeals board instead chastised the ORI's investigation as incompetent, the Secret Service's evidence as conflicting, and the investigation as tainted by political considerations. Many prominent scientists expressed outrage at what they called Dingell's overzealous witch-hunt, while moderate voices cautioned that one botched investigation should not be used to justify attempts to curb misconduct. Nonetheless, repercussions from the case were felt throughout the science community, resulting in bitter feelings toward Congress on the part of scientists and science administrators nationwide. Maxine Singer, president of the Carnegie Institution of Washington, called the Baltimore case "an American tragedy."

AFP Photo

In an address to the Pontifical Academy of Sciences, Pope John Paul II created surprisingly little controversy when he declared the theory of evolution as "more than a hypothesis."

Other scientific fields also were touched by cultural and political controversy. Anthropologists found themselves in a situation rife with racial undercurrents and ironies following the discovery of a 9,300-year old skeleton on the Columbia River in Washington State. A battle ensued between several American Indian tribes and researchers. The tribes insisted that the remains were of an ancestor and claimed the right to rebury them. The researchers theorized that the bones belonged to a Caucasian and provided important new evidence that Europeans may have inhabited North America much earlier than previously thought. Protests even halted laboratory analysis of DNA extracted from a finger bone of the skeleton, while lawyers argued over ownership and rights.

The Oakland (Calif.) Unified School District Board of Education touched off heated controversy when it announced that the "recognition and understanding of the language structures unique to African-American students," known as ebonics (a combination of the words *ebony* and *phonics,* literally translated as "black sounds"), would be incorporated into its curriculum. Noting the disproportionately low levels of academic achievement of its 27,000 black students, the school board emphasized that English language proficiency was critical to academic competency and outlined new goals that would "build on the language skills that African-American students bring to the classroom without devaluing students and their diversity." The action created a fierce debate not only among linguists and educators but also in the media. Critics accused the Oakland board of trying to supplant the teaching of standard English with ebonics, to promote the unsupported claim that ebonics is not a dialect of English but is "genetically based," *i.e.,* tied to African languages, thereby entitling ebonics speakers to specialized curricula as bilingual students, and to use language as a tool to further the segregation of African-American students within the school district as well as in society in general.

Other notable episodes laden with social and political overtones included controversies over the recommended frequency of mammograms for women under 50 and prostate-cancer testing for men over 50; the medicinal value of marijuana; the causes, diagnosis, and treatment of Gulf War syndrome; the safety of transgenic crops; and the link between human activity and global warming. Remarkably little controversy, however, was raised in October when Pope John Paul II in an address to the Pontifical Academy of Sciences stated that "new knowledge has led to the recognition of the theory of evolution as more than a hypothesis." The pontiff qualified his declaration by saying that while the human body may have evolved "from pre-existent living matter, the spiritual soul is immediately created by God."

Independence Day, the most popular movie of 1996, used a traditional Hollywood formula of pseudoscience, government conspiracies, and stereotypical mad scientists, played here by Brent Spiner (right), to tell the story of alien warfare and secret laboratory experiments in the Nevada desert.

Conspiracies and a postmodern hoax

A recent troubling development has been the proliferation of science "fictions" masquerading as science fact. Many of them have been used in support of conspiracies that have achieved wide currency in the media, particularly via the Internet. The mania over the Mars meteorite, for example, drove conspiracy-mongers to new heights. A September issue of the tabloid *Weekly World News* printed on its cover a picture of an insect that the editors claimed was that of a Martian life-form in a classified photo smuggled out of U.S. government files. NASA was implicated in the same issue in a paranoiac article entitled "NASA Receives Radio Signals from the Center of the Earth."

The tabloids, however, were not the only form of media to engage in groundless accusations of conspiracy. *Independence Day,* the most popular movie of 1996, used Hollywood hype to reinforce

pseudoscience—scientists as asocial freaks; UFO visitations, crashes, and abductions; and ESP—to craft a conspiracy narrative in which the U.S. government had captured alien spacecraft and bodies and had successfully kept the secret from the public for 50 years. The public's mania for extraterrestrials showed no signs of abating. The residents of Roswell, N.M., made preparations for the 50th anniversary celebration of the discovery near the city limits of metal wreckage, which the U.S. Air Force in a 1947 press release initially claimed was part of a flying saucer. Proceeds from the UFO-based tourist trade, including receipts from visits to the city's UFO Museum & Research Center, had already been contributing an estimated $5 million annually to the local economy and were expected to swamp the city coffers in 1997.

The most egregious liberties taken with scientific matter by mainstream media occurred in February on television, when NBC aired "The Mysterious Origins of Man." With actor Charlton Heston as host, the show contained many long-discredited fringe ideas about human evolution, including claims that human civilization dated to more than 100 million years ago and that people and dinosaurs coexisted (the archaeological evidence for which supposedly was suppressed by a great conspiratorial circle of scientists). Despite outrage voiced by scientists, NBC rebroadcast the program in June, congratulating itself on its courage to air the segment in the face of protest. Seeking to set the record straight and combat the junk science promoted by such programs—as well as by such popular television series as "The X-Files"—the Committee for the Scientific

New York University physicist Alan D. Sokal (below) generated heated debate among academics after publishing a bogus article in the prestigious journal *Social Text* (bottom). Sokal had written the article to draw attention to what he considered the irrelevance and superficiality often found in academic science writing.

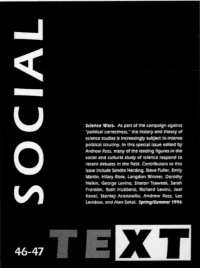

Investigation of Claims of the Paranormal, a nonprofit scientific and educational organization that uses responsible science to investigate paranormal and fringe-science claims, set up the Council for Media Integrity. One of the council's first tasks was to lobby television producers to attach disclaimers to programs that presented material not grounded in scientific fact.

With even mainstream media actively promoting conspiracies, it is no wonder that some scientific institutions found themselves hounded by wild allegations. Brookhaven National Laboratory (BNL), Upton, N.Y., was a particular target. Allegations circulated that its scientists were dissecting alien bodies recovered from crashed UFOs, that radiation from laboratory research produced mutant mosquitoes that caused an outbreak of equine encephalitis in a local state park, and that BNL researchers were implicated in the July crash of TWA Flight 800 in which 230 people died. In June CERN (European Laboratory for Particle Physics), Geneva, was the victim of actual sabotage when two strategically placed beer bottles delayed the restart of its newly upgraded Large Electron-Positron Collider.

Some of these scientific myths were so entrenched that even the most diligent research failed to dispel them. The alleged risks of electromagnetic fields (emfs), for example, continued to provide fodder for people with conspiratorial mind-sets. Following a three-year examination of some 500 studies done over the past 17 years, a panel convened by the U.S. National Academy of Sciences concluded that "the current body of evidence does not show that exposure to these fields presents a human-health hazard." Nonetheless, given the growing number of pseudoscientific media sources with a vested interest in stirring up public concern, the emf controversy is unlikely to end, and accusations of conspiracies and cover-ups undoubtedly will continue.

One might expect academics concerned with interpreting the nature and practice of science to assume leadership in resolving such situations. Not only did this fail to happen in 1996, but some academics even mounted well-publicized hoaxes in protest against their colleagues' misinterpretations of science. New York University physicist Alan D. Sokal submitted a bogus article entitled "Transgressing the Boundaries: Toward a Transformative Hermeneutics of Quantum Gravity," to *Social Text,* an academic journal edited by key figures in the philosophy and sociology of science. Sokal's article established a purported link between the physical theory of quantum gravity and the postmodernist themes of such prominent contemporary philosophers as Jacques Derrida, Luce Irigaray, and Jacques Lacan. The article was published in the Spring/Summer issue devoted to "science wars." Shortly after, in an essay published in *Lingua Franca,* a journal that covers academic matters, Sokal confessed that he had written the article as a hoax to showcase the sloppiness and vapidity of much current academic discourse about science.

The revelation was followed by vehement panel discussions, bitter speeches, impassioned articles, outraged editorials, and bemused press coverage. The controversy was even picked up by the Associated Press and made the front page of the *New York Times,* exposing to the general public the deep and bitter division among academics about the cultural meaning of science.

Books and obituaries

Despite the numerous misrepresentations of science in popular culture, a number of insightful science-related books helped to elucidate the intersection of science and society. *Conjuring Science: Scientific Symbols and Cultural Meanings in American*

Carl Sagan, considered one of the most passionate and articulate popularizers of science, died in 1996.

Life by cultural anthropologist Christopher P. Toumey examined the "looting of science for its images and metaphors" by scientists and nonscientists alike. Paul Rabinow's *Making PCR: A Study of Biotechnology* examined the events that surrounded the development of the polymerase chain reaction, providing a broad context for the "emergence of biotechnology, circa 1980, as a distinctive configuration of scientific, technical, cultural, social, economic, political, and legal elements." *Science on Trial: The Clash of Medical Evidence and the Law in the Breast Implant Case* by Marcia Angell provided a frightening account of how lawyers managed to wrest billions of dollars out of companies by using claims that lack a sound scientific basis. Steven G. Epstein's *Impure Science: AIDS, Activism, and the Politics of Knowledge* gave an astute account of the intertwining of politics and science in public health decisions about AIDS without succumbing either to the

romanticism of those who believe all science arises from human interests or to the idea that scientific work takes place independently of social decisions. David A. Hollinger, who has written extensively and perceptively on the social and intellectual forces at play in the genesis, consolidation, and exploitation of the reputation of science, contributed another book on the same theme, *Science, Jews, and Secular Culture: Studies in Mid-Twentieth-Century American Intellectual History*. *The Scientific Revolution* by Steven Shapin did a masterful job of exhibiting the social context in which the modern scientific worldview arose.

Stephen J. Gould, whose work has brilliantly exposed systematic errors in thinking about science by scientists and the public alike, made another provocative contribution with *Full House: The Spread of Excellence from Plato to Darwin*. Gould described *Homo sapiens* as a "tiny twig, born just yesterday on an enormously arborescent tree of life that would never produce the same set of branches if regrown from seed." To regard the production of complexity in evolution as an indication of directionality toward progress is a mistake, he wrote. Gould argued instead for a vast reconceptualization of what evolutionary progress means and called for "viewing a history of change as the increase or contraction of variation in an entire system (a 'full house'), rather than as a 'thing' moving somewhere," adding that "humans are here by the luck of the draw, not the inevitability of life's direction or evolution's mechanism."

Although science was marked by such notable contributions, the field also lost some of its brightest theorists and practitioners in 1996, including several scientists who had become legendary cultural figures because of their working styles, the issues they addressed, or the impact of their achievements. Among them was the mathematician Paul Erdos, whose career was once described as "one life-long, continuous lecture tour"; anthropologist Mary Leakey, one of the foremost researchers into human evolutionary history; ornithologist Roger Tory Peterson, whose bestselling guidebooks literally changed the way we see birds; and science historian and philosopher Thomas S. Kuhn, whose *The Structure of Scientific Revolutions*, the most frequently cited book in the humanities, transformed the way scientific practice was understood.

Paul Rabinow's *Making PCR: A Study of Biotechnology* examined the revolutionary development of the polymerase chain reaction within the scientific and cultural context of the early 1980s.

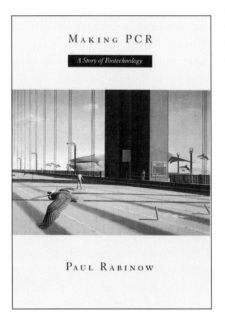

MAKING PCR

A Story of Biotechnology

PAUL RABINOW

Carl Sagan, one of the finest scientists ever to write for the general public, also died in 1996. His last book, *The Demon-Haunted World,* published in 1996, debunked pseudoscience and refuted the so-called arbitrariness of science. "He conveyed one consistent message," wrote Gould in a moving tribute. "Real science is so damned exciting, transforming, and provable, why would anyone prefer the undocumentable nonsense of astrology, alien abductions, and so forth?" Gould added that Sagan "bridged the gaps between our various cultures by showing the personal, humanistic, and artistic side of scientific activity." (For further information on these scientists, *see* SCIENTISTS OF THE YEAR: *Obituaries.*)

The real impact of science on everyday life, however, generally took much less dramatic and extreme forms. For me the most enduring image of the interplay between science and society occurred when Muhammad Ali lit the Olympic flame at the 1996 Summer Games in Atlanta, Ga. At his peak Ali was an Olympic gold medalist and then a world heavyweight boxing champion, famous for a nimbleness and arrogance that he himself immortalized in the lines "float like a butterfly, sting like a bee." Then he became a victim of Parkinson's disease, a terrible progressive illness that damages the brain's ability to control movement. Not long ago, Parkinson's sufferers like Ali would have been institutionalized, totally incapacitated

Former heavyweight boxing champion Muhammad Ali lights the Olympic flame at the 1996 Summer Games in Atlanta, Ga. Stricken with Parkinson's disease, Ali is among the millions of people to have benefited from scientific breakthroughs.

by uncontrollable shaking. Today, although the disease is not curable, much progress has been made in slowing and controlling its symptoms. As Ali unsteadily and laboriously extended his hand to light the Olympic flame, it was a reminder not only of how much science has served human life but also of how much there is to hope for from its future progress.

—Robert P. Crease

ANTHROPOLOGY

During the past year fossil discoveries and genetic studies shed new light on anthropologists' understanding of the evolution of primates and hominids. New evidence also fueled scientific debate on the early occupation of the Americas. Across the globe the discovery of Australian rock art stimulated rethinking about the origins of human creativity and other sophisticated cognitive abilities and suggested a much older date for the occupation of Australia than previously thought.

Primate evolution

Anthropologists theorize that after African and Asian hominoids split from a common ancestor, they developed different locomotion patterns. Living mostly in trees, Asian hominoids became slow climbers, an adaptation that contributed to the evolution of gorillas and chimpanzees. On the other hand, African hominoids dwelling in thin woods and savannas became specialized in terrestrial locomotion, a distinction which led to the development of the group of upright-walking hominids known as australopithecines, the earliest creatures that can be identified as direct ancestors of modern humans.

The discovery of a 9.5 million-year-old fossil hominoid identified as *Dryopithecus laietanus* promised to shed light on the divergence between hominoids that walked on all fours and those that walked erect and to give researchers a new glimpse into the critical but little-understood period of hominoid evolution 5 million–15 million years ago. Discovered near Barcelona, Spain, by Meike Köhler and Salvador Moyà-Solà, both of the Miquel Crusafont Institute of Paleontology, Sabadell, Spain, the fossil shares both the knuckle-walking

characteristics of greater apes and the arm strength of the orangutan, which provides the strongest evidence to date that *Dryopithecus* was capable of orthograde, or upright, posture similar to that of an orangutan. The fact that this fossil was discovered in Spain, which, like the African landscape, features more open land than thick forest, suggested a geographic adaptation in the evolution of erect posture.

Scientists in central Turkey discovered the fossilized remains of an ape some 10 million years old whose distinctive features include squarish eyes, a protruding mouth, and a small forehead. Discovered near Ankara by John Kappelman of the University of Texas at Austin and a team of researchers from the University of Ankara, the Finnish Museum of Natural History, Helsinki, and the Natural History Museum, London, the fossil was the most complete ever found of an ape known as *Ankarapithecus meteai*. A distant cousin of the common ancestor of the great apes and humans, *Ankarapithecus* gave scientists insight into the period between 5 million and 18 million years ago (before the split of humans and great apes), for which there is little fossil evidence.

K. Christopher Beard and Mary Dawson, both from the Carnegie Museum of Natural History, Pittsburgh, Pa., along with scientists from the Institute of Vertebrate Paleontology and Paleo-Anthropology, Beijing, discovered in Shanxi province, China, the complete lower jaw of a new genus and species of anthropoid known as *Eosimias centennicus*. On the basis of the new find, the researchers maintained that the primate suborder Anthropoidea, which includes monkeys, apes, and humans, originated some 45 million–

50 million years ago, earlier than previously thought. Emerging at a point near the evolutionary diversification of the higher primates, *E. centennicus,* although clearly related to the anthropoids, possessed characteristics unlike those of any other primate. Although early fossils of anthropoids had been discovered previously in Africa and Asia, the find was significant in that it was among the oldest and most complete examples of anthropoids found in Asia. Unfortunately, the discovery of *E. centennicus* does not solve the mystery of their origin.

Hominid evolution

U.S., Canadian, Ethiopian, and Israeli scientists used the single-crystal laser-fusion method of potassium-argon dating to reliably pinpoint the age of a hominid jaw at 2,330,000 years. The jaw was originally found in 1994 at a site near Hadar, Eth., along with other artifacts suggesting that the hominid used tools. William H. Kimbel, Donald C. Johanson, and geochronologist Robert C. Walter of the Institute of Human Origins, Berkeley, Calif., theorized that the jaw belongs to the genus *Homo* (the generally accepted root of modern humankind) and is at least 400,000 years older than other finds of this lineage. The researchers based their identification on the broad dental arch, short and flat snout, and a first molar that they said resembles that of *Homo habilis*. Researchers were able to further identify the fossil with *H. habilis* by comparing the tools associated with the jaw with tools found with *H. habilis* remains in Kenya and Ethiopia dating to 1,800,000–2,340,000 years ago. Nevertheless, firm confirmation of the species of the fossil remained a problem, and

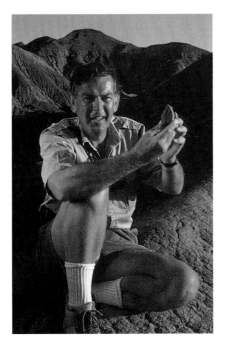

Photographs, © Enrico Ferorelli

Donald C. Johanson (left) of the Institute of Human Origins holds the world's oldest hominid jaw, believed to be 400,000 years older than other finds of this lineage. Researchers used the single-crystal laser-fusion method of potassium-argon dating (below) to reliably date the jaw, which was discovered near Hadar, Eth., in 1994.

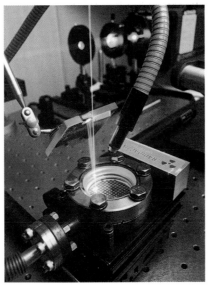

the possibility that the jaw represented a previously unknown branch of the family tree was left open.

Michel Brunet of the University of Poitiers, France, and a team of French scientists from the Museum of Man, Paris, uncovered a lower jawbone and canine tooth in Chad that appeared to belong to a new species of human ancestor that the scientists named *Australopithecus bahrelghazali*. Reported to be 3 million–3.5 million years old, *A. bahrelghazali* was the first australopithecine found that far west in Africa. Its location alone—2,400 km (1,500 mi) from contemporary fossils of the same lineage found in Ethiopia—will force scientists to rethink human origins, since the fossil's discovery suggested that australopithecines occupied more territory than previously believed.

In other hominid developments, scientists discovered the dental remains of an *A. afarensis* in Fejej, Eth. Reported to be 4,000,000–4,180,000 years old, the fossils were the oldest evidence for this species to date. Furthermore, they suggested that a number of different hominids existed in East Africa during the same time period.

In Sterkfontein, S.Af., researchers discovered fossils of *A. africanus*. According to Henry McHenry and Lee Berger of the University of the Witwatersrand, Johannesburg, S.Af., the fossils appeared to be less similar to modern humans than previous remains of *A. africanus*.

In the Danakil Desert of Eritrea, 500 km (300 mi) from the Hadar site, a team of Eritrean and Italian scientists unearthed fossils that date back some two million years, including the first skull from this area. While neither the genus nor the species was identified, Ernesto Abbate and Giovanni Ficcarelli of the University of Florence were confident that the skull, pelvis fragment, and a finger bone are of human ancestry. The discovery marked the first time that ancestral fossils had been located in this area.

From Asia came a report of fossilized human remains and evidence of a rather complex and advanced stone technology in a cave in Guizhou province, China, a discovery that may hold important clues to the earliest inhabitants of Asia. According to Lynn Schepartz of California State University, Stanislaus, and a team led by Huang Weiwen of the Institute of Vertebrate Paleontology and Paleo-Anthropology, the evidence from Panxian Dadong Cave (reported to be more than 300,000 years old) suggested that humans used the cave over a very long period of time. A contemporary of the Zhoukoudian Cave, where *H. erectus* (Peking Man) was found in the 1920s, the Panxian Dadong Cave could answer the question of whether *H. erectus* and modern *H. sapiens* inhabited China at the same time.

Chinese and Western scholars combined their resources to increase scientific knowledge about the evolution of humans in Asia and Africa. Russell Ciochon of the University of Iowa and Roy Larick of the University of Massachusetts at Amherst, along with a team of Chinese and U.S. scientists, proposed that pre-*H. erectus* hominids left Africa as long as two million years ago and arrived in China between 1.7 million and 1.9 million years ago. After examining newly discovered fossils from the Longgupo Cave in Sichuan province, the team noted physical similarities between the cave's fossils and the early African hominids *H. habilis* and *H. ergaster*. The tools associated with the cave's human fossils bore resemblances to those of early hominids at Olduvai Gorge in Tanzania. The new evidence lent support to the idea that *H. erectus* evolved in Asia as a side branch of the hominid evolutionary tree rather than as part of an African heritage leading to modern humans.

Genetic evidence continued to mount in

support of the idea that modern humans can be linked to a common human ancestor who lived in Africa some 100,000–300,000 years ago. An international team completed the largest study of the nuclear DNA of 1,600 individuals from 42 different African and non-African populations. The results led the researchers to conclude that modern humans emerged in northeastern Africa about 100,000 years ago.

Neanderthals

Until recently the earliest evidence for human activity deep in caves comprised the cave paintings at Grotte Chauvet in southern France, dated at 31,000 years. François Rouzaud, chief of the archaeology service of France's Midi-Pyrénées region; Michel Soulier, president of a local caving association; and Yves Lignereux of the National Veterinary School of Toulouse studied materials from an underground cavern in Bruniquel, Fr., that suggested that the site was visited repeatedly some 47,600 years ago, possibly earlier. While the scientists uncovered no traces of human bones or tools, they did find a complex quadrilateral structure that was constructed far inside the cave, as well as evidence of fire.

Both the use of fire and the building of complex structures have long been considered modern human accomplishments. The evidence, however, contradicts this theory. The date of the Bruniquel cave site confirmed the existence of Neanderthals in the cave well before the appearance of modern humans (the species occupied Europe and parts of the Middle East during the last ice age but became extinct about 30,000 years ago). According to some scientists, the construction of the structure suggested that Neanderthals possessed greater language

abilities and intelligence than previously thought, although this conclusion remained a matter of considerable debate.

A number of other studies during the past year addressed the question of whether Neanderthals may have been a different species from modern *H. sapiens*. Jeffery Schwartz of the University of Pittsburgh and Ian Tattersall of the American Museum of Natural History, New York City, studied the nose of the Neanderthals and identified three features that are shared by no other human or primate. Although the study did not provide conclusive evidence that Neanderthals were a separate species, it clearly suggested

that they were considerably different from *H. sapiens*.

Erik Trinkaus of the University of New Mexico and Chris Ruff of Johns Hopkins University, Baltimore, Md., analyzed the shape and inner structure of the upper arms and legs of some 17 different Neanderthal skeletons and compared them with examples of modern humans from the Middle East and Europe in an effort to determine why Neanderthals lost the evolutionary competition with modern humans. The researchers suggested that modern humans developed different social structures and activity levels. The resulting morphological changes gave modern humans a competitive edge.

Critics argue that the jump from differences in social structure to morphological differences goes too far. They charge that morphological differences resulted from biology, not behavior. On the basis of comparisons between the bony labyrinth (located within the temporal bone) of one of the fossils from Arcy-sur-Cure with that of other Neanderthals and modern humans, as well as of the fossils' association with Châtelperronian industries (an amalgam of Mousterian and Upper Paleolithic technologies), Jean-Jacques Hublin of the Museum of Man argued that there was a reproductive barrier between Neanderthals

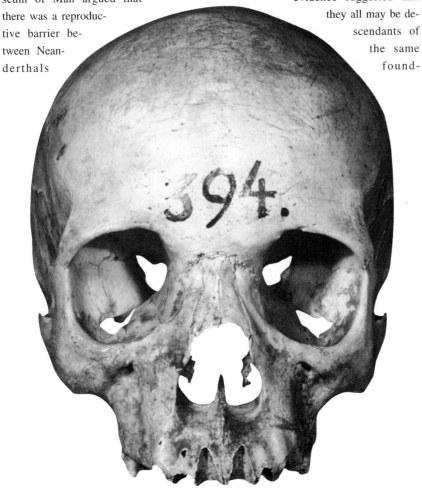

and modern humans. (*See* Feature Article: THE LIFE AND SCIENCE OF NEANDERTHALS.)

Peopling the Americas

Two new genetic studies addressed the question of how the earliest Americans migrated from Asia. A study by D. Andrew Merriwether of the University of Pittsburgh and a European research team showed that native Americans as diverse as the Alaskan Eskimos and the Kraho and Yanomami of Brazil share more gene types than previously thought. This new evidence suggested that they all may be descendants of the same founding populations of Asians, which migrated in a single wave from Mongolia.

Earlier studies that looked at shared gene types in different populations of native Americans had distinguished four lineages among these native groups. Merriwether identified additional gene types that were shared by the Kraho, Yanomami, and Eskimos and thus linked them to a single migration.

Merriwether's single-wave proposition countered a previous theory by Joseph Greenburg and Christy Turner of Arizona State University, which holds that the early Americas were occupied by people who migrated in three different waves. However, the results of a recent study by Néstor O. Bianchi of the Multidisciplinary Institute of Cellular Biology, Buenos Aires, Arg., seemed to confirm Merriwether's conclusions. His study of mitochondrial DNA (mtDNA) from 25 populations found enough genetic similarity among them to suggest that it was unlikely that the first migrants came in multiple waves.

Peter Forster of Hamburg (Ger.) University, Rosalind Hading of the Institute of Molecular Medicine, Oxford, Eng., and Antonio Torroni of the University of Rome revisited a genetic study of the mtDNA sequences of some 574 native Americans and Siberians to determine whether they had all come from a common ancestral population. The researchers detected nine mtDNA sequences in these populations

Several anatomical studies in 1996 sought to determine whether Neanderthals may have been a different species from modern humans. Among the points of comparison was the structure of the nasal cavity of Neanderthals (opposite page) and that of *Homo sapiens* (left), which demonstrated remarkable differences in size and form.

that suggested that Na-Dene speakers in Alaska. Eskimos, and coastal Siberians shared a common ancestor. On the basis of this finding, the researchers cautiously suggested that there were no more than two population waves into North America, the first occurring 20,000–25,000 years ago and the second occurring about 11,300 years ago.

Ancient art in Australia

In September 1996 researchers from the University of Wollongong, N.S.W., Australia, and the Australian Museum, Sydney, reported the discovery of what they said is the world's oldest known artwork—rock engravings estimated to be 75,000 years old. Located in northwestern Australia near a place that the Aboriginal people call Jinmium, the rock art consists of thousands of uniform circles inscribed on high sandstone monoliths. The work is more than twice as old as the oldest known European cave art and some 15,000 years older than any previous material found in Australia.

In addition to this startling find, the team also uncovered red ochre and stone artifacts that nearly triple previous age estimates for Australian settlement, pushing it back from 60,000 years to 176,000 years. The Jinmium find followed on the heels of a 1995 discovery by Rhys Jones of the Australian National University, Canberra, of rock art in Kakadu National Park, which also suggested that humans occupied Australia at least 60,000 years ago.

If the dates are confirmed, the find will have significant worldwide effects on theories concerning the origins of human creativity, including the development of art and language. Scientists usually associate

these sophisticated cognitive achievements with modern humans; artifacts discovered at the Jinmium site may demonstrate that these abilities originated with premodern humans.

—Larry L. Naylor

See also Year in Review: ARCHAEOLOGY.

ARCHAEOLOGY

In 1996 archaeologists uncovered a wide range of important findings that shed startling new light on the past. In the Peruvian Andes the discovery of the frozen body of a girl sacrificed in an Inca ceremony offered new insights into the religious life of one of South America's most highly developed Native American civilizations. Off the coast of Texas near Pass Cavallo, archaeologists added to an understanding of 17th-century North American history as work continued on the excavation of the *Belle,* the oldest French colonial shipwreck in the New World.

Intriguing evidence also came to light concerning human evolution and migration. Studies of the ancient Monte Alegran people in Brazil changed the established time frame for human occupation of the Amazon Basin. In addition, new fossil discoveries along with more accurate dating techniques suggested that early hominid expansion out of Africa occurred much earlier than previously thought.

The Inca girl of Mount Ampato

The 1991 discovery of the 5,000-year-old remains of a man found frozen in an Alpine glacier sparked much public interest in the lives of individual human beings from the past. Such rare finds have al-

lowed us to touch history in ways that even the best-preserved assemblages of artifacts can never duplicate. The recent discovery of another frozen, intact body has opened doors into the world of the Inca, whose civilization thrived in the highlands of South America just prior to the arrival of the Spaniards in the 16th century.

In September 1995 the anthropologist Johan Reinhard of the Mountain Institute, Franklin, W.Va., and his climbing partner, Miguel Zárate, hiked into a crater near the summit of Mt. Ampato in the Peruvian Andes to assess the results of recent volcanic eruptions. Soot and ash had blackened the summit, absorbing the Sun's heat, which melted snow from the 6,300-m (20,700-ft) mountain for the first time in memory. Lying attached to a large block of ice was the frozen body of an Inca girl wrapped in fine wool. Reinhard and Zárate managed to carry the body and ice block off the mountain and transport it safely to a freezer at Catholic University of Santa María, Arequipa, Peru, for further study.

Examination of the 500-year-old body revealed much about the girl and her Inca culture. Scientists estimated that she was about 13 years old and in very good health when she was killed by a blow to the right side of her head. Her death was a sacrifice to the mountains in a time of severe drought. Even today, people in the region revere the high mountains as their ancestors, regarding them as spirits who can intercede with nature on their behalf to ensure fertility and prosperity. In Inca times as well as today (human sacrifice still occurs in some of the mountain villages near Mt. Ampato, although the practice often results in prison sentences), a village might give up its most precious

Research on the 500-year-old remains of an Inca girl discovered in the Peruvian Andes shed new light on this remarkable civilization, which thrived in the highlands of South America prior to the arrival of Spaniards in the 16th century.

possession—one of its own children—to help ensure the prosperity of the whole community.

Researchers suggested that the girl was part of a procession that climbed up into the crater of Mt. Ampato at a time when little or no snow was present. After a ceremony, she was struck on the head,

wrapped in a fine woolen blanket, and buried beneath a stone platform. Tucked into the blanket was a doll, and surrounding the body were pottery, bags of maize (corn), and silver and gold statues, all ritual offerings carefully wrapped in textiles and placed in the tomb. Ongoing and future work will reveal more ordinary details of the girl's life, such as her DNA patterns, the foods she ate, and diseases she might have had.

The wreck of the *Belle*

More than 300 years ago René-Robert Cavelier, sieur de La Salle, lost his six-gun frigate in Matagorda Bay near present-day Pass Cavallo, Texas. An ambitious explorer, La Salle had traveled through much of the Great Lakes region of North America between 1671 and 1681 and in 1682 became one of the first Europeans to canoe down the Mississippi River to its mouth. Standing on the Mississippi Delta, he formally claimed much of North America for King Louis XIV of France. A year later he returned to France, where the king commissioned him to establish a colony on the Gulf Coast near the Mississippi River. The plan was to use the colony as a base from which to capture Spanish gold and silver mines in Mexico. To accomplish this task, Louis XIV gave La Salle four ships, the *Saint-François, L'Aimable, Le Joly,* and the 15.5-m (51-ft)-long *Belle.*

La Salle's vessels left France in 1684 carrying about 300 people. The *Saint-François* was seized by Spanish pirates a few days before the fleet reached the Caribbean settlement of Santo Domingo. The three remaining ships sailed on to find the mouth of the Mississippi but missed their mark by hundreds of kilometers. La Salle

landed by mistake in Matagorda Bay, where the *L'Aimable* was lost along with many needed supplies. Undaunted, La Salle set up camp on Matagorda Island and began to search for a site suitable for constructing a colony. Soon after, the *Le Joly* sailed back to France, leaving about 180 people behind to establish Fort-Saint-Louis on the mainland. Throughout 1685, using the only remaining ship and several canoes, La Salle searched by water for the Mississippi River. In January 1686 he and a small party left the ship anchored near the mouth of Matagorda Bay to begin an overland search for the river.

Shortly after his departure, however, the crew aboard the *Belle* disobeyed La Salle's orders and set sail for Fort-Saint-Louis to retrieve fresh water and supplies. A storm blew them off course. Soon they lost control, and the 45-ton ship sank in 3.5 m (12 ft) of water. Six crew members from the *Belle* along with La Salle and his party eventually made their way back to Fort-Saint-Louis. Without the ship, however, the French were stranded in a hostile land, and most of the colonists died within a year. In January 1687 La Salle left behind a small garrison and attempted to lead the remaining survivors on an overland trek to Illinois. Never a good commander, La Salle was assassinated in northeastern Texas by members of his own party.

The exact location of the French colony on the Texas coast is unknown, and until recently no one had located the wreckage of the *Belle* in Matagorda Bay. After searching since 1978, marine archaeologist Barto Arnold of the Texas Historical Commission (THC), Austin, discovered the *Belle* in 1995. Soon after, divers from the THC located one of the ship's bronze cannons and confirmed its identity. With financial support from the Texas state legislature and private donors, the THC began a large project in 1996 to excavate the buried ship. The commission erected a large steel and sand cofferdam around the ship, providing researchers with a watertight enclosure for the excavation. Work on the wreck began in June. To date, archaeologists have recovered a variety of important artifacts, including decorated bronze cannons, wooden gun carriages, rope, leather, clothes, beads, ceramic vessels, barrels of gunpowder and shot, muskets, spoons, forks, shoes, and combs. Three human skeletons were found, along with the bones of rats, mice, and a bison. Once the ship is excavated, the THC hopes to salvage the vessel itself, which is in surprisingly good condition after more than 300 years underwater.

Early Americans in the Amazon Basin

Archaeologists have argued for many years about when and how people came to inhabit the New World. Nearly every year some intriguing new evidence is presented suggesting that the first migrations from Asia took place earlier than previously thought. Despite this speculation, the best and most abundant evidence still places migration near the end of the Pleistocene Epoch—that is, around the end of the last ice age, approximately 12,000 years ago. (See *1993 Yearbook of Science and the Future* Feature Article: IN SEARCH OF THE FIRST AMERICANS.)

How these Paleo-Indians, as the first migrants are known, arrived in the Americas, however, has become a subject of renewed speculation. Assemblages of Pa-

A 1685 engraving (top) depicts the fleet of ships commanded by René-Robert Cavelier, better known as the Sieur de La Salle, on his exploration of the coast of the Gulf of Mexico. Submerged for more than 300 years after being downed by a storm, the *Belle*, one of La Salle's four ships, is undergoing excavation by researchers from the Texas Historical Commission.

leo-Indian artifacts (dating to the period from 8,000 to 12,000 years ago) are generally believed to relate to small roving bands of gatherers and hunters (or scavengers) of large, now-extinct mammals. Most Paleo-Indian sites are found in North America or along the plains and high valleys of western and southern South America. Because the locations of these artifacts are far from the eastern regions of the South American continent, many archaeologists have argued that the lush rain forests

of the Amazon Basin were not inhabited until people developed specialized plant-processing techniques after about 6,000–7,000 years ago.

New evidence may reverse some of these assumptions. Since 1991 Anna Roosevelt of the University of Illinois and Field Museum of Natural History, Chicago, has worked in the Monte Alegre region of northern Brazil. Her excavations at Caverna da Pedra Pintada have begun to change the way archaeologists think of the early inhabitants of the Americas. Roosevelt recovered abundant evidence that people had occupied the cave around 11,200 years ago, thousands of years earlier than previously thought.

Although Roosevelt's work established that the ancient Monte Alegrans were contemporaries of the Paleo-Indian groups to the west and north, they exhibited significant deviations that may reveal important new evidence about the routes of Paleo-Indian migration. Roosevelt discovered that the hunting tools of Monte Alegrans were distinct from those of other groups, as was their prey, which included a wide variety of smaller animals and fish instead of the big-game animals associated with Paleo-Indians throughout the New World. The ancient Monte Alegrans also appear to have used boats and were adept at processing many tropical plant foods much earlier than previously believed. Researchers theorized that the Monte Alegrans were different in spiritual ways as well. They painted their cave walls, using animal and geometric figures in intricate patterns, unlike Paleo-Indian cultures in other parts of North America and western South America, which left no evidence of this practice.

These differences suggest that Monte

Alegrans and other Paleo-Indians took different migration routes into the Americas. Most Paleo-Indian groups probably migrated through the interior of North America, following such large plains-dwelling Pleistocene animals as mammoths, giant sloths, horses, camels, and bison. The ancestors of the tropical Monte Alegrans, however, may have followed the seacoasts. During the Pleistocene, the lower sea levels would have left shorelines much more expansive than they are now. These coastal migrations could explain the Monte Alegrans' familiarity with boats and their maritime lifeways associated with fish, sea mammals, and plants, providing a reasonable explanation of the differences between the New World's two earliest human adaptations.

Dating early human ancestors in Asia

The past two years were notable for discoveries of early hominid fossils. In Africa and South Asia the number of ancestral candidates or their relatives that lived between two million and five million years ago grew, as did the number of fossil hominid specimens from China and other Asian countries. New fossil evidence usually does not immediately clarify scientists' understandings of ancestral relationships, and these specimens were no exception. Occasionally, however, new evidence combined with cutting-edge techniques for interpreting existing data provides a fresh perspective on the past, as it did in the case of some recently discovered specimens and artifacts assigned to the genus *Homo* from China, the island of Java, Pakistan, and Georgia.

Conventional archaeological theory suggests that one million years elapsed between the emergence of hominids in Africa and their arrival in Asia. However, new and more precise dating methods such as paleomagnetism, electron-spin resonance, and single-crystal argon (argon-argon) dating of new artifact-bearing sites indicate that hominids were in Asia much earlier than previously thought. Sites such as Riwat and Pabbi Hills, Pak., were directly dated to 1.9 million years ago. The Javanese sites of Sangiran and Mojokerto were shown to have been occupied as early as 1.6 million–1.8 million years ago. Longgupo Cave, China, which yielded hominid teeth very much like those of early African *Homo,* was dated to 1.9 million years ago. Together the dates push back the presence of hominids in Asia by about 800,000 years, which gives rise to several questions: Which species of hominids were the first to leave Africa and disperse to Eurasia? When did they migrate? What caused them to leave?

New interpretations of human evolution based on these late-breaking fossil discoveries in Asia and the development of more accurate dating techniques were presented by Roy Larick of the University of Massachusetts at Amherst and Russell L. Ciochon of the University of Iowa. They revived some of the species classifications named by the archaeologists and anthropologists Louis and Mary Leakey during the course of their work in eastern Africa, categories that had been largely discounted by paleoanthropologists and archaeologists during the past 20–30 years. The authors also cited global climate change that occurred between two million and three million years ago as a contributing factor to the course of human evolution from aus-

tralopithecines (literally, "southern apes," the earliest creatures that can be identified as direct ancestors of modern humans) to the genus *Homo*.

Their model starts about four million years ago with *Australopithecus afarensis,* one of the earliest fossil ancestors found throughout eastern Africa. *A. afarensis* evolved in tropical woodlands and seems to have existed until around 2.7 million years ago. Around three million years ago, cooler temperatures diminished the tropical woodlands in eastern Africa, replacing them with grasslands and more open savannas. Several different species arose from *A. afarensis* populations during this time, including *A. africanus* and at least one form of *Homo*. Differences between the two genera are seen in their cranial structures, which in australopithecines reflect growing specialization toward heavy plant chewing, compared with the more generalized diets, larger brain size, and tool use in early *Homo*.

Larick and Ciochon recognize the emergence around 2.6 million years ago of *Homo rudolfensis,* a species proposed by the Leakeys in the 1960s. Just before two million years ago, this population was followed by *H. habilis*. The researchers maintain that *H. habilis* was too morphologically primitive to be the direct ancestor of *H. erectus,* which appeared around 1.8 million years ago. Larick and Ciochon assign another Leakey-named species, *H. ergaster,* which arose around 1.9 million years ago, as the more likely predecessor of *H. erectus*.

Until recently, the study of human evolution largely had focused on eastern Africa, but the revised dating of the fossil record and new fossil finds in Asia suggest that one of these early *Homo* species moved rapidly out of Africa to populate much of the tropical and subtropical Old World. Which one was it? Most paleoanthropologists had assumed that *H. erectus* was the first hominid capable of traveling long distances and adapting to a variety of different environments. The new dates, however, precluded this usual suspect. Although Larick and Ciochon referred to the earliest Asian *Homo* species as "indeterminate," they implied that *H. ergaster* might be the likely species, since the ancestor who rapidly radiated out of Africa must have been tall and mobile, relatively large-brained, highly adaptable, prolific, and well versed in the use of tools and fire. The few specimens assigned to *H. ergaster* seemed to fit this description. On the other hand, these characteristics also described *H. erectus,* and new data in Africa may demonstrate that *H. erectus* evolved earlier than has been thought.

—James D. Wilde

ARCHITECTURE AND CIVIL ENGINEERING

A survey of cities around the world during the past year supported the case that architectural design is more varied now than perhaps at any other time in its history. Architects drew on a palette of styles inspired by a wide range of built forms, from medieval Gothic cathedrals and 18th-century English villages to mid-20th-century Modernist classics. Not all of these buildings, however, opened their doors without comment. While Asian cities welcomed gleaming new office towers as symbols of newfound prosperity and optimism, many European projects provoked a great deal of

Poundbury, a community on the outskirts of Dorchester, Eng., designed by Leon Krier, won the support of architectural conservatives by using the traditional forms of English villages.

critical discussion and controversy in the popular press and among people on the street.

Architectural design

In England design classicists, led by Charles, prince of Wales, continued their polarized battle with Modernist architects. The classicists maintained that architecture should develop in incremental changes along a continuum of tradition. Modernists, on the other hand, took a more drastic approach, insisting that contemporary architecture should break with the past and express today's radically changed times. Heralded by the more conservative proponents of architecture was the traditional village of Poundbury, designed by Leon Krier on the outskirts of Dorchester. Planned as a tightly knit grouping of houses similar to the urban pattern customarily found in English towns, Poundbury proved popular with the public. The first phase of 250 units was quickly rented or sold out, even as several local architects and at least one critic dismissed its traditional design as "potted history."

British classicists sustained a major

blow, however, when the German architect Daniel Libeskind was commissioned to design an addition for the venerable Victoria and Albert Museum. Using a Deconstructivist composition of angular volumes, Libeskind's design is intended to resemble a casual heap of geometric forms that looks as though it might fall apart or be blown away at any moment. In a less-radical—but far from traditional—gesture, Sir Norman Foster & Partners unveiled a curving glass-walled scheme for the 92-story London Millennium Tower. If completed, the building will be the tallest office tower in Europe.

On the Continent, architects expressed their design philosophies in a wide variety of styles. Dutch architect Rem Koolhaas provided his own interpretation of Deconstructivism in his design for a new convention center in Lille, Fr. In Turin, Italy, Renzo Piano took his cues from organic forms in his design for a large convention center carved out of a former Fiat automobile-assembly plant. The firm of Von Gerkan, Marg and Partners designed a centerpiece for a convention and trade-show complex in Leipzig, Ger., that resembled a futuristic version of London's 19th-century Crystal Palace.

For many government-sponsored projects, however, Modernism was the style of choice. Sir Norman Foster & Partners won a competition to design a media center in Hamburg, Ger., with a rectangular glass-walled scheme expressing today's straightforward version of classic Modernism. In Paris the so-called Grand Projets, including the new national library and state opera, were executed in a Modernist spirit. Even the city's preservation projects followed this trend. Near the Louvre, Francis Soler, for example, adapted a Beaux-Arts building for the French Ministry of Culture by adding a new glass extension.

Not all restoration projects in Europe departed so abruptly from the past. To celebrate its 800th anniversary, the city of Dresden began rebuilding the Frauen-

kirche, a baroque church dating to the mid-18th century. Although the structure had been gutted during World War II, many of the original materials were salvaged from the rubble. The reconstruction, which is reusing the church's sandstone blocks, is being aided by state-of-the-art technology. Thousands of digital photographs stored on CD-ROMs recorded the dimensions of more than 8,000 cut blocks. Using a three-dimensional computer model, restorationists created a blueprint marking the original location of each piece of stone.

In the United States, architects and the public were less concerned than their European counterparts with debating the correctness of design philosophies. Robert A.M. Stern Architects applied a strict historicism to a neo-Georgian building housing the new business school at the University of Virginia. Michael Graves dipped into the grab bag of Postmodernism's abstracted historic styles for the Engineering Research Center at the University of Cincinnati, Ohio. The Modernist design for

the Getty Center in Los Angeles by Richard Meier recalled the heyday of the 1930s Bauhaus School in Berlin. Cesar Pelli & Associates, working in conjunction with Yamashita Sekkei, took an orthodox Modernist slant on the Nippon Telephone and Telegraph Co. office building in Tokyo.

Even firms that had made their mark in design history by perfecting a particular architectural style set out in new directions. Skidmore, Owings & Merrill, whose early fame rested on Modernist classics such as Lever House in New York City, produced a neo-Gothic psychology building on the campus of Washington University, St. Louis, Mo. The object was to blend with the prevailing style of the campus. Modernism also was overshadowed in the design of a new music center for Phillips Exeter Academy, Exeter, N.H. Faced with the choice of echoing the historicism of the school's older buildings or taking its cues from Louis Kahn's award-winning library (a stark exposed-concrete design executed in a manner sometimes referred

The Lingotto Conference Center in Turin, Italy, was converted from a Fiat auto-assembly factory by architect Renzo Piano.

Some of the year's most daring architectural projects were built in Asia, including Renzo Piano's design for the Kansai Airport in Japan (above) and Cesar Pelli's Petronas Towers in Malaysia (right), currently the world's tallest buildings.

to as Brutalist), William Rawn Associates produced a traditional brick building that was more in keeping with the campus's prevailing Georgian style.

Not all observers were pleased with the willingness of contemporary U.S. architects to subordinate individualistic design expression to contextual considerations or with the unwillingness of their patrons—most notably the U.S. government—to support progressive architecture. For example, Robert Campbell, a Pulitzer Prize-winning architectural critic for the *Boston Globe,* applauded the European public's enthusiasm for debates about architectural issues while decrying the corresponding lack of interest in architecture in the U.S. As an example of this disregard, he cited a recent U.S. Senate subcommittee's investigation into the construction of new federal buildings in which the architecture firm of Pei Cobb Freed & Partners was censured for aspiring to create "an architectural masterwork" in its design for Boston's new federal courthouse.

Campbell reserved his praise for European projects. In a 1996 article in *Architectural Record,* he expressed his admiration for José Rafael Moneo's "inventive" Atocha Railroad station in Madrid. He cited Italian architect Piano's dramatic Kansai Airport in Japan and Nicholas Grimshaw's innovative design for the English terminal of the Channel Tunnel. According to Campbell, what the U.S. needs is a "national argument," an engagement with architecture that rivals the level of enthusiasm that Americans bring to baseball.

There were indications that Europe's creative fires may have been tempering as well. The choice of Moneo as the recipient of the 1996 Pritzker Architecture Prize, for example, was a far cry from the 1994 winner, Christian de Portzamparc, whom Campbell celebrated for his "special design character" and ability for "finding a new esthetic vocabulary." Moneo, on the other hand, was noted for his often quiet and thoughtful work, which included his U.S. debut, the Davis Museum and Cultural Center at Wellesley (Mass.) College. Instead of being cited for expressing a highly original and very personal view of architecture, Moneo was applauded for regarding the practicalities of "materials and construction to be just as important as vision and concept."

One region where architecture's verve remained undampened was the Pacific Rim. New office towers, rarities in today's overbuilt Western nations, rose out of traditionally low-roofed cities. Some broke new records for height and square footage, such as the twin Petronas Towers in Kuala Lumpur, Malaysia, which measure 452 m (1,483 ft) tall. While many Westerners decried these breaks with local tradition and character as well as the towers' extreme energy inefficiency, the design and engineering economies of Europe and the U.S. profited by the new construction. Pelli served as design architect for Petronas Towers. Other U.S. firms were spearheading projects in progress as of early 1997, including the 44- and 66-story towers of MegaWorld Place in Manila designed by Skidmore, Owings & Merrill and a new high-rise in Shanghai by Kohn Pedersen Fox Associates, which promised to eclipse the height of the Petronas Towers.

Local architects received their share of work as well. The South Korean firm of

Hak Sik Son designed a sprawling low- and moderate-income-housing project in Pusan, South Korea, and Wong Tung & Partners completed a mixed-use tower for Hong Kong.

Technology and engineering

Analysts expressed fears that the burgeoning demand for electric power around the world would lead to massive dam construction on a scale comparable to China's Three Gorges Dam, which, when completed, will inundate 13 major cities and create a lake nearly 645 km (400 mi) long. Such fears were allayed, however, by a report from the American Wind Energy Association, which predicted that the global use of wind-powered generators—machines that resemble giant plane propellers mounted on tall posts—would increase 10-fold by 2005, producing 18.5 gigawatts (billion watts) of power.

The first leg of a project to replace Boston's Central Artery was completed with the construction of a 2.6-km (1.6-mi) tunnel under Boston Harbor connecting Logan Airport with the downtown business district. According to the American Society of Civil Engineers, the artery was the largest and most complex highway project undertaken in a U.S. city. Though barely under way, the project has already garnered some prestigious awards. The society, for example, presented the Massachusetts Highway Department with its 1996 National Engineering Award. The award recognized consultant project managers Bechtel/Parsons Brinckerhoff's innovative handling of environmental problems, such as their protection of marine life during the removal of contaminated harbor sediments and their avoidance of potential traffic problems during construction. Also recognized in the award was

Sverdrup Corp.'s design of the tunnel itself, which includes the construction of North America's largest circular cofferdam and the installation of 12 steel tubes. The tubes, which measure 97.5 m (320 ft) long, form the 1.2-km (0.75-mi) underwater section of the tunnel.

Transportation innovations also occurred in Toronto, where motorists on the new "smart" highway—a 69-km (43-mi) ring road around the city—no longer need to stop at toll booths to deposit coins. Engineers hoped to ease traffic congestion and pare down staff and highway-construction costs through the use of car-mounted transponders that electronically deduct the cost of tolls from prepaid fees.

A large number of civil engineering projects throughout the world involved refitting and improving existing infrastructure. London engineers began work to stabilize the Thames Barrier, a flood-control project that since its completion in 1983 has protected the metropolis from more than 20 floods. In specially designed cofferdams below the waterline, workers shored up deteriorated bearings that permit the pivoting of the structure's 3,500-ton surge-blocking gates and installed sensors to detect future decay. In Vietnam a consortium of North American engineering firms produced designs for the rehabilitation of water-resource facilities, including flood-protection dikes around Hanoi and two of the country's largest agricultural irrigation systems. In the U.S. forecasters revised their estimates for 1997 expenditures on highways and bridges, predicting that the cost of building new infrastructure and maintaining existing facilities will jump from $7.7 billion to $13.8 billion.

—Charles King Hoyt

London engineers completed structural repairs to shore up the 3,500-ton surge-blocking gates of the Thames Barrier, a 14-year-old flood-control project in England.

A meteorite discovered in Antarctica and designated ALH84001 is believed to have been part of the original crust of Mars. According to NASA scientists, tubelike structures identified in the meteorite resemble ancient fossilized bacteria found on Earth.

ASTRONOMY

The appearance of a very bright comet and the possible discovery of ancient life on Mars were among the exciting events that marked the past year in astronomy.

Solar system

Humans have long speculated about life on the planet Mars. In the early 1900s the ideas about Martians were fed by overly optimistic estimates of the climate and reports that ground-based telescopes had detected canals crisscrossing the planet. In the 1890s Percival Lowell, the founder of Lowell Observatory in Arizona, wrote books explaining the canals as constructions of a civilization struggling to transport water from the Martian polar caps to the warmer equatorial regions. Lowell's ideas influenced generations of science-fiction writers such as H.G. Wells, Ray Bradbury, and Edgar Rice Burroughs. Today it is known that the canals of Mars were an optical illusion and that the surface conditions on the planet are very harsh. The Viking probes that arrived at Mars in 1976 found an atmosphere composed mostly of carbon dioxide, with pressure only $\frac{1}{100}$ that of the Earth's atmosphere. Temperatures were sometimes less than $-100°$ C ($-150°$ F). Liquid water cannot exist under such conditions, but frozen water is believed to be (along with frozen carbon dioxide) at the polar ice caps. The Viking orbiting cameras did, however, reveal evidence that the climate was once much different. The planet is covered with what appear to be dry stream channels and riverbeds. For there to have been running liquid water, Mars would have had to have been much warmer and have had a much denser atmosphere. This

suggests that long ago Mars may have been a favorable location for the development of life. This idea has persisted, even though the Viking landers failed to find conclusive evidence for life. Now, however, this evidence may have been found.

In August 1996 a NASA research team led by David S. McKay and Everett K. Gibson announced evidence for ancient Martian life. This came not from a space probe or a telescope but rather from a meteorite. Meteorites are interplanetary rocks that fall to the Earth. Most are believed to be leftovers from the formation of the planets more than 4.5 billion years ago. Some, however, are pieces of asteroids and planets. The collision between a planet such as Mars and a small asteroid can eject pieces of both objects into space. Most of these collisions occurred when the solar system was young. Given time, some of the pieces may encounter the Earth and, much like any other meteorite, survive the fall through its atmosphere. Of the thousands of recovered meteorites, only 12 have been identified as having come from Mars. This identification was based on gases trapped within some of them that match the known composition of the Martian atmosphere. There is no other planet in the solar system with that exact atmospheric composition. The meteorite studied by the NASA group, known as ALH84001, was identified as having come from Mars. Dating to 4.5 billion years ago, ALH84001 is far older than previous Martian meteorites and was once part of the original Martian crust. When examined with an electron microscope, ALH84001

reveals elongated tubelike structures, less than 100 nanometers (4 millionths of an inch) long, which closely resemble ancient fossilized bacteria found on the Earth. The meteorite also has carbonate globules (about 0.1 mm across) that contain very small grains of magnetite and iron sulfide. On the Earth these compounds are not normally found together. An exception occurs in the presence of certain bacteria that produce them simultaneously. The globules also contain organic molecules known as polycyclic aromatic hydrocarbons. They are associated (but not exclusively) with the decay of organic matter. The NASA team concluded that these data, taken together, are best explained by the presence of ancient bacterial life on Mars. Samples of the meteorite have been distributed to other researchers around the world in order to verify the findings. If the evidence survives critical review, this will mark one of the most important discoveries in history.

In the early morning hours of January 1996, Japanese amateur astronomer Yuji Hyakutake discovered a new comet while scanning the sky with a large pair of binoculars. This was not Hyakutake's first comet discovery, but it would become his most famous. In the days that followed, it became clear that on the inward portion of its revolution around the Sun, the comet would pass only 15 million km from the Earth—only 40 times the distance to the Moon (1 km=0.62 mi). The comet steadily brightened, and its tail grew during February as it approached the Earth. Its progress was closely followed by both amateur and professional astronomers. The comet was studied by an array of telescopes on the ground and in space. Spectral analysis of the gases in the comet's coma and tail

Bill Hutchinson, The Kenai
Peninsula Eagle Press

Comet Hale-Bopp is bright in the night sky as it streaks over a Russian Orthodox church in Ninilchik, Alaska, on April 14, 1997. Named for the two observers who first detected it, the comet was clearly visible to the naked eye for several weeks.

revealed the presence of water, carbon monoxide, carbon dioxide, ammonia, methane, methyl alcohol, ethane, hydrogen cyanide, and carbon sulfide, among others. For those who found dark viewing locations, the comet was spectacular in late March. It was plainly visible to the unaided eye near the North Star, with a long straight tail passing through the Big Dipper and arcing almost halfway across the sky. In April the comet became more difficult to see as it receded from Earth. On May 1 it passed around the Sun and began the outward portion of its 15,000-year orbit.

In March and April 1997, the Earth was treated to a second, even more spectacular, comet show when Comet Hale-Bopp swung through the inner solar system. Named for the two observers who first detected it, Hale-Bopp was clearly visible to the naked eye for several weeks.

The images of Jupiter and its moons transmitted to the Earth by the Galileo space probe continued to impress planetary scientists. The quality of the images of Jupiter and its icy moons far surpassed those provided by the Voyager probes in the 1970s. (For a detailed discussion of the Galileo mission to Jupiter, *see* Feature Article: In the Realm of the Giant.)

Pluto is the only planet in the solar system that has not yet been visited by a space probe. From the Earth it appears as a faint, tiny dot of light only 0.1 of a second of arc across, or $\frac{1}{1,800}$ the diameter of the full moon. Observations with the Hubble Space Telescope (HST) revealed surface features for the first time. A research team led by Alan Stern obtained several high-resolution images in visible and ultraviolet light. The images portrayed a dozen distinctive features, including a

north polar cap bisected by a dark strip, a bright spot that was seen to rotate with the planet every 6.4 days, linear features, and dark spots. Some of the features may be impact basins such as those seen elsewhere in the solar system. Many of the markings may be due to the distribution of frost across the planet. Pluto's orbit is highly elliptical, and so its distance from the Sun changes considerably. When it is closest to the Sun, the ices of nitrogen, carbon monoxide, and methane partially sublimate and become part of the planet's atmosphere. They refreeze when Pluto moves farther from the Sun, possibly changing the appearance of the planet.

Stars

The search for planets orbiting other stars continued in 1996, spurred on by the discovery of three cases in the previous year.

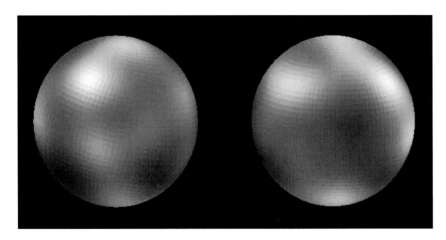

A. Stern (SwRI), M. Buie (Lowell Observatory), NASA, ESA

Computer-constructed views of the two opposite hemispheres of Pluto are based on images from the Earth-orbiting Hubble Space Telescope. The brightness variations are believed to be caused by regions of nitrogen and methane frost on the planet's surface.

By the end of 1996, there were a total of eight confirmed planetary systems. Because of their great distances, these planets were not seen directly. The star and planet appear as a single point of light. Even the best resolution of the HST will not provide a better image because the light from the planet is overwhelmed by that of the star it orbits.

The planet was detected indirectly by its gravitational effect on the visible star. The planet pulls the star in the direction of the Earth when the planet is on the Earth's side of the orbit and away from the Earth when it is on the far side of the orbit. This produces a Doppler shift, a change in the frequency of features in the star's light spectrum. The size of the frequency shift indicates the mass of the orbiting planet— the larger the shift, the more massive the planet. Except for the most massive planets, the Doppler shift is very small. Consequently, all of the planets detected thus far have mass comparable to Jupiter's or larger. If our solar system is any guide, the

detection of large planets suggests the presence of smaller planets. The implication of this research is that planetary systems are common in the universe, and so too may be life.

In general, stars are so far from the Earth that they appear as unresolved points of light even in very large telescopes. There are, however, a growing number of exceptions to this rule. The red supergiant Betelgeuse is extremely large and relatively nearby (about 500 light-years; 1 light-year is about 9.5 trillion km or 5.9 trillion mi). This has made it possible to resolve the star at visual wavelengths, using devices known as interferometers that construct images from interference patterns of light collected from separate mirrors. They show the disk of the star but little detail.

Recently, Betelgeuse was imaged directly, without an interferometer, by Andrea K. Dupree and Ronald L. Gilliland, using the superior resolution of the HST. The ultraviolet image shows a surface hot

spot that looks similar to one seen in ground-based interferometric images. Unlike the Sun, the image of Betelgeuse does not have a sharp outer edge but has a fuzzy extended atmosphere. This is because the star is a supergiant with a strong stellar wind flowing from its atmosphere.

The Sun has been shining, fairly steadily, for five billion years, deriving its energy from hydrogen fusion in its central core. In another five billion years, the hydrogen supply will become scarce. The result will be a contraction of the central core and an expansion of the outer layers. The Sun will become a red giant more than 100 times its present size. Red giants are not entirely stable. They may pulsate and eject their outer layers into space.

The result of this latter process is an object called a planetary nebula. Planetary nebulae get their name from the round appearance many have when viewed through small telescopes. They actually have nothing to do with planets. A planetary nebula is an expanding shell of gas around a hot central star. The expanding shell was once the outer layers of a red giant and the central star its core.

The transition from a red giant to a planetary nebula is brief, lasting only a few thousand years. For that reason it is rarely seen in the sky. The Egg Nebula in Cygnus may be an example. It appears as an oblong cloud that is about one light-year across and is expanding at 20 km per second.

The HST image obtained by Raghvendra Sahai and John T. Trauger shows much more detail. The central star is hidden by the nebula, but its effects are clearly seen. The nebula is surrounded by many thin, concentric shells of gas. This indicates that

The red supergiant star Betelgeuse is revealed by the Hubble Space Telescope in the first direct image of the surface of a star other than the Sun. About 500 light-years away, Betelgeuse is more than 1,000 times larger than the Sun.

the mass loss from the star has proceeded not uniformly but rather in bursts every few hundred years. There are also two pairs of oppositely directed beams coming from the central star. Their origin is not yet understood. These may indicate thin spots in the Egg Nebula that allow light from the star to escape. Another possibility is that the central star is producing oppositely directed jets of gas. There is much to be learned about this rapid phase of stellar evolution.

Extragalactic astronomy

Images of distant galaxies are also images of the past. The light from such galaxies can take millions or even billions of years to reach the Earth. These images reveal the galaxies as they appeared when the light left them. Therefore, by looking great distances into space, astronomers should be able to see young galaxies, perhaps even galaxies forming when the universe was young. Unfortunately, galaxies seen at such distances (billions of light-years) appear very small and extremely faint. Until recently, these distant galaxies appeared only as faint smudges. The galaxies that could be seen more clearly were nearer to the Earth, and they all appeared to be similar. With the advent of the HST and its sharper vision, and larger ground-based instruments such as the Keck 10-m telescope, astronomers can see farther and clearer.

The first difficulty in studying very distant galaxies is to distinguish them from those closer to the Earth. Apparent size alone is not always a good guide. The spectra of almost all galaxies show a Doppler shift toward longer wavelengths, called the red shift. This is caused by the

expansion of the universe that carries galaxies away from each other and from the Earth. Since the days of Edwin Hubble, astronomers have known that galaxies with larger red shifts are farther away than galaxies with smaller red shifts. The distance to a galaxy can be calculated from the red shift if the expansion rate of the universe is known. This approach will not work for extremely distant galaxies, however, because they are too faint for efficient spectroscopic studies to be made. In these cases a different approach is used. Light leaving the galaxy that lies in the far-ultraviolet portion of the spectrum is heavily absorbed by gas within the galaxy and in intergalactic space. This makes the galaxy very dim in the far-ultraviolet. If the galaxy is very distant, however, the entire spectrum will

be red-shifted and the dim portion of the far-ultraviolet spectrum will be shifted to the near-ultraviolet. Consequently, very distant galaxies will disappear from view when imaged through a filter that passes only near-ultraviolet light to the camera. The procedure is to take two pictures of the sky, one with and one without the filter. Those galaxies that disappear in the filtered image are very distant. While this technique does not give precise distances, it can quickly identify the most distant galaxies.

This ultraviolet-filter technique was used by Charles C. Steidel and colleagues to determine when galaxies first appeared in the early universe. Using the 10-m Keck telescope, they detected galaxies at very great distances, which indicates that galax-

255

R. Sahai and J. Trauger (JPL), WFPC2 Science Team, NASA

The Egg Nebula, imaged by the Hubble Space Telescope, is an expanding cloud of gas and dust around a hot central star that was once a red giant. A dense cocoon of dust (the dark band extending diagonally across the center) hides the star.

ies were commonly found in the universe only two billion to three billion years after the big bang. This is much earlier than predicted by some theoretical models of galaxy formation.

Although captured indistinctly, even more distant galaxies may have been imaged by the HST. Kenneth M. Lanzetta, Amos Yahil, and Alberto Fernandez-Soto used the ultraviolet-filter technique to detect objects that existed a few hundred million years after the big bang. Unfortunately, they are so distant they appear only as fuzzy specks in the HST images. They are believed to be galaxies or forming galaxies.

A better view of what may be forming galaxies was obtained with the HST by Sebastian M. Pascarelle and colleagues. In a galaxy cluster that dates back to two billion to three billion years after the big bang, they found many amorphous objects that are less than a tenth the size of a galaxy such as the Milky Way. They lie in a region only two million light-years across. The image implies that some of the objects are merging. The researchers suggested that they might be seeing the birth of a galaxy from smaller components.

The extreme heat and pressure of the big bang produced the first atomic elements: hydrogen, helium, and lithium. Other,

more massive elements were not produced in the big bang because the expansion of the universe caused the temperature and density of the universe to decline too quickly. The only place where the heavier elements could be made is within stars. Some of these stars exploded as supernovas, spreading the elements through the cosmos.

Astronomers have sought to determine when these heavy elements first appeared. Kouji Ohta, Alain Omont, and colleagues studied the light from a very distant quasar at submillimeter wavelengths. A quasar is the extremely bright nucleus of a galaxy that probably contains a massive black hole. Quasars can be seen at much greater distances than ordinary galaxies. The spectrum of the quasar they studied is highly red-shifted, which indicates that it is very distant and that it existed at a time less than two billion years after the big bang. The spectrum also shows the telltale signature of carbon monoxide from a cloud in the quasar's host galaxy. Thus, carbon and oxygen atoms existed at that time, and, therefore, so did stars and supernovas.

This work was confirmed by Piero Madau and collaborators. They found that the rate of star formation was very high in the early universe and has declined ever since. They based their findings on the

colors of distant galaxies imaged by the HST. In any collection of stars, the most massive are the hottest. These brilliant stars are blue in color, and when seen from a distance, their light dominates that of their lesser companions. Massive stars also evolve and die faster. Therefore, a galaxy with active star formation will appear blue in color.

The research team studied the colors (after correcting for the red shift) of galaxies at various distances. They sampled a group of 15 galaxies and another group of 70 that existed when the universe was 8–10% and 10–20% of its current age, respectively. The results indicate that star formation in the universe peaked at a rate 10 times that of today when the universe was less than two billion years old. The rate has declined steadily ever since.

These research projects paint a picture of a dynamic young universe that already contained well-formed galaxies producing stars at a very high rate, some of which quickly evolved, exploding and ejecting heavy elements into the galaxies. Future large ground-based telescopes and the next-generation space telescope should push this frontier even farther back into time and provide an even clearer picture of how the universe evolved.

—Ronald H. Kaitchuck

CHEMISTRY

New calorie-free fat substitutes, better medications for treating AIDS and stroke, and improved technology for producing clean-burning fuels were among the past year's advances in chemistry. Researchers determined the structure of an enzyme that may play a role in global temperature regulation, reported new advances in fullerene chemistry, and announced a new chemical technique for detecting clandestine underground nuclear tests. They also made greater use of the Internet as a research tool and developed new insights into some of chemistry's most fundamental processes.

INORGANIC CHEMISTRY

Inorganic chemistry captured worldwide public attention after the 1996 Nobel Prize for Chemistry was awarded to Richard E. Smalley and Robert F. Curl, Jr., of Rice University, Houston, Texas, and Sir Harold Kroto of the University of Sussex, Brighton, Eng., for research on fullerenes (*see* Scientists of the Year). The discovery of this new family of carbon molecules, whose most familiar member is the 60-carbon-atom, soccer-ball-patterned buckminsterfullerene (C_{60}), opened up a new branch of inorganic chemistry. Many new discoveries about these spherical, cagelike molecules also were made. The impact of instrumentation became apparent as advances in X-ray crystallography and computer speed allowed researchers to determine the three-dimensional structures of large biological molecules faster than ever before possible. One major consequence was the determination of the structure of dimethyl sulfoxide reductase, a molybdenum-containing enzyme with possibly global environmental implications. The en-

zyme produces dimethyl sulfide, a compound that may play a pivotal role in cloud formation over the oceans and, thus, regulation of Earth's temperature. In addition, researchers at the Institute for Heavy Ion Research (GSI), Darmstadt, Ger., announced discovery of a new chemical element, element 112, the heaviest yet produced in the laboratory (*see* Physics: *Nuclear Physics*).

Fullerene chemistry

Important new advances occurred in the preparation of fullerenes having metal atoms trapped inside the hollow fullerene cage or complexed to the outside face. In addition, researchers reported practical applications for compounds containing fullerenes.

The preparation of endohedral metallofullerenes, *i.e.,* fullerenes containing trapped metal atoms, was an especially active area of research. The interior cavity of C_{60}, for instance, is large enough to contain an atom of any element in the periodic table. Caged fullerene compounds hold great promise as new superconductors and materials with a host of other exotic properties. The most frequently employed techniques for preparing endohedral metallofullerenes, however, produce a mixture of endohedral metallofullerenes and empty carbon cages. Therefore, a major challenge has been to develop methods to isolate the desired compounds in high purity.

A research team led by Yoshihiro Kubozono of Okayama (Japan) University reported development of a procedure for purifying C_{60} containing one metal atom (symbolized as $M@C_{60}$, in which M is an atom of yttrium, barium, lanthanum, cerium, praseodymium, neodymium, or gad-

olinium). After extensive screening of various solvents, Kubozono found that aniline selectively dissolved $M@C_{60}$ and extracted it from a mixture of many different fullerenes. This purification technique should make large quantities of $M@C_{60}$ available, which would allow studies of chemical and physical properties.

Several research groups announced isolation and spectroscopic study of new endohedral metallofullerenes in milligram quantities. (A milligram is about 35 millionths of an ounce.) Junqi Ding and Shihe Yang of the Hong Kong University of Science and Technology reported the isolation and properties of C_{80} containing two cerium atoms trapped inside the 80-carbon-atom cage ($Ce_2@C_{80}$). The compound, which was about 99% pure, was obtained with preparative high-performance liquid chromatography (HPLC) and identified by mass spectrometry. In another report Hisanori Shinohara and associates of Nagoya (Japan) University synthesized and purified C_{84} containing two scandium atoms ($Sc_2@C_{84}$). Three structural isomers (differing molecular structures) of $Sc_2@C_{84}$ out of a possible 24 were isolated by HPLC, and a carbon-13 nuclear magnetic resonance spectrum was obtained for one of the isomers, which allowed researchers to assign a unique structure. The work should help explain how the carbon cage grows around the two metal atoms.

Chemists studying traditional organometallic compounds long have known that five-membered and six-membered aromatic compounds serve as excellent ligands (attached atoms or molecules) for certain transition metals and form very stable complexes with them. Because fullerenes contain both five- and six-membered rings, researchers also have tried to prepare transition-metal complexes of fullerenes. The goal has been the synthesis of compounds in which metal atoms bond to all the carbon atoms in a five-membered or six-membered ring of the fullerene. During the year fullerene chemists reported finally making such compounds.

Hsiu-Fu Hsu and John R. Shapley of the University of Illinois at Champaign-Urbana reported the synthesis and characterization of the first hexahapto metal complex of C_{60}, a complex in which metal atoms are bonded to six carbon atoms at once. Previous attempts to form hexahapto complexes had been thwarted by the fact that the C_{60} cage is curved. This bending orients orbitals (regions around an atom's nucleus in which electrons available for bonding are found) of the atoms of the six-membered rings away from the direction required for their bonding to a single metal atom. Hsu and Shapley solved the problem by the use of a small cluster of ruthenium atoms in which three of the atoms are situated such that they can bond simultaneously to all six carbons of a six-membered ring of C_{60}. Another team led by Masaya Sawamura and Eiichi Nakamura of the University of Tokyo reported the first metal pentahapto fullerene complex, in which a thallium atom is bonded simultaneously to five carbon atoms of a five-membered ring of the fullerene. The synthesis suggested that fullerenes can act as pentahapto ligands for many other metal atoms as well.

Deeper understanding of the properties of fullerenes led to applications in several different areas of science. R.C. Haddon of AT&T Bell Laboratories, Murray Hill, N.J., reported making thin-film transistors

based on C_{70}. An Italian research team headed by Maurizio Prato of the University of Trieste produced fullerinoproline, a derivative of the amino acid proline appended to a C_{60} cage. Synthesis of fullerinoproline opened the way for the introduction of fullerenes into biological molecules such as peptides and proteins. Naotoshi Nakashima and co-workers at Nagasaki (Japan) University reported preparation of C_{60} attached to a lipid fragment. This molecule self-assembled into well-organized membrane films with a repeating bilayer element, the same basic structure formed by the lipid molecules that constitute biological membranes. Ultraviolet absorption spectra of the films demonstrated an electronic interaction between the C_{60} groups, which allows the properties of the C_{60} to be modified in a predictable way. Shufang Niu and David Mauzeral of Rockefeller University, New York City, embedded fullerenes in lipid bilayers and studied the ability of the bilayers to transport electric charges across the membranes. Fullerenes are extremely efficient at promoting charge transfer, and aggregates of fullerenes may be responsible for the researchers' observation of the conduction of electrons across the fullerene-containing lipid bilayers. This research may lead to improved solar-energy conversion devices.

Bioinorganic chemistry

The familiar smell of air near the ocean results mainly from the compound dimethyl sulfide (DMS) produced by bacteria from dimethyl sulfoxide (DMSO) present in seawater. DMSO is soluble in water and makes its way into seawater as a product of various metabolic processes of plank-

tonic algae involving sulfur-containing organic molecules. By contrast, DMS has a low solubility in seawater, is volatile, and readily escapes to the atmosphere. Seabirds apparently can smell increased local concentrations of DMS over the ocean and use them as indicators of high productivity to find rich feeding areas in the oceans. More important for the global environment, however, oxidation products of DMS formed in the atmosphere may serve as nucleation sites for clouds. Hence, the biochemical reactions in the ocean involving DMSO and DMS may play a fundamental role in controlling the climate on Earth through cloud formation.

Bacteria convert DMSO to DMS in a process involving the enzyme DMSO reductase. The catalytically active site of DMSO reductase contains molybdenum (Mo), the only transition metal in the second row of the periodic table known to be used in biological processes. In view of the environmental importance of DMS, scientists wish to understand how the active site of DMSO reductase converts DMSO to DMS.

In a spectacular achievement a research team led by Douglas C. Rees of the California Institute of Technology determined the X-ray crystal structure of DMSO reductase in both its oxidized and reduced forms (see 1). In the active site of the enzyme, two molybdopterin ligands are attached to a molybdenum atom by sulfur atoms. An oxygen atom (O) originating from the amino acid serine is coordinated to the molybdenum. In the oxidized enzyme an oxo (oxygen atom) ligand completes the coordination sphere. In the reduced form the oxo ligand is absent and the molybdopterin's sulfur atoms are ar-

oxidized form

molybdopterin

$2e^-$, $2H^+$
(2 electrons,
2 hydrogen ions)

DMS

H_2O

DMSO

Mo

O

serine

reduced form

1 DMSO reductase active-site reaction

rayed slightly differently than in the oxidized form.

The results of the structural determinations of the two forms of the enzyme give significant insight into the way in which DMSO reductase catalyzes the conversion of DMSO to DMS. DMSO can attach to the reduced form of DMSO reductase, giving a coordinated DMSO ligand. The oxygen atom of DMSO is then abstracted from the sulfur atom by the molybdenum atom, affording DMS and the oxidized form of DMSO reductase. The oxidized DMSO reductase is returned to the reduced form by the receipt of two electrons from a electron donor, a cytochrome enzyme, and the elimination of the oxo ligand as a water molecule (H_2O). The structural results on DMSO reductase also provide information about the way related molybdenum-containing enzymes may function and, more generally, about the way nature uses metal centers and protein ligation to construct active sites of enzymes to carry out reactions that are required for various biological processes.

New molecules

Despite decades of effort, scientists have managed to identify and characterize relatively few compounds containing oxygen and either chlorine or bromine. During the past year Helge Willner and Hinrich Grothe of the University of Hannover, Ger., reported that thermal decomposition of Cl_2O_6 or Cl_2O_7 gives ClO_4, a previously unknown chlorine oxide. The molecular structure has three short chlorine-oxygen bonds and one long bond. There are even fewer well-characterized examples of bromine oxides, which are less stable than chlorine oxides. Holger Muller and associ-

ates at the Jet Propulsion Laboratory, Pasadena, Calif., prepared Br_2O and BrO_2 and characterized the molecules by millimeter and submillimeter spectroscopy. These bromine oxides are of interest because they may play a role in the breakdown of stratospheric ozone. An oxygen-containing compound, diisocyanate (OCNNCO), was prepared for the first time by the research group of Günther Maier at the University of Giessen, Ger. The synthetic route involved photolysis (breakdown by light energy) of azidoformyl isocyanate (NNNCONCO). Surprisingly, diisocyanate is resistant to formation of the isocyanate radical ($\cdot$NCO) at low temperature (80 K, $-316°$ F) and has an appreciable lifetime in a stream of dilute argon gas at room temperature.

George Olah of the University of Southern California reported indications that the heptacoordinate carbonium ion CH_7^{3+} is thermodynamically stable and may exist under certain conditions. Positively charged ions of carbon are important reactive intermediates and, because of their very high reactivity, are extremely difficult to study.

A research team led by Mitsuo Kira of Tohoku University, Sendai, Japan, made the first cyclic compound of silicon con-

taining a silicon-silicon double bond. The compound, a tetrasilylcyclobutene and an analog of cyclobutene, is important because silicon-silicon double bonds are usually highly reactive; the incorporation of such double bonds in cyclic structures would have been expected to lead to even higher reactivity and make the compound too unstable to isolate.

Controversy raged over the past several years regarding the structure of silylium ions, which are cationic (positively charged) tricoordinate silicon compounds. Although chemists generally agreed that a silylium ion must be three coordinate and planar at silicon, (i.e., it must have the silicon atom and the three attached groups lying in a plane), no known silylium ion actually fits this rigorous definition. Rather, they all show coordination to the counterion (the oppositely charged ion required to balance the charge on the silylium ion) or a solvent molecule, which leads to a four-coordinate silicon atom, and they are not planar at silicon. A team led by Christopher Reed of the University of Southern California reported the synthesis and characterization of silylium ions in which the counterions were hexahalocarboranes. The chemists reasoned that hexahalocarboranes, which are among the least coordinating anions (negatively charged ions) imaginable, might allow a planar, three-coordinate silylium ion to exist. Nevertheless, they found that even the most "ionlike" silylium species that they made still existed with a halogen atom of the

dissolve in carbon tetrachloride, evaporate

"wheels" 1–50 micrometers in diameter

hexahalocarborane coordinated to the silicon, at least in the solid state. Their results suggested that there may be no such thing as a "non-coordinating" anion and that the structures of cationic species should be carefully established to avoid incorrect assignments.

Chemistry textbooks generally describe gold atoms as being roughly equal in size to silver atoms. Recent theoretical work, however, had predicted that gold should be smaller than silver. Experimental verification of that prediction came from Hubert Schmidbaur of the Technical University of Munich, Ger. He reported X-ray crystal structures of a pair of silver(I) and gold(I) complexes that contain the same ligands and counterions and crystallize in the same lattice. These conditions allowed direct comparison of the relative sizes of silver and gold. The radius of silver(I) was 1.33 Å (one angstrom is a ten-billionth of a meter), while that of gold(I) was 1.25 Å. Thus, gold is slightly smaller than silver in the compounds examined.

Research in fullerene chemistry sparked parallel interest in other possible forms of elemental carbon. One such form involves carbon that forms linear chains of indefinite length, as opposed to the cyclic carbon arrays found in fullerenes. John Gladysz and co-workers at the University of Utah reported synthesis of a linear chain of 20 carbon atoms (C_{20}) capped at both ends with organometallic rhenium-containing groups to stabilize the otherwise highly reactive species. This rhenium complex contained the longest known carbon chain having metal atoms at each end.

Inorganic chemists have long believed that halocarbon and alkane solvents used in synthetic work do not coordinate to any metal atoms contained in the reactant molecules but serve only to dissolve the reactants. New findings, however, suggested that even those solvent molecules least inclined to share electrons can coordinate to metal atoms under proper conditions. Gregory Kubas and co-workers of Los Alamos (N.M.) National Laboratory reported a series of stable and isolable platinum complexes having chlorocarbon, bromocarbon, and iodocarbon ligands. Since halocarbons are frequently used as solvents in inorganic synthesis, these solvents should be viewed as potential ligands that might lead to stable complexes or unusual reactive intermediates.

Roeland Nolte and colleagues at the Catholic University of Nijmegen, Neth., reported preparation of micrometer-sized "wheels" composed of connected molecules of a palladium-porphyrin complex (see 2). (A micrometer is a millionth of a meter, or about 40 millionths of an inch.) They obtained wheels with diameters of 1–50 micrometers by evaporating a carbon tetrachloride solution of the complex. Higher evaporation temperatures yielded larger wheels. Experiments suggested that the wheels formed around tiny gas bubbles that occurred in the solution; the individual molecules connected to each other by means of electronic stacking interactions between the aromatic rings of adjacent molecules, using the bubble as a template. It was proposed that the porphyrin wheels might be made to act as small synchrotron-like devices to store energy as circulating electrons or in some other form.

—Charles H. Winter

ORGANIC CHEMISTRY

The search for new ways of preventing, diagnosing, and treating diseases and other human afflictions often drives scientific research. Scientists also have a desire to understand better the fundamental nature of their subject. Both factors contributed to new advances in organic chemistry during the past year. In addition, the World Wide Web, the leading information retrieval service of the Internet, greatly improved science's ability to investigate and rapidly disseminate these developments.

1   staurosporine

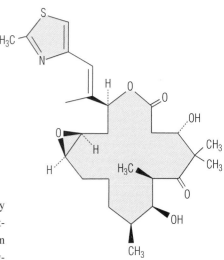

2   epothilone

Chemistry on the Internet

Although Web sites dedicated to organic chemistry have been available on the Internet for some time, their number and quality increased dramatically in the past year. These sites made it easier for scientists to understand the properties of organic molecules and the principles of organic chemistry and to communicate with other scientists around the world.

The use of Virtual Reality Modeling Language continued to expand, facilitating the viewing of molecular structures on the Internet. Peter Murray-Rust of the University of Nottingham, Eng., was developing Chemical Markup Language (CML) that will allow the incorporation of more detailed chemical symbols and concepts in Web sites than is currently possible. CML is a customized version of the standard HyperText Markup Language that is used to construct Web pages. In addition to the ongoing development of technical resources, growing numbers of new home pages established by university chemistry departments and individual scientists provided information about research, courses and curricula, and services that promote communication in organic chemistry. Several scientific journals that specialize in organic chemistry were viewable on-line. Henry S. Rzepa of Imperial College, London, organized an on-line conference for the International Society of Heterocyclic Chemists, in which the papers were posted on a Web site and discussion was aided by the use of a special electronic mail network. That conference and the expansion of information on the Internet clearly signaled a new and important way for chemists to communicate.

Chemotherapeutic advances

A number of recent advances in organic chemistry resulted from attempts to find better drugs for the treatment of AIDS, stroke, or bacterial infections. After many years of development, several new drugs called protease inhibitors became available in the U.S. for general use in treating AIDS. The drugs included ritonavir, sold under the brand name Norvir by Abbott Laboratories, Abbott Park, Ill.; indinavir sulfate, sold as Crixivan by Merck, West Point, Pa.; and saquinavir, sold as Invirase by Hoffmann-La Roche, Nutley, N.J. The medications interfere with action of HIV protease, a viral enzyme critical for reproduction of the human immunodeficiency virus, which causes AIDS. When used in combination with existing drugs such as AZT (zidovudine), the new compounds appeared highly effective in controlling HIV infection. They created genuine optimism that AIDS may become a treatable disease.

AZT works by blocking the action of another HIV enzyme, reverse transcriptase. A new and more effective reverse transcriptase inhibitor, nevirapine, or Viramune, produced by Boehringer Ingelheim Pharmaceuticals, Ridgefield, Conn., also went into use. In addition, development continued on the next generation of HIV-AIDS medications. Termed integrase inhibitors, the drugs disrupt yet another stage in HIV's reproduction cycle. New insights into the way that HIV invades human cells were gained by organic chemists, who contributed to the identification of cell-surface receptors that apparently are critical for HIV's infection of healthy cells. The accomplishment opened a new area of research for developing drugs to treat AIDS.

Stroke is the third leading cause of death in the U.S., killing about 150,000 people annually. Many potential chemotherapeutic drugs previously under development for the treatment of stroke were plagued by side effects, and research on those compounds was abandoned. During the year, work proceeded on a new series of drugs that inhibit the stroke-associated release of a damaging flow of calcium ions into nerve cells. At least three new compounds under investigation block this release by targeting receptors on the cell surface that form channels for transporting ions into and out of the cell. Compounds from Zeneca Pharmaceuticals, Wilmington, Del., and from Glaxo Wellcome, Research Triangle Park, N.C., function as antagonists (blockers) for the receptor N-methyl-D-aspartate, while another from Lilly Research Laboratories, Indianapolis, Ind., is an antagonist for the receptor α-amino-3-hydroxy-5-methyl-4-isoxazole propionic acid.

Synthesis of complex molecules

The synthesis of molecules with complex structures remained an important endeavor among organic chemists, and two major

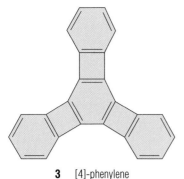

3 [4]-phenylene   **4** trisbicyclo[2.1.1]hexabenzene

achievements attracted wide attention. One molecule, staurosporine (*see* 1 on p. 261), was synthesized by John Wood of Yale University. First isolated from the bacterium *Streptomyces staurosporeus,* the compound has potential in inhibiting the protein-kinase-C family of enzymes at extremely tiny concentrations and may lead to a new treatment for cancer. The other molecule, epothilone (*see* 2 on p. 261), isolated from the bacterium *Sorangium cellulosum,* is a compound with the same mechanism of action as the important anticancer drug taxol, but it has a simpler structure and thus is easier to make. It was synthesized independently by Samuel Danishefsky of Columbia University, New York City, and K.C. Nicolaou of the Scripps Research Institute, La Jolla, Calif.

New catalysts

Developing new chemical reactions remained an important undertaking of organic chemistry, and new reagents that catalyze, or promote, chemical transformations were of particular interest. Several new catalysts and catalytic processes were reported during the year. K. Barry Sharpless of the Scripps Research Institute developed a process termed catalytic asymmetric aminohydroxylation that converts alkenes to chiral, nonracemic amino-alcohols using an dihydroquinine-phthalazine catalyst containing the transition metal osmium. (A chiral molecule is not superimposable on its mirror-image isomer; the two molecules differ as left- and right-handed gloves and are called enantiomers. A nonracemic product mixture contains a higher percentage of one enantiomer than the other, in contrast to racemic, or 50-50, mixtures of enantiomers.) Elias J. Corey of

Harvard University reported an enantiopure (comprising only one enantiomer) oxazoborinane catalyst for the Diels-Alder reaction (a highly useful method of preparing cyclic organic compounds) that targets normally unreactive alkenes and dienes. A new route to chiral epoxides was reported by Varinder K. Aggarwal and co-workers of the University of Sheffield, Eng. It calls for the reaction of an aldehyde with a catalyst derived from a chiral sulfur ylide generated in the presence of copper acetylacetonate.

Eric N. Jacobsen of Harvard reported a process that converts racemic epoxides to enantiopure 1,2-amino-alcohols using trimethylsilyl azide and a salen-chromium(III) catalyst. Victor Snieckus of the University of Waterloo, Ont., showed that chiral ferrocene derivatives are easily prepared and can serve as useful catalysts in several reactions. Chemists at Merck Research Laboratories, Rahway, N.J., invented an inexpensive method for the resolution (separation of enantiomers from a mixture) of 1,1'-bi-2-naphthol (BINOL), which, in enantiopure form, is an important component of several catalytic systems. Lucette Duhamel of the University of Rouen, Mont-Saint-Aignan, France, used potassium N-methylephedrinate in methanol as a catalytic system to abstract protons (hydrogen ions) enantioselectively in a dehydrobromination reaction. The method produces stereochemically pure alkenes.

New methods also were developed to recycle expensive chiral catalysts. For example, Kim D. Janda of the Scripps Research Institute linked a costly alkaloid derived from cinchona bark to a water-soluble polymer and recovered it after its

use as a catalyst in a Sharpless asymmetric dihydroxylation reaction.

Important industrial applications of organic chemistry also were made. They included a technique reported by John F. Knifton of Huntsman Corp., Salt Lake City, Utah, that uses a cobalt-octacarbonyl catalyst to convert syngas, which consists of carbon monoxide and hydrogen, to primary aliphatic amines. Chemists at E.I. du Pont de Nemours & Co., Wilmington, Del., developed a new polymer catalyst that, in the presence of palladium or nickel additives, yields a new, useful form of an amorphous, highly branched polyethylene.

Combinatorial chemistry

Combinatorial chemistry allows chemists to produce small amounts of enormous numbers of molecules with similar structures rapidly and efficiently. These chemical "libraries" of molecular variants can then be screened for desirable properties. Previously chemists had to synthesize each compound individually. Combinatorial techniques were becoming increasingly important in several areas of organic chemistry. For instance, there was new emphasis on the preparation of small molecules that have molecular masses (molecular weights) of less than 500 daltons. Pharmaceutical companies were embracing this new technology for screening drugs, developing new drug leads, and exploiting current leads. In late 1996 a new orally active central-nervous-system agent produced by Eli Lilly & Co., Indianapolis, was in clinical trials, possibly the first drug prepared by means of combinatorial chemistry to reach that level of development.

Recent research also extended combinatorial methodology into other areas of

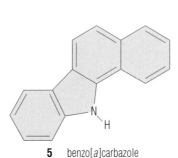

5 benzo[*a*]carbazole   **6** benzo[*c*]carbazole

chemistry. Daniel Kahne of Princeton University was the first to prepare carbohydrate monomers (simple chemical units that constitute the repeating structure of large polymer molecules) using combinatorial techniques. Combinatorial molecular recognition, an exciting new technique in combinatorial chemistry, was being used for such purposes as measuring the binding properties of compounds to cellular receptors, studying protein receptors, and identifying industrial catalysts. In protein chemistry the technique may become a fundamental tool for understanding protein binding and function.

Basic principles

New discoveries about such concepts as aromaticity and such processes as the Diels-Alder reaction promised to lead to a better understanding of the fundamental nature of organic chemistry. The six-carbon cyclic molecule benzene, although often portrayed as a ring of alternating single and double bonds, possesses six carbon-carbon bonds of equal length that have properties intermediate between those of double and single bonds. The delocalization of the electrons that form the hybrid bonds in benzene, a characteristic known as aromaticity, results in increased chemical stability of the molecule. Nevertheless, two reports during the year showed that the delocalized bonds of a benzene ring effectively become localized in single and double bonds, generating the difficult-to-form cyclohexatriene unit, when the ring is incorporated in certain compounds. One report discussed the preparation of [4]-phenylene (*see* 3) by K. Peter C. Vollhardt of the University of California, Berkeley. The other described trisbicyclo[2.1.1]hexa-

benzene (*see* 4), prepared by Jay S. Siegel of the University of California, San Diego. The observation was forcing scientists to reexamine the underlying principles of aromaticity, in which *p*-orbital electrons make the major contribution, with particular attention on the role of *s*-orbital electrons.

Organic chemists long have regarded the Diels-Alder reaction as a concerted process; *i.e.,* one in which bond-making and bond-breaking processes occur together in the reaction, without discrete stages and recognizable reaction intermediates. Ahmed H. Zewail of the California Institute of Technology, Pasadena, however, detected a diradicaloid intermediate in the retro Diels-Alder reaction of norbornene by means of ultrafast laser techniques and femtosecond-resolved mass spectrometry (techniques capable of detecting and identifying reaction intermediates that exist less than a billionth of a second). The work may lead to a reexamination of the mechanism for one of the most important reactions used in organic chemistry.

Peripheral areas

New discoveries in organic chemistry often find practical uses in unrelated fields of science. One such discovery reported during the year had important implications for the petroleum industry. Stephen R. Larter, a geologist at the University of Newcastle upon Tyne, Eng., showed that the ratio of two trace components of petroleum, benzo[*a*]carbazole (*see* 5) to the total concentration of that compound plus benzo[*c*]carbazole (*see* 6), can be used to determine the distance that oil in an underground reservoir has traveled from its orig-

inal source. This discovery may have applications in the location of new oil resources and the improved exploitation of existing resources.

—Michael B. Smith

PHYSICAL CHEMISTRY

In the past year physical chemists explored ways to cool water below the freezing point and found an unusual layer of water molecules on the surface of ordinary ice that may help explain how ice skates work. An international team of theorists and experimentalists joined forces to unravel the fine details of a chemical reaction similar to those involved in stratospheric ozone depletion. A long debate over the shape of the charged benzene molecule was settled. Electronic devices having components made of individual molecules moved a step closer to reality when chemists measured the conductivity of a single "molecular wire," found better ways to move a single molecule across a surface, and constructed an atomic-scale abacus.

Skating on thin ice

Water normally freezes at 0° C (32° F), but it can be supercooled—that is, cooled to lower temperatures while still remaining liquid. Supercooling requires the exclusion of foreign particles that initiate the formation of ice crystals and must be carried out very quickly. Experiments show that water can be cooled as low as −50° C (−58° F) without freezing. It may be that at such low temperatures water is so viscous that it cannot freeze in the time allowed in these very fast experiments. New calculations by Hideki Tanaka of Kyoto (Japan) University suggested that water can remain liquid even at −80° C (−112° F).

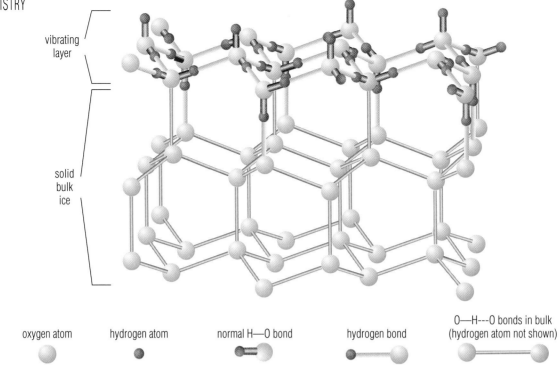

vibrating layer

solid bulk ice

oxygen atom   hydrogen atom   normal H—O bond   hydrogen bond   O—H---O bonds in bulk (hydrogen atom not shown)

Figure 1: A rapidly vibrating outermost layer of water molecules appears to exist at the surface of ice on top of more rigid layers. The surface layer may be in some intermediate state between a solid and a liquid, or it may undergo a process of continual removal and redeposit.

Many ice skaters believe that the slipperiness of ice results from a thin film of water that forms under pressure of the skate blade. A report by Michel A. Van Hove and Gabor A. Somorjai of the Lawrence Berkeley National Laboratory, Berkeley, Calif., poured cold water on this idea. Instead, they suggested that ice maintains a layer of liquid water on its surface at normal pressure and at temperatures well below the normal freezing point. Evidence came from experiments in which the researchers formed a layer of ice on a piece of platinum at −180° C (−292° F) and observed how it reflected electrons. They expected to see signals from the top three layers of water molecules in the ice structure. Surprisingly, some of the molecules were invisible to the technique, probably because they were vibrating so much that their signatures were blurred out.

Researchers offered several possible explanations for the finding. The surface layer may be neither solid like ordinary bulk ice nor liquid like water; rather, it may be in some intermediate state. Molecules in this layer appear to vibrate much more strongly than those in layers below

while staying bound to them (*see* Figure 1). It is also possible that rather than acting like a viscous liquid, the ice surface is constantly being removed and redeposited. Whichever view is correct, the surface of ice is a busy place with molecules in movement, a characteristic that may prove important in understanding reactions on ice crystals in the atmosphere that lead to depletion of the protective ozone layer.

Reaction insights

Accurate understanding of the fundamental process occurring in chemical reactions lies at the heart of physical chemistry. Solving the quantum mechanical equations for even the simplest of reactions, however, has been a major task. An international team of researchers combined quantum mechanical calculations with experiments to obtain new details about a reaction that forms hydrochloric acid:

$$H_2 + Cl \rightarrow HCl + H.$$

It is a prototype reaction for understanding the kinetics of important stratospheric-chemistry reactions such as those involved in ozone depletion. The experiments were conducted in Italy by Piergiorgio Casavec-

chia of the University of Perugia and involved collaborators from the Complutensian University of Madrid, the University of Minnesota at Minneapolis, and NASA's Ames Research Center, Moffett Field, Calif. Researchers crossed beams of chlorine atoms and hydrogen molecules at various energies and observed the amount of products formed. Groups of theorists headed by David Schwenke at Ames and Donald Truhlar in Minneapolis performed quantum calculations, which were backed up by semiclassical calculations performed by F. Javier Aoiz and colleagues in Spain.

The agreement between theory and experiment proved to be excellent, allowing researchers to explore fine details of the reaction process. One such detail emerging from the calculations was that chemical complexes can form and exist for very short times. Despite their brevity, however, such complexes can make themselves felt as oscillations in the reaction rate. Normally such subtle effects would be masked by the averaging that is involved in traditional kinetics experiments, but these sophisticated experiments confirmed their existence.

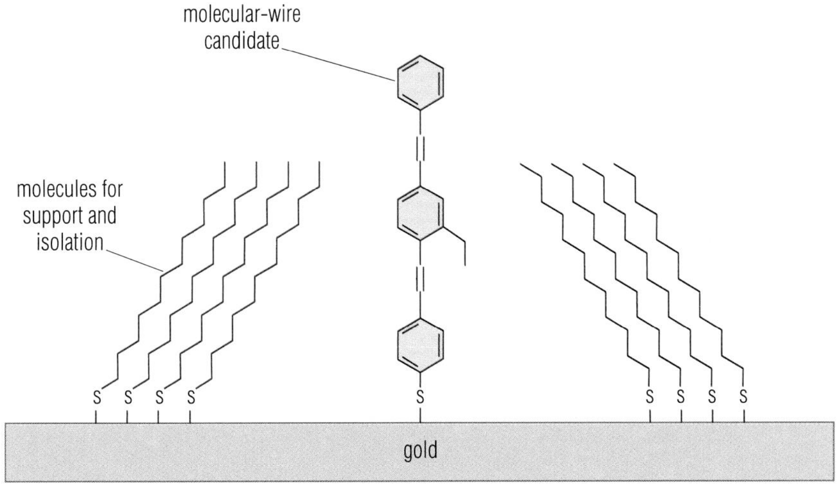

Figure 2: A candidate molecular-wire molecule is attached at one end to a piece of gold and surrounded by hydrocarbon molecules intended to provide support and isolation.

Imperfect symmetry in charged benzene

Benzene (C_6H_6) is the simplest aromatic hydrocarbon—a hexagonal ring of carbon and hydrogen atoms with its bonding electrons spread above and below the ring in doughnutlike configurations. Although neutral benzene itself has been extensively studied, the shape of the ion formed by removing one electron from the molecule ($C_6H_6^+$) has been debated for years. New insights were reported by R. Lindner and K. Müller-Dethlefs of the Institute for Physical and Theoretical Chemistry, Technical University of Munich, Ger., and E. Wedum, K. Haber, and E.R. Grant of Purdue University, West Lafayette, Ind. They made careful measurements of the way an electron is removed by laser light from benzene in a dilute pulsed beam of the molecules in argon gas. By assessing how the molecule rotates and vibrates, the researchers concluded that in its most stable (lowest-energy) form, the ion has the shape of an elongated hexagon and thus has less symmetry than neutral benzene. A second form, that of a compressed hexagon, has almost the same energy as the first. The difference in energy of the two forms is so small that on average the shape of $C_6H_6^+$ is very close to a perfect hexagon.

Molecular electronics

The quest for ever-faster computers has been rapidly approaching a roadblock as traditional methods for making semiconductor devices and other chip components reach their size limits. Conventional lithographic techniques will have difficulty in producing electronic devices much smaller

than a tenth of a micrometer. (A micrometer is a millionth of a meter, or about 40 millionths of an inch.) The production of smaller microelectronic devices and faster processors thus may require totally different approaches that employ nanotechnology—the use of tools that are in the nanometer (billionth of a meter) size range. The ultimate goal of nanotechnology in electronics manufacture is to reduce the size of tools and the electronic devices

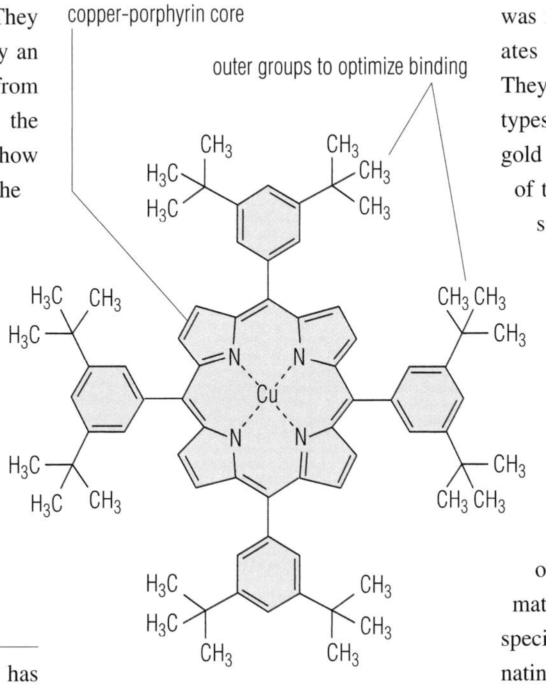

Figure 3: Attachment of bulky outer groups to a copper-porphyrin core provided chemists with a molecule optimized for manipulation by the tip of a scanning tunneling microscope on a copper surface at room temperature.

made with them to the size of single molecules.

Molecular-sized electronic devices will need molecular-sized wires for interconnections. Long molecules that contain benzene rings and double bonds have been popular candidates for such molecular wires because they are expected to have good electrical conductivity. A major problem, however, has been how to measure the conductivity of a single molecule. An important step toward molecular wires was reported by David Allara and associates of Pennsylvania State University. They constructed a film containing two types of molecules attached to a piece of gold by means of gold-sulfur bonds. Most of the molecules were of the first type—simple hydrocarbon chains bonded to the gold surface with sulfur atoms. They supported and isolated a few molecules of the second type—a candidate molecular-wire molecule synthesized by James M. Tour of the University of South Carolina at Columbia (see Figure 2). Paul S. Weiss and co-workers of Penn State then imaged just one of the candidate molecules and estimated its electrical conductivity, using a specially built microwave-frequency, alternating-current scanning tunneling microscope (STM). The back-and-forth transfer of charge through the molecule allowed its conductivity to be assessed. Although the conductivity estimate was encouragingly high, many technical challenges remained. They included finding ways of anchoring such molecules between two electrodes, which themselves must be extremely small.

Researchers at the IBM Zürich (Switz.) Research Laboratory and the National Center for Scientific Research, Toulouse, France, reported advances toward making practical nanofabrication a reality. They showed that a specific type of molecule can be moved controllably across a copper surface, using the probe tip of an STM at room temperature without breaking any bonds in the molecule. Previously, such molecular manipulation could be done only at very low temperatures. The molecule (*see* Figure 3 on p. 265) was carefully chosen so that the bulky outer groups of atoms attached to the porphyrin core optimized the binding of the molecule to the copper surface. If the molecule were bound too strongly, the STM tip would not move it easily across the surface, but if it were bound too loosely, it would not stay put once moved. At the same time, the molecule was sufficiently flexible to allow it to deform and then move in a "stick-slip" fashion when pushed by the STM tip.

The same IBM group also showed that spherical, all-carbon C_{60}, or buckminsterfullerene, molecules could be arranged in rows on a copper surface and individually pushed about in a repeatable manner. They likened this to a molecular abacus, albeit one that was very cumbersome and slow to use.

—Philip R. Watson

APPLIED CHEMISTRY

A variety of practical applications emerged from research in chemistry during the past year. They included a simple, inexpensive method for decomposing environmentally deleterious chlorofluorocarbons (CFCs), calorie-free fat substitutes, and a new, less-expensive material for rechargeable lithium batteries. The U.S. Food and Drug Administration (FDA) approved the controversial fat substitute olestra, while chemistry pointed the way toward new sources of clean-burning hydrogen fuel, more energy-efficient windows, and better technology for detecting clandestine underground nuclear weapons tests.

CFC destroyer

Most countries in the world banned the production of CFCs as of Jan. 1, 1996, as part of an international effort to limit the destruction of stratospheric ozone. Nevertheless, large amounts of CFCs remained in stockpiles. The compounds, once used in refrigeration systems and other applications, are inherently stable. Scientists have sought a safe, simple, and economical disposal method for CFCs, one capable of rupturing the very strong carbon-fluorine and carbon-chlorine bonds in these compounds.

Robert H. Crabtree and Juan Burdeniuc of Yale University reported development of such a method. It involves passing CFC vapors through a bed of powdered sodium oxalate (an inexpensive compound) heated above 425° C (800° F) for about 10 minutes. The process decomposes CFCs into easily manageable sodium chloride, sodium fluoride, and carbon dioxide.

Other available methods for destroying CFCs have been less satisfactory. Incineration requires extremely high temperatures and results in the formation of corrosive, acidic gases that require recycling or disposal. A method patented by Commodore CFC Technologies, Columbus, Ohio, pro- ceeds at room temperature and produces ammonium salts, which are then converted to harmless sodium formate, sodium chloride, and sodium fluoride. The process, however, involves highly reactive, expensive metallic sodium in liquid ammonia, a solution that is dangerous to handle.

Fat substitutes

Olestra, the first no-calorie fat substitute, was announced in 1987 by Procter & Gamble Co., Cincinnati, Ohio. It is a sucrose polyester made of table sugar (sucrose) bonded with six to eight edible oils in a molecular structure too large for the digestive enzyme lipase to break down. Procter & Gamble spent $300 million and 25 years to develop and study this first "fake fat," which is heat-stable and can be used in baking and frying. It was tested in at least 60 clinical trials involving more than 8,000 adults and children.

After considerable study and attention to concerns about side effects, the FDA approved this controversial fat substitute in early 1996. Sold under the trade name Olean, it was to be used to make low-fat potato chips and other snack foods. The FDA required these foods to be labeled with a warning that olestra may cause abdominal cramping and loose stools and may inhibit absorption of vitamins and other nutrients. Although expanded uses of olestra would require additional FDA review and separate approval, the initial approval was expected to open the door to future uses in a wide variety of foods.

In mid-1996 George E. Inglett of the Peoria, Ill., office of the U.S. Department of Agriculture announced development of Z-Trim, another calorie-free fat substitute. Z-Trim is produced by treating insoluble natural fiber from grain or other vegetable products in a solution of peroxide and alkali. The fibers burst and then undergo further treatment to yield a white, tasteless, primarily cellulose powder that, although indigestible like cellulose, does not irritate the gastrointestinal tract. When mixed with water, the powder forms a gel that mimics the smooth feel of fat in the mouth. Because it is made from ingredients generally regarded as safe, the product would not require exhaustive testing for FDA approval. According to Inglett, Z-Trim is free of the side effects associated with olestra and is suitable for use in such foods as cheese spreads, chocolate, brownies, and pancakes. Unlike olestra, it cannot withstand high temperatures and is unsuitable for use in deep frying.

New hydrogen source

Hydrogen offers great potential as a clean-burning fuel, yet no practical technology exists for producing large quantities of hydrogen at a cost competitive with that of petroleum or natural gas. Most approaches proposed to date involve the splitting of water into its components, the fermentation of crop wastes, or other technologies with undesirable features. Very little attention has been devoted to simple enzymatic approaches, such as those using enzymes (biologically derived proteins that promote specific reactions) to produce hydrogen from glucose.

A group of U.S. and British investigators reported a demonstration of enzymatic production of hydrogen from glucose that works under mild conditions, uses renewable resources, and produces a commercially valuable by-product, gluconic acid. Jonathan Woodward of the Oak Ridge

(Tenn.) National Laboratory led the group, which included collaborators from the University of Georgia and the University of Bath, Eng.

They developed a process that begins with the use of cellulase enzymes to break down cellulose into its component glucose units. The cellulose can come from a variety of sources, including scrap paper or starch. Two other enzymes, glucose dehydrogenase and hydrogenase, then are used to convert the glucose into hydrogen and gluconic acid. The gluconic acid could be sold for industrial use or converted into additional hydrogen. The researchers said that further optimization of the process would be necessary to evaluate its commercial feasibility.

Better batteries

Solid-state rechargeable lithium batteries can store twice as much energy per unit weight and volume as conventional rechargeable batteries and have begun to appear in laptop computers, cellular telephones, and other portable electronic equipment. In 1990 Sony Corp. introduced the first rechargeable lithium battery, consisting of a carbon-based negative electrode, layered lithium cobalt dioxide ($LiCoO_2$) as the positive electrode, and a nonaqueous liquid electrolyte. One disadvantage of this type of design, however, has been the high cost and toxicity of cobalt compounds. Peter G. Bruce of the University of St. Andrews, Scot., synthesized a new material, layered lithium manganese dioxide ($LiMnO_2$), which is structurally analogous to $LiCoO_2$. Manganese is less toxic and substantially less expensive than cobalt. The charge capacities of $LiMnO_2$ and $LiCoO_2$ compare favorably,

and preliminary results showed good stability over repeated charge-discharge cycles. Additional research, however, would be required for establishing the stability at different current densities and operating voltages.

"Smart" windows

Photochromic materials, which change color reversibly in response to light levels, long have been used in self-darkening sunglasses. The materials have potential large-scale applications in windows for office buildings and homes that automatically shade the interior from bright sunlight and would thus offer substantial cost savings in air-conditioning. Such applications, however, have been hindered by difficulties in controlling the transparency of conventional photochromic films. The films respond slowly to changes in brightness, remaining dark significantly long after direct sunlight has been cut off by clouds. Electrochromic films, which change color reversibly in response to electric current, are easier to regulate but require an external source of electricity.

Suzanne Ferrere and co-workers of the National Renewable Energy Laboratory, Golden, Colo., reported development of a combined photochromic film and an electrochromic film that demonstrates improved response time. Their photoelectrochromic system uses a photovoltaic film consisting of a dye-sensitized semiconductor electrode—specifically, a ruthenium polypyridine-sensitized titanium dioxide material—to collect light energy and transform it into a flow of electrons. The electrons then pass to an electrochromic film consisting of a tungsten oxide electrode, which changes color from transparent to dark blue. When the external light dims, the electrochromic film changes back to its original bleached, transparent state. Researchers said that the system has potential applications in self-powered "smart" windows that control their own transparency and respond rapidly to variations in illumination levels.

Nuclear test monitoring

Long-range seismic monitoring is a relatively accurate way of identifying underground nuclear weapons tests of devices that yield more than one kiloton. Tests of smaller devices are more difficult to discern. Arms-control officials long have sought improved chemical technology for determining whether countries have conducted clandestine nuclear tests in violation of test-ban agreements. Whereas radioactive fission products from aboveground tests are relatively easy to detect, in the case of underground tests the substances usually remain in the test cavity, beyond detection.

A photoelectrochromic cell developed at the National Renewable Energy Laboratory, Golden, Colo., changes reversibly from its bleached, light-yellow state (left) to dark blue (center) when exposed to light. Partial masking results in darkening only of the exposed portion (right).

Chemists at Pacific Northwest National Laboratory (PNNL), Richland, Wash., reported development of a new device for detecting radioactive xenon isotopes that was intended to supplement seismic and other means for detecting underground nuclear tests. Unlike many other products of a nuclear explosion, xenon is a chemically unreactive gas that does not remain below ground. The extreme pressure of a nuclear explosion pushes it to the surface, where it enters the atmosphere. The ratios of specific xenon isotopes produced in a nuclear explosion are unique and provide indisputable evidence of a nuclear detonation. PNNL researcher Richard W. Perkins said that the new xenon detector was highly sensitive in finding four kinds of xenon radioisotopes produced in nuclear weapons tests. Experts envisioned installing the device in about 100 monitoring stations located in 30 countries for test-ban treaty enforcement.

Anniversaries

Numerous anniversaries related to applied chemistry—and some to broader fields of human endeavor as well—were noted in 1996. In 1746 the British physician and chemist John Roebuck introduced the lead chamber process for production of sulfuric acid. Sulfuric acid is the perennial top industrial chemical, produced in larger quantities than any other and used in the manufacture of a vast number of industrial and commercial products. In 1796 Johann Tobias Lovits, a German chemist, first prepared pure ethanol (grain alcohol), which is used as a solvent and starting material in many industrial processes. In 1846 Norbert Rillieux, an African-American inventor and early chemical engineer, invented the triple-effect evaporator to refine sugar. In the same year, the German chemist Christian Friedrich Schönbein discovered guncotton, the basis for modern smokeless powder, and at Massachusetts General Hospital, Boston, the U.S. dental surgeon William T.G. Morton demonstrated the use of ether (ethyl ether) as a surgical anesthetic. In 1921 Phillip W. Drackett formulated a drain cleaner consisting of lye and aluminum chips, which he called Drano. In 1946 ENIAC (Electronic Numerical Integrator and Computer), the first general-purpose electronic digital computer and a forerunner of the modern computer found in laboratories, businesses, and homes around the world, was demonstrated at the University of Pennsylvania.

—George B. Kauffman

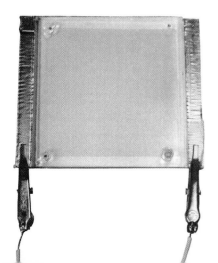

DEFENSE RESEARCH

A changing of the guard at the U.S. Department of Defense and a wave of consolidations within the defense industry made the past year a transitional one for defense research. The reforms initiated by former U.S. Secretary of Defense William Perry, which focused on using commercial technology to improve weapon systems, were expected to endure under the leadership of the new secretary, William Cohen, and spending on defense research in the United States continued to decline. The Pentagon's principal research arm, the Defense Advanced Research Projects Agency (DARPA), no longer could pursue as many promising avenues of research as it did in the past. Like many downsizing corporations, DARPA had to define its core business and apply all its assets to the areas that promised an immediate payoff. The agency's budget reflected this rethinking: down 20% in a three-year period, from $2,530,000,000 in fiscal year 1994 (equivalent to $2,750,000,000 in fiscal year 1997 dollars) to $2,180,000,000 for the fiscal year that began Oct. 1, 1996. What did not change was DARPA's two-level approach of developing one-of-a-kind systems in anticipation of near-term military requirements and maintaining the technology base over the long term by investing in the high-risk, high-payoff technologies. DARPA-sponsored research in displays and radar systems, for example, was applied to operational systems.

Continuing to dominate the defense industry in the U.S. were Lockheed Martin Corp. and Boeing Co., which announced on Dec. 15, 1996 that it would buy McDonnell Douglas Corp. for approximately $13.3 billion. Just nine days earlier Boeing completed a roughly $3 billion deal to buy the defense and space operations of Rockwell International Corp. The acquisitions were expected to make Boeing the world's largest aerospace firm, with anticipated sales of $48 billion in 1997.

The merger wave picked up momentum again on Jan. 6, 1997, as Raytheon Co. announced that it would buy the defense electronics operations of Texas Instruments Inc. for $2,950,000,000. Analysts believed the move represented an evolution in the electronics portion of the defense industry that paralleled an earlier consolidation in the airframe segment, namely, a downsizing of the industrial base to match the new global realities and the Pentagon's declining budget. As the Washington, D.C.-based Electronic Industries Association (EIA) reported in the spring of 1996, the total U.S. defense budget was projected to shrink from $254 billion to $232 billion over the next decade, though the electronics content would rise slightly from about $50 billion to some $55 billion (all figures in constant fiscal 1997 dollars).

Nonetheless, the principal support of science and technology in the U.S. continued to be concentrated in the Department of Defense, according to EIA, which surveyed eight hardware categories within the research, development, test, and evaluation (RDT&E) and procurement accounts and found that the biggest growth area was to be in aircraft, up from about $9 billion a year in 1996 spending for the combination of aeronautical electronics RDT&E and procurement to $11.5 billion by 2006. Two other categories that were also driving technology included the department's "other" category, which consisted mostly of spy satellites and similar classified programs but which also included simulators; it amounted to about $9 billion a year, of which 40% was electronics. The second category was known simply as "communications and electronics" and was worth about $5 billion a year, of which 87% was electronics.

A major event of the year was the awarding of initial contracts to Boeing and Lockheed Martin for parallel development of the U.S. Air Force/U.S. Navy/U.S. Marine Corps/British Royal Navy Joint Strike Fighter (JSF). At a Nov. 16, 1996, Pentagon news briefing to announce the two JSF semifinalists, Undersecretary of Defense for Acquisition and Technology Paul Kaminski called the JSF a "common family of aircraft" and said an estimated 3,000 fighters were to be built at a total cost of $219 billion. "We will be building three different designs here [replacements for the Air Force's F-16, the Marine Corps's AV-8B Harrier, and the Navy and Marine Corps's F/A-18 C/D], not a single design," he told reporters, "but these designs will have in common the key high-cost components—engines, avionics, and many of the high-cost structural components." Kaminski emphasized that the JSF marked a departure from the past practice of starting with a perceived threat and then using that to dictate the performance of a new weapons system. In this culture, cost and schedule were thought of as dependent variables in the weapons acquisition process.

The U.S. Army in 1996 sponsored a Joint Warrior Interoperability Demonstration (JWID) to evaluate advanced communications technologies and applications in intelligence and logistics data dissemination. The exercise was conducted August 5–30 at several sites on the East Coast and

The semifinalists for the planned U.S./British Joint Strike Fighter were the designs submitted by Boeing Co. (left) and Lockheed Martin Corp. (below left). An estimated 3,000 fighters were to be built at a cost of $219 billion, according to the U.S. undersecretary of defense for acquisition and technology.

led by the Army's Joint Task Force, Ft. Bragg, North Carolina. U.S. Air Force, Navy, and Marine units participated along with forces from Australia, Canada, New Zealand, and the United Kingdom. One of the demonstrations was the joint total asset visibility project aimed at improving tracking of materiel in the logistics pipeline. This was a problem during the Desert Shield and Desert Storm operations in the Persian Gulf War, and the U.S. Defense Department was trying to emulate commercial freight handlers in coding and constantly monitoring the status of consumables. Another demonstration was global broadcast support, using prototype equipment developed by DARPA for use in Bosnia and Herzegovina. The goal was to transfer critical data, including imagery, for such purposes as meteorology and intelligence via one-way satellite links. Par-

ticipating in the demonstration was the U.S. Air Force's *Speckled Trout,* an instrumented C-135 operating out of Andrews Air Force Base, Maryland, and employing a new active array Boeing antenna for data transfer.

Also identified at JWID was the overarching requirement of future tactical command, control, and communications systems to achieve seamless operation among a mixture of heterogeneous hardware systems so that the flow of information from the top echelons to the individual soldier in the field would appear transparent to everyone along the communications path. In its fiscal year 1997 defense technology plan for information systems, the U.S. Defense Department defined its future system as one that would "fully support wide- and narrow-band OTM [on the move]...data/voice interconnections throughout a land

battle zone at least 100 kilometers [62 mi] deep and provide robust and seamless connectivity between ground, air, and naval elements of...combat forces dispersed over distances up to 200 km [124 mi]." The OTM part of this requirement, the linking of squad-level units and even individuals into a mobile communications environment, posed the most severe technical challenge. The mechanisms selected were wireless, battery-operated devices that resembled cellular telephones, laptop computers, and other new products of the consumer electronics industry. The Pentagon's master plan for information systems also stressed affordability and interoperability with commercial infrastructures.

In an army-sponsored demonstration of technologies to improve troop training, a trainer using the Global Positioning System (GPS) of navigation satellites to record "kills" in simulated tank battles was tested in Army National Guard exercises at Gowen Field, Idaho. About 50 tanks took part in the June 1996 exercises, which consisted of attacks of 20 or more tanks against 5 defenders. The pointing angle for shooters in the vehicles was derived by using GPS interferometry. When a shooter fired, a cone-shaped beam instead of a bullet was projected across the battlefield. Damage to an intended vehicle operating within the cone at the moment of trigger pull was calculated at the base station by using statistical tables.

The U.S. Navy in 1996 tested the first of its new class of "smart ships" during sea trials in the Atlantic Ocean aimed at determining how increased use of automation could reduce crew sizes; the navy also selected a contractor team for a new class of transport ships and initiated the devel-

An officer on a U.S. Navy destroyer stands watch during Fleet Battle Experiment Alpha off the coast of California. The exercise was designed to test new concepts in coastal warfare.

opment of an advanced-technology vessel known as the Arsenal ship, intended to provide supporting fire for amphibious operations. The "smart ship," the Ticonderoga-class cruiser USS *Yorktown,* was used to check out a $6 million Integrated Control System (ICS) produced by the Sperry Marine division of Litton Industries, Inc., as the prototype for production models to reduce manning requirements throughout the fleet. Derived from technology incorporated in previous Sperry Marine installations on commercial ships, the ICS initially consisted of three subsystems: a fiber-optic local area network, an integrated bridge system, and an integrated condition assessment system. Two more were due to be added in the second phase of the development program: a damage control system and a standard monitoring and control system.

In its Dec. 17, 1996, announcement of the contractor for the USS *San Antonio* amphibious transport dock ship, the LPD 17, the navy struck the same theme: "The LPD 17 class program is the first Navy shipbuilding effort aimed at minimizing military specifications and standards that allows contractors to take advantage of cost-reducing commercial-off-the-shelf (COTS) technologies and non-developmental items." The winning contractor team, led by Avondale Industries Inc., received some $641 million to build the lead ship in the program. The LPD 17 class was scheduled to enter service in 2002 and replace 41 ships of four ship classes, including the Anchorage class LSD, the Newport class LST, the Charleston class LKA, and the Austin class LPD.

The U.S. Navy's proposed Arsenal ship for supporting troops ashore was also expected to rely heavily on COTS technology, particularly for stealth to elude enemy counterattack and to meet stringent affordability constraints. In order to achieve the desired low cost, a $520 million ceiling for the first of the planned five vessels, the development team departed from traditional military specifications and planned for a single hull about the size of a cruiser. The Arsenal ship typified the new navy emphasis on littoral (shallow water) operations, such as strike, antiair, and fire support, rather than the "blue water" operations of the past, when the Soviet Union was considered the principal adversary. By putting more firepower on ships in waters adjacent to land, according to this reasoning, fewer ground forces would have to go ashore for limited engagements. Each ship was to be armed with 512 vertically launched missiles and manned by a crew of no more than 50. Construction was scheduled to begin in 1998 with initial deployment in 2001.

The U.S. Air Force, which had previously opposed unmanned aerial vehicles (UAVs) on the grounds that they threatened to take away flying hours from its pilots, began considering a new generation of UAVs and coined a new term for post-UAV craft able to deliver firepower as well as to perform the traditional reconnaissance role of today's UAVs. The air force labeled the armed versions "uninhabited combat air vehicles" (UCAVs). These craft were intended to perform traditional piloted missions of air superiority and close air support, but would be able to do so without the pilot. By taking the pilot out of the aircraft, the air force hoped to create new shapes and functions that would not be constrained by a cockpit, human body, or ejection seat. The craft would be able to operate in conditions beyond the endurance of a human and also could be considerably stealthier.

The air force also envisioned uninhabited reconnaissance air vehicles (URAVs) that would carry sensors to produce multispectral and synthetic aperture radar images and laser radar returns at resolutions in centimeters. Another possible mission would be the deployment of low-altitude or ground-based chemical sensors for accurate discrimination of chemical and biological agents and the effluents from chemical, biological, and nuclear manufacturing plants. These sensors would be interrogated by readouts of radio frequency or optical signals by satellites or other URAVs.

In an example of post-Cold War international cooperation, a U.S. company, Ashtech, Inc., teamed with Russian scientists to develop a new, more comprehensive satellite-based navigation system for civilian use on Earth. The joint effort yielded a portable navigation receiver that cost less than $10,000 and that was capable of integrating signals from both the U.S.'s Global Positioning System and the Russian Global Navigation Satellite System (GLONASS).

The two countries' navigation satellite systems have evolved since the 1980s from military-only applications to new consumer uses, such as commercial shipping and intelligent transportation systems for managing vehicular traffic. Each system relied on a group of 24 spacecraft broadcasting navigation signals; the satellites were in different orbits and transmitted at different frequencies. By integrating the signals into a single receiver, the U.S. firm hoped to double users' access to the navigation signals.

—John Rhea

AP/Wide World

The Global Hawk, the world's largest unmanned aerial vehicle, is officially displayed for the first time on Feb. 20, 1997, in San Diego, Calif. With a range of 22,500 km (14,000 mi), it will be used for aerial reconnaissance.

A Japanese H-2 rocket launches Japan's Advanced Earth Observing Satellite on Aug. 16, 1996. Aboard the satellite was the NASA Scatterometer, a microwave radar instrument designed to sample near-surface winds over the oceans.

EARTH SCIENCES

The changing length of the Earth's day, a difference in the rotation rates of the Earth's inner core and mantle, and the possible presence of microorganism remains on a meteorite that originated on Mars were among the notable discoveries by Earth scientists during the past year. Oceanographers witnessed the creation of new ocean floor.

ATMOSPHERIC SCIENCES

The NASA Scatterometer (NSCAT) was successfully launched aboard Japan's Advanced Earth Observing Satellite (ADEOS) on Aug. 16, 1996. A specialized microwave radar instrument, NSCAT was designed to sample near-surface winds over the Earth's oceans. As part of NASA's Mission to Planet Earth Program, it was intended for long-term studies of such phenomena as the global climate, weather, air-sea interactions, and the hydrologic cycle. Scatterometers were also expected to help weather forecasters because they provide improved observations of weather systems developing over the oceans. An ocean scatterometer is a high-frequency radar device that transmits pulses of energy toward the ocean and measures the backscatter (reflected energy) from the surface of the water. It determines wind speed and direction over the oceans by analyzing the backscatter from the small wind-caused ripples on the ocean surface.

The first spaceborne scatterometer flew as part of the Skylab missions in 1973 and 1974. Scatterometers on board the European Remote Sensing Satellites (ERS-1, launched in July 1991, and ERS-2, launched in April 1995) provided high-resolution global wind and wave fields that

have proved extremely useful in studies of ocean dynamics and climate.

Climate and global change

Working Group I of the United Nations Intergovernmental Panel on Climate Change (IPCC) published its contribution to the Second Assessment Report, entitled *Climate Change 1995*. The latest assessment, approved by scientists from 96 countries, concluded that "the balance of evidence suggests a discernible human influence on global climate." While the scientists were careful to point out that many uncertainties exist about the role of humans in changing the climate, they noted that there are also many certainties. These include a human-induced increase of carbon dioxide, methane, and other greenhouse gases in the atmosphere; an increase of global mean temperature by between 0.3° and 0.6° C (0.54° and 1.08° F) since the late 19th century; melting of much of the tropical and subtropical ice caps and glaciers worldwide; and an increase in global sea level of 10–25 cm (4–10 in) during the past 100 years.

Recently developed climate models were providing increasing support for the IPCC conclusion that humans are now having a detectable influence on climate. Simon Tett and colleagues at the Hadley Centre for Climate Prediction and Research, Bracknell, Berkshire, Eng., used a coupled ocean-atmosphere model to study the effect of human-generated changes in greenhouse gases, sulfate aerosols, and stratospheric ozone in changing the vertical temperature structure of the atmosphere. They compared the model-simulated temperature changes with the observed changes from 1963 to 1987 as estimated by balloonborne instruments and found that the best agreement between the model's predictions and the observed changes occurred for the combination of greenhouse gases, aerosols, and ozone that had been generated by human activities. From a statistical analysis of the results, they concluded that recent observed climate changes were unlikely to have been caused entirely by natural climate variability.

Following a careful analysis of various global data sets, scientists concluded that 1995 was the warmest year since records began in 1861, a few hundredths of a degree higher than the previous record holder, 1990. The increase in warmth was most marked in the Northern Hemisphere. The warmth of 1995 seemed to confirm that the cooling that followed the 1991 eruption of Mt. Pinatubo was no longer a dominant factor.

Lengthening of growing season in Northern Hemisphere

Climate warming may be contributing to the lengthening of the growing season in the mid- and high-latitude regions of the Northern Hemisphere. For nearly 40 years Charles Keeling and colleagues at the Scripps Institution of Oceanography, La Jolla, Calif., have been making careful measurements of carbon dioxide in the atmosphere. Superimposed on the well-known mean upward trend in the concentration of carbon dioxide in the atmosphere is a strong seasonal variation. In the Northern Hemisphere spring, when the growing season begins, the increased photosynthesis causes a drawdown in carbon dioxide from the atmosphere, and the concentration decreases. In autumn, when plant activity diminishes, the general upward trend resumes.

Careful analyses of these oscillations indicated that the springtime drawdown is beginning about seven days earlier than it did during the mid-1970s. This indication of an earlier spring in the Northern Hemisphere nontropical regions was consistent with observed increases in winter and spring temperatures in high northern latitudes. These changes in the growing season during the past 40 years also reflected fluctuations in climate associated with the El Niño phenomenon.

Volcanoes and ozone depletion

A study published in 1996 revealed how volcanoes influence human-caused ozone depletion. Human-made substances containing chlorine and bromine, reacting on the surface of certain volcanic particles, destroy ozone in the stratosphere, producing the well-documented "ozone hole" over Antarctica in the Southern Hemisphere spring. Using a dynamical-chemical model of the stratosphere, satellite observations of atmospheric particles, and atmospheric measurements of ozone and other gases, Susan Solomon of the U.S. National Oceanic and Atmospheric Administration and her colleagues showed why the amount of ozone destruction varies from year to year over populated regions in the Northern Hemisphere. A significant portion of the annual fluctuations is related to volcanic activity. During periods following major volcanic eruptions, such as that of Mt. Pinatubo in 1991, particles emitted by the volcanoes reach the stratosphere and accelerate the destruction of ozone.

During the Antarctic spring in 1995, the ozone hole began earlier and lasted longer

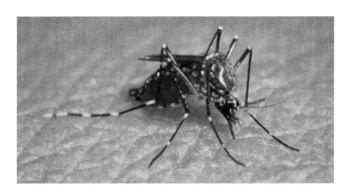

(Top) Centers for Disease Control and Prevention, San Juan, P.R.; photograph, Marco Suárez; (bottom) AFP Photo

than in any previous year on record. It resulted in the almost total destruction of the ozone layer over Antarctica.

Solar variability and climate change

Although the evidence is mounting that humans are producing a discernible effect on climate, another potentially important cause of climate variability is the variation in the Sun's output. Satellite measurements have shown that the Sun dims and brightens over the 11-year sunspot cycle with a variation of about 0.1%. Until recently most scientists thought that this variation was too small to have a significant effect on the climate near the surface of the Earth. But recent analyses of ocean temperatures and ice cores revealed strong correlations with the 11- and 22-year sunspot cycles. For example, over the past 50 years the tropical and subtropical oceans warmed and cooled by about 0.1° C (0.18° F) in time with the 11-year solar variations. Ice cores taken from the high Andes Mountains also showed 11-year cycles in the abundance of dust particles, which are indicators for wind circulations.

As with the many Sun-weather correlations that have been found in the past, a physical mechanism to explain them had not been determined by 1997. The observed climate variations appeared to be too large to be driven directly by the small variation in solar output, which implies some sort of internal feedback mechanism. Yet the correlations were strong enough to suggest that the Sun could have been responsible for up to half of the global warming of the past century, an effect sure to stimulate intensive future research on Sun-climate relationships.

A workman fumigates a neighborhood in El Salvador (above) to control the *Aedes aegypti* mosquito (top), a carrier of the dengue fever that has afflicted the area. Scientists believe that climate warming in the tropics is encouraging the spread of such diseases.

Climate change and human health

According to a panel of leading scientists, climate warming in the tropics and subtropics is encouraging the spread of diseases such as cholera, yellow fever, malaria, and dengue fever to new areas. Disease-carrying organisms—insects, rodents, and algae—are highly sensitive to changes in temperature, rainfall, humidity, and wind patterns and are altering their ranges as the Earth warms. In some areas disease carriers that thrive in warm, moist areas of the tropics and subtropics are being found at significantly higher altitudes than ever before. For example, numerous reports revealed that cases of dengue and yellow fever, along with their carrier, the *Aedes aegypti* mosquito, were found at altitudes of 2,200 m (approximately 7,200 ft) in Colombia and India, according to

Paul Epstein, a specialist in tropical public health at Harvard Medical School and a lead author of the IPCC's report on human health.

Up to half a billion people are currently infected with malaria, and 1.5 million to 2.7 million people die from the disease each year. These cases are unevenly distributed throughout the world with Africa accounting for 85%, Southeast Asia 9%, and Central/South America 2%. Climate sets the geographic limits for malaria, as it determines where both mosquito and parasite can develop and multiply. The malarial parasite requires a temperature of at least 15° C (59° F) for completing its development within the mosquito, while the mosquito requires a temperature of at least 16° C (61° F) and prefers a relative humidity above 60%. Recent studies have concluded that climate warming would affect the distribution and increase the extent of malaria, particularly in temperate countries of the Northern Hemisphere and Australia.

Global distribution of lightning

A NASA lightning-monitoring instrument that was launched into orbit in April 1995 produced the first high-quality images of lightning on a global scale. The data showed that there are up to 20 times more lightning flashes within clouds than are observed by the ground-based network. Severe thunderstorms produce lightning within clouds while the storms are growing; as storms dissipate, there is more cloud-to-ground lightning.

—Richard A. Anthes

GEOLOGY AND GEOCHEMISTRY

By analyzing ancient laminated sediments deposited on tidal flats, Charles P. Sonett and colleagues determined the number of hours in a day 900 million years ago, in the late Precambrian. Tidal flats on the edge of the sea are covered by a thin layer of water that moves in and out each day as the tide rises and falls. Sediment is moved onto the flats by the flowing water, which moves more or less vigorously depending on the strength of the tidal flow, which in turn depends on the positions of the Sun and the Moon relative to each other. During each lunar month the thickest and coarsest layer of sediment is laid down by the current of the strongest (spring) tide, and the thinnest and finest layer is laid down by that of the weakest (neap) tide. Careful measurement of the thickness and coarseness of the sediment in thousands of successive layers allowed

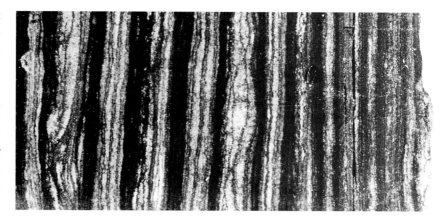

Laminated tidal sediments in ancient rock reveal the rate of retreat of the Moon from the Earth. Combining this information with the Sun's contribution to tidal friction, researchers concluded that 900 million years ago the length of the Earth's day was about 18 hours.

the researchers to determine the tidal dynamics of the system, which includes the length of the day. They found that 900 million years ago the day was approximately 18.2 hours long rather than the present 24. Consequently, the Earth was rotating on its axis 25% faster than it now is. There were 481 days in a year. Since then the Earth has slowed to the present rate of rotation owing to tidal drag from the Moon. Another feature of this dynamic connection is that the distance from the Earth to the Moon slowly increases by about 3.8 cm (1.5 in) per year.

When sea level drops several tens to hundreds of meters, the continental shelves around the world are partly exposed to erosion. When sea level rises again, these erosion surfaces are covered with new sediment and the rough break is preserved in the sedimentary record. Such buried erosion surfaces are called unconformities. A number of investigators during the year demonstrated that several sets of physical, chemical, and isotopic data all agree that unconformities of particular ages are

present throughout the world and indicate that world sea level dropped several tens to hundreds of meters many times in less than a million years (rather quickly in geologic time). A 1987 study indicated perhaps 33 such events in the last 130 million years and provided a graph of sea level against time for this interval; this former study was largely confirmed by the more recent ones.

Some of the data used to establish the presence of unconformities and their ages resulted from simple direct observation of unconformities and fossils in drill cores from sedimentary sequences on the shelves. In addition, chemical and isotopic data were useful. For example, Heather Stoll and Daniel Schrag showed that the concentration of strontium in seawater increased quickly by 20% to 70% many times just within the Upper Cretaceous Period, from 124 million to 131 million years ago; the two largest sudden increases correspond in time with two of the sea-level drops on the 1987 graph. Stoll and Schrag explained the phenomenon as fol-

Charles Sonett, University of Arizona, Tucson, and Erik Kvale, Indiana Geological Survey

lows. Many marine organisms make shells of the aragonite variety of calcium carbonate, which incorporates considerable amounts of strontium as it forms. When sea level drops and the shells are exposed, they convert from aragonite to the calcite form, and most of the strontium is released and washed into the sea. Therefore, increases in the strontium content of the sea match intervals of low sea level and exposed shelves.

The question then arose as to what would cause such rapid large drops in sea level. In recent times such low levels correlate with the formation of regional continental glaciers. It has been thought that in the Cretaceous, the age of dinosaurs, the world had a much hotter climate than at present and that ice sheets would have been impossible. The researchers, however, provided compelling evidence that regional ice sheets, perhaps on Antarctica, did exist then. At the times when the 1987 graph and the strontium abundances show that sea levels were low, the relative abundance of the heavy isotope of oxygen, oxygen-18, increased markedly in seawater. In recent times such rises in oxygen-18 match the loss of ocean water to large ice sheets. The heavy isotope becomes more abundant in seawater because the water that is evaporating and forming ice is enriched in the lighter isotope, oxygen-16, which is transported out of the sea more easily than the heavy one.

Deepest rock body

Larissa Dobrzhinetskaya, Harry Green II, and Su Wang described the discovery that a mass of rock in the Swiss Alps had formed deeper below the Earth's surface than any previously found. The Alpe

Arami body is a piece of mantle a bit less than one kilometer (0.62 mi) across, and it is mostly composed of the mineral olivine, a magnesium silicate that is the dominant mantle mineral. Such a rock body is called a peridotite. What is unusual about this olivine is that it contains a small amount of uniformly distributed tiny rod-shaped inclusions of the mineral ilmenite, an iron-titanium oxide. It is clear that the titanium and iron in the ilmenite were originally dissolved in the olivine structure when the rock body was deep in the mantle and left that state to form the ilmenite as the Alpe Arami body rose toward the surface, cooling and depressurizing; this process is called exsolution. X-ray studies of the iron-titanium oxide rods revealed different internal structures; a total of four structure types are present, one of which is that of normal ilmenite. Another structure is identical to that of the high-pressure mineral perovskite and can have formed only at pressures found at depths of 300 km or greater, more than three times deeper than the depth at which diamonds can form.

Another striking observation was that the amount of ilmenite was far too great to have formed from the olivine in which it was now included; olivine will not dissolve that much titanium under any conditions. To resolve this problem, the researchers noted that at a depth of 400 km in the mantle, magnesium silicate of olivine composition changes structure and becomes a new mineral, wadsleyite. Given its structure, wadsleyite would be able to dissolve enough titanium to have formed the ilmenite in the present crystals. The ultimate model is that the Alpe Arami peridotite is a piece of the mantle from below 400 km whose initial titanium-bear-

ing wadsleyite mineralogy was replaced by normal olivine full of ilmenite inclusions as the mantle block was carried to the surface. The model concludes that this small peridotite block came from at least four times as far down as any other mantle fragment found at the surface.

Asteroid-impact research

One of the largest and most ancient asteroid-impact features on the globe is the Sudbury structure in Canada. Luann Becker, Robert Poreda, and Jeffrey Bada described several remarkable discoveries from this impact site. In the mid-1980s a new structural form of carbon, named a fullerene, was discovered in the laboratory. Fullerenes are hollow cages, nearly spherical assemblages of as many as 600 carbon atoms around a large central space. The first significant concentrations found in nature were discovered in 1994 by groups in New Zealand and Canada. In Canada Becker, Poreda, and Bada found concentrations in a shocked fragmental mass from Sudbury. They hypothesized that the fullerenes either had formed during the impact or had existed in the impacting body and were of extraterrestrial origin, perhaps formed in the solar nebula. To narrow their choices, they examined the fullerenes to see what might be trapped in the molecular cages. Amazingly, the researchers discovered minute quantities of the inert gas helium trapped in the fullerene molecules (roughly 100 helium atoms per billion fullerene molecules). Even more amazingly, they analyzed its isotopic constitution and found that the ratio of the light helium-3 isotope to that of the heavy helium-4 was 10 times greater than the ratio in the mantle of the Earth, which indicated that the helium is not from the Earth. This very light helium is 20–30% lighter than that in the Sun and probably originated outside the solar system.

In southern Nevada outcrops of the Devonian Guilmette formation (360 million years old) contain a layer of fragmented (brecciated) limestone called the Alamo breccia. It underlies parts of six mountain ranges over at least 4,000 sq km (1,550 sq mi) and averages 70 m (230 ft) in thickness; it is the largest body of its kind in the world. In late 1995 Hugues Leroux, John Warme, and Jean-Claude Doukhan reported the discovery of shocked quartz grains in the matrix of the breccia. Shocked quartz is produced during asteroid impacts and has a unique texture, with closely spaced parallel planes of small kinks developed in the quartz structure; these are called shock lamellae and are produced only by impacts. The breccia itself is probably part of the ejecta from the actual crater, which lay within perhaps 100 km of the present outcrops. By 1997 no part of it had been found, and, given the faulting, erosion, igneous activity, and burial by younger sediments that have occurred since Devonian time in southern Nevada, it is possible that no part of it has been preserved. Nonetheless, its former existence is clear, and a new major asteroid-impact site has been added to the hundreds already known on Earth.

A key problem with the asteroid-impact-extinction model is that not all major animal groups were affected similarly; dinosaurs died out, while amphibians such as frogs, seemingly a more fragile group, survived relatively intact. One reason for this differential survival may lie in the different tolerances various animal groups have for highly acidic water. Mollusks, for example, would be exterminated at moderate acid levels, but amphibians and fish would be relatively unaffected, which is just what is observed. Resolving the differential survival question by appeal to this mechanism would add further support to the asteroid-impact hypothesis because the impact would generate acids.

The asteroid impact at Chicxulub in the Yucatán 65 million years ago ended the Mesozoic Era and eliminated many animal and plant groups, such as the dinosaurs, by a variety of mechanisms. The effects of a proposed new mechanism, acid rain, were examined quantitatively during the past year by Gregory Retallack. He studied the effects of acid leaching in the uppermost sediment below the impact layer (impactite) as well as in the impactite itself at two locations in Montana, 3,300 km from the impact site. Retallack found that the uppermost layer of preimpact sediment is a unique two-centimeter (0.8-in)-thick clay-rich rock called the boundary claystone, made almost exclusively of the clay mineral kaolinite. This clay layer was probably produced by very strong acid leaching of preexistent normal sediment in the hours after impact. A one-centimeter (0.4-in)-thick bed of impact debris (impactite) overlies the boundary claystone and was also strongly altered by acid attack. Retallack then questioned the origin of the acid. The sediments at the impact site contain abundant anhydrite (calcium sulfate), which would have been vaporized in large amounts by the impact; the sulfur would have formed large amounts of strong sulfuric acid. In addition, large amounts of nitric acid, another strong acid, would have been formed from atmospheric nitrogen and from nitrous oxide that would have been formed by the burning of large areas. These uncommon strong acids severely attacked the preexisting sediment and formed the boundary claystone and to a lesser degree attacked the accumulating impactite a short time later. They would also have strongly acidified surface water.

Plate tectonics

When the southern Atlantic Ocean began to open perhaps 130 million years ago, the driving mechanism at least in part was the local rise from deep in the mantle of columns of magma perhaps 160 km wide called plumes. As the plumes reached the surface, they erupted enormous quantities of basaltic lava, forming lava plateaus. One of these is the Paraná basalt plateau in eastern Brazil, on the eastern edge of the new South American plate. As the ocean widened and the South American and African plates diverged, traveling away from the new mid-Atlantic ridge, the Paraná basalts moved off their magma source, and magmatism was extinguished. The plume remained fixed in the mantle beneath the ridge, where it continued to emit small quantities of lava, forming the present island of Tristan da Cunha.

The standard plate tectonic model states that plates are wholly crustal and are moved not by primary mantle movements but by other forces such as ridge push, in which the plate, detached near its base, basically slides downhill atop the mantle from the high ridge crest to the deeper ocean thousands of kilometers away. By 1997 the Paraná basalts on the South American plate lay 3,000 km west of the place where they started, above the Tristan da Cunha plume, and if theory is correct, the mantle underneath them should have no trace of the former plume in it. This is, however, not the case. A study by John VanDecar, David James, and Marcelo Assumpção of seismic-wave velocities in the mantle underneath the Paraná field defined a relatively hot zone shaped like a vertical cylinder 300 km in diameter underlying the center of the field at a depth of 200 km to at least 500–600 km, about 20% of the depth of the entire mantle. The most logical model is that this hot cylinder is the former head of the plume whose basalts formed the Paraná field. If this is correct, then the upper mantle under the South American plate is locked to it, and the mantle and plate are moving away from the mid-Atlantic ridge together. This was the first time such a relationship had been indicated. Presumably, the mantle is moving owing to some as-yet-unidentified process, and the overlying South American plate is riding along. These observations provide the first compelling model for the nature of the driving mechanism and both enhances and complicates the plate tectonic model for the Earth.

—Rolfe C. Erickson

GEOPHYSICS

Powerful earthquakes and volcanoes caused hundreds of deaths, thousands of injuries, and widespread property damage during the past year. A study by seismologists of the Earth's interior revealed that the inner core is rotating faster than the mantle.

Earthquakes and volcanoes

On Jan. 1, 1996, a magnitude-7.8 earthquake struck the Minahassa Peninsula on the island of Sulawesi in Indonesia, killing eight people and damaging more than 200 houses and buildings. A local tsunami contributed to the damage in the epicentral area. On February 3 a devastating magnitude-6.5 earthquake struck near Lijiang in China's Yunnan province. The quake killed at least 250 people, injured more than 4,000, and destroyed more than 320,000 houses, leaving approximately one million people homeless. Typical houses in the area, made of mud bricks with heavy tile roofs, were not earthquake-resistant. The shaking generated rockslides in Lijiang. Sicily's Mt. Etna erupted on February 10, producing lava jets more than 200 m high (1 m=3.28 ft). A magnitude-7.9 earthquake struck Irian Jaya province, Indon., on February 17, killing at least 100 people, injuring more than 400, and damaging or destroying more than 5,000 houses. A local 6-m (20-ft)-high tsunami caused extensive damage on Biak and Supiori islands. On February 21 a tsunami at Chimbote, Peru, generated by a magnitude-7.3 earthquake offshore killed four people.

A magnitude-6.1 earthquake on March 19 killed more than 20 people and destroyed more than 15,000 houses in the Artux-Jiashi region of China's Xinjiang province. On March 28 a magnitude-5.9 earthquake struck central Ecuador, killing at least 50 people, leaving several thousand homeless, and damaging homes, bridges, and water-supply systems. On May 3 a magnitude-5.9 earthquake struck near Baotou in western Nei Mongol province, China, killing more than 18 people and causing extensive damage. Also on May 3, the Pacific Northwest region of the

In Yunnan province, a Chinese family cooks outside after their home was destroyed by a magnitude-6.5 earthquake in February 1996.

On the south coast of Iceland, a man walks by a huge block of ice that was washed ashore after a volcano began erupting beneath a glacier on Oct. 1, 1996. The eruption also caused floods that damaged roads and bridges in the area.

United States was reminded of its seismic vulnerability when a magnitude-5.5 earthquake struck western Washington state. Earthquake awareness has been high in the Pacific Northwest for the past several years, since seismologists hypothesized the possibility of a rare, very large earthquake involving faulting of the entire thrust zone from Washington to northern California. On June 15 a moderate earthquake injured one person and caused minor damage at Cruseilles, Fr., and was felt in the Alps and southern Switzerland.

Ongoing volcanic activity at Mt. Ruapehu on New Zealand's North Island peaked on June 17 with the largest eruption since October 1995. Large masses of lava were thrown more than 1.5 km, and an ash plume rose more than 11 km into the air (1 km=0.62 mi). A spectacular landslide in Yosemite National Park in California on July 10 killed one person and injured 14. The slide occurred when a 160-m-wide, 9-m-high, 7-m-thick granite slab, estimated to weigh more than 150,000 tons, broke free from a cliff face and accelerated to more than 255 km/h before crashing into the valley floor. Displaced air generated an air blast that felled more than 2,000 trees over 4.5 ha (11 ac). This event was typical of the natural exfoliation processes that have created Yosemite's beautiful scenery over recent geologic time.

An explosive eruption at Canlaon volcano in the Philippines on August 10 killed 3 mountain climbers and injured 18. On September 5 a magnitude-5.7 quake struck the Ston-Slano region along the Adriatic coast of Croatia, injuring several people, leaving at least 2,000 homeless, and causing extensive damage to villages near Du-

brovnik. Ongoing activity at the Soufrière Hills volcano on the Caribbean Island of Montserrat peaked in mid-September when an explosive eruption deposited tephra (solid material) over the southern half of the island and generated a 9.5-km-high ash plume. A magnitude-6.8 earthquake off the southwestern coast of Cyprus on October 9 injured 20 people and was widely felt throughout the eastern Mediterranean coastal region. On November 12 a devastating magnitude-7.7 earthquake struck the southern coast of Peru several hundred kilometers south-southeast of Lima. At least 15 people were killed and thousands left homeless in the region between Chincha Alta and Acari. The quake was felt as far away as La Paz, Bol., and Guayaquil, Ecuador. Caused by subduction of the Nazca tectonic plate beneath South America, this was a complex earthquake, with prominent subearthquakes (localized episodes of very high energy release) occurring 20 and 33 seconds after the onset of faulting. Other volcanic activity occurred at Popocatepetl near Mexico City, and Iceland, where volcanic eruptions beneath a glacier threatened flooding in a remote region 160 km east of Reykjavík.

Seismic hazard maps

In the past several years, earthquake studies at the U.S. Geological Survey (USGS)

have shifted somewhat in emphasis from pure research to more practical "product"- and "customer"-oriented work. This shift has been accompanied by an increased emphasis on understanding and mitigating shaking damage from earthquakes that have a high likelihood of occurring (and a decreased emphasis on trying to predict earthquakes, which has proved to be difficult).

One outcome of these changes has been a revitalization of the USGS program responsible for making national maps of earthquake shaking hazard. These maps, which quantify the spatial variations in seismic threat from future earthquakes, are used by professional organizations of structural engineers to update the seismic-design provisions of building codes. The USGS has been making seismic hazard maps for several decades, updating them periodically to reflect new knowledge. In 1997 they were using a probabilistic approach, which combines the hazard from all identifiable seismic sources and then utilizes information about their rates of activity in a statistical way. This is distinct from a deterministic approach, in which the hazard from a specific hypothetical earthquake is computed without accounting for its probability of occurrence. The maps incorporate advances from most fields of seismological research, including paleoseismology, seismotectonics, and wave propagation.

During recent months a team of USGS seismologists headed by Arthur Frankel in Golden, Colo., updated the maps again, using the latest data and a revised methodology. Several innovations made these new maps noteworthy. Instead of using various unspecified seismological or geologic or tectonic criteria to estimate seismic activity rates in so-called source zones, the USGS computed the hazard directly from the historical seismicity. This was designed to reduce subjectivity, since experience showed that even expert seismologists use different criteria for drawing zones and seldom draw them the same way. Another advance was the use of a logic-tree formalism for including competing hazard models. For example, several alternative ground-motion attenuation models (the decrease in shaking with increasing distance from the earthquake) can be weighted and combined (along with their uncertainties), using rigorous statistical techniques. Finally, Frankel's team included the hazard from more than 500 active faults with geologically determined slip rates (rates of displacement along fault lines). The new methodology was more objective and accessible than those that had been employed previously, and the new maps represented a broad consensus of the seismological and earthquake-engineering communities.

Superrotation of the Earth's inner core

In 1995 Gary Glatzmaier (Los Alamos [N.M.] National Laboratory) and Paul Roberts (University of California, Los Angeles) used a supercomputer to create by far the most successful model of the Earth's interior processes to date. They started with a randomly oriented magnetic field in a rotating Earth model that included a solid electrically conducting inner core, a liquid electrically conducting outer core, and a solid electrically insulating mantle. Their model soon organized itself into a self-sustaining geodynamo with a realistic geomagnetic field. The simulated field was remarkably Earth-like in strength and orientation; the axis of the magnetic poles was even displaced slightly from the rotation axis. The field was strong and stable for more than 30,000 years. Then, between 33,000 and 38,000 years, it became disorganized and weaker and spontaneously reversed polarity.

This behavior in the Earth's field had been well known from studies of the residual magnetism in ancient rocks, but it had never been successfully modeled. In the Glatzmaier-Roberts model the inner core, outer core, and mantle were allowed to rotate at different speeds as long as angular momentum was conserved in the system. In fact, the interactions of the various magnetic and viscous forces caused the inner core to rotate faster and the mantle to rotate slower (relative to the outer core) once the model stabilized. Perhaps not as spectacular a result as the reversal of the geomagnetic field, this attracted the attention of seismologists who recognized a feature of the model that might be testable, using the database of global seismic measurements. During 1996 seismologists Song Xiaodong and Paul Richards (Columbia University's Lamont-Doherty Earth Observatory, Palisades, N.Y.) studied 30 years of seismic data, looking for systematic changes in the travel times of phases that had followed similar paths through the deep Earth from earthquake to station. (Reliable global seismic data useful for this sort of research were not routinely collected until the World Wide Standard Seismic Network was installed in the early 1960s.) They found evidence that the inner core is rotating about 1° per year faster than the mantle, becoming the first to corroborate this prediction of the Glatzmaier-Roberts simulations.

Seismologists have recognized for several years that seismic waves travel at different speeds in different directions in the deep Earth—slowest in the equatorial plane and fastest along the north-south polar axis. This is probably due to anisotropy (the property of exhibiting different values when measured in different directions) of the iron crystals that predominate in the Earth's inner core. Laboratory studies revealed that the type of iron crystal found in the core is asymmetrical and transmits seismic energy at different speeds in different symmetry directions. Possibly owing to differential stresses, iron must crystallize in the inner core so that the fast direction is predominantly aligned north-south. More recently, seismologists recognized that the fast axis is actually tilted about 10° from north to south. This slight tilt is a key to the Song-Richards study. To see how Song and Richards succeeded, one might imagine an idealized seismic experiment. The fastest travel time axis is assumed to be slightly tilted from the Earth's rotation axis. One can then consider a regular source of earthquakes near (but not at) the North Pole and a station near (but not at) the South Pole such that 30 years ago the source-to-station path was precisely along the fast travel time axis. Then, if the inner core is indeed rotating faster than the mantle and crust, the seismic travel times will increase as the fast axis rotates out from under this source-station pair. (The mantle and crust can be considered welded together for the purposes of the experiment; any tectonic shifts between them are not a factor at the time scales of the experiment.) The travel time from an earthquake in 1994 will be measurably longer than the travel time from an earthquake in 1964. The greatest travel time will occur when the inner core has rotated halfway around relative to the mantle.

Even though Song and Richards depended on real earthquake sources and stations in less-than-ideal locations, the travel time shift was measurable and consistent. They first saw the effect in Soviet nuclear explosions measured at Antarctica. Then they studied three source-station pairs that sampled different paths through the inner core. Phases from earthquakes in the South Sandwich Islands in the South Atlantic Ocean to a station at College, Alaska (path about 27° to the rotation axis), traveled faster in the late 1960s than in the early 1990s. Phases from the Kermadec Islands to Norway (path about 45° to the rotation axis) traveled slower in the 1980s than in the 1990s. Phases from Tonga to Germany (path about 56° to the rotation axis) showed no measurable change in travel time. Their results suggested that the current orientation of the fast axis is about latitude 79° N and longitude 169° E and that the inner core rotates approximately 1.1° per year faster than the crust and mantle.

Scientists have two theories to explain the superrotation of the inner core. In one theory the rate of rotation of the whole Earth is slowing owing to tidal forces, but the inner core is doing so more slowly. In the other theory (an outgrowth of the Glatzmaier-Roberts simulations), the inner core is driven ahead by the various magnetic and viscous forces of the geodynamo itself. In the second theory the speed difference might vary over time as the geodynamo varies. If so, seismologists might be able to test the two theories someday. These discoveries will no doubt spin off other related research for years to come, as well as renew the commitment of seismologists to the unglamorous business of networks and basic observational seismology.
—Charles S. Mueller

HYDROLOGY

Concerned about possible changes in the Earth's climate due to greenhouse gases and global warming, scientists during the year worked to develop a number of techniques to reconstruct climatic histories at both global and regional scales. Researchers believed that a better understanding of climate changes in the past would improve their ability to interpret the significance of current observations as possible indicators of climate change. Hydrologists had a key role to play in these efforts. Scott Tyler of the Desert Research Institute, Reno, Nev., and his colleagues reported their reconstruction of paleohydrologic conditions for the southwestern United States. Their study site was located within the Nevada Test Site in the southern part of the state. The present-day climate of the region, which is arid, is very different from conditions that occurred there in the past. The research team measured chemical and isotopic characteristics of subsurface water collected from boreholes within the vadose zone (the region between the ground surface and the water table where the movement of soil moisture is predominantly downward). Isotopes of hydrogen and oxygen, which make up the water molecule, and of the elements dissolved in the water vary in their atomic mass owing to a different number of neutrons in the atomic nucleus. From these data, inferences were derived on the relative amount of water that infiltrated toward the water table. Higher amounts of infiltration were associated with a wetter climate. This study was the first to demonstrate how data collected from boreholes in a region with a deep water table can be used to infer paleohydrologic conditions.

The data sets studied by Tyler's team included concentrations of the radioactive isotopes chlorine-36 and carbon-14 (which are produced by cosmic-ray bombardment in the upper atmosphere and are then carried into the subsurface by infiltration of precipitation), the nonradiogenic (not produced by radioactivity) isotopes deuterium (an isotope of hydrogen) and oxygen-18, and the chloride content of the soil water. Radioactive isotopes provided the opportunity to date infiltration events. The comparative amounts of deuterium and oxygen-18 are sensitive to the temperature at the time of the precipitation and to the location of the water body from which the moisture originated. Chloride, which originates from atmospheric deposition as either chloride ions in rainfall or windblown dust particles, accumulates in the soil profile at times when there is little or no deep infiltration of soil moisture. The measured accumulation of chloride within the sediments can be used to infer how far back in time arid conditions existed. It was only

At the Aswan High Dam in Egypt, researchers determined that 25% of the annual variability in the flow of the Nile River was caused by changes in the sea-surface temperature of the Pacific Ocean.

by using multiple sets of data that the research team was able to develop a coherent interpretation of the data in terms of a paleoclimatic history.

The evidence suggested that with the present climate no water moves downward beyond the near-surface soils. The vadose zone in the study area was more than 230 m (755 ft) thick. The water the researchers sampled from their boreholes must have infiltrated during a wetter climate than currently exists. They concluded that soil water deep in the vadose zone ranged in age from approximately 20,000 to 120,000 years. Hydrologists refer to the age of the soil water in terms of the elapsed time since it first infiltrated the ground. The research team concluded that the water deep in the vadose zone resulted from recharge events that most likely occurred approximately 20,000 and 120,000 years ago, prior to full maximum glacial conditions. They suggested that a wetter climate 100,000 to 120,000 years ago led to a widespread recharge to the groundwater system, while precipitation that has occurred during the more recent wet period may not have been sufficient to induce deep infiltration everywhere.

The methods used by Tyler's research team complemented other approaches, such as studying sedimentary deposits that reveal prehistoric fluctuations in lake lev-

els, that have been developed to infer paleoclimatic histories.

Predicting river flows

All rivers are subject to seasonal and annual fluctuations in the volume of water that they carry. The development of methods for improved prediction of annual flows of rivers has been a long-standing research field in hydrology. More reliable predictions of future flow rates would aid in the improved management of scarce water supplies. Elfatih Eltahir of the Massachusetts Institute of Technology published a study that related the natural variability in the flow of the Nile River in Egypt to changes in the sea-surface temperature of the Pacific Ocean (the so-called El Niño/Southern Oscillation). After analyzing data on the variation in the flow of the Nile at the Aswan High Dam, as well as data on anomalies in the sea-surface temperature in the Pacific Ocean, for the years 1872–1972, Eltahir suggested that 25% of the natural variability in the annual flow was associated with El Niño oscillations. The remaining variability was attributed to local factors influencing rainfall and streamflow. The association between the change in the sea-surface temperature in the Pacific and rainfall in the Ethiopian Plateau, which is the source area for the Nile, was explained in terms of a positive

correlation between the atmospheric pressure in the Pacific and atmospheric pressure anomalies over the Ethiopian Plateau. A higher atmospheric pressure than normal in the Ethiopian Plateau is related to a decreased convergence of atmospheric moisture in the region and, consequently, less rainfall.

Eltahir developed a simple probability model that characterized the variability in the annual flow of the Nile River in terms of the observed sea-surface temperature in the Pacific Ocean. In complementary studies scientists developed powerful computer models of the ocean-atmosphere system that can be used to predict with good accuracy sea-surface temperatures several years into the future. Thus, it may prove possible to provide better forecasts of the annual flow of the Nile by using computer predictions of the sea-surface temperature in the Pacific. This connection between sea-surface temperature in the Pacific and atmospheric pressures in northern Africa was an intriguing demonstration of the global links in the Earth's climate.

Logging and streamflows

Important advances were reported in understanding of the impacts of logging on streamflow in forested watersheds. Evidence had been mixed in determining whether clear-cut logging and the construction of logging roads within a watershed increased the peak flows in streams during storms. Such information is essential to the management of forested lands and in the protection of stream ecosystems. Julia Jones of Oregon State University and Gordon Grant of the U.S. Forest Service research station in Corvallis, Ore., presented a comprehensive analysis of the hydrologic impacts of logging in the western Cascade Mountains of Oregon. They examined rainfall and streamflow records for five forested watersheds that ranged in area from less than 1 to 637 sq km (1 sq km = 0.386 sq mi). Long-term data records, 34 years in the case of two of the study areas and 50–55 years for the other watersheds, allowed them to assess long-term impacts of logging on streamflow. Over this time scale the proportion of the watersheds that were logged increased significantly, while sufficient time elapsed for some clear-cut areas to begin vegetative recovery.

Jones and Grant found that forest harvesting increased peak discharges in streams by as much as 50% in the small basins and 100% in the larger basins. They concluded that the main mechanism that caused the increase in peak flows was an increase in the drainage efficiency of the watershed due to the integration of the networks of roads and patch clear-cuts with the preexisting stream channel network. A more efficient drainage system was created in the watersheds, which routed rainfall more quickly to stream channels and thus increased peak flows. The duration of the data record did not permit a rigorous statistical evaluation of the impacts of logging on runoff from the largest storms that occur infrequently (for example, a rainfall amount that would occur, on average, only once in a 10-year period). Researchers have determined that it is the largest storms that have the greatest impact on vegetation adjacent to the stream channels and on sediment transport within the streams. Jones and Grant, however, saw no reason why peak discharges for the largest storm events would not also

be increased as a consequence of logging activities.

Contaminant migration

One of the most challenging technical issues facing hydrologists was the movement of contaminants dissolved in groundwater at sites where fractures (planar cracks) in the rock provide the dominant pathways for fluid flow. There are innumerable sites on each continent, underlain by geologic units that are fractured, where industrial, military, or mining activities have led to the escape of contaminants to the surrounding environment. Attempts to map the subsurface distribution of contaminants and to use these maps to predict future behavior and design remedial programs in an attempt to restore water quality were fraught with uncertainty.

A report was released by the U.S. National Research Council that provided a comprehensive assessment of present-day capabilities to describe and predict contaminant migration in fractured rocks. The report highlighted the need for better approaches to identifying and locating the relatively few fractures that typically control local directions of groundwater flow and rates of contaminant transport. This information must be incorporated into a mathematical model that can be used to understand the observed patterns of contaminant migration and to predict the fate of contaminants in future years. Hydrologists differed as to how best to incorporate data collected at a field site within a mathematical simulation model. The report called for funding of additional experimental sites, in a variety of rock types, where methods could be developed and tested to better characterize the hydrologic proper-

ties of a fractured rock mass and where competing modeling approaches could be carefully evaluated to expose their strengths and limitations.

—Leslie Smith

OCEANOGRAPHY

During the early months of 1996, oceanographers were granted a rare privilege—the opportunity to witness the creation of new ocean floor through a volcanic process known as seafloor spreading. The activity started on February 28, when researchers with the U.S. National Oceanic and Atmospheric Administration (NOAA) detected the faint rumblings of earthquakes coming from the Pacific Ocean. The rhythmic style of the tremors indicated that an undersea eruption was under way along the Gorda Ridge, a submerged mountain range off the Pacific Northwest coastline. Within 10 days a team of government and university scientists hastily arranged a research cruise and raced to the site of the eruption.

Towing instruments behind the ship, the researchers surveyed the Gorda Ridge, whose summit lay three kilometers below the ocean surface (1 km = 0.62 mi). The first evidence of the eruption that they encountered was a large pool of abnormally warm fluids floating a few hundred meters above the ridge. This cloud of dilute brine measured about one kilometer in horizontal diameter and had a temperature about 0.12° C (0.22° F) warmer than the surrounding ocean water. Although only slightly warmer than the ambient water, the so-called megaplume of hydrothermal fluids held a tremendous amount of energy, comparable to that generated by a small electric power plant.

When they returned to the Gorda Ridge

in April with undersea cameras, the researchers discovered fresh lava that had erupted along the crest of the ridge just a month earlier. The lava had emerged from a 15-km-long section of the ridge. Some of the eruptions may have been continuing while the first ship was surveying the site in March.

The Gorda Ridge is a boundary between two major pieces of ocean floor. The giant Pacific Plate lies to the west and the smaller Juan de Fuca Plate to the east. The eruption occurred because the two plates pulled apart from each other, opening a gap through which lava could ascend from inside the Earth. As the lava cooled, it created new ocean crust that bonded onto the existing plates. Called seafloor spreading, this process is responsible for generating the ocean floor around the world.

This marked only the second time that oceanographers had managed to detect oceanic earthquakes and witness seafloor spreading. Their ability to do so was greatly augmented by the U.S. Navy, which in 1993 started allowing scientists access to data from a network of undersea microphones strung out around the Pacific. This array was originally built to track submarine movements. But with the end of the Cold War, the Navy has given scientists a new set of ears with which to monitor the oceans.

The tortuous birth of an island

In a dramatic display that revealed the tumultuous growth process of oceanic island chains, the peak of a submerged volcano just off the coast of Hawaii partially collapsed in July 1996. The mountain, called Loihi, lies 27 km off the southern coast of the island of Hawaii. Loihi's base

lies on the ocean floor at a depth of 5.5 km, and the mountain rises to a broad peak about 900 m (2,952 ft) below the ocean surface. Volcanic eruptions infrequently build up the top of the mountain, and scientists estimate that it will take another 50,000 years before Loihi rises above the waves to become the next Hawaiian island.

In July seismologists at the U.S. Geological Survey at Hawaiian Volcanoes Na-

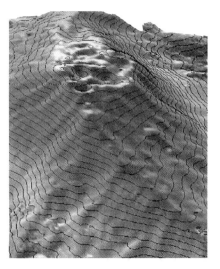

A crater named Pele's Pit occupies the former summit of Loihi, a submerged volcano near the island of Hawaii. Scientists believe that an eruption near the base of Loihi left a void in the mountain into which the peak fell.

tional Park detected an unusual swarm of small earthquakes emanating from Loihi. During the next three weeks, more than 5,000 earthquakes shook the mountain, with the largest reaching magnitude 5 in size. In August scientists at the University of Hawaii attempted to visit Loihi in a deep-sea submersible, but they were unable to survey the mountain because the water was too turbid. In September, however, they surveyed the peak and discov-

ered that its summit had collapsed. The region that had formerly been a large hill had become a crater more than one kilometer in diameter. The submersible descended into the newly created hole, and scientists discovered jets of superheated brines spewing from the floor of the crater. Around these vents thriving communities of bacteria had rapidly colonized the rock surface and were subsisting on the dissolved chemicals in the hydrothermal brines.

The researchers suspected that the peak collapsed because of an eruption near the base of the volcano. Lava pouring out near the foot of the mountain would have drained a chamber within Loihi, leaving a void. The roof of the chamber fell into the void and carried with it the peak of the mountain. This type of process may happen often as the mountain grows in fits and starts.

An undersea collapse has the potential to cause a tsunami, a set of large waves that in this case would threaten residents of Hawaii and perhaps other parts of the Pacific Basin. Volcanologists plan to improve their monitoring capabilities by installing seismometers and chemical detectors on Loihi. These instruments will be connected to the island of Hawaii through a fiber-optic cable.

Wanderers of the Atlantic

Two oceanographers from NOAA in Miami, Fla., discovered that giant patches of warm and cold water rove the Atlantic Ocean for many years and may disrupt weather in Europe. The scientists identified the temperature anomalies by studying records of Atlantic Ocean temperatures from 1948 through 1992. They focused on data for the month of January and produced maps of the January temperatures that ranged farthest from average conditions. These maps revealed the existence of broad warm and cold blobs that stretch hundreds or thousands of kilometers in diameter. Although the vertical dimensions of these anomalies remained unknown, there is some evidence that they could reach depths of several hundred meters. By tracking the position of the patches from year to year, the scientists determined that the anomalies migrated slowly around the Atlantic, often following the path of the prevailing ocean currents. But for unknown reasons, they moved at only one-third to one-half the speed of the currents. The patches typically lasted for 3 to 10 years before they disappeared. In the North Atlantic their temperatures ranged up to 4° C (7.2° F) above or below the surrounding water. In the tropics the anomalies were weaker.

As of 1997, oceanographers did not know the effect of these roving patches, but some speculated that they may alter weather in Europe. As an example the NOAA researchers proposed that a warm patch in the late 1950s contributed to an extended drought in Scandinavia at that time. Prior to this discovery, oceanographers believed that major ocean temperature anomalies remained stationary. Hints of mobile patches had emerged in the past, but researchers did not pursue those isolated discoveries. Researchers hoped to learn more about the mobile anomalies by studying computer models of the ocean.

Buried methane deposits

Scientists with the international Ocean Drilling Program during the year bored into frozen deposits of natural gas. This study confirmed that such deposits, known as methane hydrates, represent one of the largest untapped sources of fossil fuels left on the Earth. Methane hydrate is an icelike substance containing molecules of water and natural gas. The high pressures and cold temperatures of the deep sea squeeze the water and gas molecules into a solid form. Deposits of hydrates can be found around most continents, lying within the blanket of sediments that cover the continental slopes. They also exist beneath the permafrost in Arctic North America and in Siberia.

Because most methane hydrates lie in deep water far from shore, they largely escaped study in the past. Scientists did not know the extent of the resource and lacked even basic knowledge about how methane hydrates form. In late 1995 the Ocean Drilling Program drilled several holes into hydrate deposits on the Blake Ridge, 330 km off the southeastern coast of the U.S. The team's measurements revealed that sediments hold more frozen hydrate and methane gas than researchers had previously thought.

Because of the cost involved in drilling hydrate deposits, both in the sea and on land, past attempts to pump up the natural gas had not proved economically viable. But by 1997 some oil-poor nations were becoming interested in developing the methods to reap benefits from the hydrate resource. Japan was planning to collaborate with the United States and Canada in establishing an experimental drill site in northern Alaska in 1998. The Japanese national oil company planned to drill offshore hydrate deposits in Japan shortly thereafter.

Deep light

Biologists, chemists, physicists, and astronomers teamed up during the year to investigate a puzzling source of extremely dim light at the bottom of the ocean. The light, too dim for humans to see, was first discovered in the late 1980s by researchers at the Woods Hole (Mass.) Oceanographic Institution. It emanates from hydrothermal vents, openings in the seafloor that spew out superhot brines with temperatures up to 350° C (660° F).

In 1996 teams of researchers visited the hydrothermal vents, using deep-sea submersibles to collect detailed measurements of the light. The teams developed special sensors to measure the different frequencies of light emerging from the vents. The data that were acquired from these studies revealed that the light has a complex source. When the light was first found, scientists presumed that the radiation represented the thermal glow coming from the hot liquid—a phenomenon equivalent to the red light emitted by the heating elements in an electric toaster. But the frequencies measurements showed that thermal radiation alone could not account for the vent light.

Scientists thus began exploring four other possible sources of light. Minerals in the brine could be reacting together and producing light, a process called chemoluminescence. As compounds in the hot water meet the 2° C (35.6° F) water of the surrounding ocean, they may form crystals and give off light through a phenomenon called crystalloluminescence. Triboluminescence would occur if mineral grains in the fluids were generating light by knocking into each other or cracking. A fourth possibility is sonoluminescence, the emission of light that takes place when gas bubbles collapse.

Another outstanding question concerned the ways in which deep-sea organisms use the light. Researchers documented that swarms of shrimp near the vents can sense the radiation by using unusual patches of light-collecting pigments on their backs. The scientists suspect that the shrimp may use the light to maintain a safe distance from the vents. The shrimp need to hover near the brine outlets because they feed on bacteria that thrive on the sulfur in the fluid. But if the shrimp venture too close, they run the risk of being cooked by the superheated water. There is also the possibility that the light is strong enough to support photosynthesis by bacteria. If so, this would be the only place on Earth where organisms subsist on a source of light other than the Sun.

Flawed measurements of rising sea level

During the last 50 years, global sea levels have been rising at an average rate of one to two millimeters per year. Measurements made by the U.S.-French satellite TOPEX/Poseidon suggested that the rate had drastically increased between 1992 and 1995, reaching 5.8 mm per year. In early 1996 the measured rate rose even higher, to eight millimeters per year, but researchers then learned that a software glitch had caused the satellite to overestimate the rate of rise. After the problem was corrected, scientists found sea levels rising by one–three millimeters per year, a value consistent with long-term measurements.

The oceans have been swelling in recent decades, in part because warming air temperatures in many parts of the world have

been melting mountain glaciers. The heating of ocean water also causes it to expand. Knowing the speed of this process is important because rising seas threaten coastal regions and low-lying islands.

Collapsing ice

Much of the continent of Antarctica is ringed by ice shelves, sheets of floating ice attached to coastal glaciers. Scientists who studied these shelves found that they were extremely sensitive indicators of climatic warming. During the last half century, four ice shelves collapsed along the Antarctic Peninsula, which had warmed by 2.5° C (4.5° F) over the same period. By examining the temperature records over these decades, British researchers determined that ice shelves cannot continue to exist when mean annual temperatures surpass −5° C (23° F).

The most recent Antarctic casualty was the Larsen Ice Shelf, which disintegrated in early 1995. Austrian and Argentine scientists performed a postmortem on the event and determined that ice shelves can shrink slowly at first. But once they pass a critical point, the floating ice breaks apart extremely rapidly. The scientists found that the bulk of the Larsen Ice Shelf collapsed in about a week.

Antarctic temperatures are expected to warm in response to the buildup of greenhouse gases in the atmosphere. If temperatures continue to climb in Antarctica, more ice shelves will exceed their safety zones and start to collapse.

—Richard Monastersky

PALEONTOLOGY

The most dramatic and widely publicized discovery of ancient life during the past

year was a contribution to knowledge of life not on the Earth but on Mars. The excitement began with the August 7 release of a paper that was later to appear in the August 16 issue of *Science* magazine. In this paper David S. McKay of the Lyndon B. Johnson Space Center in Houston, Texas, and his colleagues reported that evidence of life had been discovered in a 1.9-kg (4.2-lb) meteorite that, judging from its chemical and isotopic composition, had originated on Mars. Radiometric dating of the meteorite, which was found in the Allan Hills region of Antarctica in 1984, revealed that it was composed of rock that had crystallized 4.5 billion years ago. Later, perhaps 3.6 billion years ago, a meteorite shattered the rock, leaving fissures in which water accumulated, thereby providing an environment in which microscopic life could flourish. Later still, according to this tentatively established historical account, another impact blew rock fragments into space, among them the meteorite, which 13,000 years ago wandered into the Earth's gravitational field and plunged into Antarctica.

Once the origin of the meteorite had been established, the remaining questions were essentially paleontological. McKay and his colleagues suggested that the carbon globules found on the fracture surfaces of the meteorite had been deposited when water laden with carbon dioxide seeped into the Martian crust. The globules resemble some bacterially induced carbonate precipitates, which lent support to speculation that tiny objects on the surfaces of the globules revealed by the scanning electron microscope may be the actual remains of microorganisms. Further evidence of biological activity was provided by particles of magnetite and iron sulfide contained in the carbon globules that resemble those produced by terrestrial microorganisms.

Some of the controversy surrounding the biological origin of these materials and structures centers on their size. Most bacteria on Earth are between 0.5 and 100 micrometers in length. (One micrometer = one millionth of a meter.) William Schopf of the University of California, Los Angeles, pointed out that the supposed Martian organisms, measuring as they do between 20 and 100 nanometers in length, are so small as to approach the limit of size necessary to accommodate the material required for sustaining life. (One nanometer = one billionth of a meter.) He went on to emphasize that no one has been able to detect in these tiny objects any internal structure that would suggest they are the remains of living bodies. Other paleontologists and geochemists maintained that the organic compounds that McKay and his colleagues believed to be indicative of life may be contaminates that entered the meteorite after its arrival on the Earth. (*See also* Year in Review: ASTRONOMY; LIFE SCIENCES: *Microbiology.*)

Paleontologists have often confronted the question of whether some structure recovered from ancient rocks represents evidence of life. The origin of stromatolites has, for example, been debated for a century. These circular, often very large structures found in rocks formed during the first two billion to three billion years of the Earth's history have been thought to be the remains of giant sponges or coelenterates, or of aggregates of various microorganisms. Although the discovery of modern structures resembling stromatolites that consist of mats of cyanobacteria

seemed to have established their biological origin, some paleontologists steadfastly maintained that the origin involved no biological activity whatsoever. John P. Grotzinger and Daniel H. Rothman of the Massachusetts Institute of Technology claimed that the structure of stromatolites from a 1.9 billion-year-old subtidal reef in northwestern Australia can be explained in wholly nonbiological terms. From examination of the inherent geometric characteristics of the structures, they concluded that stromatolites could have been formed through chemical precipitation without the involvement of organisms. Because of the great diversity of structures that have been called stromatolites, this work did not settle the issue of the origin of all of them.

A recent discovery may push back the time of the origin of vertebrates by several million years. Gavin C. Young of the Australian Geological Survey Organization and his coauthors reported the presence of phosphatic plates from Late Cambrian Period rocks (510 million years before the present) in Australia whose three-layered structure suggested vertebrate bone. The earliest previously known vertebrates are jawless fishes with bony armor and an internal cartilaginous skeleton that lived from about 470 million to 375 million years ago in Ordovician time. Differences in structure and composition between the Cambrian and Ordovician bone suggested to the authors that in Late Cambrian time an "experiment" in vertebrate evolution was occurring.

The earliest indisputable evidence of life on Earth consists of the remains of microorganisms found in rocks that formed about 3.5 billion years ago. Because these organisms were structurally complex, it is

assumed that they must be descended from earlier, simpler forms. Direct evidence of these more primitive organisms is unlikely to be found, however, because crustal rocks older than 3.5 billion years have been subject to heat and pressure almost certain to have destroyed any trace of them. S.J. Mojzsis of the Scripps Institute of Oceanography, La Jolla, Calif., and his co-workers, using techniques similar to those employed by scientists attempting to establish the presence of life on Mars, undertook a search for geochemical evidence that might, in the absence of fossil remains, permit the detection of the earliest life on Earth. They found carbonaceous inclusions in grains of apatite (calcium phosphate) from 3.8 billion-year-old rocks in western Greenland. The authors maintained that because the carbon in the carbonaceous inclusions consists of light isotopes, the presence of biological activity is suggested. If the authors' conclusions are correct, life emerged on the Earth at least 3.8 billion years before the present.

The remains of extinct birds are very rare in the fossil record. The discovery of the superbly preserved *Archaeopteryx* in the Late Jurassic Period rocks of Bavaria in 1861 provided a "missing link" between modern birds and their reptilian ancestors, but the position of this 150 million-year-old animal in the evolutionary history of birds has been a matter of dispute. The growing conviction that birds descended from dinosaurs and the recent discovery of a number of remarkable fossils of Mesozoic age (245 million to 66.4 million years ago) have provided material for an increased understanding of bird evolution. It has been discovered, for example, that the dominant birds of the Mesozoic were "op-

The theory that birds descended from dinosaurs gained strong support in 1996 with the discovery in China of a fossil dinosaur that appeared to have had a mane of downy feathers. The dinosaur, depicted as it may have appeared in life, was tentatively named *Sinosauropteryx prima*.

posite" birds, so-called because the tarsal bones in their feet fused from the top down rather than from the bottom up as in modern birds. This raised the question of the relationship between birds of the two different types. Lianhai Hou of the Institute of Vertebrate Paleontology and Paleo-Anthropology of the Chinese Academy of Sciences in Beijing, and his colleagues believe that they may be able to answer this question. They discovered a series of remarkable fossils of birds from the Late Jurassic and Early Cretaceous beds (137 million to 142 million years ago) of northeastern China. One of these birds, *Confuciusornis,* resembles *Archaeopteryx* with its recurved claws, reflecting an arboreal habitat, and its unkeeled sternum. The tarsal bones fused at the top but not the bottom suggest affinities with the "oppo-

site" birds. The same deposits yielded a fossil that the authors named *Liaoningornis;* its keeled sternum and tarsal bones fused at the bottom resemble modern birds. The authors concluded that at this early date the birds had already diverged into two separate lineages, one containing *Archaeopteryx* and the "opposite" birds and the other the ancestors of the modern birds. This conclusion by no means met with universal acceptance. Some paleontologists were not convinced that the "opposite" birds did not bear a closer relationship to modern birds, while others were withholding judgment until the dates of the specimens were more firmly established.

There is abundant evidence that the mass extinction at the end of the Cretaceous Period 65 million years ago was caused by the impact of an asteroid. In

addition to the paleontological record of the widespread extinction of animals and plants at that time, there is geological evidence of a coincident impact of a large asteroid in the Yucatán Peninsula and adjacent Caribbean Sea. Until the past year there had been no convincing evidence that other mass extinctions were caused in the same way. At the meeting of the Geological Society of America, however, Gregory Retallack of the University of Oregon presented findings that the great extinction at the end of the Permian Period 245 million years ago may have been caused by asteroid impact. He found in the Late Permian and Early Triassic rocks of Australia and Antarctica quartz grains that he believed revealed the effect of an asteroid in the form of glass-filled fractures.

—David B. Kitts

ELECTRONICS AND INFORMATION SCIENCES

In the "Information Age" of the 1990s, society has been increasingly driven by the need for more information, which is being obtained from an ever-growing number of sources at an ever-accelerating pace. This drive has affected more and more people in more and more aspects of their personal lives. This swelling demand for information has not been confined by national boundaries; the sinews of the world's telecommunications networks increasingly are connecting many areas of the globe into a universal information network. The Internet is the primary example of a global network at the forefront of the information revolution. The phenomenal growth rate of the Internet, which had attracted millions of subscribers by 1996, has been the consequence of the wide spectrum of information provided by it. Many electronics companies, such as Akai Electric Co., Ltd., and the Zenith Electronics Corp. have attempted to lower the cost of Internet access by replacing the conventional personal computer (PC) with inexpensive, easy-to-operate hardware. A leading contender is the Oracle Corp.'s Network Computer, which is seen by many people as a forerunner of a vast array of network computers that shortly will proliferate in the marketplace. Another example, WebTV Internet terminals from Philips Magnavox and the Sony Corp., connect television sets directly to the Internet through telephone lines.

ELECTRONICS

In 1996 the telecommunications and electronics industries worldwide emphasized dynamic activities in areas such as software, hardware, industrial design, and linguistic and cognitive designs. These activ-

ities were expected to result in redesigned products as well as new electronic appliances for the future. New products in novel areas of application also appeared during the year. In the quest for market share, the consumer electronics giants, by virtue of brand identification, appeared likely to have a tremendous advantage. The international business community was also tied together ever more closely by means of electronics after the International Telecommunication Union approved a recommendation that would allow businesses to be allocated a universal international toll-free phone number (*i.e.,* an international 800 number) that would be accessible worldwide regardless of the country or the carrier used.

National developments

The defense sector remained an important component of the U.S. electronics industry. Although the overall budget of the U.S. Department of Defense had plunged by about 30% since 1989 to $266 billion in 1995, the electronic components category of the department's procurement budget actually rose. Defense electronics spending accounted for about 11% of the $410 billion to $415 billion in domestically produced sales of electronic and telecommunications equipment.

Economic growth in Europe during the first half of 1996 stagnated, particularly in France and Germany. Nevertheless, some European electronics market experts expected a slight improvement in market condition for the latter half of 1996 in Europe. This cautiously optimistic forecast was based on the reduction of inventory and the impact of tax cuts in France and Germany earlier in the year, yet real

growth was not predicted to occur until 1997. France's difficulties arose partly because of severe price-cutting for telephone network equipment, a drop in sales of such equipment to China, and a slowdown in cellular phone use in Europe.

Despite Germany's lackluster economic performance in the first half of 1996, there was new activity in its electronics sector. German scientists were developing an electronic assistance system that would lessen an aircraft pilot's work in difficult situations and provide help in operating the aircraft should a need be indicated. Development of the system resulted from concern about a human pilot's flagging attention in a modern cockpit when an automatic pilot is handling the aircraft. Volkswagen AG was enhancing its product development efforts with virtual reality technology, which the company expected to use in the development and manufacture of Volkswagen, Audi, and Skoda vehicles.

In Japan the digital versatile disc (DVD; also called digital video disc) was being hailed as the most important product since the appearance of the videocassette recorder of the 1970s. Matsushita Electric Industrial Co., Ltd., and Sony were the two giant electronics companies that were pushing hard for the development and marketing of DVD technology. (See *Computers and Computer Science,* below.)

In the mid-1990s Taiwan passed Germany and moved into third place among the world's leading producers of computer-related information technology products, including motherboards, keyboards, monitors, scanners, network and graphics cards, and power supplies. Unlike their Japanese and South Korean competitors, most Taiwanese manufacturers were small-scale,

Hezekial Sepeng of South Africa runs in the 800-m final at the 1996 Olympic Games in Atlanta, Ga., in which he won the silver medal. For the first time every Olympic runner wore a computer chip, which emitted a radio signal used to track each athlete's position throughout the race.

which enabled them to adapt quickly to new technology and to shifts in the global markets.

New consumer products

The world electronics industry expanded its applicability into an ever-widening sphere of human activities by means of new or improved technology. For instance, at the 1996 Olympic Games in Atlanta, Ga., electronic chips were used for the first time to pinpoint the position of runners. Each runner wore a computer chip, created by ChampionChip of The Netherlands, that emitted a unique radio signal, which allowed for the precise tracking of a particular entrant.

A new electronic system from the ski manufacturer K2 Inc. used piezoelectric ceramic fibers embedded in the top of the ski to cancel unwanted vibrations. As the ski bends in response to an unavoidable mogul, for example, the piezo fibers generate an electric signal, which is fed to a computerized controller located in the ski's tip. The controller in turn feeds the signal back to the piezo element to cancel the vibrations and improve the skier's control.

In 1996 the immediacy of digital cameras, which made their pictures instantly available for viewing on a TV or PC screen, was further enhanced with the introduction of versions containing their own

built-in liquid-crystal display screens. The leader in the field, Casio, introduced two new models—the QV-30 Plus, featuring a 6.4-cm (2.5-in) screen, and the QV-100, which had a smaller, 4.6-cm (1.8-in) screen but a higher resolution and more internal memory. Sony's DSC-F1 digital camera allowed for the transfer of images to a PC via a high-speed infrared transceiver or directly to Sony's new DPP-M55 digital color printer.

Electronics manufacturers were well aware of the telephone's potential as an information appliance and sought to expand its traditional communications role. Consumer telephones began to appear with screens, modems, and even credit-card readers. Such "smart phones" could handle electronic mail (E-mail), conduct electronic home shopping, or make banking transactions. For example, AT&T's newly developed PocketNet cellular phone, with its built-in digital and analog modems, could be used to retrieve E-mail, make flight reservations, and check stock prices. To deter thieves from stealing cellular phone numbers with sophisticated scanning equipment and then reprogramming the numbers into stolen phones, manufacturers were developing voice-recognition systems that would make the numbers nonfunctional to anyone but their legitimate users.

Avionics

Delta Air Lines began providing an in-seat power outlet that allowed passengers (at least those in first class) to recharge their laptop-computer batteries during a flight. The EmPower system, developed by the Olin Aerospace Co., Redmond, Wash., used a special interface cable that delivered 15 v of direct-current power. An adapter adjusted the voltage level to that needed by a particular laptop. Delta was expected to decide whether to install the system throughout its fleet after several months of testing. Other major air carriers were also contemplating the installation of the system.

A new landing system for airplanes, developed by Lockheed Martin Corp., was expected to result in much safer landings. The autonomous precision approach and landing system (APALS) used the airplane's radar system to take "snapshots" of the ground around the approach path. The information received was compared with an onboard database and thereby allowed the APALS system to fix the airplane's position within a meter or two. Thus, a safe landing could be effected in low visibility, even at airports that did not have radio-navigation aids.

Global positioning system

The Persian Gulf War of 1991 and the success that electronics played in that war spurred an interest in communications and navigation systems. Success in the use of the satellite-based Global Positioning System (GPS) by U.S. forces resulted in widespread application of that system in the U.S. and Western Europe. In 1996 most Western air forces continued to procure GPS technology, and it was predicted that there would be a combined market of $31 billion for both civilian and military aircraft by the year 2005. The GPS, maintained by the U.S. Department of Defense, depended on 24 Navstar satellites placed in six different orbits at an average altitude of about 19,000 km (12,000 mi). Their orbital positions were such that any GPS

receiver on Earth was within reach of of at least two and possibly three or four satellites, which allowed for precise determination of the position of the receiver—as closely as a centimeter or less, especially if the system was used in conjunction with an Earth-based radio beacon.

By means of GPS technology, aircraft, land vehicles, and ships could be guided securely to their destinations, regardless of visibility. Farmers would be able to guide their tractors across a field at night. Even hikers could safely determine their position in the deepest forests with handheld receivers similar to those used by soldiers in the Gulf War. Starting in October 1996 in 16 cities, the Hertz Corp. offered 8,000 rental cars with such a system installed. Hertz used the Rockwell International Corp. GPS system, which could place a car to within 200 m (one-eighth of a mile) of a desired location. In 1996 about 10,000 U.S. cars were equipped with satellite-guided navigation systems.

New power sources

Important developments took place in the application of electronics to the generation of electric power. On May 22, 1996, for less than half a trillionth of a second, a laser with the power of about 1.3 quadrillion w was activated at the Lawrence Livermore National Laboratory, Livermore, Calif. This level of power corresponded to some 1,300 times the electricity generating capacity of the entire U.S. One possible use for the powerful laser was in the development of fusion power reactors.

Sony developed a lithium-ion battery for Nissan's new electric car that promised to provide the vehicle with a range of about 190 km (120 mi) between recharges.

Meanwhile, Daimler-Benz AG of Germany converted one of its minivans to run on electricity generated from a fuel cell. The prototype electric vehicle could carry six passengers at a speed of 109 km/h (68 mph). The company claimed that fuel-cell technology had greater potential than battery systems for powering electric vehicles because it produced less air pollution and did not have the same range limitations.

The first commercially available solar shingles made their appearance in 1996. Developed by the United Solar Systems Corp., the shingles were made by depositing small amounts of an amorphous silicon alloy on top of a stainless-steel sheet. It was predicted that in sunny areas such as Arizona, a 37-sq m (400-sq ft) solar-shingle roof could generate enough electricity to meet the demands of an average household.

Automotive electronics

Automotive electronic applications were growing at an estimated annual rate of 10–15%, which made for a healthy market in that industry. One important trend was the development of smart systems that would employ the intelligence of microcontrollers and digital logic circuits. Established applications such as electronic engine control were also receiving further attention. In the U.S. these developments were almost certainly helped by a California law that required onboard diagnostic systems that would show immediately the cause of failure of an automobile's emission controls.

The Donnelly Corp. developed a side-view mirror that, in addition to alerting a driver to any cars coming up from behind, used a built-in turn signal to notify vehicles in the driver's blind spot of his or her intention to change lanes. In addition, electronic sensors dimmed the mirror when the headlights of a car shone into it from behind. When the door of a parked car was unlocked, the mirror's external light illuminated an area of about three-fourths of a square meter (eight square feet).

Researchers at the Georgia Institute of Technology developed a radar-frequency transmitter-and-detector system capable of sending a wide variety of warnings to motorists. Transmitters, which would be located on police and emergency vehicles, existing overhead structures (including bridges), and other fixed sites, would broadcast messages to a special detector carried in the driver's car. The detector would include a built-in liquid-crystal display that could show a message as long as 64 characters. When the detector received a safety message from a transmitter, it would first sound a special tone to alert the driver before it displayed the message.

—Franz J. Monssen

COMPUTERS AND COMPUTER SCIENCE

Hardly anything could be more appropriate to underscore the progress made in the development of computers in the past 25 years than the announcement by Intel Corp. on Dec. 16, 1996, that it, in partnership with the U.S. Department of Energy, had developed an "ultra" computer capable of performing one trillion mathematical calculations per second. The "ultra" computer, to be based at Sandia National Laboratories, Albuquerque, N.M., would be shared by scientists at the Los Alamos (N.M.) National Laboratory, and the Lawrence Livermore National Laboratory, Livermore, Calif. The power of this com-

U.S. engineer Seymour Cray, widely recognized as the design leader of the world's first commercial transistor-based computer and father of the supercomputer industry, died in October 1996.

puter was obtained by using the massively parallel computing approach, in which 9,200 Pentium Pro chips, each of which supported 5.5 million transistors, were harnessed together to produce extraordinary speed of operation. Even more powerful chips were on the drawing board at Intel and elsewhere. By contrast, in 1971 a team of scientists, including Ted Hoff, Stan Mazor, and Federico Faggin, had designed the Intel microprocessor 4004, the first computer on a chip, which sported 2,300 transistors and was capable of 60,000 operations per second. Intel's announcement had even greater poignancy since it came only two months after the world lost one of its most innovative designers and builders of computers, Seymour Cray (*see* SCIENTISTS OF THE YEAR: *Obituaries*), virtually the father of the supercomputer, who died of

injuries suffered in an automobile accident in Colorado.

Hardware developments

The speed and power of personal computers (PCs) also climbed steadily in 1996, and there was a proliferation of new models of all makes. The best of these PCs featured central processing unit (CPU) speeds of about 300 MHz and higher. In early 1997 Intel introduced its new MMX microprocessor technology, a multimedia extension upgrade to the Pentium chip.

There were signs that digital computer technology and broadcasting were drawing ever closer together. The Federal Communications Commission (FCC) agreed, on Dec. 24, 1996, to adopt standards proposed by the Advanced Television Systems Committee for digital high-definition television (HDTV) in the U.S. It was agreed that, after a transition period of 10–15 years, during which both analog and digital signals would be broadcast, television broadcasters and television-set manufacturers would incorporate digital technology in television-signal dissemination and new television sets. The agreement stipulated that the free market would ultimately determine the actual size, shape, and resolution of images available on future digital displays, and industry experts predicted that the first digital broadcasts and sets would be available in the U.S. in about two years. No doubt, computers and computer displays would also be affected by the HDTV standard.

HDTV has been available in Japan since the early 1990s, although only about 25,000 of the expensive new television sets had been sold by late 1996. European technicians were also experimenting with

HDTV and, in fact, developed their own standard. Incompatibility problems between competing systems continued to hamper the full implementation of HDTV everywhere.

Meanwhile, the computer industry was trying to make computers and computer-like devices easier to use. WebTV, manufactured by Philips Magnavox and Sony, was the first of a new generation of Internet-access devices and would sell for approximately $350. The machine was designed to hook up to a television set and connect to a telephone line. By subscribing to an Internet service provider (ISP), a consumer could use the device to access the Internet as well as to send and receive electronic mail (E-mail). Early models came with an optional wireless keyboard but without a way to store information or to print it out. Sega, Bandai, Sanyo Electric, Samsung Electronics, Hitachi, Mitsubishi, and Zenith were among the companies planning their own TV-based devices. In a parallel business trend, many companies were considering inexpensive computers that did not have their own storage devices but rather were connected to central, networked computers that would provide programs, data storage, and printing facilities.

As an improved storage technology for computers, the digital versatile disc (DVD; also called digital video disc) loomed on the horizon. Each DVD, similar in size to a CD-ROM, would store an impressive 4.7–17 gigabytes of digital information, depending on how it was formatted, compared with the approximately 650 megabytes of storage available on a CD-ROM. In January 1996 Toshiba demonstrated a working model of a DVD player, config-

ured to show digitized films, and had units available for purchase at year-end. DVD technology would soon be available for computers in a read-write configuration, although the entertainment industry was quite concerned that the proliferation of the read-write DVD could lead to piracy of protected products such as movies, music, art, or video productions.

Although supercomputers had used parallel processing for some time, in 1996 some multiprocessor machines were coming onto the home-computer market. They included the BeBox, designed for Be, Inc., under the direction of former Apple Computer Corp. technology chief Jean-Louis Gassée, and the Apple Power Macintosh 9500/180MP. These computers, running on specially designed software, contained more than one CPU, and even though these multiple CPUs were individually slower than the fastest available, the computers were significantly faster than those running on a single fast CPU.

Apple Computer continued to be in the news. While results of its first three quarters of fiscal 1996 were disappointing, the company did show a $25 million profit in its fourth quarter. Apple's chairman, Gilbert Amelio, was attempting to reduce the large number of different Macintosh models available and to improve the company's forecasting of demand for new machines. In addition, many Macintosh clones had become available to purchasers, including those made by Power Computing, Motorola, and Umax, a fact that made the Macintosh market more interesting for software developers, whose work might, in turn, be vital to Apple's continued presence in the computer marketplace.

In a bold move designed to ensure Ap-

ple's continued profitability, Amelio announced on Dec. 20, 1996, that the company would purchase NeXT Software, Inc., owned by Steven Jobs, one of the founders of Apple, and that it had hired Jobs to return to Apple to act as a consultant to oversee the development of a new operating system and the design of new Macintosh computers. In early 1997 the company faced more big losses and the resignations of several executives, and there were rumors of large layoffs. Meanwhile it announced new products, including the fastest laptop on the market running at 240 MHz, and an aggressive new marketing campaign. Amelio indicated that he expected Apple to return to profitability in 1998.

Software developments

Developments in computer software continued to be dominated by changes in competing operating systems. For several years programmers at Apple had been working on a new Macintosh operating system (Mac OS), code-named Copland, which was to replace its System 7.x software. Late in 1996, however, Copland was scrapped. Instead, System 7 and the subsequent Mac OS 8 (expected to debut in 1997) were to be upgraded twice a year beginning in January 1997, while Apple developed a new OS, code-named Rhapsody, which was to be based, at least in part, on NeXT's operating system, NeXTStep. Meanwhile, Power Computing signed an agreement with Be to offer the BeOS, in addition to the Mac OS, on Power Computing machines.

Microsoft Corp. announced in March 1996 that it had shipped its 30 millionth copy of Windows 95, the consumer-oriented graphical OS it had introduced in 1995. Later in the year Microsoft issued a new challenge to the user-friendly Mac OS with the release of Windows NT 4.0, which would provide a graphical interface to users of the corporate-based Windows NT operating system.

Internet developments

On the Internet front, Microsoft and Netscape Communications Corp. continued to battle for Internet browser supremacy. (A browser is the software interface that allows a client to look through the contents of the Internet, to access USENET news groups and sites on the World Wide Web, and to send and receive E-mail.) In an effort to increase its market share, Microsoft began installing its browser, Internet Explorer, on all PCs using Windows 95, giving it a certain advantage over the Netscape Navigator browser. In December 1996 Microsoft announced that it had reached agreements with America Online (AOL), Prodigy, and CompuServe for those Internet content providers to offer their customers versions of Internet Explorer, joining AT&T WorldNet, Netcom, and MCI, which had already reached similar agreements. Netscape Navigator, however, had been in use longer than Internet Explorer and had a loyal following of its own, with some 80% of the market. Both Microsoft and Netscape were also developing software that would insert an improved browser into a PC operating system; the Netscape system was to be called Constellation, and the Microsoft system was to be named Active Desktop.

In a major policy shift, AOL, the largest content provider in the U.S., announced in December that it would offer unlimited access to the Internet for a flat fee of $19.95 a month, a change from its previous policy of charging a $9.95 monthly fee for only five hours of access, with additional charges for more hours. This price change triggered a huge increase in AOL customer demand for access to the Internet, and a considerable number of subscribers experienced difficulty getting online. On the other hand, Netcom, nearly three years after pioneering the market for flat-rate Internet access, decided to abandon its flat-rate pricing of $19.95 a month and to offer superior service to its business customers for a higher fee. As major phone companies, including AT&T, GTE, and others, were aggressively entering the Internet service provider business, it was likely to become more and more difficult for smaller independent ISP companies to remain profitable.

The law and the Internet

As public participation on the Internet mushroomed in 1996, U.S. government agencies moved both to control the content of Internet communications and to protect the ownership of published material. On February 8 U.S. Pres. Bill Clinton signed a telecommunications bill containing the Communications Decency Act of 1996. The act stated that anyone who transmitted "indecent materials" over the Internet to minors would be subject to criminal penalties. It also criminalized the posting of harassing or annoying material. Almost as soon as it was signed into law, the Communications Decency Act was challenged in court by the American Civil Liberties Union and other parties. A Philadelphia court granted a temporary injunction in favor of the plaintiffs on the grounds that they would likely prevail in their challenge to the act. The U.S. Supreme Court announced that it would consider the case for review in 1997.

Attempts to regulate the content of the Internet were also made at the state level. Eleven states had passed legislation in the past two years to regulate on-line content, while several other states had bills pending. Subject matter to be excluded or restricted included material deemed to be indecent, harmful to minors, related to terrorist acts or explosive materials, child pornography, or intended for the sexual solicitation of minors.

Concern about the security of data, including credit card numbers and other financial information, transmitted to others via computers led programmers to create powerful and sophisticated encryption programs. The U.S. government considered this encryption technology so important that it placed restrictions on both its publication and its export and declared much of it to be classified as "weapons," which could be exported only by persons or companies with an appropriate license.

In 1995 a mathematician and teacher, Daniel J. Bernstein, challenged the government's power to control his encryption work, specifically the publication of a program named Snuffle, as an unlawful prior restraint on freedom of speech. In December 1996 the U.S. District Court in San Francisco ruled in his favor. The decision was not binding outside California's Northern Federal District, and it was uncertain that the government would appeal the ruling. The final outcome of this case and others like it, however, would have an important impact on digital publication.

A First Amendment-based decision that went the other way dealt with a company's right to flood a private service provider (in this case, AOL) with unsolicited advertising sent to its customers. The U.S. District Court in Philadelphia ruled in November that AOL had the right to ban access by outside companies to its site because it was a private company and not a public forum.

An event bound to have considerable impact on what could be published on the Internet was an agreement reached in December by representatives of some 160 countries on a sweeping extension of existing international copyright law. The agreement, which remained subject to ratification by the U.S. Congress and the legislatures of the participating countries, would pave the way to broaden protections for the creators of digital art, software, and music on the Internet. Although U.S. copyright laws already protected traditionally published material, the agreement's specific designation of digital work and the international nature of the laws made them particularly important for artists, writers, and producers of material to be published on the Internet.

International trade developments

As 1996 came to an end, some important trade negotiations were in progress. Both in the Philippines and in Singapore, representatives of many nations, including the U.S. as well as European and Asian countries, were working on global agreements that would liberalize or abolish tariffs on computer and software products. An information technology agreement could impact about $500 billion worth of computer and software exports annually.

Computers in education

In March 1996 Clinton and U.S. Vice-Pres. Al Gore participated in California's NetDay96, a Saturday on which school staff members, parents, volunteers, and community leaders spent the day wiring schools for high-speed computer data networks. As many as 32 other states followed California's lead, and another Net-Day was declared in October, during which volunteers once again wired schools for the use of computers and the Internet. The success of NetDay96 prompted organizers and sponsors to continue the effort as an ongoing project called NetDay2000, with the goal of wiring all U.S. schools for Internet access.

The problem of how schools and other public institutions were to pay for access to the Internet remained. Clinton at one time had envisioned free access to the Internet for all schools, libraries, and rural health-care facilities. Communication companies, however, rejected the idea of free access. An FCC panel suggested its own universal-service plan, under which service to schools, libraries, and health-care operations would be provided at deep discounts of as much as 40–60% off regular rates, with institutions in low-income or poverty neighborhoods enjoying discounts of up to 90%. To pay for the service, communication companies would

U.S. Pres. Bill Clinton (right) and Vice-Pres. Al Gore share the fun with two high school students in Concord, Calif., on March 9, 1996, designated NetDay96. Later in the year, as many as 32 other states followed California's lead, with volunteers wiring schools for high-speed computer data networks.

AP/Wide World

contribute to an annual $2,250,000,000 universal-service fund.

—Hans Georg Stern

COMPUTER SYSTEMS AND SERVICES

In the 1990s the term *information society* referred to a world society in which many social and organizational changes took place as a result of the information and communications revolution. These changes transformed society from one based primarily on the manufacture and distribution of physical goods to one increasingly based on the acquisition and transfer of knowledge and information. By 1996 the technological infrastructure for the information society had become such an integral and indispensable part of many people's lives that scientists, entrepreneurs, and a large portion of the general public used electronic mail (E-mail) and the Internet as efficient and inexpensive ways to communicate data and information worldwide and to obtain access to a large variety of information services.

Along with security, pornography on the Internet became a major concern during 1996. A proposal submitted by U.S. Rep. Rick White would prevent minors in the U.S. from accessing pornography on the Internet. The proposed legislation would create incentives for on-line service providers to regulate material that could be deemed harmful to minors, provide incentives for the development of encryption techniques, and give parents a deciding role in determining what is appropriate viewing material for their children. The Information Industry Association supported the proposal because it believed such legislation represented a sensible balance between the need to protect children from pornography and the need to allow a free and open exchange of ideas on the Internet without fear of excessive regulation.

U.S. systems and services

The U.S. National Archives and Records Administration (NARA) is the agency responsible for managing the records of the federal government. In order to better inform the public of its many activities, NARA created a World Wide Web site (http://www.nara.gov) where the public could obtain information about the agency's mission, the hours and location of all National Archives facilities (including regional archives and presidential libraries), and other useful knowledge, such as descriptions of records held by the Still Picture branch and the Motion Picture, Sound, and Video branch and of the agency's major automated information systems and products.

The National Digital Library, a project of the Library of Congress, planned to digitize five million items from its collection by the year 2000—the library's 200th anniversary—and to make these freely available on the Internet. The project, which began in 1994, was expected to cost about $60 million, to be contributed by both congressional and private sources. More than 40,000 documents and photographs from the library's American history collection had been processed by 1996. Included were documents from the Continental Congress and the Constitutional Convention, 1774–89; African-American pamphlets, 1818–1907; documents from the National American Woman Suffrage Association, 1848–1921; daguerreotype photographs, 1842–62; and much more. James H. Billington, the Librarian of Congress, commented, "These primary source materials from American history provide valuable content for enriching the education of students and lifelong learners."

The American Museum of Natural History, New York, N.Y., also launched a Web site as part of its ongoing effort to expand its educational reach and bring its resources to the widest possible public. The site (http://www.amnh.org) provided general information about the museum and its programs as well as detailed information about its exhibitions, scientific research, and educational programming. The museum's home page introduced the different departments in the museum and allowed visitors to move to any area according to their individual interests. By selecting "Exhibitions" the visitor would be taken on an interactive tour of current exhibits, including a self-guided tour of selected treasures in the museum's permanent collection and "Fossil Halls," which showed users the museum's spectacular fossil exhibit and engaged them in an evolutionary journey that traced the "family tree" of vertebrates and illustrated the place of humans in the natural world. The "Education" and "Research" programs were equally interesting and informative.

The research and production staff of the privately funded U.S. Holocaust Memorial Museum, Washington, D.C., produced a combination package of the printed *Historical Atlas of the Holocaust* together with a multimedia CD-ROM. These educational tools were designed to allow users to browse through the holocaust materials thematically, geographically, and chronologically. The 300 full-color maps and photographs included on the CD-ROM locate Holocaust massacre sites, deportation and escape routes, routes of the death marches, and sites of the war crimes trials. A talking glossary pronounces all the terms used.

As part of its *Britannica Online* subscriber services (http://www.eb.com), Encyclopædia Britannica, Inc., offered several "Spotlights" on specific topics: "The American Presidential Election," a multimedia exhibit of U.S. presidential history and the electoral process, with biographies, a full tally of electoral and popular votes, and the text of inaugural addresses and other speeches; "The Olympic Games," covering the Summer Olympics from 1896 to 1996; and a "Guide to Black History," examining nearly 400 years of African-American history. Limited access was also available to nonsubscribers.

The American Presidency, a multimedia disc created by Grolier International Inc., furnishes an historical view of U.S. presidents and presidential politics ranging from the election of George Washington in 1789 to Bill Clinton's first election in 1992. Included are the full texts of each inaugural address, other presidential speeches, photographs, and hundreds of detailed articles. The content can be accessed by searching for photographs, career highlights, or items of interest.

Documents describing the finest technology produced by and for NASA over the past 20 years were made available on the *NASA Technology CD-ROM.* Included are the front pages and claims of more than 2,800 NASA patents, abstracts of approximately 90,000 NASA technical reports and congressional hearings, and abstracts of over 800 previously unpublished NASA

software programs with source code listings on a variety of subjects, such as computer-aided design, expert systems, and robotics. These selected documents constitute an invaluable source of engineering solutions and new product ideas from some of the nation's greatest technical minds.

Topographic maps have been among the most popular and versatile products of the United States Geographical Survey (USGS). These maps depict the natural and human-made features of a region, including lakes, streams, elevations, highways, and railroads. They are used for outdoor recreational purposes and in support of research and technical endeavors. In addition to printed topographic maps, the USGS has also produced topographic maps on CD-ROM. The disc includes viewing software, product specifications, and assorted text files.

Olympic Gold, a complete 100-year history of the modern Olympic games was produced on CD-ROM as an officially licensed product of both the United States Olympic Committee and the International Olympic Committee. Included on this database are a guided video of the games, official game rules, results of each event, and data about the 16,000 medal winners.

The *American Poetry Full-Text Database,* compiled by Chadwyck-Healey, is the largest electronic collection of poetry by American authors ever assembled. Included are the poetic works of over 200 writers active from the early 17th to the early 20th centuries. Authors were selected from among those listed in the *Bibliography of American Literature,* supplemented by the recommendations of a distinguished editorial board. Chadwyck-Healey also

published the *English Poetry Full-Text Database* and the *Database of African-American Poetry: 1760–1900.* All three volumes were available on CD-ROM.

Reference Service Press (RSP), a niche publishing company, specialized in the development of financial-aid directories and databases. Together with SilverPlatter Information, Inc., the two companies released three databases available on CD-ROM, and the Internet: *RSP Funding for Undergraduates, RSP Funding for Graduate Students,* and *RSP Funding for Postdoctorates and Professionals.* These databases described thousands of financial-aid programs, including scholarships, loans, grants, internships, and awards available at these different levels of training along with details regarding specific eligibility requirements, such as gender, ethnicity, and disabilities.

Gold Standard Multimedia Inc. and Michigan State University produced *Breast Cancer Lighthouse,* a CD-ROM resource on the diagnosis and treatment of breast cancer. The interactive program tells the stories of 14 women who had breast cancer and who shared their experiences, fears, and frustrations to help other women battle this disease. The CD-ROM also contains a wealth of medical information about breast cancer with sections devoted to diagnosis, treatment, and recovery. The project was funded by Michigan State University's cancer center and the American Cancer Society.

International systems and services

In a project financed partly by the European Commission, children from schools in 15 European countries took their first steps into the information society. A pilot project, Schools Adopt Monuments, encouraged students to experiment with workstations, digital cameras, scanners, and video equipment in the production and communication of materials related to the historic monuments that they symbolically adopted. By producing and sharing their work, the students could develop a deeper understanding of their own cultural heritage and its European context.

Geographic information systems (GIS) have been part of a rapidly growing, complex, and important area of the information society with many national and international applications in government, industry, and research. GIS were needed for land-management planning, environmental and health-care emergency services, and many other applications. In spite of their recognized importance, GIS services in Europe were hampered by the way relevant data were collected, stored, and distributed in the different countries. To rectify this situation, the European Commission formed the European Geographical Information Infrastructure and initiated actions to standardize the creation, collection, and exchange of geographical information.

The Frankfurt (Ger.) Book Fair was first held in 1560, only a few years after Gutenberg's invention of the printing press. In 1996 the Frankfurt Book and Electronic Publishing Fair was a most important international showcase for both cyberpublishing and conventional book publishing, where audiovisual and electronic multimedia products, including CD-ROMs, enriched databases, and electronic magazines and journals, as well as printed books, were exhibited.

The Hermitage

St. Petersburg Russia Art Treasures Tour The World's Greatest Museum

"The Litta Madonna" - Leonardo da Vinci

ЭРМИТАЖ

CD-ROM
WINDOWS

"Litta Madonna" by Leonardo da Vinci was one of the artifacts featured in *The Hermitage Art Treasures Tour*. The multimedia CD-ROM was issued by the State Hermitage Museum, located in St. Petersburg, Russia.

Two multimedia discs of Russian art treasures were released by Cascade Marketing as part of its educational CD-ROM series. *The Hermitage Art Treasures Tour* is a multimedia tour of the world-famous State Hermitage Museum, located in St. Petersburg, Russia. The *Treasures of Russia* tour provides an introduction to the history of Russian art, beginning with a view of religious frescoes and icons and continuing through the paintings and applied arts produced between the 10th and early 20th centuries. It also covers paintings by Renaissance and Impressionist artists, European crafts, jewelry, and architecture. In addition to the hundreds of full-screen images of art objects, both discs contain slide shows, maps, orchestrations, and narrations by resident art historians.

Research and development

Professors at the Harvard University Law School entered into an agreement with the Lexis-Nexis organization to create electronic course materials, including lectures and casebooks, for law schools. The first commissioned project was to develop an integrated first-year law-school curriculum covering legal analysis, research, and argumentation, which would eventually lead to the creation of a complete electronic legal education program. Under this agreement, the law faculty was furnished with the software platform needed to transform traditional course materials into electronic casebooks for use by students.

Charles R. McClure of the School of Information Studies, Syracuse (N.Y.) University, completed a study entitled "Internet Costs and Cost Models for Public Librarians." The study analyzed public library costs involved in the use of the Internet. The final report was issued by the sponsoring agency, the U.S. National Commission on Libraries and Information Science. Stephen P. Harter of the Indiana University School of Library and Information Science received a grant from the Online Computer Library Center to study the impact of electronic journals on scholarly communication. The study analyzed the extent to which newer electronic publications were being cited in scholarly peer-reviewed journals.

The College of Library and Information Services of the University of Maryland, College Park, received a $100,000 grant from the W.K. Kellogg Foundation for a pilot program designed to link the faculty of the college with the staff of the Montgomery County Public Library. Faculty investigators Paul Wasserman, Gary Merchionini, and Eileen Abels conducted an economic community survey and applied the results to build an electronic database describing the characteristics of the community.

The European Commission, through its Telematics Application Programme, was committed to improving the quality of life among disabled and elderly people residing in the European Union's member nations. The Commission funded various research projects to design and test integrated systems for enhancing the efficiency and effectiveness of services supporting independent living and activities involving education, work, leisure, mobility, and training.

—Harold Borko

TELECOMMUNICATIONS SYSTEMS

In the late 20th century, many observers were proclaiming the world's entry into the "Information Age." By 1996 the worldwide emphasis on information, rather than on agriculture or industrial production, had made this a most apt phrase. The technology that had evolved—in most cases an offshoot of solid-state electronics—and the applications of this technology seemed to many nothing short of miraculous. It appeared obvious that the leaders in the move to this information age would be the existing telecommunications companies, notably local and regional telephone companies, long-distance telephone carriers, and cable television companies. These companies, after all, were already designing systems around the new technologies and applying those technologies to real-life situations.

In the U.S., however, things changed, primarily because of the passage in the U.S. Congress of the Telecommunications Act of 1996, an update of the Communications Act of 1934. Suddenly, competition was in and monopoly was out. As a result, the existing players did not necessarily have the field to themselves. There were new entrants, and the government—represented primarily by the Federal Communications Commission (FCC)—was doing a yeoman's job in supporting these erstwhile competitors while treading a narrow line in its aim to be "pro-competition," not "pro-competitor." Nevertheless, this new act, in spite of its 322-page length, was not precise and left to the FCC a great deal of interpretation. For instance, it called for "affordable" telecommunications services and said schools should have "advanced" services.

Several different groups of companies were eager to play a major role in this exploding telecommunications industry, and each had its own definitions and its own suggestions for implementation. The emerging major players were: (1) local exchange carriers, including the seven regional telephone operating companies spun off from AT&T in 1984 (known collectively as the Baby Bells) and some 1,300 smaller companies; (2) long-distance (interexchange) carriers, notably AT&T, MCI, Sprint, and hundreds of smaller companies; (3) cable TV companies, which provided entertainment to some 63% of U.S. households via coaxial cable; (4) wireless carriers, primarily the operators of cellular telephone systems throughout the world but increasingly including the operators of personal communications services (PCS) systems; (5) direct broadcast satellite (DBS) companies, which bypassed the cable systems and broadcast television directly to homes, using satellite technology; and (6) Internet access providers, which provided access to the ever-expanding Internet through personal computers. Each of these groups of players was eager to get in the business of the other players, not so much because of the expansion of that other business but because each believed that "one-stop shopping" was the key to success.

One other service was increasingly significant: the Internet itself. Users could access companies' World Wide Web home pages and other information, while electronic mail (E-mail) was becoming a simple, modern way of communicating. Although voice transmission over the Internet (worldwide, for the price of a local telephone call) was crude and hardly satisfactory, its quality was likely to improve in the near future.

Cellular telephones

In 1983 the nation's first cellular telephone (also called cellular radio) system was activated in Chicago. Market growth was phenomenal, and within 13 years there were approximately 40 million subscribers in the U.S., with more being added at the

A modern businessman in Hong Kong talks on his cellular phone while driving. In 1996 cellular-phone system operators were using sophisticated electronics to tackle the technological challenge of providing cellular telecommunications for speakers moving from one geographic "cell" to another.

rate of 32,000 per day. Although the growth rate had tapered off somewhat, there was certainly a lot more life in the market, and many companies wanted to be a part of it. The technology of a cellular system is simple: talking channels are assigned to a particular geographic "cell" (usually several kilometers in diameter). The system operators expand or contract these cells as they see fit and attempt always to accommodate the potential subscribers in a particular cell. If, for instance, the business climate in a particular geographic area increases, then the cell serving these people should be made smaller to maintain the same density of subscribers. Adjacent cells are assigned different frequencies and are allowed additional talking channels, but several cells farther out, the same frequencies can be reassigned. Thus, the system can be expanded indefinitely.

The trick (one that can be solved only with sophisticated electronics) is to accommodate a moving speaker (for example, in a vehicle) who leaves one cell and enters another. In this case a handoff must take place; that is, the cellular phone in use must switch from the frequency it has been using in the first cell to some other vacant and assigned frequency in the second cell. Since each cell requires a central location, called a cell site, comprising a significant amount of electronics, not to mention a tower with a radio antenna reaching out to all the mobile speakers, system operators wish to handle as many subscribers as possible within each cell. This need leads to a continuing technological problem: what method should be used for the cell-site-to-user communications? In 1996 there were essentially three methods, each with several variations.

The vast majority of subscribers in the U.S. used the advanced mobile phone system (AMPS), which employed an analog (as opposed to digital) technology known as frequency-division multiple access. Although not state-of-the-art, it was quite satisfactory for most users. Unfortunately, AMPS was not particularly secure (i.e., owners of "adjusted" cellular phones can listen in on other conversations), and scrambling could be accomplished only by the addition of a considerable amount of electronic equipment.

A second system, known as time-division multiple access (TDMA), employed digital technology to break up an audio signal into a string of 0s and 1s. It was quite secure and provided approximately three times the capacity of AMPS. This advantage meant that fewer cell sites would be required for a service provider. A variation of this TDMA system, called global system for mobile (GSM) communications, had become the standard in much of the world outside the U.S. GSM offered economies of scale, acceptable voice quality, and ease of mobility. It had frequently been suggested that the GSM technology be adapted for use in the U.S.

The third system was extremely complex and used more software and hardware than the other two. Called code-division multiple access (CDMA), it was adapted from "spread spectrum" technologies of the military and was extremely secure. Furthermore, it had 20 times the capacity of AMPS. In 1996 several cellular systems were running trials on CDMA.

Personal communications services

The continuing growth of cellular communications led government and industry in the U.S. to search for additional ways to satisfy the obvious need not only for ordinary telephone service but also for special services and features, smaller telephones, and the ability to use cellular phones as one would a standard wired telephone. This search led to the personal communications services industry. Additional frequency bands were allocated for their use, and rather than assign them to the first comers or by way of a lottery, the FCC auctioned them off through a sophisticated bidding contest that brought the U.S. treasury billions of dollars.

Although some industry observers identified the PCS systems (most of which used CDMA as the modulation scheme of choice) as additional cellular systems, it was likely that they would be much more. Only time would define the many features to be provided. A looming problem in the wireless communications industry was the growing presence of antenna towers. In 1996 there were some 25,000 such towers in the U.S., and as PCS made its debut another 100,000 would likely be required. Communities were starting to recognize that this could pose a problem and were rejecting applications for permits, but few had come up with acceptable solutions.

Satellite communications

Yet another wireless telecommunications technology was the low-Earth-orbit (LEO) system. LEOs are satellites that communicate directly with handheld telephones on Earth. Because these satellites are relatively low—less than 1,500 km (930 mi), rather than the 35,900 km (22,300 mi) of a geosynchronous satellite—they move across the sky quite rapidly.

In a LEO the communications equipment on a satellite acts much like the cell site of a cellular system. It "catches" the call from Earth and passes it to an Earth-based switching system. Because of the speed of the satellite, it is frequently necessary to hand off a particular call to a second satellite just rising over the horizon. This is akin to a cellular system except that in this case it is the cell site that is moving rather than the subscriber.

Far-fetched as such a scheme might seem, by 1996 there were several in the planning stage. The most noted was Iridium, created by Motorola, which would

utilize 66 satellites. A second system, called Globalstar, would employ 48 satellites. A third, with major backing from Craig McCaw (founder of McCaw Cellular Communications) and Bill Gates (of Microsoft), was called Teledesic. It would use approximately 840 small communications satellites.

Direct broadcasting satellites

Satellites are used not only for telecommunications but also for the transmission of television signals. Studios (or their transmission affiliates) transmit TV signals to geosynchronous satellites, which retransmit them to the head-end facilities of the thousands of cable TV providers in the world. In some cases subscribers receive these signals directly themselves with the aid of unscrambling technology obtained from the originating company. Originally, the antennae required for such an operation were large—often as much as 3 m (10 ft) in diameter. As a consequence, this method of operation fell out of vogue. Technology improved, however, and the 3-m dish was eventually replaced with a 46-cm (18-in) dish. The result was the direct broadcast satellite system, in which the antenna can be clamped to a windowsill or mounted on a simple stand outside the house or on the roof. Such a system was not only physically more attractive but also less expensive. Prices for the dish plus the electronics that went with it dropped below $500, and promotions offering both for $199 were common.

The DBS systems could provide 200 or more channels, and because the transmission technique was digital (rather than analog), the quality was excellent. There was a limit, however, to the number of provid-

ers because of the limited capacity for satellites that transmit the signal to Earth. The "orbital slots" available over the Equator were carefully controlled by the International Telecommunication Union (ITU), the global body that allocated the original DBS slots in the 1980s. The ITU's rules required each nation to coordinate its satellite slots with its neighbors.

DBS systems were not without their shortcomings. Because their footprint was very large (i.e., they served a large number of subscribers), there could be virtually no local news coverage. If local coverage was important to a subscriber, then he or she also needed to receive local broadcast TV or subscribe to conventional cable TV. Another disadvantage was that a DBS system could not be interactive. In other words, whereas a standard telephone system, cellular telephone system, or PCS system could accommodate two-way conversations, the DBS system could not. Hence it could not be a replacement for a telephone system, and even ordering pay-per-view movies was a challenge.

Even a conventional cable television system could be modified to accommodate two-way conversations. Nevertheless, because such systems were designed with "broadcast" in mind, special equipment had to be added to permit upstream communications, but by 1996 this was being done by cable TV companies as fast as possible. These companies recognized that they had a wire going into more than 63% of the homes in the U.S. and that this wire was capable of carrying telephone conversations as well as TV pictures.

—Robert E. Stoffels

See also Feature Article: Robots on the Move.

ENERGY

World economic growth, increasing at more than twice the rate of population growth, was the dominant factor in determining energy demand during the past year. In 1996 world energy consumption was approximately 380 quadrillion BTU (British thermal units), compared with 350 quadrillion BTU in 1993. During this same period, U.S. consumption of energy rose from 87 quadrillion BTU to approximately 93 quadrillion BTU. The Energy Information Administration and World Energy Projection System determined that 70% of future energy growth will occur in previously less developed areas of the world. In particular, the growth in demand from Asia is expected to be explosive during the next eight years. An estimate that assumes the rapid advance of China and India to the current per capita income level of South Korea concludes that worldwide demand for oil will increase by a factor of three owing to that growth alone. While new electrical power generating capacity in North America is expected to grow by 118 GW (gigawatts; one billion watts) by 2004, Asian markets are expected to grow by 500 GW, with investments projected at $350 billion in China and $280 billion in India.

Because economic development and growth in per capita income are the principal drivers of demand, it seems certain that demand for electricity for lighting, home appliances, and industrial production will continue to grow faster than other energy forms, just as it has for the last 20 years. Forecasts of the mix of energy sources necessary to meet this increased demand vary somewhat from study to study, depending on several factors, including assumptions about technological

innovation and adaptation. Some studies predict that worldwide energy demand and supply will diverge around 2015 as rapid economic growth continues.

By 1997 natural gas was gaining a larger market share relative to other fuels, especially with the development of new electrical generating plants throughout the world. Projections indicated that natural gas would soon equal the use of coal for electrical power generation. Nuclear energy, which by 1997 supplied about 20% of the world's electricity, was increasing slightly owing primarily to growth in less developed countries and was projected to level off after the year 2000 due to plant retirements in developed countries. Renewable energy forms (hydroelectric, solar, wind, geothermal, and biomass) were growing modestly, with most of their increase attributable to several large hydroelectric projects nearing completion in China. Growth in the use of these energy forms varied significantly throughout the world.

Energy and security

Oil is the lifeblood of the industrialized world, and disruptions in oil supply can have severe economic and military consequences. Middle East oil reserves are critical to world oil supply. Each of the oil market disruptions of the 1970s, '80s, and '90s was due to political instability in the Persian Gulf region. In 1996 fully 35% of the world's oil supply came from the Persian Gulf states of Saudi Arabia, Iran, United Arab Emirates, Kuwait, Qatar, and Iraq. Because it is the easiest area from which to increase production rapidly in order to meet growth in demand for the Asian nations, Persian Gulf states are ex-

pected to gain even greater market share over the next few years. Their percentage of world consumption is expected to reach about 50% in 2010.

Yet this area continues to be the most politically unstable region, and the conflicts there promise to become even more dangerous as the combatants acquire increasing numbers of weapons of mass destruction. The vulnerability of Japan, the U.S., and other advanced nations to disruptions of, or attacks on, Persian Gulf oil-supply systems is quite high. The U.S. has once again increased its oil imports to greater than 50% of its total consumption, while fully 100% of Japan's oil is imported. In September 1996 the Trilateral Commission representing Europe, North America, and Japan published a major report entitled *Maintaining Energy Security in a Global Context.* On July 15, 1996, U.S. Pres. Bill Clinton issued Executive Order 13,010, which established a commission on critical infrastructure protection.

The vulnerability of critical infrastructures was amply demonstrated on Aug. 10, 1996, when a series of events caused the second-largest electrical power blackout ever experienced in North America. Fourteen western U.S. states and two Canadian provinces were affected in an area covering 4.7 million sq km (1.8 million sq mi). Four million customers lost power. Similar disruptions occurred in Malaysia and Kuala Lumpur. With the increasing connectivity of energy distribution systems around the world, the reliability of such infrastructures becomes a security issue.

Oil and gas

Improvements in oil and gas exploration and in enhanced recovery methods were improving the economic attractiveness of these fossil fuels. Horizontal drilling was routinely used in oil exploration and recovery. Wells were drilled horizontally for thousands of meters while being maintained well within relatively thin strata (layers in a rock formation) and across natural fractures in the reservoir. Such drilling was revitalizing development in many mature fields. Capabilities were developed so that two to four horizontal wells could be extended into the reservoir from a single vertical well.

Two-dimensional seismic analysis was used as an exploration tool. It provides a vertical slice image through the reservoir. Three-dimensional seismic analysis uses a two-dimensional array of surface sources and receivers and a sophisticated means of processing the collected data to obtain a stack of horizontal slice images through the reservoir, thus providing data as a function of depth. Recently, lower costs allowed even small independent oil companies to use three-dimensional seismic surveys to locate drill sites, and larger surveys coupled with faster computers have been providing unprecedented reservoir detail in the Gulf of Mexico.

Natural gas was becoming an attractive, lower-cost alternative for electrical power generation, particularly for utilities that were seeking to achieve compliance with emissions standards. The use of natural gas for electrical power generation had by 1997 grown to approximately 10% of U.S. electricity production, and use was also increasing as an automotive and truck fuel for similar reasons.

Maintaining the low-cost position for natural gas was challenging due to the increase in production from difficult environments, including very deep (greater than 5,000 m) onshore areas, offshore areas in the Gulf of Mexico, and certain rock formations. Transfer of technology from other applications into gas exploration and recovery was, however, having a significant impact in this regard. New drill bits based on tunnel excavation technology were under development and showed promise of drilling as much as 25% faster than current bits. To release gas from tight rock formations, advanced stimulation techniques using hydraulic fracturing were being applied, employing three-dimensional modeling to model the reservoir while the fracture was taking place.

Coal

Coal accounts for 25% of the worldwide demand for energy. This percentage has declined somewhat due to competition from other fuels such as natural gas. In the U.S. coal usage during the past year increased moderately to about 22 quadrillion BTU, while it declined in other developed countries because of fuel competition and in former Soviet Union countries because of economic conditions. In Asian countries usage increased to represent 40% of world consumption, with China alone accounting for 25% of world consumption.

Concern over environmental impact limited coal usage in some developed countries. Policies or regulations to limit sulfur dioxide caused some switching to coal with a lower content of sulfur and encouraged utilities to invest in equipment to reduce emissions. In addition to concern over sulfur dioxide, coal has the highest carbon content of all the fossil fuels. Carbon dioxide emissions per unit of energy obtained from coal are almost double those from natural gas and 20% higher than from oil. This fact and the international commitment to reduce emissions of carbon dioxide led to the development of strategies and technologies to mix other fuels with coal in order to reduce overall emissions.

Other hydrocarbon resources

Future energy supplies may likely come from other sources such as adapting low-cost or waste hydrocarbon energy forms to current fuel characteristics and requirements. An increased focus was being placed on coprocessing or coburning to utilize low-grade or waste hydrocarbons (such as plastics) with conventional hydrocarbon fuels (such as coal, oil, and gas). Additionally, new techniques for the production and transportation of low-cost hydrocarbon resources utilizing existing infrastructures were being developed. For example, the Venezuelan state oil company was producing and marketing a fuel called Orimulsion that resembled No. 6 fuel oil. The name derives from the large bitumen reserves in the Orinoco Belt of east-central Venezuela. Whereas bitumen is an extremely viscous, tarlike material, Orimulsion is a pumpable stable emulsion of 70% bitumen, 30% water (by weight), and a small amount of surfactant. As such, it can be easily transported and distributed. In the future, development of new catalysts and processes to convert Orimulsion to clean liquid transportation fuels could dramatically reduce the worldwide dependence on crude oil.

Nuclear power

With more than 430 nuclear power plants in operation worldwide producing more than 343,000 MW of electricity and 39 plants under construction projected to produce another 32,000 MW, nuclear power represents both an aging and an evolving infrastructure with tremendous inertia. Regulatory requirements and rigorous efforts to maximize plant safety through design, construction, operational, and maintenance practices also tend to slow the development and implementation of new technologies. Thus, the nuclear industry in 1997 found itself at a crossroads. In many industrialized countries some plants had been operating for more than 20 years, while in less developed countries the nuclear power infrastructure was just now being created. Older plants required new technologies in order to remain safe and to maintain public confidence; newer plants must implement technologies that are even safer than current designs to gain public confidence. In addition, new technologies that decrease the construction and operational costs of nuclear power plants will make them more economically competitive with conventional power sources. Record levels of safety performance and reliable operation have been achieved in the past five years, and further improvement was being sought with new technology and knowledge. For instance, the reactor pressure vessel that contains heat-producing fuel elements slowly degrades with time. Russian-built plants that are most susceptible to this type of aging have been annealed to restore the vessel to a like-new condition. In 1996 the U.S. nuclear power industry and regulators successfully demonstrated that Western-style plants can also be annealed in the future, well before any safety issues arise.

In 1996 the U.S. Nuclear Regulatory Commission certified the Combustion Engineering System 80+ and the General Electric simplified boiling-water reactor. The advanced pressurized-water reactor being developed by engineers at Westinghouse, the AP600, was undergoing certification review. These advanced and evolutionary plants featured simplified designs and passive safety systems that operate without the intervention of operators or active system components.

Fusion energy

From its beginnings fusion research has been seen as a long-term endeavor. The engineering challenge of containing a fusion reaction with its 100-million-degree temperatures is exceedingly formidable. Since the start of systematic work on magnetic confinement of fusion in the 1950s, however, fusion energy research has made steady advances. The last several years, in particular, have been marked by dramatic attainments. While researchers remained far from a demonstration of a practical fusion reactor, the increase in requisite understanding was demonstrated by the successes of the Tokamak Fusion Test Reactor (TFTR) project at the Princeton Plasma Physics Laboratory and at facilities elsewhere in the world.

A tokamak is a doughnut-shaped reactor chamber used experimentally to explore magnetic confinement of the fusion plasma. By November 1994, TFTR had achieved about 11 MW of fusion power per discharge from deuterium-tritium (D-T) reactions, about 100 million times the power produced in tokamak discharges 20 years earlier. The energy gain (fusion power divided by heating power) for the recent shots was 0.27. More importantly, the results showed that D-T plasmas are better behaved than the deuterium plasmas studied earlier, achieving higher temperatures and longer confinement times. TFTR's longest-run period ended in August 1996. The 20,000 plasma pulses since late 1993 represented the world's first extensive D-T magnetic fusion experiments. In the ensuing maintenance period tritium was removed successfully by several techniques and then processed by the cleanup system and trapped in special containers, demonstrating several aspects of the tritium technology needed for the operation of fusion reactors.

Fusion research is a truly international effort, with some of the prime facilities being operated in Europe, Japan, and Russia. The Joint European Torus (JET), with the largest plasma volume, has come closer than any other magnetic fusion experiment to achieving the plasmas required in a reactor. It was the first to demonstrate significant fusion power from D-T discharges, and new experiments with a 50/50 D-T mixture were planned with the aim of achieving 10 MW of fusion power for several seconds. In deuterium plasmas JET achieved conditions that are equivalent to "break-even"; that is, the fusion power produced under the same conditions with a D-T plasma would equal the plasma losses. A significant step was taken in 1996 for plasma research in Europe when the Council of the European Union approved an extension of the JET project to the end of 1999.

In Japan significant progress was achieved at the Japan Atomic Energy Research Institute's tokamak facility. In contrast to TFTR and JET, that machine was not equipped to operate with tritium. Plasma performance with deuterium plasmas has, however, yielded remarkable values of energy confinement time and central density. In August 1996 an equivalent energy gain value of about 0.7 was achieved. In October energy gain equivalents greater than one were reported.

Solar thermal energy

Solar thermal energy as a source of generating electricity was benefiting from programs that promoted its use. Capacity estimates in 1997 ranged as high as 400 MW. In 1996 the first solar thermal power plant to demonstrate efficient, cost-effective storage was dedicated and began operation near Barstow, Calif. Solar Two, a 10-MW solar power pilot plant, was built and operated by a consortium of western U.S. utilities and industry and the U.S. government. Solar Two uses a field of large Sun-tracking mirrors that focus on a receiver to heat a molten-nitrate-salt fluid

to more than 565° C (1,050° F). Because the heated salt can be stored efficiently in large tanks, it can be used to produce steam to power the plant's electric generator well after the Sun has set, providing high-value electricity to meet a utility's evening peak loads. All of Solar Two's operational capabilities were demonstrated in 1996, but extensive testing and evaluation were expected to continue for two to three years.

The solar thermal technology that uses a parabolic dish concentrator to focus solar energy to a Stirling engine to produce electricity holds the world's record of 30% for system efficiency in converting solar energy to electricity. (A Stirling engine is a type of external-combustion engine.) To make these 25-kw systems practical and cost-effective, two technology development efforts were underway. Major advances in the design of the solar receiver,

which collects the solar energy and transmits it to the engine, allowed the use of liquid sodium in a heat-pipe configuration to increase dramatically the operating temperature, efficiency, and lifetime of the receiver. Advances in the development of the Stirling engine and a parallel development of the engine for possible use in a hybrid electric vehicle design significantly enhanced the engine's efficiency, reliability, and manufacturability. Coupled with available solar dish concentrator technology, full systems utilizing these advances were expected to be demonstrated during the next two years.

Solar photovoltaic energy

Solar photovoltaic energy utilizes the photovoltaic ("light-induced voltage") effect to convert solar energy directly into electricity by using sunlight to create mobile negatively charged (electrons) and positively charged (holes) carriers in a semiconductor material. Photovoltaic systems are often cost-effective in less developed countries and isolated rural regions where no existing electrical distribution systems exist. Worldwide, these applications in 1997 accounted for approximately 400 MW. Photovoltaic systems are economical because the energy is generated near the point of use and matches the electrical load profiles.

Distributed photovoltaic systems operate in conjunction with the electric utility power grid. Types of distributed photovoltaic systems include those mounted on the roofs of buildings and those that use photovoltaic modules specifically designed to replace various building materials without affecting architectural aesthetics. An example of a commercial rooftop system is

Solar Two, the first solar thermal power plant to achieve cost-effective energy storage, uses large Sun-tracking mirrors to heat a molten-nitrate-salt fluid in a tower-mounted central receiver. All of the plant's operational capabilities were tested successfully during the past year.

Joseph Sohm—The Image Works

A Georgia Tech graduate student stands on the rooftop of the university's natatorium, on which a distributed photovoltaic system has been mounted. The system converts solar energy directly into electricity.

Gary Meek—Georgia Institute of Technology

the 340-kw system on the roof of the natatorium at the Georgia Institute of Technology. This natatorium was the venue for the swimming and diving events of the 1996 Olympic Games. Examples of building-integrated systems are photovoltaic "shingles," photovoltaic "curtain walls," and photovoltaic "awnings." An integrated photovoltaic module and roofing shingle was introduced in 1996.

Advances in putting photovoltaic technologies into applications were supported during the past year by technological improvements. Record efficiency of 17.7% (conversion from sunlight to electricity) was measured for a laboratory-made copper indium diselenide photovoltaic cell. Only a thin film (less than one-millionth

of a meter) of the material was used, and so this technology has the potential to be very inexpensive.

Biomass energy

Biomass energy is derived from wood, wood wastes, municipal solid wastes, and from other plants, including ethanol derived from corn. Biomass for nonelectrical uses in the U.S. accounts for approximately 3% of the total marketed energy consumption. In electricity generation, biomass accounts for approximately 70 billion kw-hr per year. Biomass is attractive because it is a renewable energy source.

During the last two years interest in cofiring biomass with coal has been increasing. Typically, up to 15% biomass is fired with coal in a coal facility. Such a scheme allows biomass to benefit from the specialized staff and sophisticated equipment available for large-scale coal combustion while providing some relief from the global-warming effects of coal. Bio-

mass also generally produces lower gas pollutant emissions than coal, and cofiring blends benefit from this low pollutant production. Ethanol for use as a transportation fuel additive has grown substantially, benefiting from tax credits that began in 1986 and were scheduled to continue to 2000.

Wind energy

Children seem to understand intuitively that wind can provide the power to turn a simple pinwheel. Converting wind power to electricity has, however, proven to be more difficult than even highly trained scientists and engineers believed just a few years ago. But by the end of 1996, wind energy had become a clear leader in renewable energy technologies, reaching a worldwide installed capacity of about 6,000 MW. This represents tens of thousands of individual wind turbines, enough to supply electricity to over two million American homes. More significantly, these turbines were installed in diverse locations, ranging from such less developed countries as India to such developed nations as Germany and Denmark. This growth was fueled by a "next generation" of larger wind turbines. each of which produces 500 kw to 1 MW.

Wind turbines have evolved from small, rigid configurations that produced electricity for tens of cents per kilowatt-hour to larger units that can be as inexpensive as five cents per kilowatt-hour. Advanced designs could, in the next few years, reach less than three cents per kilowatt-hour.

Geothermal energy

Electricity from geothermal energy, produced by tapping into the heat that is stored in the Earth, accounts each year for about 18 billion kw-hr in the U.S. Projected expansion owing to new technology was expected to be offset by a decline at the Geysers site in California, where reservoir water was being depleted. In 1997 total capacity in the U.S. was about 3,000 MW, as compared with the capacity from geothermal sources worldwide of about 10,000 MW.

During the past year the initial development and successful field testing of high-temperature tools for geothermal wells was conducted. The tools, which are deployed on nonelectrical lines, provide more accurate data on geothermal reservoir conditions in a more cost-effective manner than was previously possible; they measure reservoir temperature and pressure conditions, identify fractures that contain fluid, and sample the chemical composition of the fluids.

Fluids are lost in fractures or caverns in the subsurface rocks because of the highly fractured nature of rock formations associated with geothermal resources. This "lost circulation" causes significantly expensive problems in drilling geothermal wells, accounting for up to 10% of the total expense of a geothermal power project. Technology to solve lost circulation was under development; it included advanced instrumentation for measuring the flow rate and a downhole tool to improve the efficiency of cementing operations for plugging zones of lost circulation.

Process-control technology

The growing importance of computers and the dynamic changes in both computer software and hardware are increasingly evident. But not so obvious is the impact on energy technology made by computers and computer simulations. For example, an on-line, computer-controlled induction heater under development in 1997 was designed to allow a 40–60% savings in energy and cost in the case-hardening of automotive bearings and gears. Broad application of this "smart" heat-treating technology may save one quadrillion BTU over the next 20 years.

Other "smart" processes based on computer simulations have been developed to enhance the efficiency of manufacturing cast components, so that design and manufacture can be done in days rather than months. In the manufacturing of welded components, for example, computers used for close coupling of all project stages from the preliminary design through the welded product may revolutionize this industry, enabling products of improved quality to be produced much faster, cheaper, and with lower energy use. Additionally, process-control procedures being developed for petroleum refining can es-

tablish optimum process conditions for different feedstocks and desired product slates. This can potentially save billions of dollars and reduce the environmental impact of less efficient processes.

—C. Paul Robinson and Joan B. Woodard

ENVIRONMENT

In 1996 concerns about feeding the world's growing population without depleting the Earth's natural resources climbed to the top of many environmental agendas. Some analysts warned that the year's record lows in world grain reserves were an early indication that the global resources used to grow food have become overextended. In the past year the world's population grew by 87 million people, an increase that coincided with worsening soil erosion, water shortages, and desertification that claimed thousands of hectares of arable land.

One of the year's most hopeful stories was the progress made on global atmospheric issues. The Intergovernmental Panel on Climate Change, established in 1988 by the World Meteorological Organization and the United Nations Environment Programme, validated the debated connection between global warming and the burning of fossil fuels. The U.S. government, which had been slow to curb the consumption of fossil fuels, led a charge for mandatory controls on carbon dioxide emissions. The continuing phaseout of chlorofluorocarbons and other ozone-depleting chemicals also helped prevent further damage to the ozone layer, although experts predicted that it will take another 50 years for its full recovery, even at reduced rates of emission.

Environment and agriculture

There is a growing environmental urgency surrounding one of the most fundamental human needs: putting food on the table of the world's burgeoning human population. The problem was underscored in 1996 when world grain reserves fell to record lows of 229 million metric tons, a mere 46 days of supply. In November participating nations at the World Food Summit in Rome blamed the drop in grain supplies on a long-standing overuse of farmlands, which has resulted in diminishing yields and mounting problems of pollution, soil erosion, and water shortages.

Summit members warned of still greater pressure to come on shrinking farmland. To keep pace with a projected population growth of around 85 million new people each year, they acknowledged that annual grain production needed to expand by 27 million metric tons. This increase in demand, however, will come at a time of dwindling natural resources. Since 1981,

for example, 9% of the world's grain lands have been lost to urbanization, industrial installations, roads, and other developments. In the mid-1990s alone, desertification claimed 60,000 sq km (23,000 sq mi) of agricultural land annually and severely depleted the productivity of another 200,000 sq km (77,000 sq mi). Soil erosion continued to threaten the fertility of farmland. According to David Pimentel and his colleagues at Cornell University, Ithaca, N.Y., for example, some 75 billion metric tons of soil were lost to erosion, enough to grow all the grain needed to make up the diets of the world's 750 million undernourished people. Without better conservation measures, at least 1.4 million sq km (540,000 sq mi), an area the size of Alaska, will lose most good-quality soil over the next two decades.

Furthermore, in the past 15 years there has been little growth in irrigated water supplies, a critical shortfall since irrigated lands comprise ⅙ of all croplands and

produce more than ⅓ of the total output of food. (*See* Year in Review: LIFE SCIENCES: *Ecology.*)

The World Food Summit also drew attention to an alarming depletion in wild gene pools. Fresh germ plasm, often derived from wild relatives of modern crops or so-called primitive cultivars, are used routinely by plant breeders to add beneficial characteristics to commercial crops. According to the U.S. Department of Agriculture, the genetic boost has resulted in a 1% annual increase in U.S. domestic-crop production. In commercial terms, the genetic advantage translated to earned income for farmers valued at more than $1.3 billion in 1996.

In the early 1980s the U.S. National Academy of Sciences warned that existing germ-plasm collections were "completely inadequate." The academy's assessment has largely gone unheeded. Because of a protracted breeding trend toward genetic uniformity, the U.S. wheat crop lost most of its genetic variability. The U.S. is not alone. Ninety-five percent of Greece's native wheats have become extinct. In Turkey and throughout much of the Middle East, wild progenitors find sanctuary from grazing animals only in graveyards and castle ruins.

Summit participants also focused on another long-term threat to the world's food supply—increases in solar ultraviolet-B (UVB) radiation resulting from the depletion of the Earth's ozone layer. Research by Alan Teramura of the University of Maryland has shown that excess UVB radiation can severely injure a host of vulnerable plants, including several major food crops. Predicted losses in wheat yields due to UVB overexposure were es-

Rising levels of disposable income in many developing countries have resulted in the adoption of Western patterns of consumption. Here, an Avon zone manager delivers new products to company representatives in the rain forests of Brazil.

timated at 5%; the production of soybeans, a major source of the world's protein, could be cut by as much as 25%. (*See* Year in Review: FOOD AND AGRICULTURE: *Agriculture.*)

Controlling overconsumption

In 1996 several major U.S. foundations, including the John D. and Catherine T. MacArthur Foundation in Chicago, the Pew Charitable Trusts in Philadelphia, and the Merck Family Fund in Takoma Park, Md., announced the addition of a new program area that focused on the effects of material consumption worldwide. By including this new area of emphasis, the foundations recognized that their traditional focus on issues of environment, population, and development was inseparable from an analysis of the amounts and kinds of resources that people consume and the waste and pollution that they generate. Its inclusion also reflected their concern that a world projected to contain 8.3 billion people by 2025—all of them expecting to consume what they perceive as a necessary and fair share of global resources—will surely place extreme if not unsustainable pressures on the environment.

The new focus recognized the growing inequity between industrialized and developing nations concerning natural-resource consumption and environmental pollution. Although the U.S. contained less than 5% of the world's population, for example, it utilized nearly 30% of the Earth's resources. Higher levels of consumption in industrialized countries also resulted in greater amounts of waste. In 1996 the U.S. population of 265 million people pumped 1.5 billion metric tons of carbon—a major contributor to global warming—into the

atmosphere. Although the U.S. has only about ⅕ the population of China, it emitted approximately 20% more carbon into the atmosphere. Industrialized countries also generated 75% of the world's toxic chemicals and hazardous wastes.

Public-opinion polls in 1996 revealed that more than half of all Americans and an even greater proportion of interviewees in other wealthy nations acknowledged that "changes in life-style" and "reduced consumption" were part of the solution to environmental problems. At the same time, the "American dream" became a model for many emerging nations, including those of Eastern Europe and the former Soviet Union, where newly affluent people now total 150 million. The number of consumers grew in other parts of the world as well, including 350 million people in China and 80 million in India, along with millions more in the emerging countries of Taiwan, Indonesia, Malaysia, Thailand, Turkey, Venezuela, Brazil, and Argentina. The increase in disposable income was perhaps best illustrated by the growth in the purchase of automobiles. In 1996 there were as many new cars sold in developing Asia as in Western Europe and North America combined, a statistic that worried environmental analysts since motor vehicles currently account for nearly 20% of carbon dioxide emissions worldwide.

Energy

Alternative energies accounted for a small but high-growth sector of the energy industry. Solar-powered consumer electronic devices in Japan topped 100 million. In Norway 50,000 homes were powered by photovoltaics, thin silicon cells that convert sunlight into electricity.

Photovoltaic systems and other forms of solar energy have become especially cost-effective in less-developed countries, most of which lack an abundance of fossil fuels and have many isolated rural regions that are cut off from energy-distribution systems such as national grids for electricity. The numbers are still small, but growing. In Kenya, for example, 20,000 homes, less than 1% of the country's households, were electrified with solar cells. In Colombia there were 30,000 solar water heaters, while more than 25% of households in Jordan used solar hot-water systems.

By the end of 1996, tens of thousands of wind turbines throughout the world produced about 6,000 MW of power. Although this accounts for only 0.1% of the world's electricity, the use of wind power is on the rise. Generating more than 1,000 MW of power, Germany led the world in wind-power production, followed by India at 500 MW. China planned to produce 1,300 MW of wind power by the year 2000. By the year 2005, Denmark was projected to derive 10% of its electricity from wind power. In California 1,700 turbines generated enough electricity to supply all of San Francisco's households. The increased use of wind power led to a ⅔ drop in the cost of wind-generated electricity over the past decade. In many regions of the world, constructing wind generators became cheaper than building new coal plants. Indeed, wind power may soon rank as the world's cheapest power source.

Great strides also were made in energy efficiency. In Japan more than 80% of homes were lit by long-lasting and low-power compact fluorescent bulbs.

New advances in architectural design and energy technologies resulted in big

Solar energy has become an important source of electricity for many less-developed countries that lack access to fossil fuels and national power grids. Villagers in Kenya (above) rely on the Sun's rays to operate a local water pump.

energy savings for both commercial and residential buildings. Swedish architects developed a design for office blocks that are so well insulated that they are kept warm through workers' body heat alone. In the U.S., the internationally known energy-efficiency expert Amory Lovins of the Rocky Mountain Institute, Snowmass, Colo., and his wife, Hunter Lovins, who live at an elevation of 2,100 m (7,000 ft) in the Colorado Rockies, unveiled a model energy installation for their home that consumed less than $50 per year in heat. In their widely publicized solar-powered house, the Lovins reduced their heating costs by intensively insulating ceilings, walls, windows, and doors, as well as by installing the latest in heat-conserving appliances and water systems in the kitchen and bathroom.

In 1970 manufacturers produced as many bicycles as they did cars. In 1996 there were three times as many new bicycles as new cars, totalling 120 million, or about one bicycle for every 50 people worldwide. Nearly 95% of these bicycles were manufactured as cheap, efficient sources of transportation for people in less-developed countries. (For more information on energy technologies, *see* Year in Review: ENERGY.)

Government and industry

The U.S. Department of Defense's (DOD's) Environmental Security Program, established in 1993, inaugurated a new project known as the Rapid Commercialization Initiative (RCI). The RCI is part of the program's mission to facilitate the timely cleanup of decommissioned or reassigned DOD facilities that have been seriously contaminated, as well as to invest in pollution prevention by developing cleaner weapons technologies that comply with U.S. environmental laws.

A cooperative effort between government agencies and private industry, the RCI includes 10 projects that will test new technologies for monitoring and assessing pollution, emission control, pollution prevention and remediation, and environmental restoration. The goal of the project is to identify the barriers that prevent the rapid commercialization of new environmental technologies. Among the projects being explored are portable instruments that measure such serious contaminants as trichloroethylene and trihalomethanes in groundwater and chemical remediation processes that destroy hazardous hydrocarbon pollutants in soil.

Minnesota Mining & Manufacturing (3M) corporation, St. Paul, Minn., was awarded the 1996 Presidential Award for Sustainable Development and received a ranking of third-best company in the world from the Hamburg Institute, a German environmental organization, for its corporate-wide environmental initiative known as

Pollution Prevention Pays (3P) program. Instituted in 1975, the program enlisted the help of employees in eliminating pollution at its source in the company. Because of its efforts to more efficiently manage and recycle waste, the company prevented the discharge of 700,000 tons of pollutants in the past two decades. To date, the model program has saved 3M more than $750 million.

The debate on curbing global warming took on a new twist. Fossil-fuel industries, the main source of greenhouse gases, were challenged by the insurance industry, a corporate giant worth $1.5 trillion worldwide (half again as much as the oil industry). At stake were the industry's ever-rising payouts in the destructive aftermath of natural catastrophes, such as floods, droughts, and hurricanes. According to some experts, the frequency and severity of these weather events are exacerbated by the effects of global warming. In 1996 insurance leaders on both sides of the Atlantic asserted that if the trend persists, it could precipitate a crisis in the industry by the year 2000 that could have major repercussions for banks and financial programs such as pension funds. According to Frank Nutter, president of the Reinsurance Association of America, a Washington, D.C.-based group of companies that write property and casualty insurance, "Climate change could bankrupt the industry."

—Norman Myers

See also Feature Articles: AN APPETITE FOR POISON; UNNATURAL SELECTION.

FOOD AND AGRICULTURE

Worldwide grain production reached an all-time high in 1996, with steady growth predicted for the global agricultural economy over the next decade. Agricultural researchers continued to play an important role in fueling this economic expansion by developing new food-processing techniques, improving crop stocks, and pioneering cultivation techniques that lowered the costs of farming.

Exploring the connections between diet and health also was the focus of several important research efforts. Investigators continued studies of the healing and disease-prevention properties of fruits, vegetables, and herbs; developed a new fat substitute; and collected data on people's attitudes toward food and weight loss in an effort to combat the growing problem of obesity in industrialized countries.

AGRICULTURE

Driven by a desire to capitalize on high prices worldwide, farmers in several countries dramatically increased their grain acreage. As a result, the global production of grain, especially wheat, rice, and coarse grain (corn sorghum, barley, and oats) hit a new record of 1.84 billion tons, surpassing consumption for the first time in four years. Despite the surplus, prices remained strong due to the demand by major Asian markets.

The global production of meat and dairy products remained steady, but poultry production was down by 10% from 1995. The drop came after a decade of robust growth in the U.S. poultry industry that was fueled by rising demand in both domestic and foreign markets. Nonetheless, the poultry market remained strong. Since 1993 the U.S. consumption of chicken per capita

has surpassed beef and pork. Improvements in poultry management, technology, and genetic stock have enhanced feed efficiency and raised average bird weight. As a result, output of ready-to-cook poultry meat has increased almost 6% per year since the early 1960s. In the U.S. about 18% of the domestic poultry produced in 1996 was exported.

The U.S. Department of Agriculture (USDA) expected the global agricultural economy to grow about 3% over the next decade. This figure is well above the growth rate for the first half of the 1990s. Economic growth in agriculture for developing countries over the next 10 years was expected to average about 5.5%, increasing at a somewhat faster pace than it had over the past decade. These macroeconomic growth projections, combined with freer markets, fewer trade barriers, and fewer price controls, were expected to support strong increases in international agricultural trade.

Troubles in the Russian agricultural industry prompted a meeting in early 1997 between U.S. Secretary of Agriculture Dan Glickman and Russian Agriculture Minister Viktor Khlystun. The pair focused on problems in the Russian production of food and fiber, which lagged far behind the country's agricultural capacity. Their discussions served as a prelude to a meeting between Russian Prime Minister Viktor Chernomyrdin and U.S. Vice Pres. Al Gore that focused on Russia's need for agricultural assistance and its desire for U.S. support in obtaining investment credits from the World Bank, the Export-Import Bank of the United States, and the Overseas Private Investment Corporation to underwrite agricultural reform.

1996 U.S. Farm Bill

In the U.S. the Federal Agriculture Improvement and Reform Act of 1996, more commonly known as the 1996 Farm Bill, accelerated trends toward phasing out government influence in agriculture by reducing commodity price-support programs. Two previous major farm acts passed by the U.S. Congress had nudged the agricultural industry toward a greater market orientation, but the current Farm Bill, which expires in 2002, stepped up the pace in an effort to stem the rate of increase in the U.S. national debt. In addition to easing the deficit, the bill also sought to make U.S. agriculture more price-competitive in world markets.

Although the Farm Bill was expected to have minimal effects on planting levels for wheat, feed grains, and soybeans, a major shift in production was predicted in some areas. Experts anticipated that the elimination of minimum poundage quotas and the reduction in price supports for edible peanuts, for example, would trigger a decline in peanut production. Some analysts, however, predicted that by reducing supports for sugar, the government may encourage more efficient sugar production. The bill phased out dairy price supports completely by the year 2002.

Nutraceuticals

The market for nutraceutical products—foods or food components that confer medical benefits, including health promotion and disease prevention—continued to grow, representing a $17 billion industry in the U.S. alone. Among the pioneers in the area of natural-products chemistry and the study of the interconnections between food and health were researchers at Rutgers University, New Brunswick, N.J. In July the researchers published the results of an 18-month laboratory study, identifying a compound in asparagus that prevents cultured leukemia cells from multiplying. Found in the vegetable's shoots, the agent, known as asparagus crude saponin (ACS), was found to inhibit the growth of leukemia HL-60 cells by preventing their DNA from replicating. Saponins occur naturally in many plants and are responsible for the active medicinal properties of such herbs as ginseng and licorice. According to the researchers, the cultured cancer cell counts dropped substantially following the introduction of ACS, whereas counts of cultured noncancerous cells treated with the compound remained unaffected. Investigators cautioned that experiments on tissue cultures do not always produce the same results in animals. In 1997 the cancer-

inhibiting effects of ACS were being tested in laboratory rats.

The asparagus study was part of an ambitious program to collect strong scientific data illuminating the effects of natural compounds in fruits, vegetables, and herbs on human health. In addition to asparagus, the New Jersey researchers targeted several other crops for their potential health benefits, including soybeans, broccoli, purple coneflower, and tomatoes. (*See* Table.)

Biotechnology and international markets

The European Union (EU) altered its traditionally strong position against biotechnology in 1996 by allowing genetically engineered crops to become a part of the European food supply. Announcing its ruling that genetically engineered corn (maize) posed no health hazard to humans,

the EU settled an old trade dispute with the U.S. and paved the way for importation of genetically engineered American corn. Similar action was expected regarding soybeans, cotton, and tomatoes, which already were traded internationally. Disregarding the claim by many scientists that genetically altered field- and laboratory-tested crops do not compromise food safety, some consumer and environmental groups were expected to continue to boycott the products.

Despite such concerns, bioengineered crops have made their way into processed foods around the world, including packaged meats, chocolate, baby formula, and syrup. Their use was expected to increase in a wide variety of food products following U.S. approval in 1996 of nearly three dozen genetically engineered crops for consumption.

A Dow-Jones report predicted that the long-term market impact of the EU's decision to open its markets to U.S. bioengineered corn would be minimal, even though the U.S. will export 85 million bushels of corn to the EU during the 1997–98 crop-production year. According to the report, profits will be offset by the increased production due to higher-yielding seeds, resulting in lower commodity prices.

Mad cow disease

A fatal brain disease that researchers suspect may have been transmitted from infected cows to humans in Great Britain became the focus of a major pan-European research effort. Bovine spongiform encephalopathy (BSE), commonly known as "mad cow" disease, was thought to be the cause of an outbreak of a rare human

NUTRACEUTICALS		
crop	compound	health benefit
asparagus	saponin	leukemia and melanoma treatment
blueberry	unknown	antiviral
broccoli and cauliflower	indole carbinol and sulforphane	cancer prevention
cranberry	unknown	prevention and treatment of urinary-tract infection
Echinacea (coneflower)	unknown	immune-system enhancer
feverfew	parthenolide	migraine treatment
hot pepper	capsaicin	arthritis treatment
potato (skin)	unknown	antimutagen
soybean	genestein	prevention of breast and prostate cancer and menopausal hot flashes
strawberry and raspberry	ellagic acid	cancer prevention
tomato	lycopene	prostate cancer treatment

neurological disorder known as Creutzfeldt-Jakob disease (CJD). In 1996 officials investigated reports of 10 cases of a new variant of CJD in young people in Great Britain. After analyzing the proteins thought to transmit these degenerative diseases in humans and livestock, scientists concluded that proteins of the new variant of CJD resembled those of BSE more closely than proteins in older cases of CJD, suggesting a connection between the recent outbreak and BSE.

There were no confirmed cases of BSE in the U.S., and no more than a few hundred were reported in countries outside the U.K. In Britain the primary cause of BSE's spread had been traced to the use of livestock feed containing meat and bone meal (and perhaps other parts of the offal) from infected sheep and possibly cattle. More than 160,000 cases of BSE in cattle have been diagnosed in Britain over the past decade. The EU spent billions of dollars to slaughter infected cattle and to compensate British farmers for their loss.

The focus of the EU's research effort, which was expected to cost $63.5 million, will be BSE in cattle, CJD in humans, and a related disease known as scrapie in sheep. Researchers identified five priority areas including epidemiological and social studies, infectious agents and their transmission, diagnosis, risk assessment, and treatment and prevention. (*See* Year in Review: MEDICAL SCIENCES: *Veterinary Medicine.*)

High-fiber fat substitute

USDA researchers in Peoria, Ill., developed a good-tasting calorie-free fat substitute for use in foods ranging from reduced-calorie cheeses and cheese products to baked goods and food fillers. Called Z-Trim, the product is made from low-cost by-products of food processing, including the hulls of soybeans, rice, peas, and oats or the bran of corn or wheat. In the manufacture of Z-Trim, the plant fibers are broken down before being combined with water to form a substance that mimics the smooth, creamy texture of fat. Unlike olestra, a controversial new fat substitute that has caused gastrointestinal problems in some consumers, Z-Trim is made from natural dietary fibers that are considered safe and beneficial when consumed in normal quantities. (*See* Year in Review: CHEMISTRY: *Applied Chemistry.*)

Greener grass

British scientists reported that they found the key to keeping grass green, even when grass has gone dormant. During a drought several years ago, researchers at the University of Wales, Aberystwyth, noted that a test plot planted with a strain of meadow fescue remained green while surrounding plots of dormant grass yellowed. Genetic tests revealed that the grass, a natural mutant, lacked the enzyme that breaks down chlorophyll, the green pigment that enables plants to photosynthesize light energy into chemical energy. Scientists transferred the gene responsible for the enzyme deficiency into other grasses. Not only did the gene enhance the cosmetic appearance of these grasses, but it also boosted their nutritional potential for livestock grazing. Chlorophyll, for example, is bound chemically to compounds called light-harvesting proteins, which account for up to 30% of the protein in grass. Without the degradation of chlorophyll, the grasses retained much of their nutritional value.

Environmentally friendly concrete

The manufacture of lightweight concrete traditionally has relied for aggregate material on sand and gravel. Unfortunately, the mining of these resources often has damaged the environment by destroying habitats or disrupting hydrological regimes. To alleviate this problem, USDA scientists at the Western Regional Research Center in Albany, Calif., developed a method that used wheat starch, an abundant, renewable resource, as a substitute for mineral aggregate for producing lightweight, insulating concrete for use in roof tiles, floors, and fireplaces. In the production process the wheat starch, which is formed into a hard brittle substance with the consistency and appearance of sand, was hydrated and then added to a concrete mixture used in the construction of lightweight, nonstructural components. The mixture could be formed into building components with a variety of densities, shapes, strengths, and U-values (insulation levels).

Zip-skinned citrus

USDA scientists in Winter Haven, Fla., developed a process in which enzymes are used to peel citrus. The procedure involved soaking the fruit in commercially available food-grade enzymes for about 25 minutes to dissolve the albedo, the white, pithy material that keeps the peel attached to the fruit. Once the peel was loosened, it could be removed by hand in as little as six seconds.

The process allowed fruit to be peeled without breaking the citrus sections apart or losing any of the juice. It also may help eliminate some of the waste in the fruit industry. Whole fruit that does not mea-

New research helped reduce the amount of pesticides and fertilizers applied to crops. This sprayer directs precise doses of herbicides to weeds between the crop rows. High-residue cultivation controls weeds and protects the soil with a layer of plant residue.

sure up to fresh market grade because of a superficial defect in the peel, for example, can be prepeeled and still used for fresh consumption instead of qualifying only for use in the processing of juice and other fruit products.

Conservation farming

Scientists unveiled new strategies to reduce the use of herbicides and nitrogen fertilizers, thereby minimizing damaging environmental effects and lowering crop-production costs. By tilling the soil, farmers break the natural protective barrier against pests that forms between plants and the soil. USDA and land-grant university researchers demonstrated that farmers could attain effective weed control and reduce their inputs of herbicides by 50–70% by using high-residue cultivation (tillage that returns nonharvested plant materials to the soil). By restoring some vegetative cover, this tillage method reduced the exposure of the soil and plants to pests. By eliminating the need for additional applications of herbicides, farmers also real-

ized significant savings in time and labor.

Scientists also studied the ability of new high-residue cultivators to provide mechanical weed control in conservation-tillage systems. The strategy was shown to reduce inputs of herbicides, decrease soil erosion, minimize environmental risks, and decrease runoff, thus enabling farmers to comply with state and federal conservation standards.

Researchers at the University of Arkansas developed a new nitrogen-management technique to eliminate unnecessary applications of fertilizers on rice crops. Using a video camera in combination with a computerized image-acquisition unit that digitized the footage, scientists recorded the crop canopy at midseason. The method allowed them to analyze the plants' features and assess the crop's overall health. Based on the results of the computerized analysis, scientists estimated the levels of nitrogen needed for maximum yield. This image-based system proved to be more accurate at measuring the additional nitrogen needed than more traditional tech-

niques such as manual plant-area measurements or chlorophyll-meter measurements. Not only was the new technique useful in cutting nitrogen-input costs and boosting yields, but it also prevented the runoff of excess nitrogen into lakes and rivers, where it causes numerous water-quality problems.

Cleaner-tasting catfish

USDA scientists in New Orleans, La., produced detailed scientific evidence that farm-raised catfish can naturally eliminate musty "off-flavors" caused by natural compounds that are released by some kinds of blue-green algae. Once the fish are no longer exposed to the problem-causing algae, they can cleanse themselves of off-flavors.

Harnessing this capability could give a major boost to the $365 million farm-raised catfish industry in the U.S. As much as 80% of the annual U.S. catfish crop has been affected at any given time, and harvest losses and delivery delays cost farmers more than $30 million each year. To ensure a cleaner-tasting product, some farmers have transferred their fish to algae-free waters before sending them to processors. The procedure, however, is too costly for most operators. Finding ways to naturally control problem algae in fish-rearing ponds as well as enhance the natural ability of fish to purge themselves of off-flavors may equip fish farmers with an inexpensive method for providing consistent supplies of clean-tasting fish to processors.

—John Patrick Jordan and
Patricia Brazeel Lewis
See also Feature Article: RICE TO FEED THE HUNGRY.

NUTRITION

In affluent Western countries obesity moved to the top of many public health agendas. Between 1980 and 1994 the number of overweight adults in the U.S. alone increased by approximately 9%. In 1996 33% of men and 36% of women were considered overweight, with numbers increasing around the globe as growing industrialization promoted detrimental lifestyle changes, including high-calorie diets and decreases in physical activity. Research has shown that excess weight increases the risk for developing physical disabilities, diabetes, heart disease, high blood pressure, arthritis, and cancer. In affluent countries overweight people, especially women, also are socially and economically stigmatized and as a result are more likely to be poor and less healthy than their thinner counterparts.

In 1996 scientists from a wide range of disciplines produced significant developments related to obesity, including genetic testing and the development of antiobesity drugs and new weight-loss therapies.

The genetics of obesity

By early 1997 researchers had identified at least 5 genes and 10 hormones involved in the body's regulation of weight. One of the biggest breakthroughs came in 1994 with the sequencing of the *ob* gene ("ob" for obese) in mice. Researchers at Rockefeller University, New York City, discovered that a protein coded by this gene instructed fat cells to secrete a hormone called leptin, which traveled through the bloodstream to the brain, signaling it when the body had stored enough fat. The fat cells of mice that carried two copies of a defective *ob* gene (one copy inherited from each parent)

or were missing the gene altogether did not produce leptin, causing the cells to amass increasing quantities of fat. When injected with leptin, however, the mice, which had grown to three to four times their normal weight, consumed less food, burned calories faster, and lost body fat.

The role of leptin in human weight regulation proved to be somewhat more complicated. Subsequent metabolic research revealed that leptin production was not the problem in humans since fat people had high levels of leptin in their bloodstreams. Scientists suggested that the receptors on the cell surface that bind with leptin were unresponsive to the hormone's message. As a result, in obese people the brain never got the signal to stop eating no matter how much leptin was available. In 1996 researchers at Rockefeller University validated this faulty-receptor theory by identifying a receptor for leptin in the hypothalamus, an area of the brain known to regulate feeding behavior. The discovery of the leptin receptor fueled optimism that new drugs could be developed to enhance the actions of leptin in controlling body weight.

Weight-loss drugs

In developing drugs to control obesity, pharmaceutical companies concentrated on various chemicals that curb appetite, including chemicals that block the brain receptors for naturally produced compounds that stimulate eating, such as the brain chemical neuropeptide Y. In laboratory tests, for example, animals that had been starved overnight showed little interest in eating after they were injected with a chemical that blocks the neuropeptide Y signal. The approach was being tested in

early human trials by researchers at the Neurogen Corp., Branford, Conn.

Other potential therapies focused on a class of stress-related hormones, such as the corticotropin-releasing factor hormones. Laboratory animals that were injected with high levels of these hormones ate less food. In late 1995 scientists discovered urocortin, another member of this family of hormones, which curbed the appetite of laboratory animals without undesirable side effects.

Scientists also investigated mood-lifting drugs that allowed people to satisfy the appetite with less food. Drugs that triggered the release of the brain chemical serotonin, for example, provided weight-loss patients with the same sense of well-being that they got from eating certain fatty or sugary foods. Serotonin-releasing drugs also avoided the associated downsides of amphetamine-based diet pills, not the least of which was amphetamine addiction. There was some concern, however, about long-term side effects of serotonin drugs, such as pulmonary hypertension, which affected a very small percentage of users who had taken the drug for at least three months.

The National Task Force on the Prevention and Treatment of Obesity in the U.S. concluded that more research was needed to measure the long-term safety and effectiveness of popular prescription weight-loss drugs. When combined with a healthy diet and regular exercise, these drugs have helped some obese individuals lose weight and maintain the weight loss for at least a year. The task force cautioned that drugs were not the cure for obesity. It pointed out that people who took weight-loss drugs for up to six months and then stopped using them tended to regain the weight, reinforcing the need for drugs to be used in combination with diet and behavioral therapy.

Weight-loss diets

Therapies and products designed to help people trim pounds and maintain weight loss were more popular than ever. In 1995 in the U.S. alone, $70 billion were spent on health care related to obesity and $33 billion on weight-reduction products and services. Researchers cautioned, however, that the efficacy of weight-loss efforts remained dependent on many interconnected factors, including genetics, life-style practices, and socioeconomic and dietary conditions. Metabolic researchers, for example, continued to be intrigued by the question of why weight stabilized at certain degrees of adiposity, or fatness, in different individuals. One theory that seemed to grow in popularity suggested that people have a set point that determines their natural or comfortable weight, which would explain why 90% of dieters regain a part or all of their lost weight within five years. Many researchers believed that this metabolic equilibrium may be established in late adolescence. In a recent study at Rockefeller University, patients who lost about 10% of their body weight through dieting underwent a metabolic adjustment in which their bodies burned an average of 15% fewer calories. Study results suggested that if people want to maintain weight loss by strict dieting, they must limit calories on a long-term basis.

Researchers continued to investigate the impact of life-style changes on weight reduction and maintenance, including increases or decreases in physical activity, food intake or availability, pregnancy or lactation, and hormonal and drug treatment. Many results suggested that the problem of obesity has no simple solutions. Studies at the University of Minnesota at Minneapolis that examined the efficacy of low-fat dietary counseling in obesity treatment, for example, produced both positive and negative outcomes. Subjects who incorporated fat-modified products into their diets rated their diets as more palatable and reported greater compliance with treatment directions, including fewer episodes of binge eating. On the other hand, some researchers cautioned that the phenomenal increase in the availability of reduced-fat foods could lead to an increase in energy intake by consumers who mistakenly equate a reduction in fat with a reduction in calories.

Many health professionals are advocating a new approach to the treatment of obese patients that stresses the pursuit of health and happiness over the goal of getting and staying thin.

Rethinking a thin paradigm

The ranks of health-care professionals who adopted a new weight paradigm in the treatment of overweight or obese patients continued to grow. Proponents of this new thinking advocated a more neutral approach to the concept of body weight. This shift represented a radical departure from the more traditional medical and moral models of obesity treatment that viewed obesity either as the result of laziness, gluttony, and lack of will power or as a disease that needs to be treated by eating less, exercising more, and complying with authoritative guidance. Many professionals who worked with overweight people observed that the traditional models were neither accurate nor helpful in providing successful strategies for attaining and maintaining healthy life-styles.

Critics of the traditional moral and medical models pointed to the high rate of failure in most weight-loss approaches, which suggested that fatness can not be modified easily. They also charged that dieting may do more harm than good and could lead to eating disorders. Advocates of the new weight paradigm proposed that, instead of asking how people can get and stay thin, health professionals should help obese patients explore multiple options for becoming healthy and happy. These more health-affirming strategies should focus on coupling self-acceptance of body size with the development of new behaviors that emphasize an internal control of eating, increased physical activity to enhance mental and physical health, and greater attention to food quality. Future research will evaluate the success of this new weight paradigm.

—Marla Reicks

LIFE SCIENCES

The discovery of purported fossilized life forms in a Martian meteorite and the successful cloning of an adult sheep monopolized headlines in the life sciences during the past year. Researchers, however, reported other findings with equally wide-ranging implications. Botanists collected valuable new data on growing plants in the microgravity of space. Ecologists debated the accuracy of theoretical models used to predict the Earth's carrying capacity and rates of species extinction. Biologists uncovered startling new evidence about the evolution of life in the Rift lakes of Africa. Microbiologists continued to investigate the frontiers of life in some of the most inhospitable places on Earth. Molecular biologists made big strides in basic research by completing the genetic sequencing of two additional microorganisms.

BOTANY

Botanical researchers broke new ground in 1996, laying the foundation for a wide range of practical applications in the future, including the potential for establishing gardens in the microgravity of space. At the same time, basic research shed new light on already-well-studied plant processes, such as photosynthesis and the protective mechanisms of plants against drought, and strong evidence was obtained that some steroids act as plant hormones.

"Warm-blooded" plants

Warm-blooded animals are equipped with complex hormonal and nervous systems that regulate their body temperatures. Most other living things can only assume the temperature of their surroundings. A few plants, however, are exceptions to the rule, including many species of the arum family

and several species of water lilies, palms, and cycads. Skunk cabbage plants, for example, are early spring bloomers that send up an elongated flower in an open leaf sheath. To attract pollinators, their flowers become very warm, promoting the evaporation of a chemical with the odor of rotting meat. This odor attracts carrion flies and other insects that carry out pollination.

Roger S. Seymour and Paul Schultze-Motel of the University of Adelaide, Australia, discovered that the sacred lotus (*Nelumbo nucifera*) not only generates heat during this critical reproductive phase, like the skunk cabbage, but also regulates the temperatures of its flower within a few degrees. The scientists measured temperatures within the lotus blossoms, ambient

The sacred lotus (*Nelumbo nucifera*) maximizes its potential for pollination by regulating the heat of its blossoms. The warm blooms attract and invigorate pollinating insects on cold nights.

temperatures, and the rate of oxygen consumption by the flowers (a direct indication of the plant's rate of metabolic heat production) and found that the heat increased as the flowers began to bloom and stabilized within a relatively narrow range of 30°–35° C (86°–95° F) for about two to four days while the flower budded, even though ambient nighttime temperatures dipped as low as 10° C (50° F).

Most surprising was the ability of the lotus to respond to changes in temperature. As the ambient temperature dropped, for example, the rate of oxygen consumption increased, which indicated that the plant was converting more carbohydrates to energy to keep warm. Conversely, when the ambient temperature warmed to 30° C, oxygen consumption dropped. The researchers theorized that this heat-maintenance regimen may offer the sacred lotus a reproductive advantage. The elevated temperatures within the blossom coincided with the receptivity of the stigma (female flower part) to pollination. During cold nights the warm temperatures stimulated the activity levels of insects that had become trapped within the floral chamber. They were thus "rewarded" for pollination with a warm place to stay during the cold night. As the flowers opened in the morning, they released the pollen-laden insects to fertilize other lotus flowers.

Farming in space

Among the greatest limitations to establishing permanent colonies on the Moon or launching lengthy flights to Mars is the inability of scientists to sustain the basic components of life—fresh air, clean water, and a renewable supply of food—in space. To meet these basic biological needs, re-

318

searchers have explored the possibilities of growing plants on spacecraft.

To cultivate plants in space successfully, however, scientists must first resolve the problem of microgravity. Plants are endowed with a mechanism so sensitive to gravitational force that if, for example, a growing stem is tipped only a few degrees from a vertical position, it will realign itself vertically within just a few hours. Consequently, scientists have wondered about the ability of plants to thrive in an orbiting spacecraft that experiences only slight accelerational forces, typically about $^1/_{1000}$ the force of gravity at the Earth's surface, a condition referred to as microgravity. The ultimate test of a plant's ability to grow in microgravity is its completion of the life cycle from seed to a mature seed-producing plant. U.S. missions have been too short to test this goal adequately. In 1983 Soviet biologists realized seed-to-seed growth with the tiny laboratory mustard *Arabidopsis thaliana*. The plants barely survived, however, and their yield and general health were very poor compared with those of plants grown under similar conditions on Earth.

In 1996 an international team of plant scientists and environmental engineers achieved vigorous growth and formation of wheat heads (wheat flowers) with a superdwarf wheat cultivar grown on the Russian space station *Mir*.

On August 5, 104 wheat seeds were planted on board *Mir* in a special Russian- and Bulgarian-designed growth chamber. About 65 of the seeds germinated in a growing area measuring 0.1 sq m (about 1 sq ft). The plants grew vigorously, most growing up toward the lamps, while a few spread horizontally, similar to the growth

pattern of crabgrass. On December 6, U.S. astronaut John Blaha harvested the mature plants, including about 290 wheat heads. He immediately planted a second crop, which also grew well. It was harvested on January 16 just as the seed heads were forming. The specimens were frozen in liquid nitrogen and returned to Earth on the space shuttle *Atlantis* for analysis.

Upon analysis, researchers discovered that there were no seeds inside the normally formed seed heads. Studies have suggested that the lack of seed production was caused not by microgravity but by the presence of ethylene in the atmosphere of *Mir*. The gas, innocuous to humans, is a natural plant hormone known to cause many effects such as fruit ripening and—at levels much lower than those subsequently found on *Mir*—sterility in cereals such as wheat.

Despite the wheat plants' failure to produce seeds, the researchers were much encouraged by their general health and vigorous growth. Far more biomass was produced than in any previous experiment with plants in space, and undoubtedly seeds would have been produced had the ethylene been removed from the atmosphere. Using instruments built at Utah State University, the research also produced an unprecedented amount of high-quality data, including information on such environmental parameters as light, moisture, and oxygen levels, cabin pressures, plant and air temperatures, the transpiration of water vapor, and even the uptake of carbon dioxide in photosynthesis.

Gravitropism

The response of plants to gravity—the phenomenon known as gravitropism—has

resisted scientific understanding for more than a century. Scientists do know that indole-3-acetic acid (IAA), the most important of the growth hormones called auxins, plays an essential role in the ability of higher plants to respond to gravity. IAA, for example, promotes the growth of cells on the bottom of a plant stem turned to the horizontal so that increased elongation of those cells causes the stem to bend upward. In plant roots IAA inhibits the growth of cells on the bottom of a horizontal root, which allows the top cells to grow more elongated and thus bend the root downward. There is evidence that auxin is preferentially transported to the bottom of horizontal stems or roots and that the sensitivity of those cells toward auxin increases as part of the response to gravity.

In 1996 a team of researchers from the Universities of Warwick, Leeds, and Cambridge and the University of Arizona described a gene known as *AUX1* that determines the response of the mustard plant *A. thaliana* to gravity and other environmental factors. Scientists found that plants containing a mutant *aux1* gene did not respond to gravity or to applications of IAA, which led them to conclude that *AUX1* plays an important role in the plant's response to gravity. In further research the scientists cloned the *AUX1* gene, sequenced it (determined the sequence of nucleotides in the DNA that makes up the gene), and compared the sequence with those of other genes (or the proteins specified by the genes) recorded in data banks. They found that *AUX1* closely resembles genes that control the movement of amino acids across membranes. Since IAA is derived from the amino acid tryptophan, the research suggested that *AUX1* codes for a protein that regulates the movement of IAA in and out of plant cells.

Harvests of light

After more than a half century of study of photosynthesis, much is known about the process in algae, including green algae, and higher plants. Scientists know, for example, that there are at least 50 photochemical and biochemical steps in the conversion of carbon dioxide and water to carbohydrates and other compounds and the release of oxygen. Nevertheless, some studies offered important surprises.

In the 1960s plant researchers developed a hypothesis suggesting that there were two parts to the photosynthetic apparatus in the cellular bodies called chloroplasts: photosystem I (PSI) and photosystem II (PSII). The first step in photosynthesis is the absorption of light (photons) by the chlorophyll molecules in PSII. The photon energy is used to split water into hydrogen ions, molecular oxygen, and electrons.

The electrons then move into PSI, where, with energy from additional photons, they produce a special reducing compound called NADP+, a vital ingredient in converting carbon dioxide into photosynthetic products. The process is referred to as the Z-scheme because a diagram of the chemical reactions forms the letter Z.

A group of researchers at Oak Ridge (Tenn.) National Laboratory found a significant exception to this widely supported theory after developing mutants of a single-celled green algae, *Chlamydomonas*, that were able to photosynthesize without PSI. Scientists theorized that instead of relying on the reduced compound NADP+ that is created in PSI, the mutant alga

produced reduced compounds in the PSII stage that had enough energy to convert carbon dioxide into the products of photosynthesis. The researchers cautioned, however, that their work does not invalidate the Z-scheme, the photosynthetic sequence used by most green plants.

Scientists from the University of Konstanz, Ger., and Macquarie University, N.S.W., Australia, also contributed significant findings to the knowledge about the photosynthetic processes of a single-celled alga. The researchers reported on the extraordinarily efficient light-harvesting complex in the dinoflagellate *Amphidinium carterae*. Compared with plants on the Earth's surface, which typically receive an abundance of full-spectrum light, dinoflagellates grow at ocean depths that are penetrated only by blue-green light. Unlike higher plants that utilize the red and blue parts of the solar spectrum and reflect these blue-green wavelengths or utilize them inefficiently, the dinoflagellate is nearly 100% efficient in absorbing blue-green light and transferring this energy to the photosynthetic apparatus.

To determine the structure of the algae's light-harvesting center, the researchers used high-resolution X-ray crystallography. They discovered a complex consisting of coils of amino acids that formed a boat-shaped protein. Within the structure's "hull" are two chlorophyll molecules, two lipid (fat) molecules, and eight molecules of a pigment called peridinin that is responsible for absorbing blue-green light. The peridinin and chlorophyll molecules are tightly packed, which enables rapid transfer of the energy of the absorbed light to the cholorphyll and then on to the rest of the photosynthetic apparatus.

Surviving drought

Drought-tolerant plants commonly synthesize sugars or amino acids known as osmoprotectants in response to low-moisture conditions and other stresses. These compounds not only help the plant retain water but also protect critical enzymes from the denaturing effects of drying. One of these compounds—trehalose, a disaccharide similar to common table sugar, sucrose, and found in some of the most drought-resistant species—now may help drought-sensitive crops survive dry conditions, one of the main contributors to low crop yields.

A group of researchers at the Swedish University of Agricultural Sciences, Uppsala, and Primalco Ltd. Biotec, Rajamäki, Fin., transferred the gene coding for an enzyme responsible for the synthesis of trehalose-6-phosphate from a drought-hardy species into tobacco plants and dramatically increased their capacity to make trehalose. In plant trials the compound was a decisive factor in the ability of tobacco plants to survive drought. When control plants without trehalose and trehalose-enhanced seedlings were removed from the soil and allowed to dry for seven hours in air at 50% relative humidity, the control plants withered, while the enhanced plants had high rates of survival. When replanted, the control plants died, while the enhanced seedlings recovered completely. Under optimal conditions, however, the growth rates of the trehalose plants lagged behind the control plants by 30–50%.

Plant hormones

By the 1950s scientists had discovered several signaling molecules, or hormones, that regulated growth, development, and other functions of plants. They assumed, however, that the molecules that constitute an important class of hormones in animals—polypeptides, or chains of amino acids shorter than but otherwise similar to protein molecules—were too large to move through the pores in the tough, mostly cellulose cell walls of many plants. As a result, for decades scientists assumed that polypeptides did not have the same hormonal functions in plants as they do in animals.

Several studies during the year countered this assumption. In 1991 researchers isolated the first polypeptide plant hormone, called systemin, from 27 kg (60 lb) of tomato leaves. At concentrations as low as one part in 10 trillion, systemin caused tomato leaves to produce compounds that gave insects feeding on the leaves a case of "indigestion." No additional polypeptide hormones were found in plants until 1996, when a team of researchers from the Max Planck Institute for Plant Breeding Research, Cologne, Ger., and the Agricultural University, Wageningen, Neth., identified a gene that is expressed during the early stages of legume-nodule development and located the protein for which it codes—a polypeptide of about 10 amino acids with the ability to change the plant's response to the growth hormone IAA even when the polypeptide is present at extremely low concentrations.

Researchers also made dramatic new discoveries about plant steroids. Scientists have long known that plants synthesize numerous steroids, but the roles that these compounds play, if any, in plant growth and development has largely eluded them. In April, however, a group of researchers from the Salk Institute for Biological Studies, La Jolla, Calif., and the University of California, San Diego, demonstrated for the first time that a steroid is critical to plant growth and development and should qualify as a plant hormone.

The Salk researchers isolated a gene known as *DET2* that plays a fundamental role in the synthesis of the steroid brassinolide. They found that *A. thaliana* seedlings with a mutated *det2* gene exhibited a number of abnormalities. Mutant plants that germinated in the dark, for example, were short and had atypical leaf buds. Those grown in the light also were small, featured leaves that were darker green than the wild type, and had reduced cell size and other abnormalities. The subsequent application of brassinolide to mutant seedlings produced normal-sized plants. Using research terminology, the mutant plants were "rescued" by the brassinolide. This suggests that the steroid plays an important role in plant growth by regulating its response to light. According to the researchers, brassinosteroids should "be recognized as an important class of plant hormones."

—Frank B. Salisbury

ECOLOGY

"How many people can the Earth support?" is not a new question raised by modern-day ecologists concerned about the depletion of the Earth's natural resources by a burgeoning human population. Two centuries ago the Englishman Thomas Malthus noted with alarm the population explosion in industrial England and formulated his famous theory of exponential population growth in response. If the human population continued to double at a fixed rate, he theorized, the "earth would at last be overstocked, and become unable to support its numerous inhabitants."

Malthus argued that there were material limits to human growth—such as a finite amount of land on which to grow food—a concept modern ecologists call "carrying capacity."

Malthus was responding to changes brought about by the Industrial Revolution in Europe, which resulted in a near doubling of the population between 1750 and 1850. Today the rate of growth has accelerated dramatically. From the mid-1950s to the mid-1990s, the world's population increased from three billion to six billion people. If the population were to continue doubling at 40-year intervals, the number of people would reach 12 billion in the 2030s; by the 2070s the world would contain more than 24 billion human beings.

Although achievements in agricultural technology have supported human population growth far exceeding Malthus's expectations, defining the limits of the Earth's carrying capacity continues to be a matter of considerable debate. In 1996 the discussion focused on the population-prediction model devised the previous year by Joel Cohen of Rockefeller University, New York City. As demonstrated by the heated discussion, scientists were no closer to agreement about global carrying capacity than they were before.

Some researchers charged that humans already have exceeded the capacity of the Earth to sustain them, cautioning that the global population should safely total only one billion people, a mere one-sixth the present population. Other scientists suggested that the world's population could expand to one trillion people—more than 150 times the present population—without exhausting the globe's natural infrastructure. In 1996 ecologists focused on the research of such issues as food and water supplies to help establish a more accurate standard for measuring the Earth's carrying capacity.

Food and plant growth

In 1986 Stanford University ecologists Peter Vitousek, Paul and Anne Ehrlich, and Pam Matson sought to determine the percentage of the Earth's plants that were consumed directly or indirectly by humans. They used two measures: plant biomass (the amount of existing vegetation) and plant production (the amount of new plant growth each year). The researchers determined that about 15% of the Earth's total plant production—*i.e.*, new plant growth—came from crops. They tabulated the amount of new plant material that was consumed directly by people as well as indirectly through feeding domestic livestock, burning wood for heat, clearing land for crops and cities, and growing trees for building materials. Calculating these combined uses, the Stanford group estimated that in 1986 the world's five billion people consumed a total of 40% of the Earth's land-plant production. By 2036, if population predictions hold true, the world's 12.5 billion people would consume 100% of land-plant production.

Some predictions about the Earth's carrying capacity were far more optimistic. In 1994 Paul Waggoner of the Connecticut Agricultural Experiment Station in New Haven suggested that the Earth could support a population of one trillion people—nearly 1,000 times the Stanford group's estimate. Waggoner based his high estimates on the assumption that technological improvements would continue to expand food production as they have in the past

200 years, a supposition that the Stanford group questioned.

Cohen approached this controversy by building a mathematical model based on the same two parameters population ecologists commonly use for modeling: the time in which a population can double if there is nothing to limit its growth and the Earth's carrying capacity. Cohen's major innovation in the model, however, was the supposition that the limit to the number of people that the Earth can support increases over time as technology improves. In extrapolating population size into the future, the model incorporates an estimate of how much and in what direction current population growth is being affected by advancing technology. Cohen pointed out that the growth in the Earth's population recently has slowed, suggesting that increasing technology is not pushing the limit upward as fast as the population is approaching it.

Cohen also concluded that estimates of carrying capacity cannot simply be calculated by the number of people but depend on such factors as standard of living. The carrying capacity for a global population living the resource-intensive lifestyle of the average European or North American, for example, would be considerably different from a carrying capacity based on the materially simpler lifestyle of the average citizen in Africa. Raising enough cattle to feed a billion beef eaters requires more land and resources than feeding an equal number of vegetarians. Furthermore, the benefits of technology are not always distributed evenly throughout the population. The richest 10% of the world's people, for example, are now 38 times richer than the poorest 10%. Twenty-five years ago they were only 25 times richer.

Water, water everywhere?

Only 2.5% of the Earth's water is freshwater, and two-thirds of that is locked up in glaciers and polar ice caps. About 110,000 cu km (26,000 cu mi) of water fall as rain and snow across the Earth's land surface. Of this total, 70,000 cu km (16,700 cu mi) return to the atmosphere either through direct evaporation or by transpiration through plants. The remaining water runs off the land into rivers and eventually into the sea.

How human populations may be limited by these finite sources of freshwater was the theme of collaborative work by Sandra Postel of the Global Water Policy Project, Cambridge, Mass., and Stanford ecologists Paul Ehrlich and Gretchen Daily. The group argued that to feed the millions of new people each year, farmers would need to capture significantly more freshwater runoff to irrigate the roughly 50% of the nonfrozen land surface that currently is too dry to be very productive. The researchers were not optimistic about the prospects for harnessing greater amounts of existing runoff. Of the runoff that is accessible, humanity already appropriates more than 50% for various uses, of which irrigating crops is the most important. The key word is *accessible*. Some 60% of the world's total freshwater runoff either is located in out-of-the-way places or becomes available at the wrong time of year. The Amazon River, for example, accounts for some 15% of the world's total freshwater runoff and the Congo River another 3.5%. Relatively few people, however, live in these river basins. Even fewer live along another major source of freshwater—remote, Arctic rivers. Furthermore, freshwater runoff often is seasonal and unpredictable, appearing in the form of flood- or meltwater.

The researchers pointed out that technologies to capture additional freshwater are expensive, difficult, and relatively ineffective. Exotic options, such as towing icebergs, are costly and unlikely to yield appreciable quantities of water. Desalinization, which currently provides only about 0.1% of the world's freshwater, is prohibitively expensive for all but a few oil-rich water-scarce countries. Additional floodwater can be captured, using existing dam technology, but dam construction is not likely to increase. From 1950 to the mid-1980s, nearly 900 large dams were constructed annually, most of them on the cheapest and most buildable sites. Since then, however, the annual rate of dam building has dropped to 500. Postel predicted that even at current rates of construction, new dams might increase accessible runoff only by about 10% in the next 30 years. These modest gains, however,

are likely to be offset by additional consumption as the human population undergoes an expected 45% increase. By 2025 the human population will likely have less water, not more.

Shrinking forests

Increases in the human population have led to a rapid clearing of tropical forests that are home to at least two-thirds of the Earth's plant and animal species. Among the most vulnerable are the coastal forests of Brazil. Thomas Brooks of the University of Tennessee at Knoxville and Andrew Balmford of the University of Sheffield, Eng., devised a method for predicting the correlation between the rates of forest destruction and species extinction. As a case study, the researchers selected the birds of Brazil's coastal forests, which have come under considerable pressure. As the country's human population has grown, many people have moved from the interior to the

coastal cities of São Paulo and Rio de Janeiro. As a result, only 10% of the country's coastal forests remain. These forests are home to more than 200 species of endemic birds that would become extinct if the forests were eliminated.

Brooks and Balmford estimated the losses in forest area by using satellite images. Then they tackled the more difficult task of correlating forest loss with species loss. The researchers noted that the forest-cutting pattern in Brazil left "islands" of forest, often national parks, surrounded by a "sea" of agriculture. Because of this configuration, they based their method of calculation on a common ecological observation known as the oceanic island pattern. Although ecologists have noted that the number of species increases with the size of oceanic islands—Cuba has more species, for example, than the smaller island of Jamaica—the numbers are not in direct proportion to their areas. Whereas bigger

To feed the world's burgeoning population, researchers say that irrigated croplands must be expanded. Some scientists, however, warn that these growing demands on global water resources will quickly outstrip available freshwater supplies.

As Brazil's population has grown, people have migrated from the country's interior to such coastal cities as Rio de Janeiro. Under pressure by intense human development, only 10% of the country's species-rich coastal forests remain.

islands normally serve as host to more species, an island half the size of another typically will have not 50% but about 85% as many species. For an island to have only 50% as many species, it would have to be one-sixteenth the size.

Using satellite photos, the researchers determined that the remaining forest patches along the coast of Brazil ranged from 2% to 20% the size of the original forest cover. By comparing the size of the remnant forest islands with the size of the original unbroken forest and using the oceanic island pattern, the researchers were able to determine how many species these patches should contain. By subtracting the number of species calculated to be in the island remnants from the number of species that once lived in the intact forest, the researchers were able to predict the number of species that eventually would go extinct. The numbers calculated by this theoretical model closely matched the results of field data reported in 1994 by Nigel Collar and his colleagues at BirdLife International, Cambridge, Eng. The group listed the number of species on the verge of extinction, including about 60 of the endemic birds of Brazil's coastal forests.

Moreover, the researchers not only predicted how many species would likely go extinct but also pinpointed the locations of those extinctions. Forests with only 2% of their original canopy, for example, were at greater risk of losing more species than those with 20%.

What happens when the Earth warms?

When it comes to predicting the consequences of increased carbon dioxide in the atmosphere, two major questions must be answered: How much will the Earth warm? What will be the consequences of this warming? One widely held ecological hypothesis proposes that ecosystems and their associated organisms simply will adapt to new climatic niches by shifting their locations. In this scenario, for example, the plants and animals of cold-adapted forests of Canada, northern Europe, and Russia would move northward as they were replaced by the species of more southerly deciduous forests.

The ecological consequences of global warming, however, may be much more complicated and difficult to predict, according to a group of 20 scientists across North America known as the Faunmap working group. The group compiled a vast electronic database that charts the distribution of mammal species throughout North America in the last 20,000 years. The primary purpose of this database is to use the fossil record to investigate the changes in mammalian communities in a wide variety of habitats, including grasslands, deserts, and deciduous and coniferous forests.

Researchers examined changes in the mammalian fossil record and established correlations between climatic fluctuations and geographical distributions and extinctions. They discovered that some species moved more quickly into new ranges, while others were left stranded by the changed vegetation or relocated in unpredictable ways. The Faunmap group concluded that predicting the consequences of global warming may be much more difficult than previously thought.

—Stuart L. Pimm

MICROBIOLOGY

The discovery of what some scientists called bacterial fossils in a meteorite from Mars dominated the headlines in microbiology in 1996. Researchers also issued equally newsworthy reports of the discovery of new life forms on Earth and provided insights into the evolution of some of humankind's most troubling pathogens.

Life on Mars?

In 1976 NASA's unmanned Viking orbiters sent lander modules to the surface of Mars to collect soil samples. The failure of later analysis of the Martian materials to detect evidence of bacteria or bacterially derived organic materials led to the general consensus among scientists that Mars is a lifeless planet. The Viking experiments, however, could not completely rule out the possibility that life is present—or once had existed—in other regions of the planet.

In 1996 a team of NASA scientists presented the first compelling evidence that primitive life may have existed on Mars. The scientists discovered structures in a potato-sized meteorite that they claimed were the fossilized remains of ancient bacteria. The meteorite, known as ALH84001, was discovered in 1984 lodged in a sheet of Antarctic ice. About a decade later, David Mittlefehldt of Lockheed Martin compared ALH84001 with documented Martian meteorites and concluded that it had come from Mars. The NASA team corroborated his judgment, suggesting that ALH84001 was 4.5 billion years old and therefore part of the original Martian crust. They theorized that fissures developed in that part of the crust. Because they allowed fluid to penetrate, the fissures became sites of secondary mineral formation, such as carbonate globules. Later, when a large comet or asteroid collided with Mars, ALH84001 became part of the debris that was scattered into space, where it wandered for millions of years before landing on Earth 13,000 years ago.

The researchers used several independent lines of evidence to support their claim that the rock was once host to a community of Martian organisms. Simon Clemett and Richard Zare of Stanford University and their colleagues showed that fracture surfaces inside the meteorite contain polycyclic aromatic hydrocarbons (PAHs), large organic molecules that sometimes result when cellular organic matter decays. According to Clemett and Zare, the presence of the PAHs in the meteorite's interior suggested that the hydrocarbons did not enter ALH84001 from an outside source on Earth. The researchers could not definitively ascertain, however, that the PAHs were the product of living cells, since PAHs are common in some interplanetary dust particles and in certain meteorites from the asteroid belt,

where they presumably are produced in nonbiological processes.

Scientists who supported the Martian-fossil hypothesis also pointed to the presence of an iron oxide called magnetite and an iron monosulfide called pyrrhotite in the carbonate globules inside the meteorite. On Earth the only means by which magnetite and pyrrhotite have been observed to precipitate together has been through the action of bacteria. This unusual combination of minerals provided strong, but not necessarily unequivocal, evidence in support of the fossil hypothesis.

Yet another piece of supporting evidence was the presence in the carbonate globules of ovoid and rod-shaped structures resembling fossilized bacteria, albeit considerably smaller than those found on Earth. Plans were under way to analyze the structures for the telltale signs of living cells, including such organic components as amino acids and cell walls.

Although none of these observations alone proved that life existed on Mars, together they presented a compelling case. In order to confirm or discredit the hypothesis, scientists agreed, additional data needed to be gathered from new sources. The outlook for this further research looked promising.

New life on Earth

If there is life on other planets, what would it be like? One way to answer this question is to look at the diversity of life on Earth and ask whether similar ecosystems could exist elsewhere. For more than a century, scientists assumed that complex ecosystems rich in species diversity existed only on the surface of the planet in the presence

of light. In the past decade scientists have discovered unusual ecosystems in places whose conditions, like those of many planets, seemed far too harsh to support life. Perhaps the most famous was the recent discovery of marine ecosystems that thrive in the darkness around deep-sea hydrothermal vents. Key to the survival of any ecosystem are the organisms that are devoted to primary production—that is, the synthesis of cellular material from carbon dioxide, using either light energy (photoautotrophy) or chemical energy (chemoautotrophy). In these deep-sea systems, chemoautotrophic bacteria provide this critical function of primary production. They reproduce by using hydrogen sulfide from the hydrothermal vent discharge as an energy source. These bacteria are then consumed by mussels and tube worms through a complex symbiotic process. Tube worms, for example, lack a mouth, gut, or anus but contain a modified gastrointestinal tract composed of a spongy tissue called the trophosome. Trophosome tissue contains the sulfur-oxidizing bacterium *Thiovulum,* which supplies the worm with nourishment in the form of excretory products and dead cells. In return, the tube worm traps molecular oxygen and hydrogen sulfide, which feeds *Thiovulum.* In this manner a complex ecosystem has developed around the primary production of the chemoautotrophic bacteria.

Scientists were only beginning to realize the extent to which chemoautotrophy drives subsurface ecosystems. In 1996 Serban Sarbu, Thomas Kane, and Brian Kinkle of the University of Cincinnati, Ohio, described a chemoautotrophically based ecosystem in the Movile Cave, Dobrogea, Rom. In the cave, the researchers discovered bacteria with the ability to use hydrogen sulfide as an energy source. These organisms served as the primary producers for the entire cave ecosystem, which includes 48 species of terrestrial and aquatic invertebrates.

Redrawing the blueprints of life

In 1977 Carl R. Woese in collaboration with his colleague Ralph S. Wolfe at the University of Illinois at Urbana-Champaign, proposed adding a new superkingdom of organisms—Archaea—or a third branch to the existing tree of life. Woese's view ran contrary to the commonly held belief that all life could be divided into just two groups, Bacteria, which contains single-celled organisms lacking a distinct nucleus, and Eucarya, which encompasses organisms whose more complex cells contain a distinct nucleus and includes plants, animals, fungi, and protozoa. Critics argued that the bacteria-like organisms that Woese classified under the Archaea domain were too similar to bacteria to warrant a separate category.

In 1996 scientists provided conclusive evidence in favor of Woese's controversial reclassification. In 1995 researchers had reported the first sequencing of the entire genetic blueprint, or genome, of two living bacteria: the human pathogens *Haemophilus influenzae* and *Mycoplasma genitalium*. These two achievements were followed in 1996 by the sequencing of the first archaeon, *Methanococcus jannaschii,* and the first eukaryote, the yeast *Saccharomyces cerevisiae*. This mapping enabled scientists to make a full genomic comparison of the three domains. The comparison between *M. jannaschii* and *H. influenzae* revealed only an 11% similarity in their

© Luminita Sarbu

Movile Cave's rich profusion of life includes this water scorpion, the only known cave-dwelling aquatic scorpion. The cave's biological diversity is made possible by bacteria that use the hydrogen sulfide in the subterranean waters as an energy source.

genes, and that between *M. jannaschii* and *M. genitalium* only a 17% similarity.

The fossil record suggests that microbes first appeared on the planet about 3.8 billion years ago, when the climate was much warmer and there was little oxygen. Only thermophilic (heat-loving) organisms that do not require oxygen, such as *M. jannaschii,* could have survived under those conditions. Studying other archaea like it could provide clues to the origin of life on Earth. (For more information on microbes that inhabit extreme environments or on the Woese reclassification scheme, *see* Feature Article: LIFE ON THE EDGE.)

Medical microbiology

Some scientists have regarded virulent pathogens as a primitive stage in biological development, evidence that the relationship between these parasites and their hosts has not yet evolved into a more benign coexistence. Why would a parasite want to harm or kill the host, they have argued, if it relies on the host for survival, proliferation, and transmission? Bruce

Levin of Emory University, Atlanta, Ga., offered another interpretation, suggesting that virulence could indicate both the advanced and the primitive stage of the association between host and parasite. He pointed out that natural selection could favor the virulent parasites, since they have a greater capacity for infectious transmission. One example is the case of the highly virulent myxoma virus, which was deliberately introduced in 1950 in Australia to control naturalized rabbit populations. Researchers found that almost all the infected rabbits died within two weeks after exposure.

Within a short time, however, the virus mutated into a less virulent form. Researchers theorized that the process of natural selection led to the optimal level of virulence. Highly virulent strains were at a disadvantage because they killed the rabbits too quickly and thus reduced the opportunity for the virus to be picked up by mosquitoes or fleas that transmitted the virus. On the other hand, strains of the virus that were not virulent enough also were at a disadvantage. Their reduced abundance in infected animals made it less likely that they, too, would be transmitted by the biting insects. Thus, a balance eventually emerged in which the myxoma virus, although still lethal, became somewhat less virulent, which allowed infected rabbits to survive up to two weeks longer after exposure.

Such a balance, however, is not permanent. Indeed, highly virulent parasites continually emerge owing to the acquisition of small sets of new genes. A good example is cholera, one of the most persistent scourges of humankind, with seven major pandemics since 1817 having affected many millions of individuals. The causative agent, the water-dwelling bacterium *Vibrio cholerae,* is normally benign. It becomes a menace, however, after acquiring a set of genes that encode a toxin responsible for causing cholera's life-threatening diarrhea. Where do these deadly genes come from? Matthew K. Waldor and John J. Mekalanos of Harvard Medical School discovered that the toxin gene is located on a bacterial virus. When this virus infects a benign *V. cholerae* strain, it deposits its genes, including the gene encoding the toxin, in the bacterium, triggering the Jekyll-to-Hyde transformation. The transfer occurs at significantly higher rates in the mammalian gut than in a laboratory environment. Although little is known about the mechanisms of this genetic transfer, it appears that the gut provides the necessary environmental signals for the complex interaction between the bacterium, the infecting virus, and the mammalian host. These genetically altered strains of *V. cholerae* cause deadly pandemics until the virulence of the pathogen has

been defused by the biological balance struck between host and parasite.

—Lawrence J. Shimkets

MOLECULAR BIOLOGY AND GENETICS

The dedication in 1996 of a new source of extremely powerful X-rays, the Advanced Photon Source (APS) synchrotron-radiation facility at Argonne National Laboratory, ushered in a new era for structural biologists in the U.S. Previously, crystallographers working to elucidate the three-dimensional structure of proteins and fragments of DNA and RNA had to use as their source of X-rays either a much-less-powerful rotating-anode X-ray tube in their own laboratories or one of several high-energy synchrotron X-ray beams available outside the U.S. The APS will provide such a high flux of X-rays that structural information will be obtained with very short exposures, minimizing damage to the crystals in the X-ray beam and allowing smaller crystals to be investigated. The structures described below may well be the last important ones to be determined in the U.S. through the use of an X-ray source other than the APS. (*See* Feature Article: BRIGHT NEW LIGHTS FOR PHYSICS.)

Developments also took place in fields other than structural biology. For example, several large DNA-sequencing projects were completed in 1995 and 1996. Researchers in the U.S. reported the complete nucleotide sequences of the rather small genomes (genetic blueprints) of the microorganisms *Haemophilus influenzae, Mycoplasma genitalium,* and *Methanococcus jannaschii.* Whereas the first two are bacteria, the last named is an archaeon (archaebacterium), a representative of a re-

cently recognized third kingdom of living forms (along with true bacteria and eukaryotes). Its DNA sequence showed that many of its genes are more closely related to those of eukaryotes than to those of bacteria. (See *Microbiology,* above.) Also during the year two very large sequencing projects were concluded. A team in Japan reported the complete sequence of the genome of *Synechocystis,* a cyanobacterium, while two teams, one in Japan and one at the University of Wisconsin, completed the sequence of the genome of *Escherichia coli,* the workhorse of bacterial genetics.

A striking feature of the results from each of these projects was the presence of a large proportion of genes whose functions cannot be guessed from their nucleotide sequences. As this area of research moves into its next phase, methods for the rapid and efficient determination of the function of such unknown genes must be improved. It may well be that a complete functional description of a bacterial genome will be available first for *Rhodobacter capsulatus,* whose DNA sequence had not yet been completed by early 1997 but for which a facile system for analysis of gene functions already existed.

A DNA-bending molecule

The expression of genes requires the regulated transcription of the sequence of nucleotides in a DNA strand into the sequence of nucleotides in a strand of messenger RNA. Regulation in many cases is achieved by the interaction of RNA polymerase, the enzyme responsible for transcription, with a short DNA sequence on the gene called the promoter. Often, access to the promoter is blocked by a protein bound nearby, called a repressor.

In such cases the environmental cue that triggers expression of that particular gene does so by causing the release of the repressor from the DNA, allowing RNA polymerase to bind to the promoter and begin transcription. (For a description of the lactose repressor/DNA interaction, see *1997 Yearbook of Science and the Future* Year in Review: LIFE SCIENCES: *Molecular Biology and Genetics.*)

In other cases the regulation is of a different sort; the binding of RNA polymerase is not blocked, but the promoter sequence is such that it must be "activated" for the enzyme to transcribe. Activation requires the binding of another protein nearby, governed by interaction between the protein's amino acids and a particular sequence in the DNA. In the known examples of this kind of transcriptional activation, the protein that is bound nearby, called the activator, actually touches the RNA polymerase and chemically persuades it to start transcription. In some cases the activator binds to the DNA quite close to the promoter, which makes it comparatively easy to visualize the molecular interaction of activator with RNA polymerase. In other cases, however, the activator binds farther away, and it is not as clear how it manages the task of activation. One report in the past year detailed a remarkable example of the way this more distant form of activation can be achieved.

The work in question, carried out by Phoebe Rice and Shu-wei Yang in the laboratories of Kiyoshi Mizuuchi and Howard Nash, respectively, at the National Institutes of Health, Bethesda, Md., involves a small protein found in *E. coli* called integration host factor (IHF). IHF was discovered in the 1970s by Nash as a

component of the process by which the virus lambda, a virus that infects bacteria, integrates its DNA into the chromosome of the bacterial host. Later, other investigators found that IHF had additional roles in the cell, including helping transcription activators do their jobs. Sydney Kustu and her colleagues at the University of California, Berkeley, showed that IHF could bend DNA and thus allow a distant activator and RNA polymerase to interact, effectively looping out the DNA between them. The subsequent studies by Rice and her colleagues showed exactly how IHF causes the double-stranded DNA helix to make its U-turn, actually a bend of some 160°.

The protein IHF consists of two similar polypeptide chains, each containing approximately 100 amino acids. It is related in sequence to another small DNA-binding protein, dubbed HU, that is found abundantly in all bacteria and is believed to be responsible for allowing the bacterial chromosome to fold compactly enough to fit inside a bacterial cell. Bacteria do not have the proteins called histones that function in nucleated cells to promote the compaction of DNA; HU serves the same purpose. Unlike HU, IHF is restricted in the sites to which it can bind in DNA. Biochemical experiments designed to determine which parts of a DNA fragment are protected by bound IHF from chemical or enzymatic attack have defined the binding site, which extends a little beyond 25 nucleotide pairs. The crystal structure determined by Rice and her colleagues contained 35 nucleotide pairs of DNA, including the sequence AAAAAA in one half and the sequence TATCAAxxxxTTG in the other half. (The four nucleotide bases found in DNA are adenine, thymine, guanine, and cytosine,

abbreviated A, T, G, and C, respectively.) The latter sequence is characteristic of all IHF binding sites. (The x's in that sequence represent nucleotides that vary among different binding sites.)

The structure of the IHF-DNA complex is shown in Figure 1. Part of the IHF protein is a compact core; each of the subunits contains an extended ribbon-shaped part that wraps around the DNA, forming contacts in the minor groove of the helix. (The structure of the double-stranded DNA helix has a major, or wider, groove and a minor, or narrower, groove running along its length.) The sharp U-turn in the DNA is caused by two kinks put into it nine nucleotides apart. The kinks are due to intercalation, or insertion, of two molecules of the amino acid proline, one from each subunit of the protein, into the DNA helix.

Two features of the DNA helix normally prevent it from bending sharply. First, the phosphate groups that link the deoxyribose sugars to form the helix backbone each carry a negative charge. To bend the DNA at a sharp angle would require that these negatively charged groups come close together, which is energetically difficult owing to the repulsion of like charges. IHF facilitates the bending because its numerous positively charged amino-acid side chains interact with the phosphate groups and negate the repulsion. Second, the stacking of paired bases in the DNA helix (the stacked "rungs" in the DNA helix "ladder") provides another source of energy for resisting bending. IHF favors unstacking of the helix in two places—the kinks—by inserting the planar amino acid proline into the helix. A third aspect of the IHF-DNA interaction is provided by the

DNA binding site for IHF

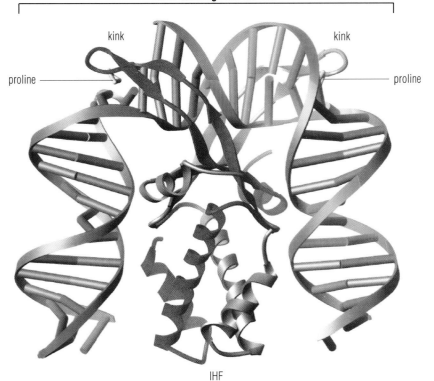

kink   kink

proline   proline

IHF

Phoebe Rice

Figure 1: In the IHF-DNA complex shown, part of each IHF subunit wraps around the DNA helix, forming contacts in the minor groove. Insertion of a proline molecule from each IHF subunit causes the helix to kink, creating a U-turn.

target sequence AAAAAA in the binding site. This particular run of adenine molecules in the DNA leads, without any further protein interaction, to widening of the major groove and narrowing of the minor groove of the helix where the run occurs. These changes cause the helix to bend.

IHF has at least two different functions in the bacterial cell. In the example illustrated in Figure 1, the particular target sequence is one contained in the DNA of the virus lambda, where it integrates into the bacterial chromosome. The integration reaction is a recombination event involving breakage and reunion of the ends of DNA molecules. Bending mediated by IHF brings the two regions of DNA involved in this rearrangement close together. Quite separate from that function, IHF is also used to activate certain promoters, as was discussed above. In those latter cases, DNA bending brings an activating protein bound at a distant site close to the promoter, where RNA polymerase is waiting for persuasion to move.

Structure of an intron domain

The idea that single-stranded RNA molecules can fold into unique three-dimen-

sional structures without assistance from proteins has taken a long time to be accepted. Whereas the characteristic helical nature of double-stranded DNA is now taken for granted, if that DNA is separated into its constituent single strands by heating or treatment with chemicals, the resulting molecules coil randomly into more compact structures, no two having exactly the same structure. So, too, it was thought to be for single-stranded RNA, in spite of the known facts that conventional base pairs can form in RNA and that those base pairs have greater stability than their DNA counterparts. (In RNA, A selectively bonds with U [uracil, which replaces the thymine of DNA], and G selectively bonds with C.) Moreover, members of a class of small single-stranded RNA molecules, the transfer RNAs, whose structures were determined in the mid-1970s, always take the form of a folded cloverleaf, with four base-paired stems and three loops, but they were deemed to be exceptional. In addition, the ribosomes, the protein-RNA complexes that are the workbenches for protein synthesis, contain well-defined single-stranded RNA molecules having dozens of stems and loops, each with reproducible

stability and chemical reactivity. The past year, however, saw the determination of the three-dimensional structure of a significant part of a self-splicing intron, a piece of single-stranded RNA with unique biochemical activity.

Introns are intervening sequences found in the coding regions of genes. These sequences are transcribed from DNA into RNA and spliced out at a later stage of processing. Introns in messenger RNA generally require an elaborate molecular splicing machine, called the spliceosome, for this purpose; the spliceosome contains small RNA molecules to guide the machine to the borders of the intron as well as proteins to catalyze the reactions that cut out the introns and splice the cut ends of the RNA molecule back together. Some introns, however, can dispense with this machinery. Instead, they fold into structures, termed ribozymes, that have catalytic activity capable of splicing themselves out perfectly.

One such intron, studied extensively in the laboratory of Thomas Cech at the University of Colorado, occurs in the ribosomal RNA of the ciliate protozoan *Tetrahymena*. The intron comprises more than 300 nucleotides. On the basis of a comparison of the sequences of several self-splicing introns, as well as data on the accessibility of parts of the sequence to biochemical modification, François Michel of the Center for Molecular Genetics, Gif-sur-Yvette, France, and Eric Westhof of the Institute of Molecular and Cellular Biology, Strasbourg, France, proposed that the intron coils and folds into two side-by-side stacked helices that join to create the site where cutting and splicing occur.

By the end of 1996 the entire intron had

yet to be crystallized, but a significant portion of it, 160 nucleotides, constituting half of the catalytic site, was crystallized in Cech's laboratory during the year and its structure determined at high resolution. The work showed that this half, termed the P4-P6 domain, folds on its own to take up the same structure that it has in the full, intact intron. Thus, the solution of the structure of this part revealed a great deal about the way that the whole molecule works.

The intron fragment is more than twice as large as a transfer RNA molecule. Its crystallization, an exceedingly difficult task, was accomplished by Jennifer Doudna, who subsequently established her own laboratory at Yale University. The structural analysis was continued in Colorado as well, and the following description is based on publications from both laboratories. The most striking feature of the P4-P6 domain (*see* Figure 2), particularly in view of the discussion of protein-assisted DNA bending above, is that the molecule accomplishes a U-turn without any help from a bending protein. Over most of its length, the folded RNA fragment is double-helical, with conventional DNA-like base pairing: A with U and G with C. A few of the pairs are G-U, which, although allowed, are weaker than the conventional G-C pair.

Completely novel with respect to structures seen in DNA, however, are two other features: a tetraloop bound to its receptor and an adenine-rich bulge that glues the two parallel helical segments together. The tetraloop is simply the sequence GAAA found at the bottom of the helix on the right in the figure. This sequence turns up in many RNA structures; it forms the hair-

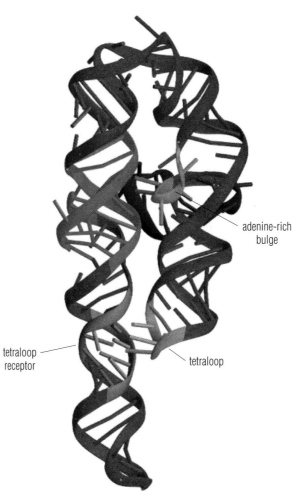

P4-P6 domain

pin that allows the single strand to fold back on itself. In doing so, its bases are projected outward in such a way that two or three of the adenines are available to make hydrogen bonds with other bases. In the case of the P4-P6 structure, those other bases, called the tetraloop receptor, are on the other helix. The details of this interaction are truly remarkable, as precise and regular as any protein structure known. Each adenine of the tetraloop makes specific hydrogen bonds with base pairs and deoxyribose sugars in the receptor, in addition to stacking one upon the other as though they were a continuation of the receptor helix. The resulting structure is compact and stable. The adenine-rich bulge occurs about one-third of the distance down the helix on the right. It contains four adenine residues, all projecting outward, two interacting with the helix on the left and two with the three-way helix

junction on the right. These interactions again involve an extended network of hydrogen bonds, but additional stability is provided by specific magnesium ions (Mg^{2+}) that neutralize the negative charges on phosphate groups brought into close juxtaposition.

All told, this remarkable structure demonstrates that some RNA molecules can be as compact and well-defined as proteins. With such characteristics it is small wonder that, like many proteins, they also have enzymatic activity.

—Robert Haselkorn

ZOOLOGY

Many exciting findings were made in the past year in zoology and related fields, including discoveries that previously had been considered improbable, if not impossible. Researchers, for example, presented evidence that suggests the existence of an-

Figure 2: The P4-P6 domain of a self-splicing RNA intron from the ciliate *Tetrahymena* achieves a U-turn without the help of a protein. The tetraloop bound to its receptor and the adenine-rich bulge are novel with respect to structures seen in DNA.

cient life on Mars. Although the purported fossil life forms do not look like little green Martians—or, for that matter, even like animals—the discovery may help zoologists understand the evolution of animals on Earth. In news with even wider implications, scientists for the first time successfully cloned an adult sheep, triggering widespread speculation about the implications of cloning for humans.

Developmental biology

Developmental biologists long have recognized that almost every cell in the human body (with the exception of the reproductive testis and ovary cells) contains the entire genetic blueprint necessary for the development of an individual. Most of these cells, however, differentiate into a particular cell type. Regulatory genes typically shut down all "unnecessary" genes in specialized cells so that nerve cells, for example, perform functions related to nerves and muscle cells correspond only to muscles. Many scientists believed cellular differentiation to be irreversible. A liver cell, in other words, could never be reprogrammed to produce an individual.

Ian Wilmut and his colleagues at the Roslin Institute, near Edinburgh, stunned the public and scientific community alike in early 1997 with a report that differentiated cells could indeed produce viable adults. Wilmut and his colleagues removed cells from the udder of a six-year-old pregnant Finn Dorset ewe and cultured them in a broth that arrested the cells' development at a stage referred to as the G_0 phase. Nuclei of these quiescent cells were inserted into enucleated egg cells (cells with their nucleus removed), and the "renucleated" egg cells were implanted into surro-

gate mother ewes. Of the 29 remodeled eggs inserted into recipient ewes, one resulted in the birth of a lamb, which was named Dolly. Dolly is a genetic carbon copy, or clone, of the nucleus-donor ewe.

The researchers' findings have extraordinary ramifications. The ability to clone complex creatures like lambs means that scientists could create entire herds that possess traits of interest to humans. Ethicists also raised concerns about the troubling potential for this technology to be applied to humans.

Life on Mars?

A group of scientists led by geologist David S. McKay of NASA's Lyndon B. Johnson Space Center, Houston, Texas, introduced tantalizing evidence indicating that life may have existed on Mars. The evidence came from what might appear as an unlikely candidate—a Martian meteorite.

The 4.5 billion-year-old meteorite, technically named ALH84001, was thought to have crashed in Antarctica 13,000 years ago. The rock featured tiny carbonate globules ranging from one to 250 micrometers (millionths of a meter) wide that researchers estimated were formed 3.6 billion years ago. Electron microscopy revealed that several globules possessed elongated tube-like structures similar in size and texture to some bacterially induced carbonate precipitates on Earth. The investigators also discovered that the Martian meteorite contained abundant polycyclic aromatic hydrocarbons (PAHs). On Earth PAHs, organic molecules commonly found in ancient sedimentary rocks and fossil fuels, indicate the existence of such biological precursors as marine plankton and early

plant life. Although they did not imply that life exists on Mars today, the materials found in the meteorite could represent the fossilized remains of past life on the Red Planet. The NASA researchers' findings, however, did not go uncontested. Many investigators suggested that the globules could easily be attributable to inorganic processes. (For additional information, *see* Year in Review: ASTRONOMY; EARTH SCIENCES: *Paleontology;* LIFE SCIENCES: *Microbiology,* above.)

Life on Earth

The earliest forms of life on Earth are bacterial microfossils, which appear in sediments about 3.5 billion years old. Since these early microfossils are structurally complex, scientists speculate that life must have evolved much earlier in time. Unfortunately, most crustal rocks older than 3.5 billion years were subject to extreme metamorphism, which destroyed any microfossils that they may have contained.

Examining ancient biogeochemical traces, an international team of researchers led by Stephen Mojzsis of the Scripps Institution of Oceanography, La Jolla, Calif., recently reported a novel approach to searching for evidence of life in rocks older than 3.5 billion years. In the marine environment, for example, microorganisms are known to segregate particular minerals, such as calcium from magnesium, as well as concentrate various organic phosphate species. Therefore, many modern and ancient sediments possess mineral signatures of organic life.

The research team used an ion microprobe to measure the carbon-isotope composition within grains of calcium phosphate taken from the world's oldest known sediments (roughly 3,850,000,000 years old) in western Greenland and nearby Akilia Island. The carbon inclusions within the grains of calcium phosphate possessed a signature that differed substantially from inorganic carbon, which suggested evidence of ancient biological activity. No known inorganic process could explain the data. Their findings pushed back the date for the emergence of life approximately 300 million to 400 million years.

Evolution

Lake Victoria, the largest of the great Rift lakes in Africa, is home to more than 300 endemic species of cichlid fish, all thought to have evolved from a single common ancestor less than 200,000 years ago. This astounding speciation is only part of the lake's phenomenal evolutionary story. Evidence has indicated that during the late Pleistocene (15,000 to 17,000 years ago), the lake was at least 65 m (213 ft) lower than its present depth of 69 m (226 ft). One question that remained to be answered was whether one or more residual lakes survived this dry spell to provide a refuge for the lake's cichlid fauna.

An international team of scientists led by Thomas Johnson of the University of Minnesota at Duluth answered this question by surveying the floor of Lake Victoria, using seismic-reflection profiling and sediment coring to determine how much smaller Lake Victoria was during the Late Pleistocene. Vertical rootlets and pollen derived mostly from grasses indicated that the lake level fell about 17,000 years ago and was not flooded again until about 12,400 years ago, and the lake basin was thus dry for several thousand years. Therefore, according to the evidence, the lake's

cichlid species must have evolved in the 12,000 years since the lake was recharged, which makes this story of evolution even more astounding. Sadly, the ability to learn more about this unique habitat and its cichlids has been compromised by the elimination of nearly every native cichlid species owing to a variety of human blunders, including the introduction of fish-eating Nile perch.

Cichlid fishes are not the only fascinating creatures to have evolved in the Rift lakes of Africa. The incredibly diverse and unique snails (gastropods) of Lake Tanganyika also have attracted the attention of biologists. Unlike most freshwater gastropods, many of the lake's snails have strongly calcified and highly ornamented shells. In fact, the degree of ornamentation (including coarse ribbing and spines) and the general shape of the shells show striking similarities to those of several marine gastropods. At the turn of the century, many malacologists categorized Tanganyikan snails in marine gastropod families. To account for these commonalities, they postulated that Lake Tanganyika had been linked to the ocean at one time.

Recent geological evidence, however, provides no support for this theory. Modern scientists have placed the endemic gastropods of Lake Tanganyika in a freshwater family of snails. Nonetheless, the question has remained as to why the lake's snails strongly resemble marine gastropods. Several years ago Kelly West and Andrew Cohen of the University of California, Los Angeles, and their colleagues hypothesized that the unusual Tanganyikan shell morphologies were the product of a coevolutionary relationship with the numerous fish and crab predators of the lake.

Snails with thicker ornamented shells appeared to suffer fewer fatal attacks from shell-crushing predators than gastropods without ornamentation.

In 1996 West and Cohen examined the microstructure of the shells, using electron microscopy, and then conducted shell-crushing experiments to see if their underlying structure actually conferred any advantage. The researchers found that the structure of the shells resembled that of plywood. Shell layers were juxtaposed such that the orientation of the sheets was offset by about 90°. The construction increased the tensile strength of the shell and retarded cracking. The researchers found a direct correlation between the number of such crossed-lamellar layers and the gastropod's chances of surviving a predator's attack. The findings revealed that although the shells' spines and ribs helped deter predation, the less-conspicuous shell microstructure was important as well. Interestingly, shell microstructure also was linked to the snail's habitat. Snails with only one or two crossed-lamellar layers in their shell walls tended to inhabit ecologically safer places to avoid predation, such as the undersides of rocks, whereas those with three or four protective layers were found in more open habitats.

Researchers also made new discoveries about another scientific enigma—the evolution of turtles (chelonians). The characteristics of modern turtles already were well developed in the earliest turtles of the Triassic Period (more than 200 million years ago). Only in the past few years have evolutionary biologists begun to piece together the history of turtles prior to the Triassic. Michael Lee of the University of Sydney, Australia, presented the results of

Surveys of the floor of Lake Victoria revealed that Africa's largest lake was a grassy plain only about 12,000 years ago. The lake's fauna, including this Nyassa blue cichlid, was one of 300 unique fish species that evolved in what scientists say was a record period of evolutionary time.

a comprehensive evolutionary study of turtles and the early reptiles considered to be their relatives, including nycteroleterids, nyctiphruretids, procolophonids, lanthanosuchids, and pareiasaurs.

On the basis of the analysis of anatomic features in representative animals from each species in the group, Lee constructed an evolutionary tree. Lee's findings demonstrated, for example, that some pareiasaurs appeared to be related more closely to turtles than to other pareiasaurs. The tree also suggested ways in which distinctive turtle morphology may have evolved. The most primitive arrangement of dermal armor (precursor of the modern turtle shell), for example, was found in the earliest pareiasaurs, which include *Bradysaurus, Embrithosaurus,* and *Deltavjatia.* The animals in these groups featured small, isolated, and bonelike disks along their backbones. Though it is unlikely that these disks conferred any protective advantage, they may have aided the posture of these animals by providing sites for muscle attachments.

Lee tracked the next stage in the evolution of armor to such pareiasaurs as *Scutosaurus* and *Elginia.* Both groups exhibited bony plates that were larger than the

disks found in the earliest pareiasaurs. In addition, the plates covered most of the animals' backs, which suggests that they served as protective armor. In *Anthodon* and *Nanoparia*—the pareiasaurs thought to be most closely related to turtles—the armor formed a rigid covering over the entire back.

Lee's evolutionary tree also revealed information about traits associated with turtle locomotion. Living turtles, for example, rely on their limbs exclusively for locomotion. The tree clearly showed the gradual shortening and stiffening of the trunk in earlier relatives of turtles, features that forced turtles to use just their limbs rather than move with the lateral-body, S-like undulation characteristic of their ancestors.

Ecology

Ornithologists have long studied how female birds choose their mates. Noting that birds often are sexually dimorphic—that is, the males and females differ in size, coloration, or both—many scientists have concluded that females often prefer males that are more colorful and ornate. One potential problem with mate-choice studies is that they may be influenced by biases and perceptions deriving from a human's

inability to see exactly what a bird sees. For instance, a researcher may assume that a female cardinal chooses a particular male for a mate because he appears redder than a competing male. What if, however, the female bird is actually looking at something other than redness?

Researchers have known for more than 20 years that unlike humans, many birds can see ultraviolet (UV) light. Recent research suggested that this ability may play a decisive role in mate selection. Andrew Bennett of the University of Bristol, Eng., reported the results of an experiment in which zebra finches were discovered to use UV light in mate-choice decisions. Researchers placed a female bird in the center of a specially designed mate-choice apparatus. From this position she could view prospective males individually through transparent filters on all four sides. Mate choice was measured by counting the number of hops made by a female facing a particular filter. Results indicated that female zebra finches had stronger preferences for males residing behind a filter that did not block UV light than for males behind one that did, although the investigators themselves could not detect the difference visually.

Over the past few years, wildlife scientists have reported abnormal sexual development, such as feminization, in male alligators and fish. Some investigators believe that the phenomenon may be due to the presence of human-made chemicals in the environment that mimic estrogens, the hormones responsible for the regulation of female reproductive functions and the development of female secondary sex characteristics. Estrogen-like compounds are found in pesticides such as dieldrin and toxaphene, plastic ingredients such as bisphenol A, and some polychlorinated biphenyls. Some researchers theorize that in addition to causing the abnormal features found in animals, environmental estrogens also may increase the risk of breast and testicular cancer or reduce sperm counts in humans.

Critics of the theory charge that most estrogen-like compounds have potencies only $1/50$ to $1/10,000$ those of natural estrogen and thus pose no real health threat. The enhanced effects of these compounds, however, when combined with other chemicals in the environment, have not been well studied. Steven Arnold of Tulane University, New Orleans, explored this question of enhancement by using genetically engineered yeast cells. The yeast cells contained genes that code for the human estrogen receptor as well as the "reporter" protein that is made by the cell when an estrogen-like compound binds to the receptor. When estrogen became bound to the receptor, the synthesis of the reporter protein turned blue. The intensity of the color indicated the strength of the binding. When four different pesticides were individually tested with this yeast-cell system, the results supported previous findings in which little or no response was recorded in the estrogen-receptor reaction. When the pesticides were paired in various combinations for the test, however, potency increased to 160–1,600 times that of the individual compounds. Although the researchers could not infer the same effects of these synergistic reactions in living vertebrates, including humans, their results certainly demonstrated that the interaction of estrogen-like chemicals and biological systems was more complex than previ-

ously thought and served as a warning that further studies were needed. (*See also* Feature Article: Unnatural Selection.)

Conservation biology

Conservation biologists have their hands full trying to effectively manage endangered and threatened species. Occasionally contributing to the problem is a disease outbreak, which can have disastrous consequences on already small populations. In the 1980s, for example, canine distemper virus (CDV), a morbillivirus that also includes measles, nearly eliminated the black-footed ferret from its only known habitat in Wyoming. Scientists are concerned that the transmission of feline immunodeficiency virus from domestic cats may devastate the Florida panther.

In 1994 six lions in the Serengeti National Park were observed with grand mal seizures and three others with recurrent facial and forelimb twitching. Within three months of the first observation, 11 lion carcasses were found, which indicated a serious disease outbreak. In 1996 Melody Roelke-Parker of the Serengeti Wildlife Research Institute, Arusha, Tanz., reported findings of an investigation into the outbreak in an effort to determine its cause and formulate a strategy for prevention. Tissue and serum samples were obtained from lions that died or were killed in a moribund state, from anesthetized individuals with signs of the disease, and from healthy lions. Since the Serengeti lions were a large, well-studied population, sera also were available from healthy lions sampled between 1984 and 1994. Tissues from the dead lions showed lesions that were similar to those found in zoo cats that had died from CDV in the U.S. To confirm

the initial diagnosis, mono- and polyclonal CDV antibodies were used to test for the presence of CDV antigens in affected tissues and all available lion sera. All the tests suggested that the disease was indeed caused by CDV.

Later in 1994 CDV-infected lions were identified in the northern and western areas of the Serengeti National Park and in the Masai Mara National Reserve, Kenya. The overall lion population in the Serengeti ecosystem, estimated at 3,000 individuals prior to the outbreak, dropped to 2,000 by 1995. The investigators believed that the epidemic had such a devastating effect because the unexposed population had not built up any resistance to CDV. Only one of the lions sampled between 1990 and 1993, for example, showed evidence of CDV antigens in its blood sera.

The investigators then attempted to determine the source of the CDV in the Serengeti epidemic. Their primary suspect was the large population of domestic dogs that live in local villages adjacent to the park. Tests showed that CDV was prevalent in the serum of dogs, and incidences of the disease had increased between 1991 and 1993. A dog death from CDV was confirmed in 1994. Because dog-lion interactions are unusual, the virus probably traveled from dogs to spotted hyenas, which range around human settlements, and subsequently to lions. The researchers concluded that the large population of domestic dogs may serve as a reservoir for various diseases and recommended initiating a canine-vaccination program.

—Charles Lydeard

See also Feature Articles: An Appetite for Poison; Kjell B. Sandved: Wonders on the Wing; Rice to Feed the Hungry.

MATERIALS SCIENCE AND ENGINEERING

Scientists in Japan, Germany, and the United States reported significant advances during the year in the production of heat-resistant silicon-based fibers for ceramic composite materials. Among other developments was commercialization of a process for making components from intermetallics, which are alloys based on metal-metal compounds, and the growing commercial use of single-site catalysts for the production of important polymers.

CERAMICS

Progress occurred during the past year in developing silicon-based fibers capable of withstanding extremely high temperatures for use as reinforcement in ceramic composites. Fiber-reinforced ceramic matrix composites are new materials with great advantages in a wide range of applications. These include jet and rocket engines, gas turbines, filters for coal-fired electric power plants, and brake disks and pads for automobiles. Ceramic components permit cleaner and more efficient operation, especially in turbine applications, and thereby aid conservation of fuel and reduction of environmental pollution.

Ceramic composites are lightweight, temperature-resistant materials that owe much of their strength and toughness to reinforcing fibers. The fibers, dispersed throughout the ceramic material, deflect and stop cracks that would otherwise cause catastrophic failure of a ceramic part under mechanical stress. Ceramic composites have an engineered capability of accumulating local damage without failing that far exceeds that of traditional, unreinforced ceramics. New fiber-reinforcement materials are needed, however. The fibers must be durable in harsh environments, such as the scorching conditions inside jet engines, and yet also be cost-effective and compatible with manufacturing processes. This is especially true for applications requiring long-term operation at very high temperature, in excess of 1,100° C (2,000° F). Significant progress toward this objective occurred during the past year in Japan, the United States, and Germany.

Fiber research in Japan and the U.S. focused on silicon carbide (SiC). This fiber is typically spun from organosilicon polymers based on polycarbosilane (PCS) and is then converted to the ceramic state through heat treatment. Silicon carbide fibers are very fine, with a diameter of 10–15 micrometers (millionths of a meter), and can be spun to produce yarn containing 500 or more filaments. Fibers are often strong and stiff. A disadvantage, however, has been their tendency to perform poorly when subjected for long periods in air to temperatures above 1,100° C. Researchers finally were able to implement the procedure for achieving both improved high-temperature performance and greater strength and stiffness. It involved avoiding excessive amounts of carbon or silicon and limiting the amount of oxygen that exists as an impurity in the fibers.

Nippon Carbon Co., Ltd., of Japan developed a new silicon carbide fiber containing near-equal amounts of silicon and carbon on an atomic-percentage basis. Named Hi-Nicalon Type S, the fiber consists of 68.9% silicon, 30.9% carbon, and 0.2% oxygen by weight. The oxygen content is limited by the use of a curing process that employs a beam of electrons. To maintain its geometric integrity, the newly spun fiber, which is in a polymeric state, must be made rigid before its high-temperature conversion to the ceramic. This rigidifying step, termed "curing," causes the formation of chemical cross-links between the polymer chains. Cross-links reinforce and strengthen the molecular structure. The conventional cross-linking process uses oxygen and thereby incorporates significant amounts of oxygen into the fiber. This reduces the ability of the finished fibers to perform well at high temperatures. Nippon Carbon's use of radiation curing results in a dramatic reduction in oxygen content.

UBE Industries of Japan had previously developed silicon carbide fibers containing small amounts of titanium. During the past year it developed similar fibers that consist of silicon carbide and zirconium. Named Tyranno, the new fibers have near-equal atomic percentages of carbon and silicon and low oxygen contents. Researchers achieved the combination by modifying the structure of the polymer and by changing the conditions under which the spun fiber is converted to the ceramic state. Oxygen content as low as 3% by weight was achieved, and this resulted in improved oxidation resistance and in mechanical properties that were retained after exposure to high temperatures.

The Dow Corning Corp. in the U.S. developed a new silicon carbide fiber named Sylramic. It also has near-equal atomic percentages of silicon and carbon, plus 5% by weight of three titanium and boron compounds. Tests showed that Sylramic could withstand 10 hours of exposure to temperatures of 1,550° C (2,800° F) in an argon atmosphere without significant loss in fiber strength. Oxidation studies at 1,200° C (2,200° F) indicated behavior similar to bulk silicon carbide. Dow

Corning targeted this new fiber for applications requiring continuous use at temperatures as high as 1,400° C (2,550° F) and began supplying sample fiber to prospective customers.

The University of Florida, in conjunction with the 3M Co., also developed two new silicon carbide fibers. They are spun from PCS, but the Florida polymer is sufficiently rigid when freshly spun that it does not require curing before conversion to ceramic. This eliminates the need for an oxidative or radiative curing step. One fiber type contains 60–62% silicon, 37–39% carbon, and 0.5–1.5% oxygen by weight. Named LoX, for low oxygen, it retains high strength after short-term exposure to 1,500° C in argon. LoX is amorphous, but a crystalline version can be made if the spun polymer is heated to temperatures higher than those used for conventional LoX fiber. The crystalline version would

Sylramic, a silicon carbide fiber recently developed in the U.S. by Dow Corning Corp., demonstrated in tests that it could withstand 10 hours of exposure to temperatures of 1,550° C (2,800° F) in an argon atmosphere without a significant loss of fiber strength.

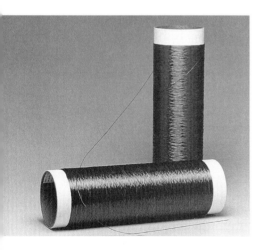

have resistance to higher temperatures than would the amorphous, but it would cost more to produce.

Bayer AG in Germany took a different approach for its advanced fiber, which is spun from a polyborosilazane precursor polymer. When the fiber is heated in nitrogen, it yields an amorphous fiber containing silicon, boron, nitrogen, and carbon (SiBN$_3$C). The oxygen content is about 2.5% by weight. If the spun fiber is heated in ammonia, the carbon is removed and the fiber becomes Si$_3$B$_3$N$_7$. The SiBN$_3$C fiber may remain amorphous to a temperature of 1,800° C (3,300° F). Preliminary data revealed that the fiber exhibits significant resistance to creep (an undesired change in dimension over a long period when under a mechanical load).

—Allan P. Katz

METALS

Alloys based on intermetallic compounds (intermetallics) such as the nickel aluminide Ni$_3$Al attracted great attention in the automobile and metal processing industries during the past year. Although intermetallic alloys are highly corrosion resistant and strong at high temperatures, their commercial application has been hampered for several decades by difficulties in producing useful shapes. Renewed interest in intermetallics has been sparked by the invention of a practical casting process suitable for large-scale production of nickel aluminide components.

Intermetallics are alloys based on specific compounds between different metals including nickel and aluminum (Al$_3$Ni$_2$, NiAl, and Ni$_3$Al), titanium and aluminum (TiAl and Ti$_3$Al), niobium and titanium (Nb$_3$Al), molybdenum and silicon (MoSi$_2$),

and iron and silicon (FeSi). Intermetallics are highly alloyed compared with conventional metal alloys. A typical plain carbon steel, for example, is composed of iron alloyed with only 0.4% carbon, 0.6% manganese, and even smaller concentrations by weight of other elements.

Intermetallics have a variety of properties that differ from conventional metal alloys. Many intermetallics have lower density owing to their high concentration of lighter materials such as aluminum and silicon. Many also have a high melting point. The nickel aluminide NiAl, for example, melts at about 1,700° C (3,100° F), which is higher than the melting points of either of its components; aluminum melts at 660° C (1,220° F) and nickel at 1,452° C (2,650° F). The high melting point of intermetallics results from strong chemical bonding between the different metals. In addition, many of these alloys have an ordered crystal structure. In conventional solid-solution alloys, an alloying element (solute) substitutes randomly in the crystal structure for the base metal (solvent). In ordered alloys the different atoms are arranged in a specific periodic pattern. The strong chemical bonding and ordered crystal structure enable intermetallics to retain their strength at higher temperatures than conventional alloys. Their combination of low density, heat resistance, and oxidation resistance makes intermetallics attractive structural materials for turbine engine components and other high-temperature applications.

Unfortunately, most intermetallics are intrinsically brittle and thus are weak and unpredictable when they are loaded in tension. This characteristic also makes them difficult to process into useful shapes. Owing to their great strength at high temperatures, they cannot easily be forged or rolled. Because of their high brittleness and hardness, they cannot be machined easily. For these reasons most intermetallics have been produced by powder processing. One powder production process involves ball milling elemental metal powder such as nickel and aluminum. In the mill the metal particles are repeatedly bonded together and fractured in a mechanical process that eventually produces fine particles of the intermetallic compound. These powders can be formed into shapes by pressing in a die and then densified by a sintering heat treatment. The disadvantages of powder processing include high cost, the potential for contamination of the powder, large shrinkages that occur in sintering, and residual porosity, which can act as the strength-limiting flaw in the final component.

Researchers at Oak Ridge (Tenn.) National Laboratory in the early 1990s developed the Exo-Melt processes for melting and casting nickel aluminide intermetallics. It involved a new method for loading the furnace to take advantage of the exothermic (heat-generating) reaction between nickel and aluminum. In this process pure aluminum and nickel pellets are arranged in an oxide refractory crucible with all of the aluminum in the top half of the crucible. Upon heating by an electric current in an argon atmosphere, the aluminum melts and trickles down into the solid nickel, dissolving it. Heat thus released further melts the metals and fosters the alloying process. The large amount of heat released reduces by nearly 50% the power necessary to produce the alloy. Recently the Exo-Melt process was commercialized in

conjunction with United Defense LP, Anniston, Ala. The most successful alloys produced in this effort were based on Ni_3Al, with small additions of chromium, molybdenum, zinc, and boron.

By itself, Ni_3Al is too brittle for applications involving large tensile stresses. It has several other attractive properties, however, including excellent oxidation resistance and unusual mechanical behavior. Not only do Ni_3Al alloys retain strength at high temperatures, but their strength actually increases slightly up to about 800° C (1,470° F), before decreasing at higher temperatures. In contrast, conventional heat-resistant alloys such as stainless steel lose strength continuously with increasing temperature.

One of the first commercial applications for the new cast Ni_3Al alloys was in fixturing, grating, and structural members in heat-treating furnaces. Compared with stainless steels, Ni_3Al alloys have much lower solubility for carbon. They thus have higher resistance to carburization, the tendency to dissolve carbon from the furnace atmosphere and become brittle. The superior properties of the alloys would be of little practical value, however, without a casting process that allows economical production of large components with complex shapes. Indeed, the ability to cast intermetallics to final or near-final shapes without extensive additional machining should lead to many new commercial applications in the near future.

—Kevin Trumble

POLYMERS

Single-site catalysts (SSCs) made a dynamic impact within the last year on technology for producing polyolefins, one of

the largest and most important groups of plastics. Polyolefins are made from long chains of olefins (hydrocarbons having one double bond) and include familiar plastics such as polyethylene, polypropylene, polybutylene, and polyisoprene. Some are used to manufacture synthetic fibers for carpeting, automobile seat covers, filters, and other products. The impact of SSCs was especially great in the production of linear low-density polyethylene (LLDPE) and polypropylene (PP). In 1996 alone, approximately 200 patents involving SSCs were granted in the United States.

SSC is significant because it allows much better control of molecular architecture and molecular weight distribution (MWD) compared with conventional polymerization methods, such as Ziegler-Natta catalysis. Ziegler-Natta catalysts comprise titanium halides and alkyl aluminum compounds that can control molecular development during polymerization. The disadvantage of these catalysts is that they contain multiple active sites for polymerization. As a result, they yield polymers that lack a homogeneous molecular architecture and have a relatively broad MWD. By contrast, SSCs contain only one type of active center and produce a highly desirable uniform molecular architecture and a narrow MWD.

The most common SSCs are based on a metallocene system developed by Walter Kaminsky during his graduate studies at the University of Hamburg, Ger. The system contained two compounds, methylalumoxane (an organoaluminum oligomer $[-O-AlCH_3-]_n$, in which n is less than 20) and a metallocene complex based on zirconium and two cyclopentadiene (C_5H_6) rings. In recently developed metallocene

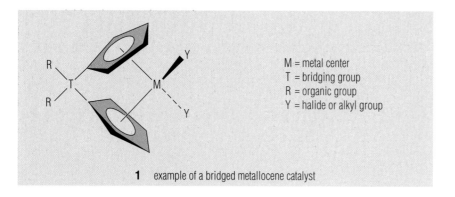

1 example of a bridged metallocene catalyst

catalysts, the two rings are bridged to maintain their fixed position relative to each other and to widen the angle between them (*see* 1). This approach provides much better control over polymer architecture. For example, new catalytic systems developed by the Dow Chemical Co. are able to copolymerize ethylene with styrene or hindered olefins (olefins with bulky side groups that physically hinder contact with the double bond).

Group VIII metal catalysts (including nickel, platinum, and palladium) that are single-site but not metallocene were also developed during the past year. Using this catalyst system, Maurice Brookhart at the University of North Carolina at Chapel Hill demonstrated a low-pressure, low-temperature method to copolymerize polar monomers with ethylene. (Polar monomers are molecules containing atoms of different electronegativity than carbon, such as oxygen and nitrogen.) Previously, this reaction required polymerization by free radicals under energy-intensive conditions in a high-pressure reactor. (Free radicals are atoms and molecules that possess at least one unpaired electron.)

SSCs' ability to control molecular architecture and molecular weight had its greatest impact on LLDPE development. LLDPE is a semicrystalline polyethylene copolymer made from a polyethylene chain with a small number of α-olefin chains inserted to form branches. An α-olefin is a relatively short, open-chain hydrocarbon with a single double bond located at the end of the chain. Branching is important because of its influence on the polymer's ability to crystallize. Crystallization, in turn, affects the physical properties of the bulk material. Consequently, manu-

facturers often promote branching in order to tailor properties such as stiffness and puncture resistance. Branches typically contain two to six carbons.

Several factors determine the extent to which the polymer will crystallize to form "spherulites." These include the number of branches per chain, spatial distribution of branches, and the consistency of branching between individual chains. Spherulites consist of blocks of flat crystallites called lamellae, which are formed by the folding of linear segments of the polyethylene chain. These blocks are interconnected by chain segments that hold neighboring lamellae together, which thus strengthens the spherulite. The remaining chains fill in the voids and constitute the amorphous (noncrystalline) region. In terms of mechanical properties, the lamellae provide rigidity, whereas the amorphous region provides flexibility.

Since branches cannot be accommodated in the lamella, their presence disrupts chain folding. This obstruction decreases lamella thickness and increases the number of interlamellar connections. If the branching arrangement is random, sections with fewer branches will form thicker lamellae than sections with extensive branching. If the branching arrangement is ordered, spherulite formation is more difficult, which results in thin lamellae. These materials typically have less stiffness and higher flexibility. Films made from these resins have improved puncture resistance, improved heat-sealing performance, reduced moisture and oxygen permeability, and greater toughness compared with conventional LLDPE.

The past year also was marked by the commercial development of new polypro-

pylene resins produced by SSCs. Polypropylene has three possible structures, defined by the arrangement of pendent methyl (CH_3-) groups relative to the plane of the polymer backbone (*see* 2). In isotactic PP, the pendent groups are located on one side of the plane, forming a crystalline polymer. Syndiotactic PP has a regular alternating pattern of pendent groups on either side of the plane, which results in a less crystalline form than isotactic PP. Consequently, syndiotactic PP lacks the stiffness of the isotactic form but has better impact resistance and clarity. Atactic PP is a result of random pendent group arrangement, which causes it to be amorphous and rubbery.

Manufacturers can use metallocene catalysts to tailor properties of specific molecular structures. For example, in current grades of isotactic PP, molecular irregularities can lead to a detrimental atactic component. By using metallocene catalysts, researchers can arrange the distribution of these irregularities such that the contribution of truly atactic PP to the bulk material is diminished. This type of control over molecular structure has led to properties that differ significantly from conventional isotactic PP. Metallocene-derived PP with a melting point of 140° C (280° F) can have the same mechanical properties as a conventional-grade PP with a melting point of 160° C (320° F).

The use of single-site catalysis has not been restricted to polyethylene and polypropylene. A joint venture between Dow Chemical Co. and Idemitsu Kosan Ltd. introduced the development of syndiotactic polystyrene, which had been previously unobtainable without the use of metallocene catalysts. Syndiotactic poly-

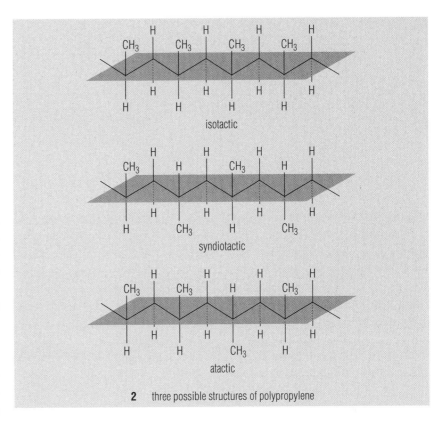

isotactic

syndiotactic

atactic

2 three possible structures of polypropylene

styrene offers significantly better thermal, chemical, and moisture resistance than conventional polystyrene. Metallocene catalysts have also been used to polymerize several cyclic olefin monomers.

—David E. Collins

MATHEMATICS

After several years of suspense and excitement about the proof of Fermat's last theorem, the achievements in mathematics during the past year were not as spectacular yet were surprising in their own way. A computer proved a mathematical theorem that had frustrated mathematicians for decades and a solution came to light at last for exactly predicting the motions of interacting celestial bodies. A new largest prime was discovered, and pi was computed to a record 6.4 billion decimal places. Meanwhile, as physicists began designing the first quantum computers, mathematicians and computer scientists were designing algorithms to run on them.

Computers and mathematics

Through programming the use of assumptions and rules for deduction, mathematicians have used computers in the past to find proofs of mathematical results. These have been either brute-force enumeration of cases (as in the four-color theorem) or else fairly straightforward derivations, occasionally simpler than known proofs. At last, however, a computer has used deductive logic to prove a significant mathematical theorem that mathematicians did not know before to be true. In fact, mathematicians had worked on the underlying conjecture for more than half a century. The theorem, in the field of equational algebras, was conjectured by Herbert Robbins, then at Harvard University, in the 1930s; it asserts that a particular set of three equations is powerful enough to capture all the laws of Boolean algebra.

Boolean algebra is named after George Boole (1815–64), a pioneer in expressing logical arguments in algebraic form. Today Boolean algebra is the basis for the logic of electric circuitry in computers. A Boolean algebra is an algebraic system with two operations, "addition" and "multiplication," which satisfy a standard set of axioms. Both of the operations are commutative ($x + y = y + x$ and $xy = yx$) and interact in accordance with distributive law ($x(y + z) = xy + xz$) and associative law ($x(yz) = (xy)z$ and $x + (y + z) = (x + y) + z$). In addition, there is an additive identity 0 and a multiplicative identity 1 (such that $x + 0 = x$ and $x1 = x$ for every element x); each element x has an inverse x^c (such that $x + x^c = 1$ and $xx^c = 0$); and both operations are idempotent—that is, any element applied to itself under one of the binary operations equals itself (for any element x, $x + x = x$ and $xx = x$). A simple example is the collection of all subsets of a set, with set union as the addition operation and set intersection as the multiplication operation. Indeed, this example is generic, since any Boolean algebra can be represented as a Boolean algebra of sets.

In particular, an algebra satisfying additive commutativity, additive associativity, and the Robbins condition, $((x + y)^c + (x + y^c)^c)^c = x$, is called a Robbins algebra. The new result is that every Robbins algebra is a Boolean algebra. It had been known since 1933 that additive commutativity, additive associativity, and the Huntington equation, $(x^c + y)^c + (x^c + y^c)^c = x$, are equivalent to standard axioms for a Boolean algebra. Also in the 1930s, Robbins had conjectured that the Huntington equation could be replaced with the simpler Robbins condition, but this conjecture was not proved until October 1996, when a computer theorem-proving program was used. The computer proof, obtained by William McCune, took place at the Argonne (Ill.) National Laboratory.

The n-body problem

The n-body problem in celestial mechanics is as follows: Given exact initial locations, masses, and velocities of n bodies moving under Newton's laws of motion, find functions that describe exactly their locations at all future times. The case $n = 2$ (two-body problem) was solved by Johann Bernoulli in 1710. In 1888 Henri Poincaré showed that the case $n \geq 3$ can include chaotic behavior and that the general problem cannot be solved by the method of integrals, in which one seeks functions that are constant for all values of the positions and velocities. Mathematical folklore ever since has held either that the general n-body problem for $n \geq 3$ is unsolvable or that the problem is still open.

The case $n = 3$ (three-body problem) was solved in the form of an infinite series in 1909 by Karl Sundman, except for initial conditions that may lead to a triple collision of the bodies. The method used for that solution does not extend to higher n, which may have led to the mathematical folklore. In 1991, however, Quidong ("Don") Wang, a graduate student at the University of Cincinnati, Ohio, achieved an infinite series solution for the n-body problem, except for some special cases (including collisions). Only in 1996, however, did his achievement receive wide recognition in the mathematical community. His solution is not practical because the series solutions add up very slowly to the exact values. Nonetheless, since Newton and Bernoulli, important practical special cases have been solved with sufficiently good approximations to send spacecraft throughout the solar system.

Algorithms for quantum computers

Quantum computers theoretically offer a greatly increased amount of memory and the ability to solve problems that traditional computers cannot do in a reasonable period of time. In a quantum computer the usual bits of data (0 and 1) of the binary number system used in digital computers would be replaced by quantum bits (qubits, pronounced like *cubits*). In accord with the laws of quantum mechanics, qubits would behave both like particles and like waves and would be simultaneously both 0 and 1. An ordinary digital computer with n bits of memory can display and work on only one computational state at a time. By contrast, a quantum computer with n qubits of memory would exist in 2^n states all at the same time. The great advantage of a quantum computer would be that computation could be done simultaneously along many paths, as opposed to the step-by-step process of computation in traditional computers. A quantum computation, such as a search through an unordered list for a particular name, would consist of using the wavelike properties of qubits so that names not matching the search item would fade (cancel themselves out), whereas matching names would be amplified (reinforced).

Physicists have not yet built a quantum computer, first proposed in 1985 by David Deutsch of the University of Oxford, and are not likely to be able to do so soon. However, much as Alonzo Church (1903–95) and Alan Turing (1912–54) studied and analyzed the capabilities of a digital computer before one was ever built, mathematicians and computer scientists have already designed algorithms (systematic mathematical procedures that produce solutions to problems) to exploit the structure and advantages of a quantum computer. In 1994 Peter W. Shor of AT&T Bell Laboratories designed a quantum-computer algorithm for factoring large whole numbers, which in principle makes the time-consuming problem of factorization manageable. Two years later his co-worker Lov K. Grover devised a quantum-computer algorithm for extremely quick searching of an unordered database in a time proportional to the square root of the number of items in the database. A standard digital-computer algorithm must examine on average half the items before finding the desired one (if it is present) and all of the items before discovering that the desired item is not present. Grover also discovered how to use a quantum computer to calculate statistics efficiently from large data sets.

New primes

The record for largest-known prime (a positive integer with no exact positive integer divisors except itself and 1) was broken twice during 1996. The two record holders are the 34th and 35th Mersenne primes, $M_{34} = 2^{1,257,787} - 1$ and $M_{35} = 2^{1,398,269} - 1$. The latter has 420,921 decimal digits. A Mersenne number is an integer of the form $2^p - 1$, where p is a prime. Some Mersenne numbers are themselves primes, and they are called Mersenne primes. It is relatively quick to check if a candidate Mersenne number is prime; checking M_{34} took only six hours on a Cray T94 supercomputer, and checking M_{35} took 88 hours on a 90-megahertz Pentium personal computer. The major time involved in a discovery like this is in testing and discarding thousands of other Mersenne numbers that turn out not to be prime.

Like recent predecessors, M_{34} was found at Cray Research, this time by David Slowinski and Paul Gage. Its successor, M_{35}, however, was discovered by Joel Armengaud of the Great Internet Mersenne Prime Search (GIMPS), in an effort by more than 700 volunteers who employed otherwise-unused time on their personal computers to find Mersenne primes. In fact, George Woltman, founder of GIMPS, had been 90% of the way through checking M_{34} when the announcement came from Cray Research.

More and more digits of pi

In 1873 William Shanks (1812–82) employed John Machin's (1680–1750) identity

$$\tfrac{\pi}{4} = 4\,\tan^{-1}\left(\tfrac{1}{5}\right) - \tan^{-1}\left(\tfrac{1}{239}\right)$$

to calculate the value of pi to 707 decimal digits. It was not discovered until the 1940s that Shanks's digits were in error after the 527th digit. Until the 1970s machine calculations continued to use Machin's and other classical formulas. With such formulas, calculating pi to twice as many correct decimal digits requires evaluating twice as many terms of the formula.

Beginning in the mid-1970s, however, mathematicians discovered iterative algorithms (computational procedures in which repetition of a sequence of operations yields results successively closer to a desired result) that are considerably more efficient than the classical formulas. The calculation for each iteration must be done to the number of decimal digits of the desired final result. Each iteration approximately doubles, triples, or multiplies by an even larger number the number of correct decimal digits. An algorithm that multiplies the number of correct digits by n with each iteration is called an nth-order algorithm. There are algorithms for pi of every order. Although a higher-order algorithm requires fewer iterations for achieving a given number of correct digits, each

Paul Erdos, one of the century's greatest mathematicians, died on Sept. 20, 1996. At the age of 20 he discovered a proof for a classic theorem of number theory that states that there is always at least one prime number between any positive integer and its double.

iteration requires more calculations than a lower-order algorithm. Consequently, algorithms of low order (2 to 4) turn out to be the fastest iterative algorithms.

The latest record, more than 6.4 billion decimal digits of pi, was set by Yasumasa Kanada of the University of Tokyo in October 1995. He used two different algorithms, combinations of algorithms of orders 2 and 4; each took five days on a Hitachi supercomputer. Thanks to new algorithms of the 1990s, individual digits of pi represented in base 16 can be calculated with relatively little computation. It does not appear, however, that there are corresponding simple formulas for individual decimal digits.

Why is there interest in so many digits

of pi? Apart from the desire to set a record, these calculations—like the testing of Mersenne numbers—are an excellent test of computer hardware and software, and the search for digits of pi has spun off new computational techniques with applications in other areas. Finally, it has long been conjectured that on average each decimal digit occurs with equal frequency (one-tenth) in the expansion of pi and that in some sense the digits occur randomly. So far, with a large number of digits calculated, these conjectures appear to be true, though no one has any idea how to prove them.

Milestones

Donald Knuth of Stanford University received the Inamori Foundation's 1996 Kyoto Prize in the category of Advanced Technology, with a monetary award of $460,000. Knuth, among the world's best-known computer scientists, retired recently at age 57 to complete his seven-volume *The Art of Computer Programming,* which he started in 1962 and suspended for many years to create the TeX computer document publishing system and the METAFONT font-design system. He estimated that it would take 20 more years to finish the remaining four volumes. Willard van Orman Quine of Harvard University, known for his work on mathematical logic and in philosophy, received the Kyoto Prize for Creative Arts and Moral Sciences. Among notable mathematicians who died in 1996 were Paul Erdos (*see* SCIENTISTS OF THE YEAR: *Obituaries*) and Garrett Birkhoff, researcher in lattice theory and coauthor of the classic *A Survey of Modern Algebra.*

—Paul J. Campbell

MEDICAL SCIENCES

In 1996 physicians and dentists made major strides in the fight against devastating human diseases. Deaths due to cancer dropped, while new combination drug therapies dramatically prolonged the lives of AIDS sufferers. Gum disease, the second leading cause of tooth loss, was on the decline because of better dental care and antibiotics that target disease-causing bacteria. Veterinary research delivered some good news to household pets and their owners by expanding the knowledge about cat-scratch disease and developing an analgesic skin patch that provided postsurgical pain relief for dogs.

GENERAL MEDICINE

The year 1996 may well be remembered as the point when medical science's persistence finally began to pay off in the struggle against two of the most-feared diseases in the modern era: cancer and AIDS. Low-tech life-style changes such as quitting smoking largely accounted for the first steady drop in cancer death rates in the 20th century. On the other hand, it took all the muscle that high-tech science could muster to design drug therapies that have raised hopes for life-prolonging, perhaps even curative, treatments for AIDS.

Despite the aura of optimism in many fields, the year was not without controversy and uncertainty. Debate continued to swirl around such politically and ethically charged issues as whether "mad cow" disease can be passed on to humans, the causes of Gulf War syndrome, and prioritizing recipients of liver transplants.

Cancer

U.S. National Cancer Institute Director Richard Klausner called it the news for which he—and the rest of the medical community—had long been waiting: for the first time since 1900, the overall U.S. cancer death rate appeared to be on the decline. Researchers at the University of Alabama, Birmingham, found that the death rate for all types of cancer fell more than 3% from 1990 to 1995. The researchers credited most of this historic drop to lower levels of smoking among U.S. men, along with improved efforts to detect cancer in its earliest, most treatable stages.

On the treatment front, U.S. Pres. Bill Clinton in March directed the Food and Drug Administration (FDA) to speed approval of promising new cancer drugs, using as a model the new streamlined process for approving AIDS drugs. The move could cut as much as three years off the time it takes for a cancer therapy to move from the laboratory to the clinic. The new policy also authorized U.S. medical facilities to provide patients whose cancers are untreatable by existing therapies in the U.S. with treatments that have been approved in Canada, Australia, or Europe.

Scientists also learned more about the basic underpinnings of various types of cancer, including prostate cancer. An international team from Sweden's Umeå University, the U.S. National Institutes of Health (NIH), Bethesda, Md., and Johns Hopkins University, Baltimore, Md., identified the general location of the first gene believed to predispose men to developing prostate cancer. The researchers speculated that mutations in the gene, located on chromosome 1, may account for about 3% of all prostate cancer cases. The discovery also may help them learn more about the mechanism of nonhereditary cases. Before their work can have any practical applica-tions in diagnosis or treatment, however, researchers cautioned that they must pinpoint the exact location of the gene.

Harvard University researchers reported encouraging early results from a new blood test aimed at identifying the men most likely to develop a dangerous form of prostate cancer—the type with rapid growth fueled by the male hormone testosterone. The test examines variations in a gene coding for a protein that determines how sensitive the prostate is to testosterone. The researchers said that, if their findings are confirmed by larger studies, the test might be used in tandem with the current prostate-specific antigen (PSA) test, which helps to detect prostate tumors but does not convey their severity.

In a massive project designed to address long-standing concerns that oral contraceptives may cause breast cancer, scientists from 25 nations analyzed 54 studies involving more than 53,000 women with breast cancer and more than 100,000 healthy women. The study compared Pill users who had discontinued using oral contraceptives for 10 or more years to nonusers and found no long-term link between birth-control pills and the risk of developing breast cancer. On the contrary, the study suggested that oral contraceptives may provide some protection for women who do develop breast cancer. Analysis of breast-cancer patients showed that users of the Pill were much more likely than nonusers to have developed the kind of cancer that had not spread beyond the breast and therefore was the easiest to cure.

Researchers helped to settle another major unresolved question pertaining to breast cancer: does treatment with the drug tamoxifen after breast-cancer surgery im-

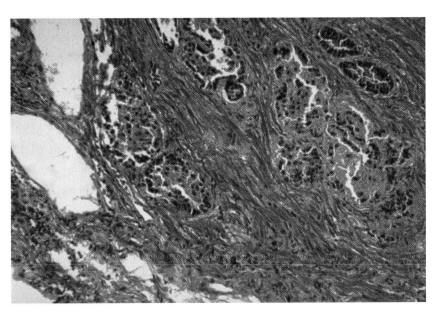

Researchers reported important new information about the genetic predisposition of some men to prostate cancer, shown here in the dark stains sprinkled throughout this microscopic view of a tissue sample taken from a prostate gland.

prove a woman's chance for survival? The answer is a resounding yes. Studies conducted by the U.S. National Surgical Adjuvant Breast and Bowel Project and the Swedish Breast Cancer Cooperative Group showed that women who took tamoxifen for five years after having early-stage breast-cancer surgery were up to 18% more likely to be cancer-free a decade after their operations than women who had not taken the drug.

AIDS and other infectious diseases

In the despair-ridden years that followed the first identified case of AIDS in 1981, few in the medical community dared to dream about—much less publicly discuss—the possibility of curing the deadly retroviral disease. In the past year, however, tangible hopes for a cure emerged—

hopes grounded in the impressive performance of a new breed of combination therapies that features drugs known as protease inhibitors. A team from New York City's Aaron Diamond AIDS Research Center reported no sign of the AIDS virus in the blood of 21 of 26 infected men who had undergone nine months of treatment with a three-drug "cocktail" consisting of the standard anti-HIV (the virus that causes AIDS) drug zidovudine (AZT), the drug lamivudine (3TC), and the protease inhibitor indinavir. In contrast, only one of 27 men who took a two-drug mixture of AZT and 3TC showed no signs of the virus in the bloodstream.

Similar encouraging data were reported from Canada for a three-drug regimen combining AZT, 3TC, and the protease inhibitor ritonavir. According to health officials in British Columbia, the introduc-

tion of combination therapies that included protease inhibitors cut the death rate among province residents infected with the AIDS virus from 70 per 1,000 in 1994 to 23 per 1,000 in the last three months of 1996. Such treatment strategies were thought to have the best chance of succeeding in the earliest stages of infection, when levels of the AIDS virus are lower and the virus has done less damage to the immune system. Researchers cautioned, however, that the only sure way to find out if the new combination therapies actually provide a lasting cure is to see if the AIDS virus returns after the patients stop their medication—a risky step that no patient appeared to have yet taken as the year drew to a close.

Drug intervention also may have been responsible for reducing the number of AIDS cases among babies in the U.S. The U.S. Centers for Disease Control and Prevention (CDC) credited increased testing of pregnant women for the AIDS virus—and increased use of the drug AZT in those who were infected—for a 27% drop in the number of babies who contracted AIDS from their mothers between 1992 and 1995.

Despite the encouraging news about AIDS treatments, the global outlook for the disease remained far from bright. Noting that the annual cost for combination drug therapies was as much as $20,000 per patient—a price that precludes treatment for 90% of AIDS sufferers in developing nations—Peter Piot, head of the United Nations' program on AIDS, warned that the "only true hope for the entire world is prevention." Piot also urged the medical research community to step up efforts to develop a vaccine to protect against the

AIDS virus. "The [AIDS] epidemic is not over—far from over—not even close," said Piot, adding that 1.5 million people died of AIDS in 1996 and the rate of infection was rapidly increasing in Eastern Europe and India.

Throughout the summer a team of U.S., French, and Belgian researchers uncovered a series of clues about natural immunity to AIDS that may lead to better designs for both drugs and vaccines. The researchers found that about 1% of white people have a genetic variation that appears to protect them from infection by the AIDS virus. Such people, according to the researchers, have a mutation in the gene that produces a protein used by the AIDS virus to infect cells. The mutation renders the cells resistant to the viral attack. No similar genetic variants were found in the Central African and Japanese people included in the study.

Two studies found that a simple and relatively inexpensive device may be able to lower the death toll from malaria, a mosquito-borne parasitic disease. Researchers found that draping beds with mosquito nets impregnated with insecticide reduced the number of children admitted to hospitals with severe malaria by 41% in Kenya and 17% in Ghana each year. According to the World Health Organization, children accounted for most of the 1 to 1.5 million fatal cases of malaria reported worldwide each year.

The ongoing quest to develop a malaria vaccine met with mixed results. In September a prototype vaccine called SP66 produced disappointing results in tests involving more than 1,300 refugee children in Thailand. Researchers from the Walter Reed Army Institute, Washington, D.C., however, reported promising results from

tests of another experimental vaccine on seven people who had never been exposed to malaria. Only one of the seven people who received the vaccine, which combines proteins from the malaria parasite with those from the hepatitis B virus, developed malaria when they were later injected with live malaria parasites.

Stroke and neurological disorders

In 1996 doctors found a powerful new weapon in their effort to reduce the brain damage of strokes, the leading cause of adult disability in the U.S. In June the FDA approved the use of the clot-dissolving drug known as tissue plasminogen activator (t-PA) for the emergency treatment of ischemic stroke, which is caused by a clot blocking the flow of blood to the brain. The drug already was widely used

The majority of victims who succumb to the mosquito-borne disease malaria are children. Studies in Kenya and Ghana found that draping beds with netting sprayed with insecticides resulted in a significant decline in the number of children admitted to hospitals with the disease.

Andy Crump—WHO/TDR/Still Pictures

to treat heart attacks. The approval came on the heels of a NIH study that found that patients who received t-PA within three hours of an ischemic stroke were at least 30% more likely to recover with little or no disability than untreated patients. The approval of the first emergency treatment for stroke underscored the need for both health-care workers and the public to recognize its early signs, since t-PA is most beneficial when used within three hours of a stroke's onset.

Less dramatic were the steps made in the understanding and treatment of Alzheimer's disease. In November the FDA approved a second drug for Alzheimer's disease, donepezil. Like tacrine, the only other government-approved Alzheimer's drug, donepezil is not a cure for the progressive neurological disorder that results in the loss of memory and speech and motor skills, eventually culminating in dementia. A 30-week study, however, found that Alzheimer's patients who took donepezil performed better on assessment tests measuring such abilities as memory and language skills than those who did not take the drug.

Also in November researchers from the Veterans Affairs hospital in Tacoma, Wash., released results from the first controlled study evaluating the effects of the female hormone estrogen on Alzheimer's disease. In the study of 12 women with Alzheimer's, six subjects who received estrogen doses via skin patches doubled their scores on memory and concentration tests while the six who received placebo medication showed no improvement. Experts cautioned that larger studies were needed before any recommendation could be made on whether people should take estrogen

supplements to delay or prevent Alzheimer's disease.

The year also saw rising fears in Great Britain and other European countries about the risk posed to humans by "mad cow" disease, a fatal neurological disorder in cattle. Although such concerns have been around since the mid-1980s when the disease, formally known as bovine spongiform encephalopathy (BSE), first hit the British livestock industry, worries that consumption of infected beef may make humans sick escalated in March following a report by a scientific advisory panel assembled by the British government. Focusing on the cases of 10 young people in Great Britain who had an unusual strain of Creutzfeldt-Jakob disease, a human neurological disorder with symptoms similar to BSE that usually strikes the middle-aged or elderly, the scientists concluded it was "likely"—although not clearly proven—that the victims' symptoms were related to eating infected beef.

Gulf War syndrome

Simmering concerns about the health of U.S. veterans who served in the 1991 Persian Gulf War finally boiled over in the wake of new revelations by the U.S. Department of Defense. In 1994 a panel of distinguished scientists said it had found no links between chemical weapons and Gulf War syndrome, a constellation of joint pain, chronic nausea and fatigue, insomnia, and other ailments reported by thousands of veterans. In fall 1996, however, Pentagon officials admitted that shortly after the war U.S. military engineers blew up parts of a large Iraqi ammunition depot containing chemical weapons—actions that could have exposed as

In response to public fears about consuming beef from British-raised cows infected with "mad cow" disease, this London McDonald's posted a sign assuring customers that its hamburgers were made with imported meat.

many as 20,000 U.S. soldiers to nerve gas and other blistering agents.

In response to the Pentagon announcement, the head of the 1994 scientific panel, Nobel Prize-winning geneticist Joshua Lederberg, called for a reevaluation of the group's conclusions and urged that more work be done to determine the long-term health effects of exposure to low doses of nerve gas. Two government studies uncovered no difference in the disease-related death and hospitalization rates of Gulf War veterans compared with those of similar soldiers who did not serve in the war. Many veterans, however, greeted the government researchers' conclusions with skepticism.

345

Heart disease

Efforts to find alternatives to heart transplants for people suffering from severe heart disease suffered a tragic setback in March when 64-year-old Abel Goodman, the world's first person to receive a permanent electric heart, died unexpectedly in England five months after the device was implanted alongside his own heart. Doctors at Oxford's John Radcliffe Hospital had removed the battery-powered heart because they thought his natural heart had regained enough strength to function on its own. However, Goodman developed an irregular heart rhythm and died just 30 hours after the revolutionary device was removed.

Researchers at Allegheny General Hospital, Pittsburgh, Pa., presented results from the first study comparing conventional heart-bypass surgery, in which surgeons cut the breastbone to fully expose the heart, with a new "keyhole" bypass technique, in which several small chest incisions allow doctors to access the heart through special scopes. The study evaluated the outcomes of 48 people who had the keyhole surgery and 55 who had conventional bypass. Researchers found that the keyhole patients had fully recovered in two to three weeks, compared with six to eight weeks for conventional patients. In addition, hospital costs were 40% lower for the keyhole patients, whose average hospital stay was three days, compared with eight days for patients undergoing conventional bypass surgery.

In December a multicenter study of more than 2,100 heart-bypass patients found that about 6% of bypass patients may suffer significant, perhaps permanent, brain damage as a result of the operation.

Researchers noted that about half of the cases of brain damage were attributable to strokes caused by the operation, while the other half involved inexplicable symptoms that were very similar to Alzheimer's disease. Although it has long been known that some bypass patients have thinking and memory difficulties during their recovery periods, most doctors regarded such problems as only temporary.

In the prevention of heart disease, exercise and diet continued to be the watchwords. A new U.S. study indicated that it may never be too late in life for the heart to benefit from exercise. Researchers from the National Institute on Aging (NIA), Johns Hopkins University, and the Veterans Affairs medical center in Baltimore found that an aerobic exercise program improved the cardiovascular function of older men regardless of whether they were couch potatoes or endurance-trained athletes when the regimen began. "You don't lose the ability to get into condition," said NIA's Edward Lakatta, who headed the study.

On the dietary front, some startling data were presented on the apparent benefits of vitamin E on the heart. A British team concluded a 17-month study of 2,000 people with serious heart disease and found that those who took a daily dose of at least 400 international units of vitamin E had a 75% lower chance of suffering a heart attack than those who took dummy pills. The U.S. recommended daily allowance of vitamin E is currently 15 units for men and 12 for women. Cardiologists called for more studies of both people with heart disease and healthy people before recommending that their patients take large doses of vitamin E on a daily basis.

Transplants

A number of firsts occurred in the field of transplantation during the past year. On the bright side, the first multicenter study of bone-marrow transplantation for sickle-cell disease showed that the procedure can cure young sickle-cell patients if the donor is a matched sibling. An international team of researchers reported startling results in which 90% of children with sickle-cell disease were alive and nearly three-quarters were symptom-free two years after receiving marrow donated by a brother or sister who provided a close tissue match. Sickle-cell disease, a painful blood disorder that can lead to disability and premature death, affects about one out of every 400 African-Americans.

Not all the news, however, was glowing. The risks of transplantation were highlighted with the first report of a heart transplant recipient who received prostate cancer along with the life-saving organ. In February 1994 a 58-year-old patient at the University of Pennsylvania School of Medicine received not only a heart from a donor but also some of his cancer cells accidentally. The donor, who died of a brain hemorrhage, had an invasive form of prostate cancer that was not discovered until the transplant surgery was well under way. Ten months later doctors found the donor's type of cancer growing on one of the recipient's ribs. As of January 1997 the patient was still alive.

As the demand for donated organs continued to outstrip the supply, the issue over allocation procedures grew even more contentious. The United Network for Organ Sharing (UNOS), a nonprofit agency that oversees many aspects of U.S. organ donation and transplant policy, announced that starting in 1997 it would no longer put chronic, seriously ill patients at the top of its list for liver transplants. Instead, UNOS officials said priority would be given to otherwise healthy people who suffered acute liver failure. Currently about 800 people in the U.S. die each year while waiting for liver donors. UNOS's policy shift to giving priority to patients with the greatest chance of survival spurred renewed debate over whether the U.S. should set up a national waiting list for organs or stick with the regional system that began in 1991. Under the current system, patients in some regions have to wait far longer for new livers than comparably sick people in other regions.

Reproduction

If pregnant women needed any more reasons to stop smoking, it may have come in the form of new study findings released in April: women who smoke are 50% more likely to give birth to mentally retarded babies than those who do not. The study team headed by researchers from Emory University, Atlanta, Ga., said the risk of smoking was independent of other factors believed to increase the chance of mental retardation, such as alcohol use, economic status, and the mother's age.

In other disturbing news, researchers from Macquarie University, Sydney, Australia, presented preliminary evidence that as much as 60% of the lead found in pregnant women's blood comes from lead that has leached out of their bones during pregnancy. Although more follow-up research was needed, the findings suggested that a girl who grows up in a lead-polluted environment may later pass a significant contaminant load on to her offspring. Lead

According to a new study by researchers at Emory University, women smokers are 50% more likely to give birth to mentally retarded babies than nonsmokers. The risk was determined to be independent of other life-style factors, including alcohol use, economic status, and the mother's age.

is known to cause developmental delays and mental retardation in children.

In a drive to prevent potentially fatal bacterial infections in newborns, U.S. public health experts called for a new treatment strategy targeted at pregnant women. The CDC in May recommended that all pregnant women be tested at 35–37 weeks of pregnancy for group B streptococci, a class of bacteria that can cause pneumonia, meningitis, and other life-threatening infections in infants. Currently about one in 500 U.S. newborns are stricken with such strep infections.

Researchers also reported that a simple screening test for a common cervical infection can dramatically reduce women's risk for pelvic inflammatory disease, an acute inflammation of the pelvic cavity. The disease is a major cause of infertility and ectopic pregnancy. A team from the University of Washington and Group Health Cooperative of Puget Sound, Seattle, Wash., found that women who were routinely screened and treated for chlamydial infections were nearly 60% less likely to develop pelvic inflammatory disease than unscreened women.

The U.S. Food and Drug Administration approved the first antibiotic treatment against *Helicobacter pylori* bacteria (highlighted in yellow, opposite), the cause of most intestinal ulcers.

CNRI/Science Photo Library/Photo Researchers

Obesity and diet

If fat is where it is at, the U.S. was the place to be last year. Government statistics released in October showed that, for the first time, overweight Americans outnumbered those of normal weight. Although the reasons for the nation's growing girth are unknown, health experts blamed reductions in physical activity and excessive eating. According to government researchers, 59% of U.S. men and 49% of U.S. women were heavier than they should be.

One possible new weapon in the battle of the bulge was dexfenfluramine—the first antiobesity drug to hit the U.S. market in 22 years. When the FDA approved the appetite suppressant in April, however, it warned that the drug should be used only under a doctor's supervision because of the risk of hypertension in the lungs, a potentially fatal disorder. Since dexfenfluramine alters brain chemicals to make people feel full without eating as much, some physicians and consumer advocates also expressed concern about the drug's neurological effects. Brain damage was seen in animals that were given 10 times the dose of dexfenfluramine recommended for use in humans, but no similar problems have been reported in human studies.

Excess weight can be far more than just a cosmetic problem. Research showed that women who were obese at the time they got pregnant were at least twice as likely to have babies with debilitating neural-tube defects than women who were thinner. Furthermore, one study found that, unlike the effect in thin women, increasing the amount of folic acid in the obese women's diet did not reduce the risk of having a baby with neural-tube defects.

However, losing weight may not be de-sirable—or even healthy—in all situations. In a study of nearly 3,700 elderly women, a NIA team found that women who lost 10% or more of their weight after age 50 had twice the risk of hip fracture as women whose weight remained stable.

Osteoporosis and aging

Efforts to combat osteoporosis—a bone-thinning disease that affects one in five white women over age 50 and is a common cause of disabling fractures—made significant strides during the past year. In November a seven-center study of nearly 900 women showed that giving older women hormone-replacement therapy after menopause not only slowed the thinning of bones but also thickened the spine and hipbones.

Doctors and pharmacists remained on the alert for serious side effects associated with use of a new nonhormonal drug for osteoporosis. When it was approved in 1995, the drug alendronate was billed as a good alternative to hormone-replacement therapy for osteoporosis sufferers who wanted to avoid the hormonal therapy's side effects or cancer risks. In March, however, the drug's manufacturer, Merck & Co., issued warnings noting that more than 30 patients had suffered stomach irritation serious enough to require hospitalization.

Evidence also emerged that mental health may play a role in maintaining healthy bones. A team from the U.S. National Institute of Mental Health reported in October that depression may increase a woman's risk for developing thin bones. In their study of 48 women, the researchers found that women with a history of major depression had hipbones that were 10–14% less dense and spines that were 6.5% less dense than those of nondepressed women of similar age. The thin bones also gave sufferers of depression a risk of hip fracture that was 40% greater than nondepressed women.

In a discovery that may have implications for osteoporosis and a host of other medical conditions related to aging, scientists in April announced they had isolated the gene that causes a premature aging disease known as Werner's syndrome. People who have defective copies of the gene, which appears to play a vital role in DNA's ability to repair itself, develop gray hair, cataracts, osteoporosis, heart disease, and other age-related ailments in their 20s, and most die before age 50. Researchers hope that further research may reveal the role of the Werner's syndrome gene in the aging process of healthy people as well.

Other treatment advances

The past year was also marked by an array of treatment advances for everything from appendicitis and ulcers to poison ivy. Researchers from Massachusetts General Hospital, Boston, reported the development of a new X-ray method that may reduce the number of appendectomies performed. Currently doctors must perform surgery to determine conclusively if a person's abdominal pain is caused by an inflamed appendix. In one in five people the appendix is not the problem. The new technique, which the researchers called focused appendix computed tomography (FACT), makes it possible to take an X-ray picture of the appendix by using a dye that is infused into the intestines through a rectal tube.

The FDA in April gave its official blessing to the first antibiotic therapy targeted

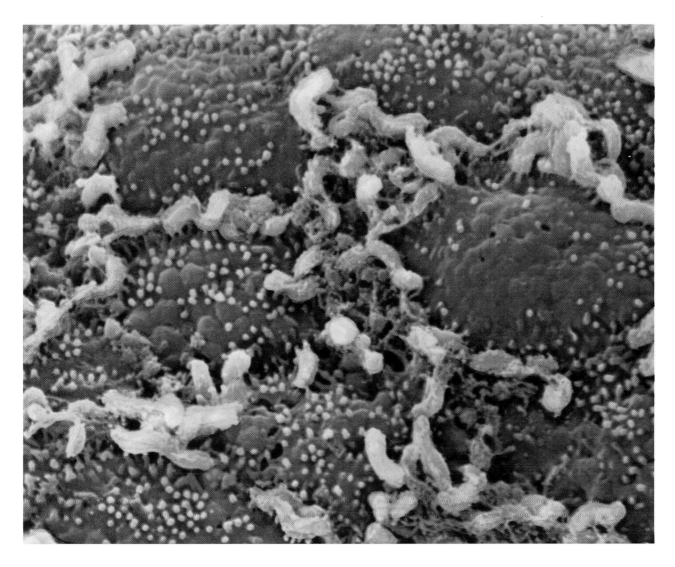

at intestinal ulcers. Although studies revealed that antibiotics were effective against the bacterium *Helicobacter pylori*, which was proven in the 1980s to cause most ulcers, the medication was not routinely prescribed. The drug therapy that won U.S. government approval teams the antibiotic clarithromycin with the antacid omeprazole—a combination thought to provide the greatest chance of relieving ulcer symptoms, promoting healing, and preventing ulcer recurrence.

Underscoring that research need not be monumental to be useful, medical science took another whack at poison ivy during the past year. In August the FDA approved the first drug aimed at protecting against the painful, itchy rashes that many people develop after touching poison ivy and related plants. The drug bentoquatam is the active ingredient in a skin lotion that re-searchers said acts as a barrier against poison ivy's irritating oils. A previous product billed as giving humans the edge against poison ivy—a shot that was supposed to "immunize" against the allergic reaction triggered by the plant—was pulled off the market because it often failed to work.

—Rebecca Kolberg

DENTISTRY

In 1996 researchers developed an impressive array of new technologies, procedures, and treatments for some of the most common dental concerns, including gum disease and root canal therapy. New research revealed, however, that unfortunately throughout most of the world one of the simplest and cheapest forms of dental treatment—prevention—continued to be lacking. According to George K. Stookey of the Indiana University School of Dentistry, Indianapolis, research has shown that prevention is key to good oral health; yet many countries have been slow to act on these results. Stookey, who has conducted dental research around the world, pointed out that in Japan, for example, dentists focused primarily on filling cavities caused by tooth decay rather than stressing dental practices to prevent cavities. Not surprisingly, statistics revealed that only 44% of Japanese visited a dentist during a 12-month period compared with 66% in the U.S. Of the Japanese patients who visited a dentist during this period, 64% needed a cavity filled, compared with only 19% of U.S. dental patients.

In countries such as Venezuela, Ecuador, and Brazil, where a lack of centralized infrastructure prevented health officials from adding sodium fluoride to many

Cameramann International, Ltd.

Studies of international dental practices revealed important differences in attitudes toward dental care. On average, only 44% of Japanese patients visit their dentists in a 12-month period, reflecting a trend in dental care that focuses less on prevention than on repairing problems caused by tooth decay.

household drinking-water supplies, the cavity-fighting chemical was added to common table salt during the manufacturing process. China, on the other hand, began a study to assess the health effects of high fluoride levels on residents who live in areas where the drinking water naturally contains fluoride concentrations between 8 and 15 parts per million. In the U.S. the recommended level is one part per million.

Managed care

Under the motto "Dentistry: Health Care That Works," the American Dental Association (ADA) continued to lobby the U.S. Congress on issues of managed dental care, voicing its concern about the effects of program cost-cutting on the delivery of quality dental care. Testifying before a

congressional committee, ADA Pres. William S. Ten Pas maintained that too many managed-care plans control costs through micromanaged clinical decisions, rationing by inconvenience, and denial of beneficial care. "We see a very real danger of the patient's health becoming secondary to the bottom line," he said. Ten Pas also pointed out that managed-care programs soon may dominate the profession, forcing doctors to enroll or else watch their practices shrink.

War on gum disease

U.S. dentists may be winning the battle against the second leading cause of tooth loss—gum disease—as indicated by the decline in the number of severe periodontal cases reported in 1996. Roy C. Page of the Schools of Medicine and Dentistry, University of Washington, said that better

oral hygiene may have been a key reason. Other factors for the decline included regular dental care and the fluoridation of drinking water.

Several new approaches to diagnose and treat severe gum disease more effectively also were made more widely available. Periodontal Screening and Recording Program (PSR), a probing method, detects and measures the progress of periodontitis more accurately than the traditional diagnostic tool, X-rays. In the PSR process the patient's mouth is divided into six zones. A special probe with a colored band is inserted into the space between the teeth and gums to measure the depth of the pockets between them and the amount of gum tissue attached to the teeth. Based on the visibility of the probe's colored band, the dentist assigns a score ranging from zero to four to each area of the mouth. In a study of 24 patients at the University of Medicine and Dentistry of New Jersey, Newark, researchers found that PSR provided more accurate measurements of gaps between teeth and gums and of gum-attachment levels than did the commonly used bitewing X-rays.

Dental researchers also focused on the development of an antibiotic treatment to help combat the bacteria that contribute to gum disease. To date, the three bacteria that cause gum disease have been identified. According to Page, "This is a major breakthrough because previously it was thought that as many as 10 to 12 bacteria were directly or indirectly involved in the progression of the disease." Unfortunately it may be many years before a vaccine is developed to prevent periodontitis. Because the disease often is hereditary, future research also may include genetic tests that identify people whose gums are most likely to be susceptible to the bacteria.

In the meantime, periodontitis sufferers may obtain some relief from substances found in eucalyptus leaves. Researchers Kenji Osawa and Hydeyku Yasuda of Lotte Central Laboratory, Saitama, Japan, discovered that an ethanol extract of the dried leaves of *Eucalyptus globulus* "showed appreciable antibacterial activity" against bacteria associated with both dental caries (tooth decay) and periodontal disease. Scientists believe that bacteria such as *Streptococcus mutans* synthesize insoluble complex sugars called glucans from sucrose by secreting the enzyme glucosyltransferase (GTase). Adhering to tooth surfaces, the glucans then form dental plaque that obstructs the diffusion of organic acids produced by oral microorganisms. The acid buildup leads to decay and contributes to gum disease. "This is the first time," Osawa said, "that a natural substance has been found to have both antibacterial activity and act as an inhibitor of GTase. The eucalyptus extract might be a promising natural substance for a new cariostatic drug and thus be useful for maintaining good oral health."

Dental X-rays as diagnostic tools

Two new studies indicated that dental X-rays can be used as diagnostic tools for strokes and osteoporosis. In a study conducted by researchers at the Veterans Affairs Medical Center, Sepulveda, Calif., researchers screened the cephalometric X-rays of 1,063 healthy men between the ages of 25 and 85 for atherosclerotic lesions, or blockages, in the carotid artery that carries blood to the brain. They dis-covered that 2% of the subjects had blockages that were visible in these X-rays of the head, which are commonly used by orthodontists and oral and maxillofacial surgeons to evaluate the jaws and face for deformities. Arthur Friedlander, the study's lead researcher, recommended that dentists urge patients with blocked carotid arteries to consult with a physician since not only is arteriosclerosis the most common cause of stroke, but a calcified carotid artery also is a strong marker of coronary artery disease.

Researchers at the School of Dentistry, University of Washington, compared the results of three standard techniques for measuring bone density with those of the dental X-rays of 111 women and found that dental X-rays are just as effective as traditional methods in diagnosing osteoporosis. According to Anne-Marie Bollen of the department of orthodontics, the pixel intensity, or fineness, of the X-ray image allowed researchers to readily discern bone density. Furthermore, she pointed out that dental X-rays were more commonly available and less expensive than other imaging techniques.

Vote of confidence for amalgam

Following a meeting at the ADA's Chicago headquarters, international dental experts concluded that, based on current scientific knowledge, amalgams (mercury-silver fillings) were a safe, durable, and cost-effective material for restoring teeth, contrary to several erroneous news reports that many countries had banned their use. The continued use of dental amalgam was supported by the World Health Organization, the FDI World Dental Federation, and the ADA.

Cinnamon linked to oral lesions

Researchers speculated that the red-hot taste of cinnamon that people crave causes oral health problems, including painful sores, inflamed taste buds, and a burning sensation in the tongue and mouth tissue. According to Michael A. Siegel of the University of Maryland at Baltimore Dental School, foods containing cinnamon, including gum and candy, can lead to mouth ulcers in patients who consume large amounts of it for extended periods of time. "We're seeing cinnamon being used as a flavoring agent in more and more products such as chewing gum, candy, pastries, rice cakes, herbal teas, breads, and cereals," he pointed out. "What people don't realize is that cinnamon is an irritant, a caustic substance that can dry out and irritate the oral soft tissue lining."

Most health professionals, however, fail to associate these symptoms with a high consumption of cinnamon products and often mistakenly give patients tests for diabetes, anemia, lupus, or other systemic diseases. According to a study conducted at the University of Louisville (Ky.) School of Dentistry in 1992, patients with unexplained mouth sores and irritation were treated for cinnamon-induced stomatitis, an inflammatory disease of the mouth. Most of the participants who reported consuming large amounts of cinnamon said their symptoms healed within weeks once they stopped eating cinnamon-laced foods.

Root canals easier and less painful

Root canal therapy, a treatment that preserves a tooth after the dental pulp (the soft tissue in the center of the tooth) has been

An ethanol extract from dried eucalyptus leaves showed promise as an antibacterial agent that can help prevent tooth decay and periodontal disease.

damaged or destroyed by trauma or disease, were being performed painlessly in less than an hour, thanks to several new dental devices. The endodontics industry's most far-reaching innovations included automated files to clean and shape the canals and new methods for filling the tooth's hollowed center.

These advances enabled dentists to complete a routine molar root canal in about 30 minutes instead of two hours. Locating root canals within teeth also was made easier. Richard Rubenstein of the University of Pennsylvania adapted a microscope used in cataract surgery for endodontic surgery. According to Rubenstein, "The use of this instrument and [these] procedures allows access to previously inaccessible areas."

Chlorhexidine

New research showed that tooth plaque was substantially reduced in people who used a chewing gum containing chlorhexidine. In a study conducted by Loma Linda (Calif.) University School of Dentistry and the Karolinska Institute, Stockholm, researchers examined the formation of dental plaque on the teeth of volunteers who chewed gum containing one of three addi-

tives—chlorhexidine, xylitol, and sorbitol. Study participants were instructed to chew the gum three times daily for 20 minutes following meals. The chlorhexidine gum showed significantly reduced plaque values compared with the other two products.

—Lou Joseph

VETERINARY MEDICINE

Two veterinarians achieved special distinction in 1996. Rick Linnehan, the first veterinarian to become a member of the Astronaut Corps, served as a crew member on a 17-day mission aboard the U.S. space shuttle *Columbia*. As part of the Life and Microgravity Spacelab crew, Linnehan participated in the mission's study of the effects of prolonged periods of microgravity on people and other organisms. He and his crewmates were subjected to a variety of physiologic analyses, including tests that measured the loss of muscle mass and calcium from bones. Preventing these losses is of critical concern for future space-station personnel who will conduct extended missions in microgravity environments.

Linnehan also contributed to the spacelab's animal studies, demonstrating that microgravity slowed both the growth

of musculoskeletal systems in rats and the development of fish embryos.

For research contributions to the field of immunology, veterinarian Peter Doherty of St. Jude Children's Research Hospital, Memphis, Tenn., shared the 1996 Nobel Prize for Physiology or Medicine with longtime collaborator Rolf Zinkernagel of the University of Zürich, Switz. (*see* SCIENTISTS OF THE YEAR). Their prizewinning research, conducted between 1973 and 1975 at the John Curtin School of Medical Research, Canberra, Australia, was extremely important to the basic understanding of how the human body's cellular immune system (specifically, cytotoxic T cells) recognizes foreign antigens. Their work had clinical applications for controlling autoimmune reactions associated with diseases such as rheumatism and multiple sclerosis, graft rejection in organ transplantation, and vaccine design.

Bovine disease

Bovine spongiform encephalopathy (BSE), more commonly known as "mad cow" disease, continued to be a major concern in the U.K. Public fears about BSE were heightened in March 1996 when the British government released information suggesting a possible link between exposure to BSE and 10 cases of a new human variant of Creutzfeldt-Jakob disease. The U.S. Department of Defense responded to the announcement by promptly terminating procurement of British beef and sales of it to U.S. military communities in Europe. The European Commission and Third World countries placed a ban on all exports from the U.K. of live cattle, bovine semen, and embryos, as well as meat and other products that might enter the animal or human food chain.

To eradicate BSE, the British government coordinated the slaughter of cattle that were more than 30 months old, the group at highest risk of being infected. By the beginning of 1997 about one million cattle had been destroyed, dramatically decreasing the incidence of new BSE cases. Epidemiologists predicted that BSE in the U.K. should be completely eradicated by 2001, even though a seven-year study of maternal transmission of BSE by the U.K. Ministry of Agriculture, Fisheries, and Food suggested about a 1% likelihood of maternal transmission. Researchers considered this number insufficient to sustain the BSE epidemic. (For additional information on BSE, see Year in Review: Food and Agriculture: *Agriculture*.)

Equine diseases

In March a special seminar was held in Lexington, Ky., to review information on the disease equine protozoal myeloencephalitis (EPM) and to refine recommendations for its control. This disease is caused by *Sarcocystis falcatula (neurona)*, a protozoan parasite that invades and damages the central nervous system. Research at the University of Kentucky indicated that horses contract EPM after consuming food and water contaminated by feces from infected opossums. Additional research at the University of Florida used genetic-sequencing techniques to demonstrate that wild birds serve as the intermediate host for the parasite. Opossums become infected when they consume a parasite-ridden bird. Infected horses, however, do not transmit the disease to other animals.

Horses suffering from EPM display a variety of neurological symptoms, including lameness, incoordination, and muscle atrophy. Diagnosis usually can be confirmed by testing for antibodies against the parasite in the cerebrospinal fluid of horses with neurological signs. Approximately 20% of infected horses die. Although no vaccine is available, prolonged drug therapy is effective in about 50% of the cases.

Researchers at the Animal Health Trust in Newmarket, Suffolk, England, explored the role of the naturally produced signaling molecule nitric oxide in regulating high pulmonary-artery pressure, a major cause of exercise-induced pulmonary hemorrhage in racehorses. During races many animals experience a marked increase in blood pressure that can lead to pulmonary bleeding as well as to spontaneous rupture of a major blood vessel and death. In a series of controlled workouts on a treadmill, researchers used nitric oxide and drugs to vary the horses' pulmonary-artery pressure. When the horses were given supplemental nitric oxide by inhalation, their blood pressure decreased. On the other hand, when the animals were given drugs that reduced natural production of nitric oxide, their blood pressure rose. These findings provided excellent data for the development of future methods to prevent and control exercise-induced pulmonary hemorrhage in racehorses.

Feline and canine diseases

Several new drugs that help prevent and control flea infestations in cats now may help stop the spread of cat scratch disease, an illness in humans caused by a scratch or a bite from a cat infected with the bacterium *Bartonella henselae*. How cats become carriers of the organism has been the subject of considerable study. Researchers at the University of California, San Francisco, and the University of California, Davis, found that infected cats transmitted the organism to noninfected cats only when fleas were present to act as the vector. The results of this research indicated that the spread of *B. henselae* can be reduced by controlling flea populations.

A bacteriologist at the Ontario Veterinary College, Guelph, compiled information on a new canine disease that is similar to the so-called human "flesh-eating" disease (necrotizing fasciitis) associated with severe streptococcal infections. The disease in dogs, as in people, progresses rapidly, involves toxic shock, and has high mortality rates. Differences in the DNA patterns of the infectious organisms isolated from affected dogs indicated that more than one highly virulent bacterium was involved.

Researchers at the University of Missouri, Columbia, the University of Illinois, Urbana, and Angell Memorial Animal Hospital, Boston, demonstrated that succimer, an oral drug approved by the U.S. Food and Drug Administration for the treatment of lead poisoning in children, was effective in treating the same problem in dogs. A derivative of dimercaprol, also used in the treatment of lead poisoning, succimer had a greater specificity for lead and a greater margin of safety than drugs previously used to treat canine lead poisoning. Succimer chelates (chemically ties up) lead and promotes its urinary excretion. Animal studies have indicated that it also has great potential for treatment of poisoning by other heavy metals.

A research team at North Carolina State University demonstrated the effectiveness of a skin patch, containing the analgesic drug fentanyl, that provided postoperative pain relief in dogs for up to three days. Unlike the effect of transdermal delivery of fentanyl in human postoperative patients, in dogs there was no incidence of respiratory depression.

Vaccines

The Greater Yellowstone Interagency Brucellosis Committee proposed a management plan to eliminate brucellosis from wild bison and elk in the Greater Yellowstone Park area by the year 2010. The potential spread of the disease to cattle by migration of infected bison from the park into Montana, Idaho, and Wyoming threatened the goal of eradication of brucellosis from the U.S. livestock population by the target date of Dec. 31, 1998.

When transmitted to cattle, the disease causes abortions, infertility, and reduced milk production. The development and marketing of a new brucellosis vaccine prepared from *Brucella abortus* strain RB51 will greatly aid the bovine-brucellosis eradication program and may be of value for controlling infection in wildlife. A major advantage of the new vaccine is that the immune response of vaccinated animals differs from that of naturally in-

fected animals, enabling managers to separate vaccine-protected animals from infected ones. This separation was not possible with the previous vaccine prepared from *B. abortus* strain 19.

A research team at the University of Saskatchewan developed a subunit vaccine against bovine herpes virus-1 (BHV-1) disease. Once an animal has been infected with the virus, it becomes a lifetime carrier and source of infection for other cattle. The subunit—one of the glycoproteins that constitute the virus's outer coat—induced an effective immunity against virulent BHV-1. Until recently, however, it was difficult to produce large quantities of the

subunit using the virus as the source. Researchers solved this problem by developing a unique mammalian cell-expression system that incorporated the specific glycoprotein gene. The system enabled cellular secretion of large quantities of the glycoprotein, which precluded its toxic accumulation within the cells. In addition, the cells were adapted to grow in a culture medium without serum, which reduced the cost of obtaining the purified glycoprotein for vaccine production. The researchers believed that this system will facilitate the mass production of glycoproteins for preparation of other vaccines.

—John M. Bowen

Bison that migrated out of the boundaries of Yellowstone National Park were captured and sent to slaughterhouses in Montana. The controversial action was prompted by area ranchers who feared the potential spread of brucellosis from infected bison to cattle.

McCrystie Adams

OPTICAL ENGINEERING

Progress continued on a new generation of large telescopes, as the largest optical telescope in the continental United States became operational late in 1996. Consumers began to reap the benefits of years of basic and applied optics research with the introduction of new commercial products. One was a new high-capacity optical disk that could hold a full-length movie and sound track. The other was a new camera format that combined elements of digital photography with traditional silver-halide films. In other developments, researchers reached new milestones in transmitting data over optical fibers, and military officials decided to develop a ballistic missile defense system using airborne lasers. Laser technology also was selected for cleaner, less expensive production of nuclear power plant fuel in the 21st century.

Telescope technology

Technology for making and testing large telescope mirrors and for correcting image distortion caused by atmospheric turbulence led to the development of a new generation of large ground-based telescopes. Many have primary mirrors 8–10 m in diameter—a size once regarded as impractical (1 m=3.28 ft). A telescope's primary mirror collects faint light from celestial objects. These huge instruments can see farther into the universe, with greater clarity, than ever before possible.

The biggest and most powerful optical telescope in the continental U.S. took its first look at the universe late in 1996. The milestone event, known as "first light," occurred for the William P. Hobby-Robert E. Eberly Telescope (HET), located in the Davis Mountains of western Texas. The approximately $13.5 million instrument

was built by a group of U.S. and German universities, including the University of Texas at Austin, Pennsylvania State University, Stanford University, Georg-August University of Göttingen, and Ludwig-Maximilians University of Munich. Its novel cost-saving design eliminated many of the most expensive features of a standard telescope. HET's primary mirror, for instance, has a diameter of 11 m, the largest in the world, but it was made from 91 identical hexagonal mirror segments that were produced at less cost than a single mirror.

Another cost-saving feature is HET's approach to tracking objects as they move across the sky. In traditional observatories the entire telescope is rotated, under precise control. HET tracks objects by moving only a few focusing instruments, reducing by more than 10 times the amount of weight that must be moved. As a result, HET's cost was approximately 15% that of a telescope of similar size. HET was expected to become fully operational late in 1997. Astronomers planned to use it to study black holes, to discover the origin of chemical elements in the Milky Way Galaxy, to search for planets that are orbiting stars, and for other research.

The second of two 10-m telescopes at the W.M. Keck Observatory on Mauna Kea, Hawaii, became fully operational in 1996. Astronomers proceeded with plans to couple images from both instruments to obtain extremely detailed images of distant objects. The Very Large Telescope (VLT) program at the European Southern Observatory, on a mountaintop site in Chile, also established several landmarks. Construction of buildings at the observatory site neared completion, and technicians fin-

ished work on the primary mirror for the first of four VLT telescopes. Plans called for the first telescope's completion by the end of 1997. The other three were scheduled to be completed at intervals of approximately one year. Each will have a primary mirror 8 m in diameter.

In 1996 Spain announced plans for the construction of a large-aperture telescope in the Canary Islands. Work was almost complete at the two telescope sites, located in Hawaii and Chile, of the Gemini 8 Meter Telescopes Project. The mirror "blanks," or unfinished slabs of glass, for the primary mirrors were completed, and one was shipped to France in May 1997 for final finishing.

Final finishing work also proceeded on the 6.5-m mirror that will replace the six smaller mirrors at the Multiple Mirror Telescope in Arizona. Similarly, the 8.3-m mirror for the Japanese Subaru telescope in Hawaii neared completion. The first of two 8.4-m blanks for the Large Binocular Telescope on Mt. Graham in Arizona was cast in January 1997. This pair of telescopes, mounted on a single base, was designed to have a light-collection capability equivalent to that of a telescope with an 11.8-m aperture.

Fiber optics

Fiber optics continued to be important in modern telecommunications because of the enormous information-carrying capacity of light transmitted over optical fibers. Two strands of optical fiber, thinner in diameter than a human hair, can carry as many telephone conversations as a cable of copper wires 10 cm (4 in) in diameter. Such high transmission rates are essential for speeding the flow of computer data. By

1997, transmission rates averaging 10 Gbps (gigabits per second; 1 gigabit=1 billion bits) were becoming the world standard for optical fibers. Systems with rates averaging 40 Gbps were starting to emerge from the laboratory into practical applications.

Optical engineers in 1996 reported an advance toward the next standard with a new experimental transmission record in

The William P. Hobby-Robert E. Eberly Telescope, shown with 7 of its 91 primary mirror segments in place, saw "first light" in late 1996. Located in the Davis Mountains of western Texas, it is the largest and most powerful optical telescope in the continental United States.

which 80 gigabits of data were transmitted farther than 350 km over a single fiber (1 km=0.62 mi). The record was achieved at the Siemens AG test facility in Munich, Ger., in a joint research project with Corning Inc., Corning, N.Y. A modified Corning SMLF-LS fiber with the signal optically amplified at intervals of 90 km was used. The transmission rates were equivalent to about one million voice channels. Researchers said that such new high-capacity fibers, when put into everyday use, will reduce the cost of fiber-optic systems and make them more widely available for specialized and consumer uses.

Multiplexing optical signals

Wavelength-division-multiplexing (WDM) is expected to be widely used in the next generation of fiber-optic transmission systems. WDM involves transmitting lightwave signals of different wavelengths, or colors, over a single strand of fiber. An electronic device termed a multiplexer transmits the signals at different wavelengths, and a demultiplexer at the output end separates them. WDM is attractive because it allows transmission capacity to be expanded to meet increased demand. It also can be used to expand the capacity of existing fiber-optic systems without the need for expensive installation of additional ducting and fibers.

Researchers at Fujitsu Laboratories Ltd. in Tokyo reported a milestone in WDM technology when they successfully transmitted signals at more than 1 Tb/s (terabits per second; 1 terabit=1 trillion bits) for the first time. In the experiment, 55 optical signal sources were used to transmit at a rate of 1.1 Tb/s. The researchers said the achievement confirmed their belief that ex-

tremely high transmission rates are possible with WDM and also helped to establish the optimal conditions for transmissions at such rates.

Laser advances

In 1996 the U.S. Department of Defense awarded a $1.1 billion contract for the development of a revolutionary airborne high-energy laser defense system against ballistic missiles. The system will use a high-power chemical oxygen-iodine laser (COIL) mounted in a military version of a Boeing 747 jumbo jet. A large-aperture beam director will be located in the nose of the aircraft, which would fly in the vicinity of ballistic missile installations and be prepared to shoot the beam at missiles during launch.

Since the laser beam travels at the speed of light, the aircraft could remain relatively far from the launch site. The COIL beam would be powerful enough to destroy enemy ballistic missiles instantly. A group of firms, including Boeing, TRW, and Lockheed Martin, were chosen to develop components of the system. The first tests of the beam on ballistic missiles are expected in 2002.

Laser-based technology

Enriched uranium used as fuel in nuclear power plants has long been produced by means of a chemical process termed gaseous diffusion. Freshly mined uranium oxide contains two primary forms, or isotopes, of uranium, ^{235}U and ^{238}U. Nuclear power plants need uranium with increased amounts of ^{235}U, and gaseous diffusion has been the best way to produce this enriched form.

In 1996, however, the U.S. Enrichment

Corp., a government-owned firm in Bethesda, Md., that produces and markets uranium enrichment to more than 60 electric utilities in 14 countries, decided to move ahead with the development of a full-scale plant for producing enriched uranium with a new laser technology that is cheaper, more reliable, and more environmentally safe than gaseous diffusion. Termed atomic vapor laser isotope separation (AVLIS), the process uses a precisely tuned laser to enrich uranium. The laser beam optically excites and ionizes atoms in a vapor stream of natural uranium. The ionized ^{235}U isotope can then be collected and used to produce a product suitable as nuclear fuel. AVLIS plants are less expensive to build, require less electricity than gaseous diffusion plants, and produce less low-level nuclear waste and conventional toxic waste.

Hybrid photography

Digitization of photographic images has emerged as a growing challenge to conventional photography. By 1997 relatively inexpensive cameras incorporating some features of digital photography were widely available to consumers, and home computer users could use special drives to digitize photographs. Conventional photography is based on the light-sensitive properties of silver halide. When exposed to light, crystals of silver halide undergo a chemical change that captures a latent image, which processing converts into an actual image. In digital photography, images are stored as binary numbers on disks and other magnetic storage devices used in personal computers. The images can be edited, manipulated, and processed in a variety of ways.

A major advance in traditional photography occurred in 1996 with the introduction of the Advanced Photo System (APS), which was initially researched and evolved by Eastman Kodak Co. Canon, Fuji, Minolta, and Nikon aided in the development of system standards. APS combines silver-halide photography with some features of digital photography in an effort to improve image quality. APS uses a special film with a magnetic layer added to the entire surface, including the image area. Magnetic particles in the layer store information about picture-taking conditions on each frame of the film. During developing, photofinishing equipment reads the digital information on each frame and automatically adjusts printing conditions. The system also enables consumers to customize photographs by automatically recording photofinishing instructions on a picture. The film can encode 400 bytes of information on each frame. (1 byte = 8 bits.) Lower-priced cameras use a small light-emitting diode to encode data on the film. More expensive models encode the data magnetically.

Digital versatile discs

After years of research and development, a new generation of optical storage devices termed the digital versatile disc (DVD; also called digital videodisc) was introduced. Toshiba, Compaq, Philips, and a number of other firms announced plans to market the first DVD read-only memory drives, or DVD-ROMs. These devices play an optical disk that appears much like a conventional audio disc or a CD-ROM. Indeed, most of them can play audio discs and CD-ROMs. But these new players are designed specifically for the new high-

density DVD, in which each layer on a single-sided disc can store 4.7 billion bytes. That is enough capacity to enable a DVD to hold a standard 133-minute feature-length motion picture with high-quality sound.

Conventional CD-ROMs can hold about 680 million bytes. The high capacity of the DVD is achieved by tighter packing of the data pits that are written and read by a laser, by the use of lasers of shorter wavelengths, and by recording the data in layers on the disc.

Although movies will be the major use for DVDs, the discs also can store many hours of CD-quality stereo music, digitized graphics and photographs, and computer programs. Many firms also announced plans to market popular movies on the discs in 1997.

Machine vision

Other imaging applications resulted from the wide availability of various new sensor arrays. Researchers at Carnegie Mellon University, Pittsburgh, Pa., reported a form of machine vision that could have future practical applications, such as self-driving cars for greater safety and efficiency. They developed a machine vision system termed the Rapidly Adapting Lateral Position Handler (RALPH). It used a conventional video camera connected to a computer that performed on-line image analysis to guide an automobile in a drive across the U.S. Changing road conditions provided many challenges, indicating that the concept was not yet ready for widespread application, but the experiment demonstrated the potential of machine vision for everyday tasks.

—Robert R. Shannon

PHYSICS

After more than 70 years of effort, physicists in the past year reported producing a liquid metallic form of hydrogen, the lightest of all elements. Nuclear scientists synthesized a new element, 112, the heaviest yet produced. A major innovation occurred in atomic physics with the development of the first atom laser. In other advances, researchers developed a quantum logic gate that could greatly improve the power of future computers. Evidence was found for the existence of "glueballs," aggregates of subatomic particles that are thought to carry one of the four elementary forces in nature. Physicists continued building new instruments in the search for gravity waves. Progress also occurred in the quest to detect neutrinos and determine if these ghostly subatomic particles have mass.

ATOMIC, MOLECULAR, AND OPTICAL PHYSICS

Researchers in the past year announced development of the first atom laser, a major advance in laser science. Physicists devised a quantum version of a computer logic gate, an important advance toward building a superpowerful quantum computer, which could work many times faster than existing computers. In other achievements, it was shown how the strange behavior of a quantum system can decay into the familiar "classical" behavior of objects in the everyday world. Physicists also reported one of the first applications of wave-packet technology, which may have important practical uses.

First atom laser

In one of the most important advances since the invention of the first working laser in 1960, physicists at the Massachu-setts Institute of Technology (MIT) reported development of the first atom laser. The atom laser produces highly coordinated beams of atoms, just as traditional lasers do with light. The achievement may lead to innovations in nanotechnology, which involves the manufacture of microscopic machines and the manipulation of matter at the atomic level.

An ordinary laser produces light that is very different from sunlight or the light from a lamp. Unlike other light sources, lasers emit photons (particle-like packets of light energy) that are all in the same quantum state. As a result, laser light is monoenergetic; that is, every photon in a laser beam has the same energy and, therefore, a single color. Sunlight or lamplight, by contrast, is made of many different colors. In addition, laser light is coherent, having a wave front that varies in a predictable manner over time. By contrast, other light sources produce light that is incoherent, so that later wave fronts have no predictable relationships to earlier ones. Moreover, laser beams travel in a single, well-defined direction, unlike sunlight and lamplight, which radiate in all directions.

Scientists in 1995 successfully produced the state of matter that would become the source for a laserlike beam of atoms. It was a Bose-Einstein condensate (BEC), a collection of gaseous atoms cooled to temperatures just billionths of a degree above absolute zero (0 K, −273.16° C, or −459.69° F). The atoms were so cold and densely packed that they fell into the same low-energy quantum state and acted coherently as a single unit. (See *1997 Yearbook of Science and the Future* Year in Review: PHYSICS.) Nevertheless, researchers lacked a method for extracting atoms from the condensate and producing a coherent beam of atoms.

In the past year Wolfgang Ketterle and co-workers at MIT devised a technique for extracting a controlled fraction of atoms from a BEC of sodium atoms. They applied radio-frequency (rf) radiation to the condensate, which was trapped in a small space by magnetic fields. Each atom in the condensate possesses a property known as spin. The value of its spin describes the way that the atom responds to a magnetic field. Initially, all of a condensate's atoms have exactly the same spin value, which corresponds to a state in which they are pushed toward the center of the trap. The rf radiation, which contains magnetic fields of its own, "flips" the spins of some atoms and reverses the effect of the magnetic forces on them. As a result, those atoms are expelled from the trap and form a beam.

In the MIT experiment the bursts of atoms that emerged from the condensate were all in the same quantum state. By contrast, atoms in conventional atom beams are distributed over a wide range of quantum states. Unlike most other atom beams, the beam produced at MIT acted like a single "matter wave." It could be manipulated and controlled just like light waves from a laser.

The MIT group also demonstrated that their atom-laser beam has coherence properties directly analogous to the coherence of the light waves produced by an optical laser. They showed coherence by creating a pair of atom-laser beams that fell side by side. As time passed, each beam expanded, and the two beams overlapped. In doing so, they produced an interference pattern of light and dark bands that was detected

Michael Andrews, Marc-Oliver Mewes, and team leader Wolfgang Ketterle (left to right) gather around the equipment that they and their co-workers used to demonstrate the first atom laser.

by an electronic camera. Such a pattern could have been created only if the atoms in each beam acted as a single wave with consistent, predictable properties.

An atom laser differs from an optical laser in several important ways. For example, whereas an optical laser creates photons during the laser process, the atom laser simply cools an existing supply of atoms to very low temperatures and makes a beam from them. Unlike laser light, an atom-laser beam cannot travel great distances through air, since its atoms will interact with those in the air. Unlike photons, which are massless, atoms have mass. As a result, gravity causes the atom-laser beam to fall to the ground just like a beam of ordinary atoms.

Despite such differences, researchers expected the atom laser to lead to significant improvement in the precision of atomic clocks and other procedures involving measurement of atoms. Atom lasers may foster a revolution in nanotechnology by allowing scientists to deposit atoms on surfaces with unprecedented precision. Researchers may use atom lasers to make submicroscopic structures and machines that are more sophisticated than previously possible. Atom-laser devices will have some limitations, however. They will remain operable only in extreme vacuum

conditions. Because of their presently small flux rate, the first atom lasers will be able to make nanostructures only very slowly. Nonetheless, physicists predicted that the atom laser, just like the optical laser, will have many applications that could not even be imagined at the time of its discovery.

Quantum logic gate

Computers process information by converting data into strings of binary digits, which are 0s and 1s. Binary digits (bits) pass through devices known as logic gates. A logic gate is a collection of transistors and other electronic components that constitute a logical operation, such as AND, NAND, NOT, or OR, based on Boolean algebra. Logic gates make up electronic circuits, which in turn make up electronic systems wherein many components work together to perform a task. Logic gates perform specific operations on bits. A NOT gate, for instance, converts 0s into 1s and 1s into 0s. By connecting a series of gates in a certain way, computers can perform complex mathematical calculations.

Researchers at the U.S. National Institute of Standards and Technology (NIST), Boulder, Colo., reported development of a new logic gate that obeys the peculiar rules of quantum mechanics. This "quantum

logic gate" consists of two quantum bits (qubits). A qubit is a quantum system (such as an atom) having two states that represent the 0 and 1 of conventional binary logic. Unlike ordinary bits, which can exist only as either a 0 or a 1, qubits have the strange ability to exist simultaneously as a 0 and a 1. This duality offers the potential for carrying out enormously complicated calculations beyond the power of ordinary logic gates.

The NIST researchers created the two-qubit quantum logic gate by trapping a single beryllium ion in nonuniform electric fields. The first qubit was the ion's outer electron, which could exist in two energy levels corresponding to 0 and 1. The second qubit was the ion's vibrational level. The vibrational level describes the amount of energy an ion needs to move from the center of the trap. An ion in the lowest vibrational level (which represents a value of 0) would most likely be found at the center of the trap, whereas an ion in the next higher vibrational level (which corresponds to a value of 1) would most likely be found a certain distance from the center. The researchers worked under conditions in which the two qubits—the ion's vibrational properties and the electron's energy level—became interdependent.

The NIST investigators demonstrated the Controlled-NOT Boolean logic operation, which is equivalent to the Exclusive-OR (XOR) operation in conventional computing. An XOR operation is true (equivalent to a binary value of 1) if only one of the inputs is true but not both. The researchers used a series of laser pulses to operate the gate. One qubit acted as the "control" bit, and the other acted as a "target" bit. If the control bit (the vibra-

A pulsed beam of coherent sodium atoms propagates from an atom laser at five-millisecond intervals (below). Released from a magnetically trapped Bose-Einstein condensate, the pulses spread out while being pulled downward by gravity. When two atom-laser beams fall side by side, they expand, overlap, and produce a characteristic interference pattern of dark and light fringes (bottom), analagous to the behavior of coherent laser beams.

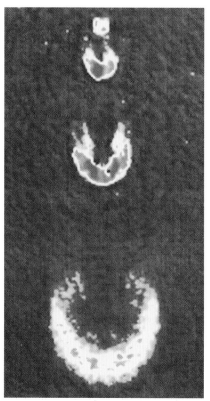

Photographs, Michael R. Andrews, MIT

tional state) was 0, then the target bit (the electron energy level) would keep its original value. If the control bit was 1, then the target bit would change its value from a 0 to a 1, or vice versa.

The power of a quantum logic gate lies in the fact that a qubit can exist as a 0 and a 1 at the same time. For example, firing a laser pulse at an electron in an atom for exactly half the usual time needed to move the electron from a lower state to an upper state can put it into an "equal superposition" of the two states. In this condition the electron acts as if it is in both states equally and possesses both 0 and 1 values. Performing a Controlled-NOT operation on the gate thus would be equivalent to performing the operation on both values at the same time.

The quantum uncertainty principle indicates that it is impossible to read out all of the information from such a quantum calculation. Nevertheless, the process still could be used to develop very powerful computer programs and other algorithms, which are sets of instructions for solving problems. Other researchers have shown theoretically that a quantum computer constructed with thousands of quantum logic gates could crunch extremely large numbers that are used as top secret codes and rapidly break these codes. Physicists, however, warned that systems with more than about 10–100 quantum logic gates may become "decoherent." Such a system would lose its quantum properties. Nonetheless, other scientists calculated that a quantum computer could function with a small amount of decoherence. Researchers thus were pushing ahead with efforts to build systems with two or more quantum logic gates.

Quantum decoherence

In the everyday world, objects exist in only one place at one time. Things are much different, however, in the ultrasmall quantum world of atoms and subatomic particles. Atoms, photons, and other quantum particles can exist in a superposition of states in which they behave as if they were in two places or in two different conditions at the same time. Under certain circumstances, for instance, a single photon seems to pass through two parallel slits simultaneously. Decoherence is the collapse of the quantum superposition into a single definite state, the conditions that exist in the everyday world.

Serge Haroche, Jean-Michel Raimond, Michel Brune, and their colleagues at the École Normale Supérieure, Paris, reported quantitative measurements of this decoherence process. The researchers put individual rubidium atoms into a superposition of two energy states. The energy states are extremely high-energy levels known as Rydberg states. In a Rydberg state the atom's outermost electron enters such high orbits above the nucleus that the overall size of the atom swells. In the experiments, the rubidium atoms grew to 2,500 times normal size. The researchers then passed the atoms through an opening known as a microwave cavity. It consisted of two face-to-face mirrors containing an electromagnetic field comprising a few photons in the microwave portion of the spectrum. The microwave field can be envisioned as a wave consisting of peaks and valleys having well-defined locations. Each of the two Rydberg states of the rubidium atom shifted the microwave field's phase—the position of its peaks and valleys—by different amounts. Thus, the microwave field itself was put into a superposition of two states. As the microwave field exchanged energy with its surroundings, however, the superposition eventually collapsed into a single state.

The researchers observed the decoherence process by sending a second rubidium atom through the cavity after the first. A comparison of energy states of emerging pairs of atoms separated by various time delays allowed the researchers to determine whether superposition of the microwave field persisted by the time the second atom reached the cavity. Decoherence was observed to proceed faster when the time delays between the two atoms increased and when researchers increased the differences in phase shifts caused by each Rydberg state. Studying decoherence helps researchers understand how quantum systems lose their unique quantum-mechanical properties; thus, it has important implications for determining the feasibility of building a quantum computer.

Wave-packet technology

Most people regard atoms and molecules as solid particles located at definite positions in space. Under the right conditions, however, atoms, molecules, and all other particles of matter can act like waves. They can spread out in space and combine with other waves to produce interference patterns and other effects typical of waves.

Physicists in Canada and Israel exploited the wave nature of molecules to separate bromine molecules (Br_2) made of different bromine isotopes. Their achievement represented one of the first applications of a new wave-packet technology that may find numerous other practical uses. Albert Stolow and colleagues at the National Research Council of Canada and the Weizmann Institute of Science, Rehovot, Israel, used femtosecond lasers, devices that produce pulses of laser light only several quadrillionths of a second (femtoseconds) in duration. Normal optical lasers produce light of a single wavelength. By contrast, femtosecond lasers create several light waves, each having a different wavelength; the various waves combine to produce a truncated light wave. Such a combination of waves, which add together in a consistent and predictable fashion, forms a wave packet. In the experiment, each individual wave in the femtosecond laser pulse had the ability to boost a Br_2 molecule to a higher-energy quantum vibrational state, which describes the probable distance between the two atoms in a bromine molecule. When the femtosecond pulse struck a gas of Br_2 molecules, it caused each molecule to exist in a superposition of quantum vibrational states. Each of these states can be visualized as a wave with peaks and valleys. The combination of states thus formed a wave packet in each Br_2 molecule.

The resulting wave packet can be described as a wave with a constantly changing pattern of peaks and valleys. At certain times the wave packet formed a single peak, which corresponded to a single definite distance between the atoms in the Br_2 molecule. At other times the wave formed many peaks and valleys, corresponding to a range of possible separations between the atoms in the molecule.

Although bromine molecules made of the isotope bromine-79 ($^{79}Br_2$) are chemically identical to molecules made of bromine-81 ($^{81}Br_2$), $^{81}Br_2$ is slightly heavier because of the two extra neutrons in the nucleus of each of its atoms. The slight differences in their masses cause slight differences in their vibrational states, which means, in turn, that their wave packets evolve in different fashions. After the researchers had applied a femtosecond laser pulse to form wave packets in the bromine molecules, they applied a second laser pulse when the $^{79}Br_2$ and $^{81}Br_2$ wave packets each contained a single peak and were 180° out of phase from one another. For the Br_2 wave packets, 180° out of phase meant that one kind of molecule had its atoms separated by the minimum distance and the other kind had its atoms separated by the maximum distance. The second laser pulse had the greatest chance of ejecting electrons from molecules with the minimum interatomic separation and therefore ionized these molecules. The researchers then used an electric field to separate these charged molecules from the neutral molecules containing the other isotope.

In principle, this isotope-separation technique can be applied to diatomic (two-atom) molecules of any element. Researchers also envisioned other applications for wave-packet technology, including controlling the course of chemical reactions, storing multiple pieces of computer data in a single atom, and creating ultrafast electronic switches.

—Ben P. Stein

ELEMENTARY-PARTICLE PHYSICS

Physicists during the past year developed increased confidence in the accuracy of the standard model used to explain the particles and forces that make up the universe, identified entities having properties of subnuclear-particle aggregates called glue-balls, and continued development of new instruments designed to detect gravity waves and neutrinos. They also continued searches for a new elementary particle that could answer long-standing questions about why particles have the mass values that they do.

The standard model

Since the mid-1980s physicists have become increasingly confident that all particles and forces in the universe (save gravity) can be described by a mathematical theory called the standard model. Somewhat analogous to chemistry's periodic table of the elements, the standard model organizes all currently known fundamental particles and their interactions and encompasses the understanding of their combinations to form the known complex particles, such as protons, neutrons, and mesons.

The standard model includes six fundamental strongly interacting particles of fractional electric charge, known as quarks, and six (mostly) lighter particles, known as leptons, which do not experience the strong interaction. The 12 particles are grouped into three generations, and corresponding to each particle is an antiparticle having the opposite electric charge (or some other quantum property). From experiments over the past several years at the European Laboratory for Particle Physics (CERN), Geneva, physicists have confidence that there are no more than three generations and no more massive fundamental particles within each of the generations. The 12 particles and their properties are shown in Table I.

There are also four forces through which the fundamental particles interact. The most familiar are the force of gravity and the electromagnetic force. In the nuclear and subnuclear domain, the strong and weak forces are also important. It is now understood that the weak and the electromagnetic forces are fundamentally interrelated and may be regarded as special cases of a more general electroweak force. Quantum field theory argues that each of the forces, or interactions, is mediated by a quantum of the force field. The four forces and their field quanta (or field particles) are summarized in Table II. The field quanta under certain conditions may be radiated by the particles with which they interact. The electromagnetic quantum, the photon, thus is radiated by oscillating electric charges. It constitutes electromagnetic radiation most familiar as light, radio waves, and X-rays. Quanta of the weak interaction, the W and Z intermediate vector bosons, differ from the other field quanta in that they have non-zero—and rather large—rest masses. Both were discovered at CERN in the early 1980s. Since 1989 the Large Electron Positron (LEP) colliding-beam facility at CERN has provided energies from the col-

TABLE I. ELEMENTARY PARTICLES[1,2]

	charge[3]	generation I	generation II	generation III
quarks	$+\frac{2}{3}$	u (up) 2–8 MeV	c (charm) 1–1.6 GeV	t (top) 176 GeV
	$-\frac{1}{3}$	d (down) 5–15 MeV	s (strange) 100–300 MeV	b (bottom) 4.1–4.5 GeV
leptons	-1	e (electron) 511 keV	μ (muon) 105.7 MeV	τ (tau) 1.777 GeV
	0	ν_e (electron neutrino) less than 7 eV[4]	ν_μ (muon neutrino) less than 170 keV[4]	ν_τ (tau neutrino) less than 24 MeV[4]

[1]Each particle has an antiparticle with the opposite electric charge (or other quantum property).
[2]Masses (under particle names) are in energy units of billions, millions, or thousands of electron volts (GeV, MeV, keV); on this scale the mass of a hydrogen atom is about 938 MeV.
[3]Electric charge is in units of the magnitude of the electron's charge, 1.6×10^{-19} coulomb.
[4]Neutrino mass numbers are upper limits; all direct measurements of neutrino mass are compatible with zero.

TABLE II. FUNDAMENTAL FORCES OR INTERACTIONS

force	source particles	field quantum	mass of field quantum
electromagnetism	all electrically charged particles	γ (photon)	0
weak interaction	all quarks and leptons	$W^\pm$ (intermediate vector bosons) Z^0	80.3 GeV 91.2 GeV
strong interaction	quarks and gluons	g (gluon)	0
gravity	all particles with mass	G (graviton)	0

The weak interaction and electromagnetism are now understood to be special cases of a unified electroweak interaction.

lision and annihilation of electrons and positrons (the antimatter counterparts of electrons) that are sufficient to produce and study the Z boson in quantity.

In 1996, for the first time, the collision energy at LEP was raised high enough—161 GeV (billion electron volts)—to produce pairs of W bosons (W$^+$ and W$^-$; to conserve electric charge, the W bosons must be produced in pairs). The availability of these field quanta permitted excellent measurements of their properties, which in turn led to increased confidence in the standard model and to a more precise determination of its parameters.

In 1995 and early 1996, at least two measurements had suggested a problem with the standard model. First, the rate of decay of the Z boson into bottom (b) quarks appeared greater than that predicted by the model. More recent data and analyses, however, brought this measurement into agreement with the model. Second, data from the CDF detector facility at the Fermi National Accelerator Laboratory (Fermilab) near Chicago had shown departures from calculated expectations in the collisions between a proton and an antiproton. Occasionally two quarks, one from each of the colliding particles, scatter off each other very hard. The interaction is manifest in the detector as two jets of mesons, the total energy and momentum of each jet reflecting the energy and momentum of the scattered quark. In early 1996 physicists reported data from the CDF indicating a cross section (in effect, the probability) for such hard scatters that was greater than that calculated from the standard model. This result fueled excited speculation that the quark possessed a substructure and thus was not a fundamental,

indivisible object. However, data from the D0, another detector facility at Fermilab, helped reduce the discrepancy, which left the model again quite solid and compatible with indivisible, pointlike quarks.

Glueballs

Photons of electromagnetic radiation do not interact with each other. Consequently, two beams of light can cross the same region of space without affecting one another. It would be quite another matter, however, if photons carried electric charge. Gluons, the field quanta that mediate the strong force, have a property analogous to electric charge called the color property, which is also shared by the quarks. Each gluon possesses one of three whimsically designated "colors" (red, green, or blue) and thus can interact with both quarks and other gluons. For this reason, physicists long ago predicted the existence of particles formed by aggregations of gluons; the particles were given the fanciful name glueballs.

During 1996 physicists working at CERN's Low Energy Antiproton Ring (LEAR) identified invariant mass states produced in annihilations of protons and antiprotons (the antimatter counterparts of protons) that fit the predicted properties of glueballs. These states had an invariant mass of about 1.5 GeV (about 1½ times the mass of a proton), and they decayed rapidly into pi mesons.

Gravity waves

Although gravity was the earliest force understood by science, virtually all of scientists' knowledge of gravity relates to its static properties: the attraction of one object to another—for example, the attraction

between two stars. This situation is analogous to the attraction between a negatively charged particle such as an electron and a positively charged one such as a proton. Nevertheless, in the same way that electromagnetic radiation arises from oscillating charged particles, gravitational radiation has been predicted to arise from rapidly oscillating masses. In 1993 U.S. astrophysicists Joseph Taylor and Russell Hulse were awarded the Nobel Prize for Physics for having observed the progressive minuscule increase in the speed with which two stars in the binary star system PSR 1913+16 are rotating around each other and correctly interpreted this change as resulting from energy loss due to the emission of gravitational radiation. Direct observation of gravitational radiation, however, remained to be achieved.

In 1996 a large program led by physicists at the California Institute of Technology (Caltech) and the Massachusetts Institute of Technology was under way to observe gravitational radiation directly. The researchers were building two facilities for the Laser Interferometer Gravitational-Wave Observatory (LIGO), designed to detect gravitational radiation from rotating binary stars. The first full-scale LIGO facility, near Richland, Wash., was expected to be fully operational by 1999; it has two arms, each 4 km (2.5 mi) long and placed at right angles to one another. Each arm is an evacuated tube equipped with mirrors at the ends. A laser beam is split into two beams, one of which is then sent along each arm. The interference pattern formed by the recombination of the reflected beams is sensitive to a change in the relative lengths of the two arms caused by absorption of gravitational

A construction worker stands inside one of two tubes, each 4 km (2.5 mi) long, being built for the Laser Interferometer Gravitational-Wave Observatory near Richland, Wash. The facility is designed to make direct observations of gravitational waves emanating from cosmic sources.

radiation by the Earth's crust. A proof-of-principle interferometer with arms 40 m (130 ft) long went into operation in 1996 on the Caltech campus.

Neutrino mass and oscillations

Neutrinos are the least massive of the elementary particles in Table I. Indeed, their rest masses have long been thought to be zero, although there is no theoretical reason for this to be so. Neutrinos with masses greater than zero would have interesting implications for physics, one of the more profound being that the identity of a neutrino could change, or oscillate, among the three neutrino types—electron neutrino, muon neutrino, and tau neutrino. By early 1997 no experiment had succeeded in finding any direct unequivocal evidence of mass for any of the neutrinos; only upper limits to the masses had been set. If, however, neutrinos have mass and oscillate, a beam of one kind of neutrino, such as the electron neutrino, would spontaneously transform to contain some of the other kinds of neutrinos.

Three sets of observations suggested that such oscillations may occur. First, the Sun is a copious source of electron neutri-

nos, and a value for the flux of these particles has been predicted from scientists' theoretical understanding of the nuclear reactions taking place in the solar core. Nevertheless, many years of collective measurements of solar neutrinos by separate groups in the U.S., Italy, Russia, and Japan all reported the same finding: a big deficit in the number of electron neutrinos detected compared with the number expected. This difference could be due to the oscillation of a fraction of the electron neutrinos into muon or tau neutrinos.

The second set of observations came from the detection of neutrino interactions in underground detectors that were originally built to search for evidence that the proton decays. The neutrinos in question, muon neutrinos and electron neutrinos, are produced from the decays of muons and pi mesons. The muons and pi mesons, in turn, are produced by cosmic ray interactions with atoms in the Earth's atmosphere. Although the ratio of muon neutrinos to electron neutrinos produced from these interactions was calculated to be close to 2:1, the observed ratio was much closer to 1:1, which suggests the oscillation of some of the muon neutrinos into another type.

A third set of data came from an experiment at the Los Alamos (N.M.) National Laboratory wherein a proton beam was used to produce pi mesons, which in turn decayed to muons and muon neutrinos. A well-shielded detector set up at some distance from the neutrino source then detected interactions of the neutrinos. Significantly, in addition to detecting muon neutrino interactions, the experiment detected a small number (22 from the latest data) of electron neutrino interactions. While the number was modest, it had more than doubled since the first reports in 1995. Again, neutrino oscillations appeared to be the most plausible explanation for the presence of the electron neutrinos.

During 1996 a very large detector was completed and began data collection in a mine near Kamioka, Japan. It consists of a tank containing 50,000 cu m (more than 13 million gal) of water. Since neutrino interactions with matter are extremely rare, the large volume of water increases the likelihood of detection. The neutrino interactions produce charged particles—electrons and muons—that create the telltale blue light called Cherenkov radiation as they travel through the water at high velocity. The faint light is detected by photomultiplier tubes lining the tank walls. In addition to setting new limits to (or perhaps observing) proton decay, the new detector, called Super-Kamiokande, should accumulate much better statistics on both solar neutrinos and cosmic-ray-produced electron and muon neutrinos. Its observations, together with more data from other experiments under way or planned in Europe, the U.S., Japan, and Antarctica, may clarify the question of neutrino masses and oscillations in the near future. (See *Nuclear Physics*, below; *1996 Yearbook of Science and the Future* Feature Article: THE ELUSIVE NEUTRINO: A WINDOW ON THE UNIVERSE.)

Problems and challenges

Numerous problems and challenges remain for elementary-particle physics. A major one involves the question of why elementary particles have any rest mass, when current theory indicates they could just as easily be massless. Peter Higgs, a Scottish physicist, proposed a mechanism by which the particles naturally acquire their masses. His theory requires a new, very massive elementary particle, called the Higgs particle, or Higgs boson. As of early 1997 no evidence had been found for such a particle despite careful searches at CERN and Fermilab. If the particle exists, it should be experimentally detectable, although finding it may require greater energy than that available from current accelerators.

Six decades of experience have shown physicists that ever more powerful accelerators are essential for new discoveries in the subnuclear world. In the U.S., physicists were very disappointed in 1993 by the cancellation of their planned Supercon-

ducting Super Collider (SSC) because it was too expensive. The European physics community, however, had built their existing LEP facility at CERN with a tunnel large enough to accommodate a future proton-proton colliding-beam facility. Installation of this Large Hadron Collider (LHC) was approved in 1994, with plans for its completion about 2005. Its collision energy will be 14 TeV (trillion electron volts), a considerable increase over the Fermilab Tevatron's 1.8 TeV, although still less than the 40 TeV that had been planned for the SSC. Physicists hope that questions such as those concerning the Higgs particle, if not resolved with the current accelerator facilities, will be answered with the LHC.

—Lawrence W. Jones

NUCLEAR PHYSICS

In a landmark achievement nuclear physicists in Germany created a new chemical element, 112 on the periodic table. It was the heaviest ever synthesized and led to increased optimism about the possibility of making other superheavy elements that have longer half-lives. Researchers also made important progress in understanding the chemical properties of element 106, despite its extremely short half-life. Other studies challenged some of the most generally accepted ideas about subatomic particles called neutrinos.

Element 112

After a decade-long lull from 1985 to 1994, when no new elements were discovered, nuclear physicists again were expanding the periodic table of elements. The table once consisted of only 92 elements, all found naturally on Earth. The

lightest is hydrogen, 1, and the heaviest, uranium, 92. In 1940 the table began to expand with the discovery of the first of a whole series of transuranium elements. In 1994 physicists at Germany's Institute for Heavy Ion Research (GSI), Darmstadt, synthesized 110 and then 111. During the past year they reported creation of the next in the series, 112.

Heavy elements are made by fusing two lighter atomic nuclei. Researchers accelerate a beam of one kind of nucleus and use it to bombard a target containing the fusion partner. Nuclei that reach a certain minimum threshold energy overcome their electrostatic repulsion and combine to form a new heavy nucleus. Over the years this technique has extended the periodic table by more than a dozen elements. Progress has been slow, however, because of a fundamental limitation in the technique. The nuclei must be brought together with great energy, part of which becomes internal excitation energy in the fused system. Very heavy nuclei can be relatively stable in their ground, or unexcited, state, but they fission, or split apart, readily when excited. Thus, heavy nuclei formed in these fusion reactions must avoid fission in order to be observed.

In the past, physicists tried many different combinations of beam, target, and bombarding energy in a search for the optimal way to fuse nuclei without causing their subsequent fission. The GSI researchers finally found a way around the problem. They used the reaction

$$^{70}Zn + {}^{208}Pb \rightarrow {}^{278}112 \rightarrow {}^{277}112 + {}^{1}n$$

to form the mass-277 isotope of element 112 by bombarding a lead target with high-energy zinc atoms. The initial nuclei, zinc-70 (^{70}Zn) and lead-208 (^{208}Pb), were

365

carefully chosen for the experiment. The target nucleus, ^{208}Pb, is especially stable, and its fusion products have less excitation energy than normal. The projectile, ^{70}Zn, has just the right number of protons, 30, to fuse with lead's 82 protons to make element 112, and the zinc isotope chosen has as many neutrons as possible. The researchers chose a beam energy of 344 MeV (million electron volts), sufficient for fusion to occur but low enough to allow the new nucleus to get rid of its excitation energy by emission of a neutron (^{1}n) before it fissioned.

Even with such carefully selected conditions, the probability that the reaction actually would occur was extremely small, with only about one in a trillion reactions yielding the desired product. A sophisticated detection system therefore was required for measuring the new element. The newly produced nucleus started out with a substantial velocity from the projectile impact and recoiled out of the lead target along with many other reaction products. This secondary beam was sent through a mass separator, which used a combination of electric and magnetic fields to separate the products. The separated element was then implanted in a solid-state detector that recorded the arrival of the nucleus and any subsequent radioactive decays.

In three weeks of running the experiment, GSI researchers found only two atoms of the new element. Proof came from observation of the characteristic chain of radioactive decay that the two atoms underwent. Each decayed by emitting a series of alpha particles, which consist of two protons and two neutrons. With each emission the nucleus lost two protons, and after five alpha particles were emitted, the nu-

cleus became a well-known isotope of element 102, nobelium.

Observation of the alpha decay energies and isotope lifetimes provided valuable new information on the stability of very heavy elements. The lifetime of element 112 was 0.3 millisecond (thousandth of a second), long enough to transport it in a beam to the detector but too short to study it by other methods. In early 1997 the GSI researchers were working to produce element 114, an element long expected to be especially stable. The most stable of the isotopes predicted for this element, however, would probably be beyond the reach of the researchers' heavy-ion fusion approach.

Chemistry of element 106

Another kind of milestone in the study of the heaviest elements has been the elucidation of their chemical properties. The first chemical observations on element 106 were made during the past year, also by researchers working at GSI. Element 106, given the provisional name seaborgium, is in the same column of the periodic table as tungsten, molybdenum, and chromium. However, seaborgium's neighboring element, 105 (provisionally dubnium), does not resemble other elements in its assigned column. Thus, nuclear chemists were uncertain about seaborgium's properties. Since researchers could produce only a few atoms of the element at a time, experiments had to be planned with great care.

Because the fastest chemical separations possible occur at gas interfaces, gas-phase chromatography was chosen to explore seaborgium's chemistry. Seaborgium's column mates tungsten and molybdenum have volatile oxychlorides, so the research-

ers sought to form similar compounds with seaborgium. The carrier gas in the chromatography apparatus had some added chlorine and oxygen, which was known to produce oxychlorides of tungsten and molybdenum. The volatile compounds are transported along the column when the temperature is higher than some value that is a characteristic of the element.

Seaborgium for the experiment was produced in a heavy-ion fusion reaction between nuclei of neon-22 and copper-248. Seaborgium first had been made more than 20 years earlier, using a different reaction, but the particular isotope that was created was too short-lived to study chemically. GSI researchers used a different reaction in an effort to produce heavier isotopes with longer half-lives. The seaborgium and other reaction products knocked out of the copper target were transported to the chromatographic column by a helium carrier gas. Once separated, the elements went to a detector that recorded the radioactive decays of the chemical products. In that way seaborgium was identified by its passage as a compound through the column at temperatures in the range of 300° C (570° F). Seaborgium's passage through the column indicated that its chemical properties are similar to those of tungsten.

The experiment provided researchers with valuable new information about the nuclear decay processes that occur in seaborgium. It produced two new isotopes with half-lives as long as a half minute, significantly greater than that of the first isotope made.

Neutrinos with mass?

Physicists generally have believed that neutrinos have no mass, travel at the speed of light, and interact in only one spin orientation. Those assumptions are incorporated in the standard model, the central theory that explains interactions between forces and particles in the universe. Results of a three-year experiment reported in 1996, however, added to growing doubts about those assumptions.

Whereas direct measurements have established only upper limits on neutrino mass, indirect methods using neutrinos produced in nuclear reactions in the laboratory or emanating from astronomical sources like the Sun have far greater sensitivity. The question of whether neutrinos have a nonzero mass is linked to the question of whether they remain stable as they travel over a distance—for example, from their source to a detector—or whether they oscillate, *i.e.,* spontaneously transform their identities, along the way. Three kinds of neutrinos are known to exist, and physicists theorize that if the particles have mass, one kind might transform to another. If they have no mass and thus always travel at the speed of light, such transformation would be impossible because for any object moving at light speed, time stands still.

Serious doubts about the immutability of neutrinos began with the so-called solar neutrino problem, which involves the observed rate of neutrinos emitted by the Sun. Nuclear reactions in the Sun produce neutrinos, which can be detected on Earth by the nuclear reactions they produce. A decades-long experiment observing reactions of neutrinos with chlorine nuclei consistently found that solar neutrinos bombard Earth at only one-third the rate predicted from astrophysical theory. More recently, experiments using other nuclear reactions to detect solar neutrinos confirmed a shortfall in observed neutrino rates. Two experiments making use of gallium as the interacting nucleus found only half the predicted rate, and a third experiment, which used a large tank of water as a detector medium for neutrinos that interact with electrons, found a similar deficit in solar neutrinos. These detectors can identify nuclear reactions involving mainly the type of neutrinos known as electron neutrinos. Physicists thus speculated that the deficit occurs because some electron neutrinos from the Sun oscillate to another type en route to Earth.

The experiment completed in 1996 took a different approach. Instead of using solar neutrinos, it employed antineutrinos made by colliding a particle beam with a target in an accelerator at Los Alamos (N.M.) National Laboratory. The antineutrinos then were sent to a detector positioned about 30 m (100 ft) away. The conditions of the experiment were such that only muon antineutrinos were sent toward the detector, which in turn was designed to register only electron antineutrinos, which are more energetic. A detection thus would indicate that a muon antineutrino had transformed into an electron neutrino along the way. The detector consisted of a tank of organic liquid with phototubes on its inside walls to record the following reactions:

$$\bar{v}_e + p \rightarrow e^+ + n; \quad n + p \rightarrow d + \gamma.$$

In the first reaction an electron antineutrino ($\bar{v}_e$) converts a hydrogen nucleus (a proton; p) in the liquid to a neutron (n), while the neutrino itself is simultaneously converted to a positron (e^+). The positron gives a flash of light as it leaves the reaction, and the pattern of the light signal is measured with the phototubes. In the second reaction, after a short time the produced neutron is captured, possibly by another proton, to form a deuteron (d; the nucleus of deuterium, or heavy hydrogen, consisting of one proton and one neutron). Energy released in this process (γ) also produces recordable light signals. The measurement technique is extremely sensitive in two ways. First, two independent signals are involved, that of the positron track and that of the neutron capture. Second, the location of the reaction is determined by the way light is distributed into the different detectors. This sensitivity allows detection of a very small reaction rate despite external noise.

During the three years of obtaining data for the experiment, the researchers found 22 detection events that could not be explained as background noise. They concluded that the events were evidence for neutrino oscillation. Researchers emphasized the importance of confirming the findings, since previous experiments with neutrinos from an accelerator had detected no unusual reactions. The new experiment, however, was substantially more sensitive and could detect weaker effects.

Other neutrino sources also were being used in an effort to detect possible neutrino oscillation. Nuclear reactors produce large amounts of electron antineutrinos. Because of their electron-like character, these neutrinos are relatively easy to identify with detectors. To look for neutrino oscillation, researchers measured declines in the observed neutrino rate in relation to the distance between the reactor and the detector. As of early 1997 the results of these experiments had been consistent with massless neutrinos. (See *Elementary-Particle*

A mirror made of a yttrium film covered with a protective palladium layer gradually changes from a shiny reflective metal to a yellowish transparent insulator (top to bottom) on exposure to hydrogen gas.

Physics, above; 1996 Yearbook of Science and the Future Feature Article: THE ELUSIVE NEUTRINO: A WINDOW ON THE UNIVERSE.)

—George F. Bertsch

CONDENSED-MATTER PHYSICS

Materials that can be transformed from reflecting to transparent in a few seconds, a giant Kerr rotation, and the creation of metallic hydrogen were among the significant developments of the past year in condensed-matter physics.

"Switchable" mirrors

In 1996 scientists at the Free University of Amsterdam reported the discovery that metal-to-insulator transitions in yttrium and lanthanum hydrides are accompanied by a spectacular change in optical properties that could be used to produce "switchable" mirrors having industrial and commercial applications. These mirrors change from shiny, metallic, and reflective to yellowish, transparent, and windowlike.

Explaining this behavior requires an understanding of the close relationship between a material's electrical conductivity and its transparency or reflectivity. Traditional mirrors are made from a glass sheet coated with a reflective metal, such as aluminum. In addition to being good conductors of electricity, metals usually reflect light well. Insulators, on the other hand, often let light pass through. Thus, one way to make a switchable mirror is to use a metal-to-insulator transition. Various types of materials are known to exhibit such transitions. Often they involve a change in crystallographic structure in response to some external factor such as temperature

or pressure. The new switchable mirrors, however, rely on an effect involving a change in chemical composition. The phenomenon occurs in yttrium and lanthanum hydrides, YH_x and LaH_x, as x (the number of hydrogen atoms per metal atom) changes from 2 to 3. YH_2 and LaH_2 are metals, whereas YH_3 and LaH_3 are insulators.

Researchers long have wanted to study the metal-to-insulator transition in hy-

drides of rare earth elements such as yttrium and lanthanum. Such studies have been hampered, however, by the unstable and fragile nature of some of these hydrides, which fall apart into a powder upon handling. To avoid reactivity and fragility problems with the hydrides, J.N. Huiberts and associates coated yttrium and lanthanum films with a very thin (5–20-nanometer [billionths of a meter]) layer of palladium. Palladium is quite permeable to hydrogen, and thus hydrogen gas can readily diffuse through the thin coating to the rare earth elements and form the hydrides. To demonstrate the effect, the researchers enclosed each film in a glass container that was gradually filled with hydrogen gas. They simultaneously measured the electrical resistivity and the light-transmission properties of the films and found that the metal-to-insulator transition involved a striking change in transparency to visible light. This transformation happened as the hydrogen concentration in the hydride approached a critical value of $x = 2.86$.

A metal-to-insulator transition involves the opening of a band gap in the spectrum of electronic energy levels in the material. In a metal the highest occupied electronic level occurs in the middle of a band, which is a continuous distribution of energy levels. In an insulator, on the other hand, there is an energy gap between the highest occupied state and the lowest empty one. As a result, photons of light need at least that amount of energy to excite an electron. Photons of insufficient energy will pass through the material instead of being absorbed or reflected. Most metal-to-insulator transitions involve opening a small band gap, which makes the material transparent only to infrared light. The new metal-to-insulator transition, however, involves the sudden creation of a wider band gap well into the region of visible light.

The origin of the effect is not yet fully understood. Although the Amsterdam research team determined that several structural phase transitions occur as yttrium and lanthanum take up hydrogen, these do not coincide with the metal-to-insulator transition. These involve changes in the packing of the metal atoms from a hexagonally close-packed structure to a face-centered, close-packed cube. The hydrogens can fill either tetrahedral interstices, where they are surrounded by four metal atoms, or octahedral ones, where they are surrounded by six metal atoms. The open question is whether the material's behavior truly defies existing theories about electronic states in materials or whether there is an as-yet-unidentified structural transition involved.

A record Kerr rotation

As is well known, certain materials such as those used in sunglasses produce polarized light—*i.e.*, they let through only that component of the light wave's vibrating electric vector that is oriented at a certain angle, called the polarization angle. It has long been known that light reflected from a magnetic material experiences the Kerr effect—a slight rotation of its polarization angle, termed the Kerr angle. Manufacturers of magneto-optical disks exploit the Kerr effect in special high-speed and high-volume data-storage applications. Conventional CD-ROMs encode digital information in minute pits produced by a laser beam on the disc's surface. Magneto-optical disks have tiny magnetic domains that

rotate the polarization angle of a laser beam that impinges on them. Because the magnetic information on them can be written and erased easily by means of a magnetic field, such disks have the important advantage of being writable (with a magnetic recording head) as well as readable (with a laser beam) as many times as desired. This important application has developed even though the Kerr angle is relatively small in the materials currently used for magneto-optical disks. Although physicists have searched for compounds with larger Kerr angles, no material until the past year showed a Kerr angle greater than a few degrees.

In 1996 researchers reported the discovery of a material, cerium antimonide (CeSb), with a record Kerr angle. A group from the Swiss Federal Institute of Technology, Zürich, found that CeSb exhibits a 90° Kerr rotation. The rotation occurs in magnetic fields of about five tesla and at a temperature of 1.5 K (−456.98° F), just a little above absolute zero. Whereas an explanation of the phenomenon remains to be fully developed, the discovery of a material with 90° rotation of polarization opens the way to new applications in laser technology, such as the reduction of undesirable feedback in laser cavities.

Liquid metallic hydrogen

In the 1920s physicists predicted on the basis of theoretical calculations that extremely high pressures and temperatures would squeeze hydrogen, the lightest of all chemical elements, into a metallic state. Ever since, generations of physicists have tried, unsuccessfully, to produce metallic hydrogen. Researchers at the Carnegie Institution of Washington, D.C., for instance,

tried for many years to achieve this goal in solid hydrogen at low to ambient temperatures and extremely high static pressures in diamond-anvil cells.

The dream finally was achieved in 1996 by Samuel T. Weir, Arthur C. Mitchell, and William J. Nellis at the Lawrence Livermore National Laboratory, Livermore, Calif. They used shock compression techniques to produce the metallic state in liquid hydrogen at much higher temperatures (3,000 K; 4,900° F) and lower pressures (1.4 megabars) than previously tried. In the experiments the researchers fired a metal disk from a two-stage gas gun at speeds of about seven kilometers per second into a target. The target comprised a layer of liquid hydrogen in a chilled sample holder placed between sapphire anvils. The shock wave produced by the impact of the disk reverberated, increasing the pressure without letting the temperature rise to levels that would dissociate the hydrogen.

Special electronic devices in the anvil performed ultrafast measurements of the sample and provided conclusive evidence for the existence of metallic hydrogen. From the conductivity measurements, the researchers determined the band gap as a function of pressure and found it to be about 0.3 eV, which is comparable to the average kinetic energy of the electrons at those temperatures and therefore accounts for the metallic behavior. The results had relevance to studies of the giant gas planets Jupiter and Saturn, which are believed to contain metallic hydrogen deep within them.

—Walter R.L. Lambrecht

See also Feature Article: BRIGHT NEW LIGHTS FOR PHYSICS.

PSYCHOLOGY

The trend toward multiculturalism continued to change the course of many professional disciplines during the past year, and the field of psychology was no exception. Cross-cultural issues achieved increased visibility in professional publications and conferences. Psychologists from many less-developed nations found outlets for greater professional participation and recognition in the establishment of national academies of science and other professional organizations.

Despite this growing internationalization (see *International Psychology,* below), psychology continued to reflect U.S. dominance in practice, research, and theory. Professionals grew increasingly concerned about the mental health of U.S. children exposed to a culture of violence and fear. A growing elderly population prompted numerous studies on the effects of aging on memory. Researchers took a new look at the results of previous research that discouraged the use of rewards in learning situations.

Toward a global psychology

One of the most significant developments in psychology was its growing inclusion of cross-cultural perspectives. Unlike the other sciences, psychology's emergence as a formal discipline has been nurtured primarily on U.S. soil. No other country, for example, has come close to matching the numbers of psychologists who have been educated, trained, and employed in the U.S. (Each year approximately 70,000 college students major in psychology; an additional 12,000 obtain master's degrees, and another 4,000 are awarded doctoral degrees.) Moreover, American theories and practices have set the standards for the

study and practice of psychology throughout the world.

The inauguration of a new section called "International Perspectives in Psychology" in the discipline's principal journal, *American Psychologist,* was an indication of the field's growing internationalization. According to the section's editors, a goal of the feature was "to foster bidirectionality for the exchange of psychological knowledge, ideas, and practice from developing and other industrialized nations in the hopes of influencing and broadening the knowledge and practice base of psychology here in the United States."

Reducing the insularity of contemporary U.S. psychology is expected to improve the ways in which U.S. psychologists serve the needs of an increasingly multiethnic and multiracial society. It also should facilitate the formation of a truly international psychology, encouraging a greater openness to promising or tried-and-true psychological methods in countries that have dismissed them as part of a more general resistance to U.S. domination of the field—most notably France, Hungary, New Zealand, and parts of the former Soviet Union.

Finally, the exchange will give U.S. psychologists an unprecedented opportunity to benefit from the contributions of foreign psychologists and to develop forums for mutual enrichment. This international exchange will become especially important in the future as psychologists are asked to pool their resources and contribute new perspectives on growing global problems, such as how to best utilize individual and social resources in coping with the medical and emotional needs of aging, multicultural populations.

Using rewards: myths and reality

For the past quarter century, psychologists have been critical of the practice of using rewards to motivate participants in such learning situations as classrooms and on-the-job training. Opponents claim that the practice is ineffective, even counterproductive. Using measurements such as the amount of time people devoted to a task or their reported attitudes toward it, researchers cited experiments showing that extrinsically motivated (that is, reward-dependent) subjects do more poorly on assigned tasks after rewards are discontinued than control subjects who perform on the basis of intrinsic motivation—*i.e.,* activities engaged in for their own sake, involving pursuing personal interests or exploring creative potential. Critics maintained that although reward-dependent people appeared to work harder at a task, the results were less creative and the subjects less enthusiastic about the task. They attributed these outcomes to the participants' negative feelings about being controlled by others rather than being able to determine their own tasks. Widely accepted, the results of these studies have been enormously influential and have led to a decline in the use of rewards in many instructional practices, especially in tasks that emphasize creativity and personal commitment.

In a comprehensive literature review published in *American Psychologist,* Robert Eisenberger of the University of Delaware and Judy Cameron of the University of Alberta raised serious questions about the outcomes of these studies. The researchers found that in only one type of experimental situation was there any statistically reliable evidence that rewarded subjects did in fact perform more poorly on subsequent tests after the rewards were withdrawn. Eisenberger and Cameron concluded that the argument against the use of rewards, therefore, was an overgeneralization based on a relatively narrow set of circumstances. Furthermore, they maintained that these conditions could easily be avoided.

According to the researchers, subjects devoted less time to a task once the reward was withdrawn (and therefore demonstrated less intrinsic motivation) only in circumstances defined by the following conditions: the subject expected the reward, and the reward was granted independent of the subject's quality of performance or task completion.

To counter what Eisenberger and Cameron called a "myth" about the use of rewards, they provided evidence demonstrating that the practice of rewards had no measurable negative impact on—and sometimes even increased—both intrinsic motivation and creativity. In cases in which subjects received tangible rewards for quality-dependent or completion-dependent tasks, Eisenberger and Cameron found no appreciable reduction in intrinsic motivation as measured by the amount of time that subjects spent on an activity after the reward was withdrawn. In fact, subjects who had been verbally rewarded spent more time on a task after the rewards were removed than before they were introduced. Furthermore, after receiving a verbal reward or a tangible reward that recognized the quality of their performance, participants reported more favorable opinions about the task. The researchers also cited the findings of recent studies indicating that rewards for displays of high creativity encouraged greater creativity, even when subjects shifted to new tasks. The findings suggest that reward, when used appropriately, has a much more favorable effect on task interest and creativity than is generally supposed.

Memory and aging

As the world's population has steadily grown older, concerns about its psychological well-being have mounted. Among the most worrisome of mental problems in the elderly are memory failures. To examine how memory changes with age, Lars-Göran Nillson of Stockholm University began a 10-year study in 1988 of 1,000 randomly selected Swedish subjects, ranging from 35 to 80 years of age. Recently he and his colleagues completed follow-up tests on the 900 survivors from the original sample.

Nillson tested three types of memory: episodic (memory of experienced events), semantic (memory of knowledge and general information), and priming memory (the unconscious biasing effect that some immediately prior experiences have on subsequent memory, such as the ability to recall names of automobiles after being shown the word *automobile* for a very short time interval).

Test results indicated several marked differences between older and younger subjects. Older adults had considerably poorer episodic memories. Semantic memory at first also appeared to show a serious decline with age. However, when education levels were factored out—the 35-year-olds averaged 14 years of schooling, compared with only 7 years for the 80-year-olds—the difference disappeared. No age differences were found in the capacity of priming memory among the populations.

The results, which suggest that memory is extraordinarily resistant to aging, was supported by the data of an American pioneer in aging research, psychologist K. Warner Schaie of Pennsylvania State University. Schaie has directed studies of mental functions in aged subjects for more than 35 years. He pointed out that the nervous system slows down with aging, so time-dependent tasks necessarily show some memory deficit. Episodic memory—and therefore the ability to learn—under limited time conditions is typically poorer in older people. As a way to ensure the persistence of semantic and priming memories, Schaie emphasized the importance of remaining cognitively active in middle age—such as seeking new experiences and adapting to change.

Monika Knopf of the Johann Wolfgang Goethe University, Frankfurt am Main, Ger., reported several innovative techniques used in her research on memory and aging. Knopf found that when both younger and older subjects were asked to memorize a list of words, their memory of some of the words on the list, such as *water* and *eggs,* was markedly improved when the subjects combined actions with words, such as pouring a glass of water or counting the number of eggs in a bowl, instead of simply reciting the words. Moreover, she reported that participants demonstrated an increase in memory just by planning or intending to perform the actions. Knopf tentatively attributed these differences to the richer encoding of details involved in the planning or acting out of actions, such as counting eggs while placing them in a bowl, compared with the bare-bones verbal process involved in merely reciting the words.

"Lingering Questions of a Child," a 1997 painting by Michael Tice, illustrates the blur and jumble of most memories in human consciousness. Researchers have found that people lose their exact memories of routine events after a period of about 10 days.

Self-reports: truth or consequences

Psychologists rely on the information supplied by their patients or study subjects in making diagnoses or gathering data in research projects. A recent conference sponsored by the U.S. National Institutes of Health, Bethesda, Md., convened 30 participants to discuss the problems in the accuracy of such self-reports. The group produced some interesting and potentially useful conclusions about the role of memory in self-described feelings and behaviors.

Conference participants noted that memory is especially unreliable when it concerns routine behaviors. People generally lose their exact memories of routine events after a period of about 10 days. When asked to provide dates for their children's immunizations, for example, the parents in one study were found to do little better than chance when their answers were checked against clinic records.

On the other hand, memory is considerably more reliable about unusually stimulating or emotional events.

Conference participants also cited the common problem of deliberate falsification of information. Using surreptitious electronic monitoring, one study of asthma sufferers, for example, found that to avoid a reprimand from their doctors, 14% of the patients discarded unused inhaler medication the day before a clinic visit.

These problems notwithstanding, health professionals rely on their patients to report many kinds of information that cannot be readily obtained in any other way, such as sexual behaviors and subjective thoughts and feelings. One of the goals of the recent conference was to systematically assess the complexities and pitfalls of self-reports so that researchers and practitioners could reduce respondents' bias and encourage accuracy.

Treating childhood disorders

Psychologists developed several promising new approaches to handling disturbed children. At the University of Florida, researchers made considerable headway on the problem of conduct disorders, concentrating on the early treatment of what they called oppositional defiant disorder (ODD), a syndrome marked by chronic disobedience and resistance to authority. Eighty-one low-income families whose children, mostly boys, had been diagnosed with ODD participated in the 13-week program.

In each session the therapist observed the interaction between parents and their children from behind a one-way mirror. Using small radio receivers, the therapist provided guidance to parents on how to reinforce desirable behaviors and ignore obnoxious ones in their children. Avoiding negative admonitions, parents were trained to suggest constructive play activities and to compliment the children on their compliance. In later stages the therapy concentrated on improving the effectiveness of positive parental reinforcement.

Parents who finished the therapy reported that they had gained better control over their children, a skill that many of them found transferable to untreated siblings. At least half of the families said that they were able to maintain the improvements in their children's behavior over several months.

A study conducted in Dunedin, N.Z., by psychologist Avshalom Caspi of the University of Wisconsin, Madison, demonstrated that if left untreated, behavioral problems manifested in childhood persisted into adulthood. Researchers tracked a group of children from the age of 3 to 21 years. Following an evaluation at age three, each child was placed into one of five categories: well-adjusted, confident, reserved, inhibited, or undercontrolled (characterized by irritability and recklessness). When psychologists examined the children at age 18, they placed most of them into the same categories. When re-evaluated at age 21, the subjects were found to have diagnostic features consistent with their earliest descriptions. Those who had been categorized as inhibited at age three, for example, were now more likely to have diagnostic signs of depression; those who had been described as undercontrolled often exhibited symptoms of an antisocial personality disorder and were more likely to report interpersonal conflicts or to have committed multiple crimes.

Bully-proofing America's schools

The National Association of School Psychologists estimated that each day 160,000 children in the U.S. miss school out of fear of being bullied. In response to this national problem, psychologists in a Colorado school district launched a "bully-proofing" program in one of its elementary schools and developed a multifaceted program designed to counter aggressive behavior. This program included teaching children new skills for defusing tense situations, introducing classroom discussions on the problem, and creating a new school norm in which bullying was seen as "un-

cool." As a result of the program, bullies lost their position of dominance, victims became less vulnerable, teachers learned how to help children resolve conflicts, and parents were relieved by the improved school security.

Treatment of the bullies also was an integral part of the program. Psychologists found that the typical bully was not only defiant and impulsive but also popular and powerful. Unless immediately applied, punishment, such as suspension, was not a particularly effective deterrent for aggressive behavior. Instead, therapists concentrated on rechanneling the energies of these children by appealing to them for help in controlling school events or protecting younger and more vulnerable children.

Social toxicity and the culture of fear

Psychologist James Garbarino of Cornell University, Ithaca, N.Y., urged his profession to consider children's mental health problems in a broader social context. Garbarino blamed the increasing incidence of psychological problems in inner-city children on the chronically defective social environment in which they live, a condition he termed social toxicity.

Garbarino's data were persuasive, albeit not surprising. For example, he discovered that in 1974, 10% of American children and adolescents were found to be in need of help from mental health care providers; 15 years later that figure had jumped to 18%. According to a recent Harris Poll of 6th- to 12th-graders in urban communities, one-third of the children feared that they would be fatally shot; among African-American and Hispanic-American chil-

dren, the figure rose to more than one-half. In another study 43% of elementary schoolchildren in Ohio worried about being kidnapped. According to Garbarino, too often psychologists overlooked the impacts of what he called "a culture of fear" in their evaluations of children.

He maintained that a contributing factor to the children's fears is the prevalence of large, overcrowded high schools. Children in schools with populations in excess of 500 students suffer from a damaging isolation and depersonalization regardless of the goodwilled efforts of teachers and counselors. Garbarino called upon psychologists to take the lead in advocating smaller schools that encourage closer ties between students as well as between students and their teachers.

—Melvin H. Marx

International psychology

International congresses and meetings continued to foster direct exchanges about psychological research and practice. More than 4,200 psychologists from 85 countries participated in the 26th International Congress of Psychology held in Montreal in August 1996. In addition to reports of recent research on some of psychology's more traditional concerns, such as aging and memory or the role of emotion in psychotherapy, prominent psychologists addressed a number of more recent, topical issues. Scientists discussed new ways to study the connections between mind and body, including the effect of psychological experiences, especially stress, on the vulnerability to disease and the relationship between anger and heart disease. Other topics covered the sociological aspects of psychology, including the changing roles

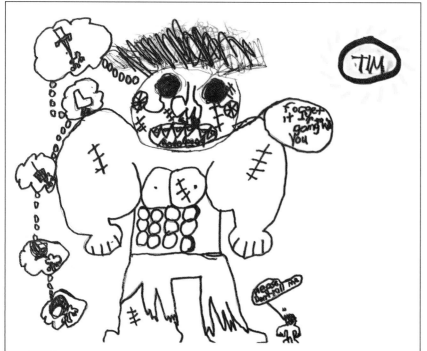

This drawing by fourth-grader Tim Nichols illustrates the fear and intimidation that children commonly experience in U.S. schools. Nichols's work was part of a manual developed by Colorado's Cherry Creek School District to counter bullying behavior in schools.

of women in psychology around the world, the effects of rapid social change on personal and family life and child development, and the development of educational programs to reduce the incidence of AIDS. Special symposia focused on psychology in the Arab world, Latin America, sub-Saharan Africa, and Asia.

Recent initiatives helped psychologists from less-developed countries and from countries with limited funds to participate in the congress and other international meetings. The organizers of the Montreal congress earmarked substantial funds to pay registration fees and other expenses and continued to support Advanced Research Training Seminars (ARTS), which were held nearby for psychologists from less-developed countries. International and regional conferences and meetings also were held to foster exchange between psychologists from less-developed countries under the sponsorship of the International Union of Psychological Science (IUPsyS), the International Association of Applied Psychology (IAAP), and the International Association for Cross-Cultural Psychology (IACCP). These initiatives showed an increased commitment on the part of inter-

national psychological organizations and congress organizers to ensure more adequate representation of psychologists from all regions of the world at international meetings.

Four new member countries joined the IUPsyS, an association that represents the field of psychology in countries with an active, organized community of psychological scientists, bringing the total number of national members to 61. New members included the Association of Albanian Psychologists, the Czech-Moravian Psychological Society, the Psychological Society of South Africa, and the Uganda National Psychological Association.

The growing interest in international contributions to the field of psychology was reflected in the establishment of an additional quarterly psychological journal that focused on international psychology. *European Psychologist* was being published in cooperation with the European Federation of Professional Psychologists' Associations and other European psychological organizations.

As a result of the growing interest in cross-cultural psychology, increasing numbers of researchers were investigating the

extent to which regularities of human behavior are found across different cultures. Psychology research, for example, has revealed five common factors, or dimensions, that can be used to describe personality, regardless of culture. They include extroversion, agreeableness, conscientiousness, emotional stability, and openness to experience. Different cultures, however, emphasize some factors over others. When Chinese describe themselves or others, they refer to conscientiousness more often and agreeableness less frequently than Americans.

Michael Harris Bond of the Chinese University of Hong Kong and Peter B. Smith of the University of Sussex, Brighton, Eng., documented the results of growing international research like this in a review of recent books and articles on cross-cultural psychology in the 1996 *Annual Review of Psychology*. Noting the promising developments that have emerged from recent East Asian research, the authors urged the expansion of similar research initiatives in South America, Africa, and countries of the former communist bloc. Such research is especially important to offset the overwhelming number of U.S. projects that continue to make up the bulk of psychological research.

An increasing number of psychologists from less-developed countries were being inducted into national academies of science or similar organizations. In 1996 Q.C. Jing of the Institute of Psychology, Chinese Academy of Sciences, Beijing, became the first psychologist inducted into the Third World Academy of Sciences.

—Mark R. Rosenzweig

See also Feature Articles: OUR SLEEPY SOCIETY; ROBOTS ON THE MOVE.

SCIENCE POLICY

In 1996 Western European countries, in common with the United States, continued to face the challenge of maintaining the breadth and excellence of their scientific research systems in the face of persistent fiscal constraints. Japan demonstrated that it recognized its responsibilities of international leadership in science, while taking steps to expand and stabilize its research and education system even in the face of a continuing economic recession. Meanwhile, the most prominent Asian economies expanded, as they applied their growing scientific capabilities with unconcealed exuberance.

INTERNATIONAL

In 1996, as in previous years, governments and private firms in North America, the 15 member nations of the European Union (EU), and Japan accounted for approximately 90% of the world's investments in, and performance of, research and development (R&D). Despite the continued dominance of the North America-Western Europe-Japan triad, the emergence of several other economies, particularly in East Asia, with respect to both R&D and technology-intensive trade has been the most significant long-term international science policy trend. These emerging economies, in common with North America, Western Europe, and Japan, have relied on national science policies as one key strategy for addressing national social and economic objectives, including international trade. That several have enjoyed such striking recent success may be owing to the fact that those policies have been designed in large measure to catch up with the more fully mature and integrated systems of the still dominant triad.

Europe

Among Western European countries, France, Germany, Sweden, and the United Kingdom—like the United States—invested more than 2% of their gross domestic product (GDP) in R&D, while several others, including Denmark, Finland, Italy, and The Netherlands, invested substantially more than 1.5%. In contrast, R&D investments in almost all countries outside the North America-Western Europe-Japan triad were less than 1% of GDP. The total (primarily government plus industrial) R&D investments in most Western European countries, however, had either leveled off or declined in inflation-adjusted terms during the 1990s.

Western Europe boasted a range of research capabilities across the entire spectrum of science and engineering disciplines. Basic research continued to flourish, despite pressures to demonstrate short-term economic benefits that appeared to be both more intense and more sustained than in the United States. As in the U.S., reductions in the growth rate of government R&D investments could be accounted for in part by imperatives to reduce budget deficits (which were in all cases larger as a fraction of GDP than in the U.S.), as a precondition for a single European currency, due to be introduced in 1999.

Despite broad similarities, differences between the science policies and outcomes of the principal Western European countries continued to be apparent. Germany, recently second only to Japan among major nations in its R&D investments relative to its economy, slipped behind France during the period 1995–96. German government investments continued to be con- strained owing to the unanticipatedly high costs of integrating the former East Germany, while industrial investments were curtailed in part as a result of increasingly strenuous competition from East Asia.

As in the United States, human resource issues were becoming important aspects of science policy in Europe. The U.S. model, in which university research was closely coupled with Ph.D.-level training, was increasingly attractive, suggesting that a larger fraction of available public research funds ought to be devoted to research in universities. Yet European universities were struggling with sharply increased enrollments (a phenomenon known as "massification") encouraged by negligible tuition charges and continuing high unemployment rates. Implications of massification for the research capacities of universities remained a serious concern.

The word *multinational* conveys the most significant difference between the United States and Western Europe in the organization and conduct of science. In 1996 the budgets of the scientific programs of the EU continued to increase, enhancing the importance of that organization as an arbiter of scientific research. At the same time, several major European multilateral research facilities outside the EU's jurisdiction, including the European Laboratory for Particle Physics (CERN) and the European Synchrotron Radiation Facility (ESRF), faced significant budgetary uncertainty as a result of Germany's July 1996 announcement of its intention to reduce its annual contributions by amounts ranging from 3% to over 9%, depending on the facility involved.

Farther east, Russia's once superb research capabilities continued to erode as a result of sharply curtailed government investments and the emigration of many first-rate scientists, as the country continued to seek political and economic stability. In contrast, by July 1996 the Czech Republic, Hungary, and Poland had all become full members of the Paris-based Organisation for Economic Co-operation and Development (OECD). Although their admission was based primarily on economic as opposed to scientific criteria, these countries sent delegates to science and technology-related committees of the OECD and displayed a newfound confidence that reflected the fact that their national science systems had turned the corner and were poised to become full-fledged members of an increasingly integrated European research system, which, despite its problems, was certain to remain one of the world's most broadly based and vital.

Imre Dunai (right), the Hungarian minister for trade, attends a press conference marking Hungary's invitation to join the Organisation for Economic Co-operation and Development. New Eastern European members were expected to participate in an increasingly integrated scientific research system.

Japan

Although Japan's R&D investments had been decreasing since 1993, owing primarily to a decline in private-sector contributions, its expenditures, measured against its economy as 2.7% of GDP, were still the largest of any major nation. Of these investments, approximately 80% were accounted for by private industry and 20% by the central government.

Despite its undoubted R&D capabilities, Japan voiced increasing concern that its research system lacked the breadth and flexibility that the country required to maintain its status as a dominant scientific power. Accordingly, on July 2, 1996, the Japanese Cabinet adopted the Science and Technology Basic Plan intended "to promote science and technology policies com-

prehensively, systematically and positively from a new viewpoint…and to provide concrete science and technology promotion for five years from the 1996 fiscal year to the 2000 fiscal year."

The most impressive feature of the basic plan was the government's commitment to double its 1992 R&D investments by fiscal year 2000 (which would begin on April 1, 2000), so that its share of those expenditures would be comparable to government shares in the U.S. and Western Europe. The plan also pledged to redirect R&D resources toward the solution of global-scale problems, such as environment, food, energy, and natural resources. Significantly, the plan also emphasized the promotion of basic research, "which produces the common intellectual property for hu-

mankind." To this end, it proposed to integrate universities more effectively into the national research system, to improve education and research in graduate schools, and to expand significantly postdoctoral research opportunities.

The government as well as many scientists expressed concern that despite Japan's status as a major scientific nation, the general public possessed insufficient understanding of, or appreciation for, science and technology. Additionally, as in the U.S. and Europe, a decreasing fraction of young people were electing careers in some scientific disciplines, particularly the mathematical and physical sciences and engineering. In the West this trend was regarded as troublesome. In Japan, however, it had assumed the dimensions of a national crisis related, in the Japanese view, to deficiencies in broader public attitudes toward science and technology. Thus, the Basic Plan assigned a high priority to science promotion to the public, particularly among young people. As a means for eliciting greater publicity for this approach, the Japanese government hosted an international conference on public understanding of science in November 1996. Participants agreed on the desirability of a concerted international effort to comprehend the complex factors conditioning public attitudes toward science. However, many remained skeptical about whether the provisions of Japan's Basic Plan could rapidly reverse the disinclination of young people in that country—and elsewhere—to pursue careers in some fields of science and engineering.

South Korea

Viewed from a science policy perspective, South Korea remained the most exuberant of the newly industrialized economies of East Asia. During 1995–96 South Korean GDP grew at an annual rate of more than 8%, compared with 3–4% annual growth rates in the U.S., Western Europe, and Japan. This growth was fueled, in part, by South Korea's R&D investments and, in turn, was permitting the country to maintain and increase those investments, which for the past five years had increased at an annual rate of 20%. Measured in terms of its economy, South Korean R&D investments were 2.3% of GDP, comparable to France, Germany, and the U.K. and only slightly less than those of Japan and the U.S. Of those investments, over 70% were accounted for by the private sector, an industrial share matched only by Japan.

Like Japan, South Korea was moving to broaden and strengthen its research system. It had announced its intention to expand capabilities for basic research, including the creation of an institute for advanced sciences modeled after the Institute for Advanced Studies, Princeton, N.J. The country was also moving aggressively to assert its aspirations to be recognized as a world scientific leader through multinational organizations such as the OECD and among the Asia-Pacific Economic Cooperation (APEC) countries. In particular, in September 1996 Seoul, S.Kor., was host to the second meeting of the APEC ministers of science, the first having been held in Beijing a year earlier.

Chinese Premier Li Peng (center right) confers with Pres. Jiang Zemin at a political conference in Beijing. Li chaired the government's Leading Group of Science and Technology in China's drive to become a world scientific power.

China

Because of its immense population, substantial geographical extent, and uneven regional development, China cannot be compared in any meaningful way with emerging East Asian economies, such as South Korea. Rather, it remains unique— and spectacular. The size of its economy continued to grow at an annual rate of 7% or better and, measured in terms of local purchasing power, exceeded that of Japan and was more than 60% as large as that of the United States.

The development and deployment of scientific resources was an essential element in China's development strategy. Although the country invested only about 0.6% of its GDP in R&D, the government had pledged to triple that proportion by the year 2000. In 1996, in an effort to exploit its scientific resources more effectively, the government established the Leading Group of Science and Technology, chaired by the Chinese premier with representatives from the country's principal scientific bodies. This committee had approved four major facilities: an innovative 4-m (13-ft)-wide field telescope for sky surveys, a new synchrotron radiation source and the upgrading of an existing source, and a national seismographic network. Taken together, their approval provided incontrovertible evidence of China's drive for recognition as a world-class rather than simply a regional scientific power.

India

India, in terms of both population and scientific potential, also defied easy comparison. By the time the country gained its independence in 1947, modern science was already well established at a handful of

The U.S. Space Shuttle *Columbia* blasts off on a mission in April 1997 to conduct microgravity experiments and test hardware and procedures for the International Space Station. In fiscal 1996 and again in fiscal 1997, NASA was the only major nondefense U.S. government agency that faced cuts in research and development appropriations.

NASA

centers, and India ranked as Asia's undisputed scientific leader. By 1996 the country had produced more world-renowned scientists, including more Nobel laureates, than any other Asian country. Yet its R&D investments were only about 0.7% of GDP, and it had been notably less successful than China or the emergent East Asian economies in deploying its scientific resources for economic development.

Beginning in 1992, the Indian government moved to dismantle many of the bewildering bureaucratic regulations that had been regarded as a significant source of the country's sluggish development, including regulations that discouraged foreign investments. One result was a virtual explosion in small, private, science-based enterprise. Bangalore, in the south, was bidding to become the software capital of the world, while advances in other areas, such as biotechnology, were also impressive. A 1996 report of the government's Council of Scientific & Industrial Research opened with the assertion, "A new vision of India as a major player in the global setting has been articulated. The wave of change sweeping the country and the world has thrown up [a] myriad of opportunities and at the same time posed daunting challenges for all sections of Indian society." Given its solid and broadly based scientific infrastructure, its multiple ties with the West, and the open, democratic character of its society, India, too, could emerge as a major scientific power during the first years of the next century.

Multinational initiatives

For many countries, national science policies have become an important strategy for addressing social and economic objectives.

Such policies, however, when pursued too aggressively or defensively, can be viewed with suspicion or even hostility by other countries, particularly trading partners. One countertrend has been a decided if sometimes hesitant movement toward seeking areas of common interest and undertaking cooperation through multinational organizations such as the OECD and APEC.

A major OECD analysis, *Technology, Productivity and Job Creation,* released in April 1996, concluded that on balance, technological change increases employment levels. It also emphasized the essential role played by institutions—primarily universities—that conduct long-term research in the economic vitality of the mature economies of OECD member countries. The "jobs" study was notable in demonstrating the utility of a multinational approach to a common set of problems. It also underlined the imperative, evident in many OECD countries, of linking scientific research more closely and directly with common socioeconomic objectives.

In 1996 APEC, which was founded in 1989, nearly 30 years after the OECD, did not as yet possess the substantial and sophisticated analytical capabilities of the latter. Yet it had perhaps demonstrated more faith in the long-term benefits of basic research than had the older organization. As a case in point, the principal item on the agenda of the APEC ministers at the September science summit was how to encourage greater creativity in scientific research.

Information technologies

Technological change itself has provided a significant impetus toward the search for

multinational approaches to generic science policy issues. The rapid development of information technologies illustrates this. By the late 1990s the Internet, originally conceived of largely as a means for facilitating communication among scientists and academics, had emerged as an essential tool of international commerce. It was not only changing the ways in which scientific data were exchanged but also altering the ways in which scientific research itself was conducted in several fields.

Although the further development of information technologies was largely in the hands of commercial interests, governments were beginning to understand the importance of access to these technologies by their national scientific communities. In 1996, for the first time, several countries also began to explore multinational approaches to issues associated with the effects of information technologies on the conduct of science and on the resultant contributions of science to national objectives. A June 1996 international conference held near Copenhagen explored the current and likely effects of information technologies on national science systems and cooperation among those systems. It concluded that a concerted multinational effort is essential to ensure universal access and, thus, to exploit the potential of information technology to strengthen the promising but by no means universally accepted trend toward the internationalization of science policy.

UNITED STATES

No doubt 1996 was an unsettling year for U.S. science policy. January 1 marked the beginning of the third week of the second partial government shutdown occasioned

by the failure of Pres. Bill Clinton's administration and the Republican-controlled Congress to agree on the government's fiscal year 1996 budget, an agreement that should have been reached prior to Oct. 1, 1995. Among the principal federal agencies that conduct and support R&D, only the Department of Defense (DOD) and the Department of Energy (DOE) had received their 1996 budgets and remained open as the year began. Although R&D appropriations for these two agencies were respectable, many foresaw dire consequences for overall federal R&D funding in any final compromise between the administration and Congress.

Amazingly, when a budget compromise was finally in place a few weeks later, R&D fared reasonably well, at least measured against earlier expectations. The fiscal year 1996 budget of the National Institutes of Health (NIH) had increased by

almost 6% relative to 1995, whereas that of the National Science Foundation (NSF) remained essentially level. Among the principal nondefense R&D agencies, only NASA suffered a decline, although of less than 1%. Equally significant, earlier attempts by a few congressional Republicans to abolish the Department of Commerce and the DOE and their science and technology-related programs had floundered.

Congress, apparently unwilling to revisit the rancor that had marked the 1996 budget process during an election year, reached agreement with the White House on the fiscal year 1997 budget with few public indications of contention. Indeed, for the first time in recent memory, the government was fully and unconditionally funded prior to the new fiscal year, which began on Oct. 1, 1996. Once again, R&D fared well, with NASA alone among the principal nondefense agencies that experi-

enced a decline in its R&D budget from the 1996 level.

Viewed in the aggregate, U.S. R&D investments remained impressive. In 1995 (the last year for which data were available) total expenditures were estimated at $171 billion, exceeding the combined totals for Japan and the principal countries of the EU. Measured in terms of the economy, R&D investments were 2.4% of GDP. That ratio had declined from its 1993 level of 2.6%, compared with ratios for Japan and Germany of 2.7% and 2.5%, respectively, during the same year.

This decline in the R&D/GDP ratio was among several concerns about the future of federal R&D. The Clinton administration had won its short-term budget battle with Congress, but it had conceded the imperative to balance the federal budget by fiscal year 2002 and, like Congress, had proposed to do so primarily at the expense of the domestic discretionary account, which includes all nondefense R&D expenditures. In mid-July 1996 the American Association for the Advancement of Science (AAAS) projected the likely impact on agency R&D budgets of the differing administration and congressional budget-balancing proposals. According to these projections, the NIH and NSF budgets would remain essentially flat under both the administration and congressional scenarios, meaning that each would experience inflation-adjusted decreases ranging from 6% to 8% over the next five years. The R&D budgets of the DOE and NASA could, according to AAAS projections, experience more serious declines ranging from 20% to 40% in inflation-adjusted terms.

National laboratories

The DOE's budget prospects were particularly unsettling. Although the department's R&D appropriation increased from an estimated level of approximately $6,060,000,000 in 1996 to approximately $6,260,000,000 in 1997, the amount devoted to magnetic fusion research in 1997 was barely more than the $227 million appropriated in 1996. While the 1997 funds would permit continued U.S. participation in the International Thermonuclear Experimental Reactor, it would further weaken the domestic effort in the field. In particular, the promising Tokamak Fusion Test Reactor managed by Princeton University was slated to be shut down.

The Princeton facility, which had a 1995 budget of approximately $106 million, was among 19 federally funded research and development centers (FFRDCs) managed by universities under DOE contracts; an

In 1996 budget cuts forced the U.S. Department of Energy to end funding for the Tokamak Fusion Test Reactor at the Princeton University Plasma Physics Laboratory. In 1994 the reactor had created a brief fusion reaction that produced more than 10 MW of electricity.

additional five FFRDCs were managed by industrial firms. The best known of these facilities were often called national laboratories. The DOE's 1995 expenditure for all of its FFRDCs was $3.5 billion, over half its R&D budget. Among the university-managed facilities, two—the Los Alamos (N.M.) National Laboratory and the Lawrence Livermore National Laboratory, Livermore, Calif., both managed by the University of California—had been primarily, although not exclusively, involved with nuclear weapons R&D. The DOE's 1995 contribution to these two facilities was about $1.1 billion, comparable to the total budgets of seven laboratories, including the Brookhaven National Laboratory, Upton, N.Y., and the Fermi National Accelerator Laboratory, Batavia, Ill., that devoted considerable resources to supporting research by university-based user groups.

The 1995 report of the Task Force on Alternative Futures for the Department of Energy National Laboratories chaired by Robert W. Galvin, retired chairman of Motorola, Inc., was strongly supportive of the unique "energy mission" of the national laboratories. The report went on to note, however, that substantial cost savings would result by eliminating duplication of programs among the laboratories as well as by streamlining their management and made specific recommendations to these ends. By year-end, 1996 action had yet to be taken on the Galvin recommendations. Meanwhile, the DOE was slated for a severe reduction in its R&D budget over the next five years and would no doubt be obliged to substantially reduce its contributions to the national laboratories. In this constrained environment, competition between the defense-oriented facilities and

the larger group that serve the needs of universities was likely to intensify.

Science and political action

In 1996 the prospect of declining federal support led a group of prominent scientists to engage in overt political action by mimicking a technique employed with some success by registered lobbying organizations such as the American Association of Retired Persons and the National Rifle Association. Although the partisan activities of most U.S. scientists were probably limited to voting and occasionally signing petitions or writing to their congressional representatives, U.S. science policy itself had become a highly political activity. This was increasingly evident as the competition for research funding intensified vis-à-vis other claims on the federal budget. Many scientific societies, for example, demonstrated considerable skill in lobbying key congressional committees to maintain or increase the level of support for research, while taking care to protect their tax-exempt status.

In September 1996 a newly formed organization called Science Watch, Inc., went a step farther by issuing a scorecard on the "pro-science" voting record of individual members of the House of Representatives. The organization, composed of 10 distinguished scientists and engineers, rated members of the 104th Congress on how they responded to 30 roll-call votes on the House floor, most of these having to do with appropriations for federal science and technology agencies. The most widely publicized outcome of this survey was that the average "pro-science" voting records of Democrats in the House was 72%, in contrast with the Republican av-

erage of 35%. Rep. Robert Walker, retiring chairman of the House Science Committee, assailed the survey, claiming that it equated being "pro-science" with being a "big spender." He pointed to a possible methodological flaw in that single voice votes in favor of (or against) an appropriations bill were not recorded, whereas roll-call votes on often minor amendments were. Others, including Washington representatives of leading research universities, decried the survey on the grounds that it threatened to politicize science. Despite such protests, one consequence of looming constraints on federal research funding might well be increasingly overt political action on the part of the U.S. scientific community.

Database copyright treaty

During much of 1996 the U.S. scientific community argued vehemently that dire consequences would result if funding levels for research were not maintained. In the midst of this budget-related activity, one telling incident suggested that science policy remained isolated from broader national concerns. Although the importance of science is at least tacitly acknowledged throughout the government, nonscience agencies sometimes display a lack of understanding of, or perhaps indifference to, the conditions required for a flourishing scientific enterprise. A case in point involved a failed attempt by the U.S. Patent and Trademark Office (PTO) to convince Congress to enact legislation that would have provided what critics regarded as excessive copyright protection for electronic databases. In August the PTO attempted to breath new life into this failed venture by means of a proposed international treaty scheduled to be negotiated in December at a meeting of the World Intellectual Property Organization (WIPO) in Geneva. This treaty was among a package of three stimulated by advances in information technology. The first proposed to extend existing copyright protection to musical recordings generated by computer. The second proposed to extend protection to literary works available electronically. According to U.S. critics, the third database treaty, the provisions of which were similar to the legislation proposed earlier by the PTO, would have given database providers far greater control over their products than do existing laws and international conventions that protect literary and artistic works. To scientists, who depend increasingly on free access to and exchange of substantial bodies of data in electronic form, the treaty would have had a chilling if not a devastating effect. Accordingly, when the U.S. National Academy of Sciences became aware of the proposed treaty in October 1996, it mounted a vigorous counter-campaign. As a result, the U.S. government withdrew its support for the proposed treaty during the December negotiations in Geneva. Instead, the WIPO negotiators agreed to reconsider it in 1998. WIPO did reach agreement on the other two treaties, subject to ratification by the U.S. Senate and comparable foreign legislative bodies.

Government Performance and Results Act

Two years before the Clinton administration agreed on the need to balance the federal budget, it took steps to reduce the size of the federal workforce and streamline the management of the bureaucracy. The Government Performance and Results Act (GPRA), enacted in 1993 at the administration's request, was a key element in the latter strategy, even though it had gone almost unnoticed outside Washington, D.C. The act required that the fiscal year 1999 budget requests of all government agencies (which the president would transmit to Congress late in January 1998) include strategic plans approved by the Office of Management and Budget (OMB), setting forth agency missions in measurable terms. Agency budgets for fiscal year 1999 and for each subsequent year were to include explicit performance goals derived from those strategic plans. Beginning in fiscal year 2000, agencies would be required to submit annual reports to the OMB and Congress on actual performance measured against those goals.

The GPRA posed a serious dilemma for agencies the principal mission of which was to conduct and/or support research. The results of scientific research, particularly basic research, are very often unknowable in advance, while the long-term socioeconomic effects of a project are even less predictable. How, then, can realistic performance criteria be established, let alone measured annually, for agencies that support research? In 1996, with preparation of their fiscal year 1999 budgets only a little more than a year away, agencies such as the NSF and the NIH, which had historically defined their missions in terms of supporting research primarily on the basis of intrinsic merit, struggled to adapt to GPRA requirements. One approach favored by the NSF would recognize that such agencies are components of larger systems that include the research communities they fund directly, in addition to other members of those communities, such as industrial firms, state governments, and local school districts. Performance goals might then be established in terms of the effectiveness of direct agency support in stimulating productive interactions among those partners within the community—and with other sectors of U.S. society. However, this approach implied that the performance of agencies critical to the U.S. scientific enterprise might, in the future, be gauged in terms of the performance of the nongovernmental institutions with which they interacted. It would run counter to the long-standing conviction that scientific research—particularly basic research performed in universities—should be judged on its own intrinsic merits rather than on its socioeconomic impacts, but rising demands for accountability in the expenditure of public funds might yet undermine this deep-seated tenet.

Changing U.S. research system

The possibility that the GPRA might ultimately require universities to evaluate the outcomes of their research in terms of societal benefits in order to qualify for federal support was scarcely on academic radar screens in 1996, the prospects of decreasing federal research support being of more immediate concern. In 1996 academia remained a distant second to industry and only slightly ahead of government in terms of research performance. Yet for almost 50 years, universities have constituted the vital core of whatever research system may be said to exist in the United States. They have maintained that status primarily because they are the only set of institutions capable of performing research without regard to short-term applications and because they have succeeded in linking research with the training of successive generations of new scientists and engineers required by the U.S. research system. The danger was that the center might not hold.

At the beginning of the 1990s, private industry and the federal government accounted for roughly equal shares of total U.S. R&D investments. In 1995, however, industry accounted for 59% of those investments, compared with 36% invested by the federal government, while a variety of other sources accounted for the balance. This disparity between industrial and federal R&D expenditures appeared likely to increase, with potentially unsettling consequences for the academic sector. By 1996 almost 25% of current federal R&D investments supported research in universities; less than 3% of industrial R&D was devoted to that purpose. The second largest source of support for academic support next to that of the federal government derived from the institutions themselves, and these funds were unlikely to grow significantly. Tuition and related fees, for example, accounted for almost 20% of the total receipts of the approximately 200 universities that performed the bulk of the research in the academic sector, but undergraduate tuition, which had been increasing at a rate greater than inflation for the past 5–10 years, was unlikely to continue to rise significantly.

Where, then, were universities in the late 1990s to obtain the support required to maintain the center of the U.S. research enterprise? The answer was by no means clear. Indeed, universities more often have received advice on mimicking private industry by downsizing and merging schools and departments than assurances that adequate support might be forthcoming. No

doubt a majority would adapt, survive, and even prosper, but whether the academic research system as a whole could maintain its status as the vital center of the U.S. system was another matter.

As recently as the mid-1980s, several large firms in the industrial sector performed substantial amounts of long-term research in their own corporate laboratories. A decade later, however, virtually all industrial research focused on the solution of specific short-term problems, often by drawing on long-term university research. An April 1996 report of the Council on Competitiveness, pointedly titled *Endless Frontier, Limited Resources,* exhorted the federal government to maintain its support for the academic sector, conceding that industry cannot assume the unique role played by universities. At the same time, the council conveyed a confused signal to academia by stating unequivocally that education rather than research should be its primary mission.

Despite the plea by the Council on Competitiveness and other organizations, the academic sector faced the prospect of declining research support, resulting in the erosion of its research capabilities and, perhaps, even maginalization. The consequences to the nation of a research system dominated by the short-term needs of industry had yet to be seriously addressed.

Research in the U.S. economy

Science and Engineering Indicators— 1996, the most recent of the National Science Board's series of biennial reports, included a new chapter, "Economic and Social Significance of Science and Engineering Research," that summarized results of attempts by an array of economists to

quantify the tangible returns from research investments. Among other things, these studies concluded that social rates of return from public research investments have been at least 30%, and considerably more than 30% in some industries. Academic research does, in fact, lead to substantial commercial payoff, but often with a considerable time lag. The report estimated that 11% of new products in the information processing industry and 27% in the pharmaceutical industry have depended partially on academic research.

Despite the acknowledged tangible benefits of much, although by no means all, academic research, many analyses take it as a given that financial support will decline, at least in inflation-adjusted terms. The very title of the Council on Competitiveness's report was calculated to convey this message. Its principal conclusion was that all sectors of the U.S. research system—industrial, academic, and governmental—must become more efficient in the face of fiscal constraints and that effective partnerships between and among these sectors provide the essential key to accomplish this end. The Galvin report on the future of the national laboratories conveyed a similar message.

In 1996 it was clear that both the structure of the U.S. research system and the links between that system and the broader economy were in flux, and the long-term outcome was not at all obvious. It was obvious, however, that science policy in the future was likely to become increasingly linked with other policies and, therefore, increasingly enmeshed with politics, whether or not the scientific community chose to recognize those likelihoods.

—William A. Blanpied

Shannon Lucid (left) and other members of the *Atlantis* crew try Russian food while docked with the Russian space station *Mir* in March 1996. Lucid then joined the *Mir* crew and remained with them for 188 days, a record for a woman and for an American.

SPACE EXPLORATION

Several new space ventures were begun or moved closer to the launch pad during the past year. The United States and Russia continued the largest cooperative manned program with joint operations by the U.S. space shuttles and the Russian *Mir* space station as both nations prepared for the 1997 launches of the first elements of the International Space Station (ISS). The exploration of Mars was renewed with the launches of two U.S. probes, although a Russian probe failed to leave Earth orbit. And communications companies prepared to start launching low-Earth-orbit satellites that promise to revolutionize the world's electronic connections. In business, Boeing Co. acquired Rockwell International Corp.'s space and defense operations. With the acquisition came the space shuttle. Boeing's planned merger with McDonnell Douglas Corp., which would have added the Delta family of launchers, had not been finalized by mid-1997. Boeing would gain the remainder of the ISS prime contracts with both purchases.

MANNED SPACE MISSIONS

Operations to build a permanent space station picked up speed as the U.S. and Russia continued joint operations aboard *Mir*, which passed its 10th anniversary, and built elements for the ISS. The U.S. and Russia each flew two manned missions to *Mir* during 1996, and the U.S. started 1997 with another shuttle mission to the station.

The Soyuz TM-23 spacecraft (February 21–September 3) delivered cosmonauts Yury Onufriyenko and Yury Usachev to *Mir*. Sergey Avdeyev, Yury Gidzenko, and Thomas Reiter (a German aboard as part of the EuroMir program) returned on February 29 aboard the Soyuz TM-22 space-

craft. Space shuttle *Atlantis* (March 22–31) delivered astronaut Shannon Lucid to *Mir*. Other members of the *Atlantis* crew included commander Kevin Chilton, pilot Richard Searfoss, and mission specialists Ronald M. Sega, Linda Godwin, and M. Richard Clifford. *Atlantis* also carried the Spacehab module containing supplies for *Mir* and experiment hardware operated by the crew. Godwin and Clifford conducted a six-hour space walk to attach the Mir Environmental Effects Payload (MEEP) on the *Mir* docking module. The payload included the Polished Plate Micrometeoroid and Debris experiment, the Orbital Debris Collector experiment, and the Passive Optical Sample Assembly I and II experiments. This was the first time that U.S. astronauts had carried out a space walk around a Russian craft. The Soyuz TM-24 spacecraft on August 17 carried Valery Korzun, Aleksandr Kalery, and Claudie André-Deshays, a French rheumatologist and neuroscience expert and the first Frenchwoman in space. André-Deshays returned two weeks later with Onufriyenko and Usachev aboard Soyuz TM-23.

Lucid was replaced in *Mir* by John Blaha during another visit by *Atlantis* (September 16–26), which was two months late because two hurricanes swept through the launch area and because con-

cerns existed about the safety of the shuttle's solid rocket boosters. This stretched Lucid's stay from a planned 115 days to 188 days, a record for any woman and for any American. Blaha was retrieved in January 1997 by *Atlantis* (January 12–22), which left Jerry Linenger as his replacement. Among the experiments conducted by the *Atlantis* crew was the second venture for KidSat, a program that lets U.S. middle-school students control the video cameras aboard the shuttle and select which parts of the Earth will be seen.

During 1996, between February 8 and December 9, *Mir* cosmonauts conducted a series of seven space walks to repair and upgrade their aging home. On February 8 Gidzenko and Reiter, who in 1995 had become the first non-Russian to conduct a space walk at *Mir*, retrieved two space debris sample cassettes that had been in orbit since 1995. Work to repair an antenna was postponed when they were unable to loosen bolts on the antenna. During a space walk in May, Onufriyenko and Usachev filmed part of a Pepsi-Cola commercial with a giant model of a Pepsi can outside the station. The ad reportedly was worth more than $1 million to the Russian space agency. On December 2 Korzun and Kalery installed U.S.-built solar panel arrays delivered earlier by *Atlantis*. These were prototypes of the arrays that the U.S. was building for the international space station. Korzun and Kalery went outside again on December 9 to connect the solar panels and to install an antenna for later shuttle dockings.

In addition to manned missions, *Mir* was visited by four unmanned spacecraft. Progress M-31, M-32, and M-33 delivered supplies, and on April 23 the Priroda science module was launched, adding facilities for microgravity materials sciences and for remote observations of the Earth. Priroda was the fifth science module to be added to *Mir* since its launch in 1986. Three more shuttle missions (STS-84 in May; STS-86 in September; STS-89 in January 1998) and three Soyuz missions (TM-25 in February; TM-26 in June; TM-27 in December) to *Mir* were planned through early 1998.

Joint Russian-U.S. operations aboard *Mir* were designed to establish the confidence and experience for the two nations in each other's spacecraft and to develop operational techniques to support assembly of the ISS starting in late 1997. The station was to be assembled through 2002 from modules launched from the U.S., Russia, Europe, Canada, and Japan. The first two of as many as 45 flights were to be launched by Russia on November 28 and the U.S. on December 5. Russia planned to orbit the Functional Cargo Element, a craft with a flight-proven design that was intended to provide electrical power, orbital control, and other utilities during the initial buildup. The U.S., using the space shuttle, planned to orbit Node 2, the first connector element for the station (Node 1, the prototype used in tests, was to be launched later). Assembly was to proceed

in two phases, the first to complete the "core" station capable of supporting a crew of three by 1998 and the second to complete the station for a crew of six by 2002.

When completed, the station would weigh 181,500 kg (400,000 lb) and house six laboratory modules (one each from the U.S., Europe, and Japan and three from Russia), two habitat modules (one U.S. and one Russian), and two logistics mod-

Claudie André-Deshays in August 1996 became the first Frenchwoman in space when she joined the crew of *Mir*. A neuroscientist, she studied for 16 days the effects of weightlessness on members of the crew.

ules. The largest structure was to be a series of six trusses extending left and right with the modules attached at the center point and four pairs of solar cell "wings" extending from rotating joints at the ends. The U.S. lab module was to be attached to the truss center. In front was to be Node 1 holding the European and Japanese labs at each side and providing a docking port for the space shuttle. Extend-

ing aft was to be an array of Russian lab, habitat, and service modules, including two Soyuz spacecraft serving as lifeboats. A Canadian robot arm system on tracks would be used to position modules as they arrive at the station.

The space shuttle also flew five missions supporting other areas of science and technology. *Endeavour* (Jan. 11–20, 1996) deployed and retrieved the OAST (Office of Aeronautics and Space Technology)-Flyer, an automated spacecraft carrying equipment to test satellite navigation, measure spacecraft contamination, and measure the effects of solar radiation on explosives used to separate spacecraft elements. It also retrieved the Space Flyer Unit, which had been launched by Japan in March 1995 and which carried materials science experiments and astronomical instruments. *Columbia* (Feb. 22–March 9, 1996) reflew the Tethered Satellite System, which was designed to deploy a satellite on a 20-km (12.4-mi) Kevlar-nylon-copper tether that would generate an electrical current as it sliced through the Earth's magnetic field. As the tether neared the end of its reel, it suddenly snapped at the shuttle end, and the satellite sailed free. Investigators later determined that even the residual dust left when the tether was assembled in a clean room was enough to build a static electric charge that burned through the tether. Nevertheless, scientists collected a great deal of data during the three-hour deployment. The mission continued with a series of experiments on the automated U.S. Microgravity Payload.

Planned releases were the order of the day for *Endeavour* (May 19–29, 1996) when it carried the Inflatable Antenna Experiment and the Satellite Test Unit. The inflatable antenna, which was attached to the Spartan 207 satellite, inflated to a length of 28 m (92 ft) with a dish that was 15.2 m (50 ft) in diameter, demonstrating a new approach for large radio antennas in space. Spartan 207 was retrieved after it released the antenna. The Satellite Test Unit demonstrated a new passive method for stabilizing satellites. *Endeavour* also carried the Spacehab module, which contained materials science and technology experiments.

The Life and Microgravity Spacelab mission, flown by *Columbia* (June 20–July 7, 1996), carried 22 experiments involving fish embryos, rats, bonsai plants, fluid dynamics, metallurgy, and protein crystal growth. The life sciences experiments were designed to further the understanding of how life adapts to the weightless environment of space.

During the last mission of 1996 (November 19–December 7), the shuttle *Columbia* operated with two satellites deployed at the same time. The first was the Wake Shield Facility, making its third flight after technical problems prevented its first two missions from carrying out the task of processing electronic materials in the ultrahard vacuum created in a spacecraft's wake. The other was ORFEUS-SPAS, a German satellite carrying a large ultraviolet astronomy telescope. ORFEUS-SPAS operated for several days independently of *Columbia*. Two six-hour space walks by mission specialists Tamara Jernigan and Thomas Jones were canceled after the air lock's external hatch jammed. A postflight investigation revealed that a screw had loosened and become wedged inside the mechanism.

The rate for manned space missions continued to be steady during 1997. In addition to space station activities mentioned above, the shuttle *Discovery* in February went into orbit near the Hubble Space Telescope. During 33 hours of space walks, astronauts Mark Lee, Steven Smith, Gregory Harbaugh, and Joseph Tanner repaired and upgraded the telescope; it was then raised to a higher orbit to offset the natural decline in altitude that will take place before the astronauts' next visit in 1999. Also planned for the year were launches of the Microgravity Science Laboratory, the infrared CRISTA-SPAS, and a test model of Japan's experiment module for the ISS.

Both NASA and the National Space Development Agency of Japan were moving toward the development of smaller craft that might ferry crews and cargoes in the 21st century. NASA was developing the X-38 concept for a crew return vehicle (CRV) that would take the place of Russia's Soyuz spacecraft as a lifeboat for the ISS. The X-38 was derived from the X-24 reentry body, which was developed and tested by the U.S. Air Force in the 1970s. Such a design would allow a six-person space station crew to return to the Earth within 4½ hours of an emergency, compared with 18 hours for a ballistic return vehicle that has less ability to fly "cross range" to a landing site. The CRV also would be fully automated and land under a parafoil so that a disabled crew could return without worrying about being fit to control the craft.

SPACE PROBES

Four satellites were added in 1996 to the flotilla exploring the Earth-space environ-

ment, but another four were lost when the first Ariane 5 vehicle was destroyed during launch. The U.S. launched Polar (February 24) and the Fast Auroral Snapshot Explorer (FAST, August 21), and Russia launched the Interball Auroral Probe and Magion 5 together on August 29. As its name suggests, Polar sails over the Earth's magnetic poles, where the magnetic field lines are vertical and leave the Earth exposed to plasma (electrified gases) and charged radiation from the Sun and the extended tail of the Earth's magnetic field. One of Polar's instruments quickly confirmed that a fountain of low-energy plasma escapes from the poles into space. About 50 tons a day of oxygen, nitrogen, hydrogen, and helium are lost in this manner. This fountain had been undetected because previous spacecraft were unable to neutralize their own electrostatic charges (caused by exposure to sunlight), which would repel the low-energy plasma. Another Polar instrument uses special filters to observe the entire aurora borealis both in daylight and in darkness. This allows detailed study throughout the year instead of principally when the north pole is in the long winter night. FAST carries instruments to analyze the electrons and ions that accelerate up and down the magnetic field lines and cause the auroras.

The Russian-Ukrainian Interball Auroral Probe was equipped with instruments to measure the magnetic fields, plasma, and other energetic particles flowing into the aurora. Interball also released the Czech-built Magion 5 subsatellite, which was to trail Interball and provide complementary measurements. Its solar panels failed to deploy, however, and the craft was lost. The European Space Agency (ESA) attempted to launch an ambitious set of four spacecraft, called Cluster, which would have flown in formation to study how plasma and particles vary across small distances. All four satellites were, however, lost aboard the ill-fated Ariane 5 rocket. ESA planned to revive the mission by using spare parts and hardware salvaged from the crash.

The greatest excitement generated during the year came from NASA's announcement in August of the discovery of possible Martian fossils in a meteorite found in the Allan Hills of Antarctica. The find revived interest in the renewed exploration of Mars and in a second look at data from the Viking spacecraft that landed on Mars in 1976. The Allan Hills meteorite is one of several that scientists have sought in "blue ice" glaciers in Antarctica. The expectation was that rocks found sitting on or frozen in the ice were deposited by meteor falls rather than by transport from nearby hills. NASA sponsored several such expeditions in hopes that such meteors might also be secondary debris blasted from the Moon or Mars by powerful meteor impacts that were common in the early history of the solar system. The theory was supported by chemical and radioisotope analyses of several such finds that matched chemical assays conducted by the Viking landers. The Allan Hills meteorite—ALH84001—was the first found in the 1984 expedition, but discovery was delayed by misclassification of the rock. Proper identification about a decade later was followed by studies in which special lasers blasted small bits of the stone free so that trapped gases could be analyzed. These yielded polycyclic aromatic hydrocarbons formed (but not exclusively) when

microorganisms break down. In addition, scanning electron microscope studies showed microfossils corresponding to bacteria recently discovered on Earth. While the discoveries are exciting—and hotly debated—they came too late to influence the first round of missions to Mars. NASA and Russia, however, were examining ways in which later missions might be modified to look for signs of life. (For additional information, *see* Year in Review: ASTRONOMY; EARTH SCIENCES: *Paleontology;* LIFE SCIENCES: *Microbiology.*)

Three missions were launched to Mars; unfortunately, only two survived departure. NASA's Mars Global Surveyor and Mars Pathfinder were successfully launched on November 7 and December 4, respectively. Russia failed in its effort to launch the ambitious Mars 96 spacecraft, which comprised a large orbiter, two small soft landers, and two surface penetrators.

Mars 96 was launched on November 16 atop a large Proton rocket. It reached orbit, but the fourth stage misfired and sent the probe into an unstable orbit that decayed the next day; its remains were strewn across the southeastern Pacific Ocean. Suspicion for the failure fell on the Russian space program's tight financial situation, which had left many workers unpaid for months and has resulted in widespread vandalism of ground facilities.

Both Mars Pathfinder and Mars Global Surveyor departed in fine form. Although both were launched on similar Delta rockets, the lighter, smaller Mars Pathfinder was expected to overtake the Mars Global Surveyor and arrive at Mars first, on July 4, 1997. Unlike other missions, Pathfinder will go directly to the surface. It will be braked first by a heat shield, then by a parachute, and finally by rockets attached to its parachute's risers. An array of air

The Mars Pathfinder spacecraft is inspected before its mission to Mars. Launched on Dec. 4, 1996, Pathfinder was scheduled to arrive at Mars on July 4, 1997. It would then descend to the planet's surface to assay its chemical composition.

bags will inflate to cushion the landing of the pyramid-shaped spacecraft on the surface. After the spacecraft finishes bouncing, the faces of the pyramid will open to right the spacecraft and expose solar cells to sunlight. Small stereo TV cameras will rise above the craft on an extendable mast, and a small rover, dubbed Sojourner, will roll off one of the petals under remote control from the Earth. Sojourner will carry cameras and a small radiation source to assay surface chemistry by measuring alpha particles, protons, and gamma rays scattered back by the soil as it explores up to 500 m (1,640 ft) away from the lander. Pathfinder's primary mission will end August 4, although NASA will operate the spacecraft for as long as it runs.

Mars Global Surveyor is scheduled to go into Mars orbit on September 12, and from September 21 until Jan. 16, 1998, it will execute a series of passes through the upper atmosphere to reshape its orbit. While this delays the start of the science mission, it reduces overall costs by cutting the weight of the spacecraft, since the planet's atmosphere acts as a brake in place of additional propellant. Mars Global Surveyor will spend one Martian year (about 687 days) studying the planet with a visible light camera, laser altimeter, and space plasma sensors.

Pathfinder and Global Surveyor will be followed, every 26 months, by a series of more capable explorers, including the Mars Surveyor Orbiter (December 1998) and Mars Surveyor Lander (January 1999), for a landing in 2000 near the south pole, where water ice—and life—are most likely to be found. Other missions include Japan's Planet B orbiter (January 1999), another NASA Surveyor Orbiter and Lander

pair in 2001, and two Surveyor landers in 2003. During the past year NASA announced that as part of its New Millennium program it would add two 2-kg (4.4-lb) penetrators to hard-land up to 200 km (125 mi) away from the Surveyor Lander. Each probe will carry hardened instruments to measure physical properties just below the surface. NASA hopes that a mission in 2005 will return in 2008 with samples of soil for more detailed study. Manned missions to Mars probably will not be attempted until closer to the mid-21st century, as a National Research Council study indicated that cosmic radiation would cause too much damage to tissues during a mission that likely would last three years or more.

Another startling discovery was the announcement on December 3 that the Moon's south pole shows signs of harboring water ice in permanent shadow. "We think we have found ice," said Paul D. Spudis of the Lunar and Planetary Institute, Houston, Texas. "We are not positive, but we see signals consistent with ice and we think it's there." Such a find has been desired by scientists for decades and was predicted by Arthur C. Clarke in the 1950s. Detailed studies of radio echo from the Clementine spacecraft, launched in 1994, revealed signals that most likely come from ice. The echoes, taken inside the rim of the 2,500-km (1,553-mi)-wide South Pole-Aitken Basin in April 1994, showed an amplification in strength and a low change in polarization that are typical of reflections from ice. This area, in perpetual shade, would always experience temperatures of about 50 K (−225° C; −375° F), which would prevent ice from sublimating into space.

If water ice is present, the lunar south pole could become that world's most valuable real estate, since water is necessary for life support and is an important rocket propellant (when separated into hydrogen and oxygen). Although the possibility of life on the Moon is remote, the presence of water would greatly aid operations to explore the solar system.

The first two missions to the Moon since Clementine were scheduled for launch in 1997: Japan's Lunar-A in August and NASA's Lunar Prospector, one of the new Discovery missions, in September. Lunar A will carry three surface penetrators equipped with seismometers and heat probes. The orbiter will relay data back to Earth. Lunar Prospector's one-year mission is to build on the Apollo legacy by mapping the Moon's surface composition, gravity and magnetic fields, and volatile release activity. It will carry alpha particle, neutron, and gamma-ray spectrometers to measure lunar surface chemistry by radiation scattered back into space. The neutron spectrometer, in particular, is expected to provide quick confirmation of Clementine's ice discovery. Lunar Prospector also will be the first deep-space mission for the Lockheed Martin Launch Vehicle-2, a new booster rocket built from existing solid rocket motor designs.

The Galileo spacecraft continued to return startling data and pictures of Jupiter's moons, though at a reduced rate because the high-gain antenna would not open fully early in the mission. Galileo arrived at Jupiter on Dec. 7, 1995, and has flown past each of its large moons—Europa, Callisto, Ganymede, and Io. (For additional information on Galileo, see Feature Article: IN THE REALM OF THE GIANT.)

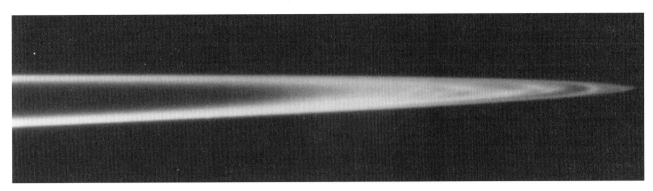

The Cassini spacecraft was being readied for an Oct. 6, 1997, launch to Saturn. The mission is composed of the Cassini orbiter carrying the Huygens probe on a seven-year odyssey that will use a Venus-Venus-Earth-Jupiter gravity assist trajectory to redirect and accelerate the craft. After arrival at Saturn the Cassini orbiter will release the ESA-built Huygens probe to enter the atmosphere of methane-shrouded Titan, Saturn's largest moon. Cassini will orbit Saturn 30 times during its primary mission.

One astronomy satellite was launched during the year, and one was shut down. NASA launched the Italian/Dutch Satellite per Astronomia a raggi X (SAX), which carries an X-ray astronomy telescope. The aging International Ultraviolet Explorer (IUE), launched in January 1978, was turned off on Sept. 30, 1996, after having operated almost 16 years longer than its planned mission. IUE was one of the most productive and successful astronomy satellites ever launched.

APPLICATIONS SATELLITES

Japan, India, and the U.S. launched several new craft to monitor the Earth's environment and resources from orbit. The most complex craft was Japan's Midori Advanced Earth Observation Satellite (August 17), which carried instruments, some provided by the U.S. and France, to monitor wind and ocean-surface temperatures, aerosols, ozone, and greenhouse gases. India's IRS-P3, launched on March 21, 1996, was equipped with a wide-field visible-and-infrared scanner to study crop conditions, geology, and snow cover. The craft also carried a German optoelectronic scanner to monitor ocean chlorophyll, sediment, and currents. The sole U.S. contribution was the Total Ozone Mapping Spectrometer–Earth Probe (July 2), which featured a single polychromator designed to observe the atmosphere in six ultraviolet wavelengths in order to see changes in stratospheric ozone content. China launched and retrieved the FSW-2 3 craft (October 20–December 6), which served the nation's commercial and military concerns.

Scheduled for 1997 were the launches of Lewis and Clark, the first two craft developed under NASA's Small Spacecraft Technology Initiative program to demonstrate advanced spacecraft technologies. The 288-kg (634-lb) Lewis would be equipped with an Earth-imaging hyperspectral imager, a spectral imager, and an ultraviolet cosmic background instrument. The 278-kg (612-lb) Clark was designed to carry a camera with 3-m (10-ft) resolution in black and white and 15-m (49-ft) resolution in multiple colors, instruments to measure air pollution, an X-ray spectrometer, and the atmospheric tomography instrument for three-dimensional pollution mapping. Both spacecraft incorporated advanced electronics and structures in order to reduce both weight and mission costs.

Japan will make a major contribution to studies of global hydrology when it launches in August the Tropical Rainfall Measuring Mission. It will measure rain quantities and distribution in tropical and subtropical areas. Japan is providing the H-2 launch vehicle and the precipitation radar, and NASA is contributing the satellite and other sensors, including a microwave imager, a visible and infrared scanner, a monitor of the Earth's radiant energy system, and a lightning imaging sensor.

Russia was in the unenviable position of having no spy satellites in operation for several months during 1996, further testimony to the difficulties that its military and civilian space programs were encountering. A single satellite was destroyed during a launch attempt at the Plesetsk facility on June 1. Russia did, however, launch electronic ocean surveillance and electronic intelligence (ELINT) satellites during the year.

The U.S. National Reconnaissance Office (NRO) on December 20 launched what is believed to be the first of a new generation of KH-11 spy satellites, carrying a primary mirror with a diameter of about 3.8 m (12.5 ft). Technical press reports said that in addition to the new KH-11, the U.S. had two older KH-11 optical spy satellites and two Lacrosse imaging radar satellites in operation. Other NRO launches included a Satellite Data System relay satellite, an ELINT satellite, and a group of four ocean-surveillance spacecraft launched on a single Titan 4.

In November the U.S Air Force selected the Lockheed Martin Corp. to build the $2 billion Space-Based Infrared System, which will replace the current constellation of Defense Support Program (DSP) satellites that are designed to warn of long-range ballistic missile launches. Because it can take up to five scans at 10 seconds per scan to provide an initial track on a launch, DSP is inadequate for the task of warning of Scud missiles, which complete their burn in 55 to 80 seconds. The new satellites will use a faster scanner and "staring" focal plane arrays to alert military commanders in less than 20 seconds. The first of five of these craft is to be launched in 2002.

The U.S. also launched two Navstar Global Positioning System (GPS) satellites on July 15 and September 12 but lost the first of a new series of GPS craft on Jan. 17, 1997, when its Delta 2 launch vehicle exploded without warning less than 30 seconds after liftoff. Most activity in this field was on the ground as providers developed new systems to use navigational satellite signals that allow the user to determine a position by comparing time differences between clocks on different satellites with well-defined locations. Ashtech, Inc., developed a single-board receiver that uses signals from both the U.S. GPS and Russian Global Navigation Satellite System (GLONASS) and thus increases system availability to 100% by making all 48 satellites available.

Shipping companies started implementing the Global Marine Distress and Safety System (GMDSS). Eliminating the traditional "SOS" telegraphy, it requires all ships to be equipped with systems that alert nearby shipping and rescue authorities in the event of a wreck or other emergency. GMDSS embraces shipboard computers, the GPS receivers to broadcast position without the crew's having to do so, and International Mobile Satellite Organization (Inmarsat) communications satellites.

Industry consolidations and the impending launches of dozens of low-Earth-orbit (LEO) satellites were the major events in communications satellite launches during the year. Lockheed Martin acquired most of Loral Corp. for $9.1 billion. In March 1997 Loral Space & Communications Ltd. purchased AT&T's Skynet Satellite Services for $478.1 million. GM's Hughes Electronics Corp. announced that it would

merge its Hughes Communications Galaxy subsidiary with PanAmSat Corp. to form the world's third largest communications satellite operator. In early 1997 the Raytheon Co. announced that it would buy the defense operations of Hughes Electronics.

The International Telecommunications Satellite Organization (Intelsat) and Inmarsat moved to reorganize themselves to match the growing wave of privatization of communications operations and to drop certain protective measures. Efforts to open international telecommunications markets stalled when the U.S. in April insisted that mobile satellite services be excluded from a proposed agreement that was to have been accepted on April 30 by the World Telecommunications Organization. A new agreement was expected in 1997.

The mobile satellite services at the heart of the U.S. complaint barely existed in 1996 but were expected to grow rapidly starting with the 1997 launch of the first Iridium satellites. As of early 1997 most communications satellites operated from geostationary orbit, 35,680 km (22,170 mi) high, where the orbital period is 24 hours. Thus, a satellite keeps pace with the Earth, and ground stations need not track a moving object. (A handful of satellites use different orbits to satisfy special needs.) The new wave of LEO satellites will operate at orbits only 667–10,355 km (414–6,434 mi) high and use advanced switching technology to hand a signal off from one satellite to another as they pass into and out of view of the user. The approach is made possible by more sensitive digital electronics that allow low-power signals to be detected, amplified, and relayed without large dish antennae. This technology is

immensely attractive to less-developed countries, where deploying landlines or even microwave repeaters is impractical.

Iridium, developed by a consortium led by the Motorola Satellite Communications Division, planned to deploy 66 satellites orbiting at 780 km (485 mi) with launches from sites in China, Kazakstan, and California starting in 1997. During 1996 Motorola conducted its first full "end-to-end" test simulating a call from one terminal to another via satellite. The total number of LEO and medium-Earth-orbit satellites could top 300, including ventures by Globalstar (48 satellites), TRW's Odyssey (12), Orbital Sciences' Orbcomm (36), GE Americom's Starsys (24), ICO Global Communications (12), and Russia's Gonets (12; the first three, which also monitor environmental disasters, were launched on Feb. 19, 1996).

An intermediate form of this service became available in January 1997 when the Comsat Corp. offered the $3,000 Planet 1 service, which uses a notebook-size terminal that provides voice, data, and fax communications through four Inmarsat 3 satellites that also link ships and airliners. The first three Inmarsat 3 craft were launched April 3, September 6, and December 17. LEO systems were expected to take over a large portion of the voice and data communications market, while geostationary communications satellites would retain most of the video work, which requires large bandwidth and uninterrupted communications.

The telecommunications industry was stunned by the loss on Jan. 11, 1997, of the Telstar 401 communications satellite, operated by AT&T's Skynet, as a result of an apparent solar outburst. Skynet said that both telemetry and communications links were lost as the spacecraft was making a routine maneuver to adjust its position in geostationary orbit. The satellite was launched Dec. 15, 1993, and was expected to operate through 2006. Scientists believed that a coronal mass ejection, a blast of plasma trapped in a magnetic field, from the Sun caused the failure. Such events can inject large quantities of energetic particles into the Earth's magnetosphere and thereby impact satellites and even terrestrial power grids. Several satellites had been damaged by geomagnetic storms in past years, but Telstar 401 was the first known total loss. More surprises can be expected over the next few years as the sunspot cycle builds toward what scientists think will be one of the most intense "solar maximums" in decades.

LAUNCH VEHICLES

The past year saw its share of launch vehicle failures, the most tragic being the explosion of a Chinese Long March 3B as it attempted to launch an Intelsat 708 satellite on February 14. Flaming wreckage fell on a nearby village and killed more than 50 people and destroyed 80 homes, the worst such accident in recent memory. In August another Long March launcher left a communications satellite in a low, useless orbit. The failures led Intelsat, among others, to cancel plans for launches by China.

ESA's new Ariane 5 exploded on its first launch attempt, June 4, when the vehicle self-destructed 37 seconds after liftoff. An investigation revealed that the fault lay in the failure to modify the guidance system, which had been adapted, virtually unchanged, from the Ariane 4 series of

On its first launch attempt, on June 4, 1996, the European Space Agency's new Ariane 5 rocket exploded 37 seconds after liftoff. The failure was blamed on a guidance system that had been adequate for previous vehicles but had not been modified sufficiently for Ariane 5.

vehicles. Engineers failed to account in the software for the greater height and acceleration of the Ariane 5 vehicle. As a result, it sensed it was failing and shut down, which caused the range safety system to destroy it. Russia's Proton launch vehicle suffered two failures, the Mars 96 mission and an unrelated Raduga communications satellite launch on February 19. The U.S. Pegasus XL, which was launched from an L-1011 carrier aircraft, stumbled when it orbited two astronomy satellites (one U.S. and one Argentine) on November 4 but failed to release the two craft.

Two new space launchers were introduced, Japan's J-1 vehicle, which lofted

the Hyflex test vehicle, and the U.S.'s Multi-Service Launch System (MSLS), derived from Minuteman II ballistic missiles that had been removed from service under arms limitation treaties. Most MSLS launches were expected to be suborbital flights for missile defense tests; some satellite launches were planned.

Noteworthy developments included the selection of Lockheed Martin to build its VentureStar concept as the X-33 Reusable Launch Vehicle (RLV) demonstrator, and the start of work on a launch platform and control ship for the Sea Launch program. The RLV program grew partly out of the DC-X Delta Clipper vertical takeoff/verti-

VentureStar, developed by Lockheed Martin, was selected by NASA as the Reusable Launch Vehicle (RLV) X-33 demonstrator. The operational version of the RLV will be able to take off vertically and land horizontally and carry up to 22,700 kg (50,045 lb) of payload to the space station.

cal landing demonstration program initiated by the U.S. Department of Defense. In 1995 the DC-X program was transferred to NASA and, after renovations to add advanced structures and other changes, in 1996 resumed flight as the DC-XA Clipper Graham in honor of the late U.S. Air Force lieutenant general Daniel Graham, who had promoted the program. NASA conducted four flight tests with the DC-XA between March 27 and July 31. On the last flight the vehicle was destroyed when one of its four landing gear legs failed to extend. An investigation determined that a hydraulic line had not been reconnected after maintenance, and that no procedure had been established for checking the connection.

Lessons from the DC-X and DC-XA programs were to be incorporated in the X-33 RLV demonstrator program. Bidding for the project were three teams led by Lockheed Martin, Rockwell International, and McDonnell Douglas, builder of the DC-X. In July NASA selected Lockheed Martin. Rockwell had offered a familiar shuttlelike craft, and McDonnell Douglas proposed a growth version of the DC-X. Lockheed Martin won with a different approach, the VentureStar, which is based on a design it offered in 1969 for the space shuttle. The wedge-shaped craft will be able to take off vertically and land horizontally. It will be propelled by a linear aerospike engine, a unique design in which its injectors are arranged in two lines along the base of the vehicle. This approach allows the engine to be shaped to the best aerodynamic shape of a craft rather than the craft's being shaped to accommodate the engines. Advanced electronics and ultralightweight structures will be used to allow an operational VentureStar to carry up to 22,700 kg (50,045 lb) of payload to the space station. Initially it will be unmanned and complement the manned shut-

tle, but designers were considering possible manned versions.

That lies in the future; in the near term, Lockheed Martin must build a suborbital test model 20 m (66 ft) high and 21 m (69 ft) across and in 1999 begin a series of 15 test flights reaching from California to as far as Montana and at up to 15 times the speed of sound. A key part of the test program will be the quick turnaround of the vehicle after each flight.

Unconventional launches for conventional rockets were planned for the Sea Launch program, which was refitting an offshore oil platform to serve as a launch pad for Russia's Zenit 3-SL. First launches were planned for mid-1998 from the Pacific Ocean south of Hawaii. This approach allows launches from near the Equator, where the Earth's rotation provides more initial velocity.

—Dave Dooling
See also Year in Review: ASTRONOMY.

TRANSPORTATION

Advances in transportation technologies during the past year were spurred on in part by government policies and regulations that encouraged greater connectivity between the modes of transportation services, by enhanced awareness of the environment, by technological advances for each of the major modes, and by the need for faster and more accurate information. In most instances transportation-related ventures were paid for with fewer tax-supported funds. On the private-sector side of the ledger, companies throughout the world were beginning to realize that the globalization of trade and the removal of restrictive international—and in some cases domestic—commercial and transportation regulations would lead to new and emerging business opportunities.

Legislative changes

With the establishment of the 257,500-km (160,000-mi) National Highway System (NHS) in 1995, the U.S. Congress set the pace for strengthening the nation's transportation system for the 21st century. By 1997 much of that system was located within or connected to so-called strategic highway corridor networks via the Interstate Highway System. Although the NHS included only 4% of the U.S. roads, it carried 43% of the total interstate traffic and 69% of combination truck traffic. Approximately 90% of the nation's population lived within 8 km (5 mi) of the system.

The legacy of the NHS—establishing a national policy focused on transportation in the 21st century—influenced other government transportation-related policies and programs. With the expiration of the Intermodal Surface Transportation Efficiency Act (ISTEA) of 1991 scheduled for 1997, the U.S. Congress faced the challenge of honoring its commitment to a balanced budget while supporting the health and vitality of the country through more efficient transportation infrastructure and operations. Without proper funding, states and metropolitan areas must either cancel planned improvements to their local transportation networks or find the money elsewhere.

No matter how the funding is accomplished, the smooth and efficient transfer of passengers and cargo between the modes (airports, ports, rail stations and yards, etc.) will have to be made in a new era marked by less federal control and investment. Since the late 1800s the Interstate Commerce Commission (ICC) has had a powerful influence on how the modes relate to one another in terms of regulating the industry's rates and services. On Jan. 1, 1996, the ICC, however, was replaced by the much smaller and weaker Surface Transportation Board, which was charged with resolving the continued merger of the nation's rail freight industry and other surface transportation business issues. One such merger was finally approved in 1996 when the Union Pacific Railroad purchased the Southern Pacific to form one of the largest single rail freight companies in the United States (the largest such merger took place in 1995 between the Burlington Northern and the Santa Fe). As a result, there remained fewer than a handful of so-called Class I railroads, those which have either national or extensive regional influence on how shippers can transport their cargo by rail. In 1996 Conrail and CSX, two of the three largest rail freight carriers east of the Mississippi River, announced that they planned to merge; the third, Norfolk Southern, intended either to prevent this merger or else become part of the final arrangement. The merger proposal was not expected to be resolved until late 1997.

Meanwhile, the relaxation of the national speed limit from 55 mph (89 km/h) to 65 mph (105 km/h) and faster on most major highways was under close scrutiny. Policy makers and legislative leaders will have to deal with questions about the safety of vehicle operation on roads designed and built for speeds below what are now allowable. Accidents on other modes of transportation added to the highway concerns and raised questions throughout the world as to what governments were doing to protect the safety of passengers and crews. All of this needed to be accomplished in the face of reduced government funding and involvement, a balancing act that seemed certain to remain at the center of budget debates for years to come.

Like the airline, railroad, and highway industries before it, the U.S. maritime industry by 1997 was being dragged reluctantly into the deregulation era. Congress planned to take a fresh look during the year at proposals to eliminate tariff filing requirements and allow confidential contracting between a carrier and its customers, a standard procedure in the other industries. At the same time, there was also pressure to eliminate the Federal Maritime Commission, the federal agency designated to regulate the industry in order to prevent rate and service discrimination by the carriers.

Meanwhile, market trends appeared to be adding pressure to the search for an industrywide agreement on ocean shipping reform. Lower ocean freight rates could prove to be a catalyst for compromise because carriers might be more willing to discard the conference system for the chance to increase market share through long-term contracts. (Conferences were organizations formed by ocean carriers, with the blessing of the U.S. government, to establish rates and services for different commodities on a specific trade route to prevent ruinous competition.) There was, however, considerable opposition from smaller carriers and shippers, who felt that the larger carriers would have them at a disadvantage if this were to take place. Their arguments were strong enough to hold off complete deregulation in 1996.

With regard to intermodalism in 1997, the private sector had in many instances taken the lead in terms of what the industry would look like for the rest of the 20th century and for the next few decades in the new millennium. The freight industry continued to form new carrier alliances—sometimes with major shippers—and to develop integrated information systems, all of which were designed to contribute to lower costs and more efficient delivery services.

Environmental issues

It was generally believed in the U.S. that the environmental regulations passed in the last three decades—such as the National Environmental Policy Act, ISTEA (with its renewed emphasis on safer and cleaner transportation systems), the Clean Air Act, and the Clean Water Act—significantly influenced the ways in which both the public and private sectors thought about the environment. Nevertheless, many believed that these and future pieces

of environmental legislation needed to be streamlined in order to be better coordinated and easier to administer.

At the same time, both the public and private sectors required more effective technical tools for environmental analysis, especially when dealing with wetlands and when removing unsightly structures to improve visual quality. The social and economic impacts of environmentally sensitive projects and regulations also needed to be addressed. This required geographic information systems and computer-aided design systems to be used more widely by public- and private-sector planners and operators. For air pollution, states such as California and Oregon led the U.S. in opening the discussion on air-quality standards, especially those to be set for urban areas. Analyses apparently demonstrated that, of the six major pollutants targeted by the Clean Air Act, three (carbon monoxide, nitrogen oxides, and volatile organic compounds) have a small impact on emissions or are politically not feasible for more effective regulation. As an alternative, the discussion was redirected to consideration of effective emission-reduction transportation strategies that would focus on cleaner-burning fuels, vehicle technology, and vehicle maintenance. In addition, states such as New Jersey, which had one of the most heavily used major interstate highways in the country (I-95), were considering the possibility of offering price incentives and penalties for off-peak and peak travel on their highway systems.

Other examples of new efforts that were underway to reduce environmental pollution included the Traffic Noise Model for highways, which was completed in 1996. Sponsored by the Federal Highway Ad-

ministration and the states, with technical expertise provided by the U.S. Department of Transportation and the Volpe National Transportation Systems Center, the model was designed to make sophisticated but inexpensive highway-noise analysis available on microcomputers.

Rail transportation

Despite the downturn in the growth of intermodal rail traffic in 1996 (down 6–7%, compared with 10–15% in 1995), new technology was helping railroads to handle growing volumes of traffic and also to improve service. For example, the increased use of alternating-current traction locomotives lowered fuel costs and improved operational efficiencies. To provide improved information to carriers and shippers about the locations of their equipment along the entire rail line, increasing numbers of locomotives and railcars were being electronically tagged.

With the reduction in Class I railroads in the U.S., many of the larger railroads began selling their secondary and branch lines to privately operated regional and short-line railroads. Many states invested in these smaller businesses because of the potential economic benefits from continued rail freight services. These investments included track and facility rehabilitation to improve connectivity with other modes.

On the passenger side in the U.S., the National Railroad Passenger Corporation, better known as Amtrak, had to turn to the states in which it operated in order to maintain service on intercity routes. In line with this goal, Amtrak started in 1996 to electrify its rail operations in the 257-km (160-mi) rail corridor between New Haven, Conn., and Boston. This line would eventually permit the use of high-speed trains, extending such service from Boston to Washington, D.C., a distance of 735 km (457 mi). This project was scheduled for completion in 1999. The goal was to reduce travel time between Boston and New York City to under three hours for Amtrak express trains and allow Amtrak to add up to 16 round-trip Metroliners between Boston and New York.

Waterloo Station in London was redesigned during the past year to further improve rail service from London to the Channel Tunnel. A trip from Waterloo Station through the tunnel to Paris took about three hours in 1997.

In Europe passenger trains have run at speeds of more than 240 km/h (150 mph) since the early 1980s, while in the U.S. they were not expected to reach even 240 km/h until 1999. By 2000, high-speed rail was predicted to expand to an even greater part of Western Europe, but to only a corner of the U.S. This expansion would include further improvement of the tracks that link London with the Channel Tunnel. In 1997, a trip from London's Waterloo Station through the tunnel to Paris's Gare du Nord took about three hours at speeds of up to 300 km/h (186 mph; 160 km/h in the tunnel).

Marine transportation

The rapid increase in the size of containerships and the potential impact of those ships on ports continued to make commercial headlines throughout the world during the past year. P&O Nedlloyd (the result of a merger between P&O Containers of the U.K. and Nedlloyd Lines of The Netherlands) scheduled for delivery in 1997 and 1998 four 6,674-TEU (20-ft-equivalent unit) containerships—the largest ever built. Each of these vessels will be almost as long as the U.S. Navy aircraft carrier USS *Enterprise* (320 m [1,049 ft] versus 342 m [1,123 ft]) and almost as wide at

Dredges deepen the navigational channel at Atchafalaya delta in the Gulf of Mexico near Morgan City, La. Many large and midsized ports were facing the need to deepen their channels in order to accommodate the new containerships, which included the largest ever built.

the waterline (43 m [140 ft]). Meanwhile, the controversy continued about the impact these ships would have not only on channel depths but on the terminals. To handle such large vessels, terminal facilities were being introduced in Europe and in East Asia that included tractors—manned or unmanned—that could pull three and more trailers. The objective was to keep the flow of containers being loaded or unloaded from the ship moving with as little interruption as possible. This represented another step toward the ultimate goal of achieving the "seamless" terminal, where cargo—containerized or in more traditional form, such as bulk—would move on and off the ship and through the terminal without stopping. A key component of this would be the information systems that link all of the terminal's activities with shippers, carriers, government agencies, and ancillary freight-handling services, such as customs-house brokers and freight forwarders.

Although the terminal issue could be resolved by introducing advanced cargo-handling equipment, the final answer in the case of many of the large and midsized ports was the need to dredge channels deep enough to accommodate safely some of the world's largest containerships. The dredging, which often must add at least 4.6 m (15 ft) to the depth of most ports, was expensive, and an additional cost was incurred in removing the dredged material from the channel. In many ports, such as the Port of New York and New Jersey, these disposal strategies had reached a crisis point, an institutional gridlock in which each of the parties concerned concluded that they could not or would not compromise. The environmentalists, sometimes using existing environmental laws to support their case, claimed that both the removal and the final disposal of the dredged material would cause long-term environmental damage, especially in regard to highly toxic materials that had settled in channels and berthing areas that had been fed by decades of pollution. The ports, along with carriers and the services and labor organizations affected by these proposed restrictions on dredging, claimed that if dredging was restricted, larger and more economical ships would have to bypass their port, with the consequent loss of jobs and tax revenue.

Although river traffic in the U.S. continued to expand, lock capacity and maintenance were by 1997 reaching their safe and economical limits. For passengers traveling on inland waters, enhanced ferry operations, using both traditional and state-of-the-art passenger vessels, were either starting up or under development in a number of states including Alaska, California, New York, Massachusetts, and Washington, as well as Puerto Rico.

Not only were cargo ships becoming larger, they were also being designed to travel at speeds as fast as 42 knots (about 48 mph). Consequently, by 2000 a fleet of containerships that would be able to cross the North Atlantic in just four days could be in operation. For example, FastShip Atlantic, Inc., planned to build a fleet of containerships, each able to carry 1,448 TEUs at speeds of 42 knots. Instead of containers being lifted on and off the ship, they would be stacked two high onto a train that would ride on a cushion of air and be pulled on and off the vessel. The goal would be to move all containers out of the terminal within six hours of the ship's arrival at the pier instead of the one or more days currently required in most container ports. Plans by other shipyards, such as Europe's Kvaerner Masa, were moving ahead with a similar type of fast ship, with particular emphasis on operations in the Pacific Ocean.

For passenger service, 40-knot catamaran ferries were beginning to become competitive in Europe, especially in the North. One such vessel, the *Stena Explorer,* had a capacity of 375 cars—or 50 trucks and 120 cars—and 1,500 passengers. The propulsion system, like that of the proposed containerships, consisted of gas turbines, reduction gears, and water jets. In the case of the *Stena Explorer,* this combination generated 100,000 hp.

Aviation

Although domestic and international commercial carriers enjoyed another year of higher earnings and profits, there were signs that the trend could change in the years to come. Rising labor costs and lack of government funding for certain programs could easily put the industry back into the red. To remain profitable it was necessary to keep costs low. Until recently that had been accomplished in a number of ways, including holding down wages across all categories of labor. On the technological side, ticketing of passengers was expected to involve the so-called ticketless ticket. Estimated to save carriers about $8 per passenger, tickets would be issued on cards about the size of the average credit card that could be purchased at kiosks or other ATM-like machines scattered in different locations. Furthermore, passengers could use home or office computers to book flights and make other travel arrange-

ments, thereby speeding up the confirmation process.

For improving efficiency of the aircraft while in the air, an integrated communication-navigation system that would permit pilots to fly the most direct, efficient routes and, for the most part, free them from the present aerial "highway" system received serious consideration by both the U.S. and international aviation community. That system, together with the greatly expanded use by aircraft of the Global Positioning System, could, however, prove less attractive for certain aircraft. For instance, the threat of reserving airspace only for aircraft equipped with the sophisticated and expensive free-flight technology might force already hard-pressed general and business aviation into even less-efficient operating conditions.

To reduce aircraft noise levels, a new version of the Integrated Noise Model was being prepared. It would integrate analyses of noise from military aircraft, provide better noise contours, and run on a microcomputer. At the same time, the U.S. Federal Aviation Administration (FAA), the National Aeronautics and Space Administration (NASA), and the aviation industry began work on the development of a "stage four" commercial aircraft that would be quieter than any being built today.

Although the U.S. commercial aviation system continued to be among the world's safest, the psychological impact of recent air-carrier accidents, including the crash of Trans World Airlines flight 800 near Long Island, N.Y., prompted considerable concern from leaders and the general public. It forced the air transportation administrators in some countries to reexamine their present administrative and regulatory

structures. Although this tightening of the system procedures seemed certain to contribute to making aviation safer, it was also likely to place greater financial constraints on the industry and lead to higher costs for air travel for the general public and cargo. Nevertheless, discussions were under way to build passenger aircraft that could carry as many as 525 passengers on nonstop trips from New York City to, possibly, Hong Kong. Boeing, using a larger version of its 747-400 series as the basis for its design, and its European counterpart Airbus Industrie had discussed such planes with potential customers for several years, but by the close of 1996 it appeared that the delivery of the first aircraft of that type was still several years and about $5 billion–$7 billion from reality.

For air cargo, the trend toward increased numbers and average weight of package express shipments would require more wide-body aircraft and more frequent flights. While the average weight of an air express package in the U.S. market in 1996 was about 2.7 kg (6 lb), that weight was expected to rise—along with package girth—closer to the average nonexpress air-cargo package weight of 90 kg (200 lb). Not only would this have an impact on the market for large aircraft, but it also would increase the difficulty of moving cargo through a customs station. Consequently, customs clearance procedures would have to be streamlined. Automated electronic systems could clear the cargo at an airport before the plane landed. For moving air cargo on the ground between airports and other major distribution facilities, a new type of rail locomotive with five specially configured railcars was recently launched by German rail operator

The Hanshin elevated expressway, which links Kobe and Osaka in Japan, was reopened late in 1996 after a 10-km (6-mi) section was repaired. The section had collapsed when a powerful earthquake struck Kobe in January 1995.

Deutsche Bahn. It was designed to move time-sensitive air cargo on the ground faster and with greater schedule reliability by bypassing congested highways, many of which were located in and around major airports.

Highway transportation

By 1997 almost 50% of U.S. urban expressways were estimated to be operating at capacity during peak hours; the resulting traffic congestion was estimated to be causing annual losses of more than two billion hours to drivers and their passengers and $40 billion to businesses. One effort to improve this situation was the Intelligent Vehicle Highway System, which originated in ISTEA. This $660 million program included integrating and operating systems for purposes of traffic-signal control, management of accidents, electronic fare collection, and highway-rail crossing protection. Progress also was being made on the development of light-emitting-diode devices that would provide comparatively low-cost highway illumination. Although this technology was relatively new, it had by 1997 achieved rapid acceptance in such traffic-control products as signal lamps because of its low power consumption and durability.

The controversy concerning regulations on large trucks on U.S. highways continued during the past year. Some industry associations and carriers wanted to use long combination vehicles (LCVs), such as triple 8.5-m (28-ft) trailers, which, including the tractor, were as long as 31.7 m (104 ft) and had a total weight of 48,000–52,000 kg (105,000–115,000 lb). Proponents of these units claimed that they would reduce labor costs for shippers by

one-third and fuel costs by 27%. Discussions were also under way on allowing double 14.6-m (48-ft) trailers to be used in competition with single 16.2-m (53-ft) trailers, which were becoming the norm on most highways.

Information systems

As the 21st century approached, the changes in transportation were expected to be worldwide. Internet communications capabilities would become available to the industry. The processing, integration, and accessibility of information were expected

to become in the year 2000 what the container revolution was in the second half of the 20th century. Moving information would be considered on a par with moving products. Transportation and logistics organizations would be designing and operating global information networks of data collection, communications, and processing in addition to designing and operating physical networks of vendors, carriers, distribution centers, plants, and customer facilities.

By 1997 many of the next century's transportation and logistics information systems were already in place. In the early 21st century, industry observers predicted, logistics data would be collected from two-dimensional bar codes with individual serial numbers painted in invisible ink. Miniature coding would be used for small products such as computer chips and precious stones. In some applications, data would be collected from sensitized paint that would respond to a radio frequency with a unique identification code. Voice recognition would be the primary human input to this field. Smart cards, traveling with passengers or cargo, seemed certain to become a common means of recording and processing transportation information, including security clearances.

Transportation leaders foresaw the massive data required for managing global transportation and logistics operations being compressed into laser holograms or solid-state cubes for instant access to multimedia information. Powerful analytic tools would explore these huge data warehouses for operating variances and for clues for strategic planning and performance improvement.

—Gerhardt Muller

SCIENTISTS OF THE YEAR

HONORS AND AWARDS

The following article discusses recent awards and prizes in science and technology. In the first section the Nobel Prizes for 1996 are described in detail. The second section is a selective list of other honors.

NOBEL PRIZE FOR CHEMISTRY

The 1996 Nobel Prize for Chemistry was awarded to a group of British and U.S. researchers who discovered fullerenes, a previously unrecognized form of molecular carbon, the discovery of which opened a new branch of chemistry. Fullerenes are hollow, spherical clusters of carbon atoms bonded together into highly symmetrical, cagelike structures. Bonds in the prototype molecule, C_{60}, resemble the seams on a soccer ball. Geometrically, C_{60} is a polygon with 60 vertices and 32 faces, 12 of which are pentagons and 20 of which are hexagons. In the 1985 paper describing their work, the researchers chose a whimsical name for C_{60}. They called it buckminsterfullerene after R. Buckminster Fuller, the U.S. architect whose geodesic dome design, the best-known example of which was the U.S. pavilion for Expo 67 in Montreal in 1967, had a similar structure. Chemists also refer to C_{60} molecules as buckyballs. The name and the elegant netlike structure of fullerenes galvanized the public imagination in a way that few other basic advances in chemistry had. "For chemists the proposed structure was uniquely beautiful and satisfying," the Royal Swedish Academy of Sciences said in its citation. "It corresponds to an aromatic, three-dimensional system in which

single and double bonds alternated, and was thus of great theoretical significance." The prize, worth $1,120,000, was shared by Richard E. Smalley and Robert F. Curl Jr. of Rice University, Houston, Texas, and Harold W. Kroto of the University of Sussex, Brighton, Eng. Kroto, Curl, and Smalley conducted their landmark experiment over a period of 11 days in 1985. The Academy of Sciences noted the assistance they received from graduate students James R. Heath and Sean C. O'Brien, who did not share in the award.

When the researchers began work, there were six known crystalline forms of the element carbon, including two kinds of graphite, two kinds of diamond, chaoit,

and carbon (VI). One way to make fullerenes is to allow vaporized carbon to condense in an atmosphere of inert gas. Gaseous carbon is produced by focusing intense pulses of laser light on a carbon surface. The carbon atoms then mix with a stream of helium gas and combine to form clusters that consist of atoms numbering from a few to hundreds. Besides C_{60}, the fullerene family includes many other configurations, including C_{56}, C_{58}, C_{62}, C_{70}, C_{76}, and C_{84}. Cooling the helium removes the fullerenes, which allows scientists to determine their exact structure, using mass spectrometry. Smalley, Curl, and Kroto were working in diverse areas of research that coalesced in their prize-

Sharing the 1996 Nobel Prize for Chemistry were Harold W. Kroto (left), Robert F. Curl (bottom left; pictured with his wife, Jonel Arnanda), and Richard E. Smalley (bottom right).

winning work—the kind of serendipitous discovery responsible for many such advances in science.

At the time of their discovery, Kroto was using microwave spectroscopy techniques to analyze gas in carbon-rich giant stars and clouds of gas in interstellar space. He had discovered long, chainlike molecules of carbon and nitrogen in both stellar atmospheres and gas clouds. Kroto wanted to study the vaporization of carbon to find out how these carbon chains form, but he lacked the apparatus to vaporize carbon. He mentioned the problem to a friend, Curl, an international authority on microwave and infrared spectroscopy who worked with Smalley. Curl told Kroto that Smalley had designed and built an instrument that seemed perfect for Kroto's research. Smalley was an authority on cluster chemistry, the study of aggregates of atoms or molecules that range in size between the microscopic and the visible. Specifically, Smalley was interested in clusters of metal atoms of potential use in electronic semiconductor materials. His laboratory instrument, a laser-supersonic cluster beam apparatus, could vaporize almost any known material into a plasma of atoms and then be used to study the resulting clusters. Kroto contacted Smalley, who agreed to collaborate on the project.

Kroto thus traveled to Rice University to work with Smalley and Curl on carbon vaporization and long-chained carbon molecules. The spectra from the first experiments did indeed have peaks that indicated the presence of those molecules. The spectra, however, also had peaks corresponding to a seventh, previously unrecognized form of carbon. Peaks on the spectra suggested molecules containing even numbers of car-

bon atoms—from 40 to more than 100. Under certain laser-vaporization conditions, most of the new carbon molecules had a structure of C_{60}. Kroto arrived at Rice on Sept. 1, 1985, and on September 12 the three scientists dispatched a research paper announcing the discovery of the structure of C_{60}; the report was published on November 14.

Scientists met the news of the discovery of C_{60} with mixed reactions ranging from criticism and skepticism to enthusiastic acceptance. Curl and Smalley continued their work from 1985 to 1990 at Rice, while Kroto returned to Sussex to conduct his research. They reported additional evidence that supported the proposed C_{60} structure, among other findings. During this period C_{60} remained mainly a laboratory curiosity because Smalley's apparatus could produce only minute quantities of fullerenes, amounts insufficient for many studies. In 1990, however, when physicists Donald R. Huffman of the University of Arizona and Wolfgang Krätschmer of the Max Planck Institute for Nuclear Physics, Heidelberg, Ger., announced a simple technique for producing large quantities of fullerenes, research in this area intensified greatly. Huffman and Krätschmer used an electric arc between two graphite rods in a helium atmosphere to vaporize carbon. Then they condensed the vapor and isolated carbon clusters with an organic solvent. They analyzed the carbon condensate and confirmed the structure of C_{60}. As a result, new substances were produced from these compounds, with new and unexpected properties. An entirely new branch of chemistry developed, having applications in such diverse fields as astrochemistry, superconductivity, and materials sci-

ence. Although practical uses for fullerenes have yet to be developed, intense research is under way on fullerenes and variations that include sheets of carbon atoms connected like chicken wire and microscopic tubes called carbon nanotubes that have a bonding framework similar to that of C_{60}.

Kroto was born on Oct. 7, 1939, in Wisbech, Cambridgeshire, Eng., and received a Ph.D. from the University of Sheffield, Eng., in 1964. He joined the faculty at Sussex in 1967 and was named Royal Society research professor in 1991. Smalley was born on June 6, 1943, in Akron, Ohio, and worked as a research chemist with the Shell Chemical Co. before receiving a Ph.D. from Princeton University in 1973. He joined the Rice faculty in 1976. Curl was born on Aug. 23, 1933, in Alice, Texas, and received a Ph.D. degree from the University of California, Berkeley, in 1957. He joined Rice University in 1958.

NOBEL PRIZE FOR PHYSICS

Three U.S. scientists won the 1996 Nobel Prize for Physics for their 1972 discovery of superfluid helium-3 (^{3}He), one of nature's most bizarre liquids. A superfluid lacks the internal friction that exists in normal liquid and thus flows without resistance. Superfluid ^{3}He, for example, can ooze through cracks and pores that normal liquids cannot penetrate, climb the walls of containers and pour out, and even flow uphill.

Douglas D. Osheroff, David M. Lee, and Robert C. Richardson, however, did not receive the prize, which totaled $1,120,000, because ^{3}He can perform such magical tricks. Rather, superfluid ^{3}He allowed scientists to study directly in macroscopic—or easily visible—systems the strange quantum mechanical effects that previously could be studied only indirectly in the microscopic world of molecules, atoms, and subatomic particles. "The study of this exotic quantum liquid has led to concepts that are of general importance," the Royal Swedish Academy of Sciences said in its citation.

The research, for instance, helped scientists understand how the first structures began to form in space microseconds after the big bang, the primordial explosion that formed the universe. Superfluid ^{3}He is anisotropic; it displays different properties in different directions along which the property is measured. The physical transitions from one form of superfluid ^{3}He to another have been used as a model for the cosmological phase transitions thought to have occurred a split second after the big bang, the Academy of Sciences said. Experts believed that in the early universe such transitions may have formed strange, linelike defects termed cosmic strings. These strings, in turn, may have formed the first physical structures in the universe. Cosmic strings have special properties that make them ideal candidates for giving rise to structures that evolved into the first stars and galaxies. For instance, cosmic strings cannot have ends and must form closed loops. They are trillions of times thinner than an atom and yet so immensely dense that a cosmic string one meter long would weigh 10^{20} kg.

Superfluid ^{3}He also may help in understanding and developing high-temperature superconductors, the academy added. These ceramic materials, discovered in 1986, lose resistance to the flow of electricity at higher temperatures than did previous superconductors. Like superfluid ^{3}He, they also have different properties in different directions. The superfluid thus might be used to model their behavior and develop general theories about how to make materials that become superconducting closer to room temperature.

In 1996 Lee and Richardson were professors at Cornell University, Ithaca, N.Y., and Osheroff was a professor at Stanford University. At the time of the discovery of superfluid ^{3}He, Richardson and Lee were senior researchers at Cornell, and Osheroff was a graduate student on their research team. Superfluids—by no means new to science when the Cornell team began its research—had been the topic of decades of research, and work on them had won several previous Nobel Prizes. The group was not looking for superfluidity but was instead studying other aspects of ^{3}He. The researchers were experts in low-temperature physics and had built their own cooling apparatus at Cornell. In their initial measurements of cooled ^{3}He, however, a problem occurred with their thermometer as temperatures dropped below a few thousandths of a degree of absolute zero (−273.15° C, or −459.67° F). Therefore, they decided to monitor the internal pressure of the ^{3}He sample while applying external pressure that varied with time.

"It was the research student Osheroff who observed a change in the way the internal pressure varied with time," the Nobel citation pointed out. Even the most experienced senior researchers are tempted to dismiss such small deviations as more or less inexplicable peculiarities of the

Winning the 1996 Nobel Prize for Physics were Douglas D. Osheroff (below), Robert Richardson (bottom left), and David M. Lee (bottom right).

equipment, the citation explained. "He did not put the observation aside as being due to some feature of the apparatus, but instead insisted that it was a real effect." Since the researchers were not initially studying superfluidity, their first published paper on the research in 1972 misinterpreted reasons for the effect. Nevertheless, the group quickly carried out a series of additional experiments that identified the creation of superfluid ^{3}He. Lee, Osheroff, and Richardson wrote a scientific paper announcing the discovery and sent it to *Physical Review Letters.* Though their paper was initially rejected because a referee regarded the finding as impossible, the authors appealed the decision, and the report was published. Soon thereafter, two other groups of scientists—one working in Finland and the other in the United States—verified that the new phase of ^{3}He was superfluid and could flow without resistance.

Lee was born on Jan. 20, 1931, in Rye, N.Y., and received a Ph.D. from Yale University in 1959. Osheroff was born on Aug. 1, 1945, in Aberdeen, Wash., and received a Ph.D. in 1973 from Cornell University. Richardson was born on June 26, 1937, in Washington, D.C., and received a Ph.D. in 1966 from Duke University, Durham, N.C.

NOBEL PRIZE FOR PHYSIOLOGY OR MEDICINE

Peter C. Doherty of Australia and Rolf M. Zinkernagel of Switzerland shared the 1996 Nobel Prize for Physiology or Medicine for their simple explanation of how the immune system distinguishes virus-infected cells from normal cells. In this key step in battling viral infections, specialized white blood cells termed cytotoxic T cells, or killer T cells, somehow recognize virus-infected cells and then eliminate them, but these T cells leave normal body cells unharmed.

The two scientists' discovery established a foundation for understanding how the immune system makes critical decisions about whether a cell is "self" or "nonself." A normally functioning immune system does not harm "self" cells that are part of the body, yet it can recognize, and target for death, infected cells, invading microorganisms, and other foreign materials or antigens. A finely tuned recognition system is critical for distinguishing normal cells from virus-infected cells and microbes that must be destroyed.

"The work fundamentally changed our understanding of the development of the immune response," said the Nobel Assembly at the Karolinska Institute in Stockholm, which awards the physiology or medicine prize. "Apart from vaccines, the work has guided attempts to use the immune system to hunt down and destroy microscopic cancer cells that have escaped from tumors. It has also helped scientists as they design ways to suppress harmful immune system attacks on the body's own tissue, as seen in multiple sclerosis and diabetes."

Doherty and Zinkernagel conducted their landmark research on laboratory mice between 1973 and 1975 while at the John Curtin School of Medical Research in Canberra, Australia. In 1996 Doherty was chairman of the department of immunology at St. Jude Children's Research Hospital in Memphis, Tenn. He was born on Oct. 15, 1940, in Brisbane, Australia, and received a veterinary medicine degree in 1966 from the University of Queensland, Australia, and a Ph.D. in 1970 from the University of Edinburgh. In 1996 Zinkernagel headed the Institute of Experimental Immunology at the University of Zürich, Switz. He was born on Jan. 6, 1944, in Basel, Switz., and received an M.D. degree in 1970 from the University of Basel and a Ph.D. in 1975 from the Australian National University, Canberra.

At the time the research began, Doherty was serving as a department head at the Curtin School, and Zinkernagel had gone to Australia from Switzerland as a postdoctoral research fellow. Though Zinkernagel had not specifically planned to work with Doherty, he found that laboratory space was at a premium and sought a space in Doherty's laboratory. The two decided to collaborate on immune system studies. At that time scientists recognized the existence of the two main components of the human immune system. One was antibody-mediated immunity, an immune response that results from the production of proteins termed antibodies, which circulate in the blood and recognize and destroy bacteria and other foreign material. The other was cell-mediated immunity, which involves the production of cytotoxic T cells. Organ transplant studies have shown that T cells selectively kill organs transplanted into the body from an unrelated donor. T cells attack foreign, or nonself, cells because they recognize certain protein molecules—the major histocompatibility complex (MHC) antigens—on the surface of foreign cells. The antigens differ from those in the individual's own body and thus are recognizable as foreign. The cells of all higher vertebrates carry MHC proteins. The proteins differ so substantially from individual

to individual that they function as a unique molecular identification code. Relatively little was known about the precise recognition mechanisms involved in cellular immunity when Doherty and Zinkernagel began their research. Scientists assumed that the MHC antigens had other functions, but they did not know what they were. Likewise, most biologists were convinced that an invading microbe in itself was enough to trigger an attack by killer T cells.

When Doherty and Zinkernagel began their collaboration, they wanted to identify causes of the fatal destruction of brain cells in mice infected with lymphocytic choriomeningitis virus (LCMV). In their experiments they developed an assay to test their theory that killer T cells caused the damage while attacking virus-infected cells. They mixed T cells from sick mice with mouse cells infected with LCMV and found that the T cells indeed did destroy the infected cells. By a coincidence, however, both the T cells and the infected cells came from mice that were members of the same inbred strain. They thus were as genetically alike as identical twins and had identical MHC antigens.

When Doherty and Zinkernagel mixed the T cells with virus-infected cells from another strain of mice, they received a surprise. The researchers had expected that the cytotoxic T cells, primed for attack, would strike the instant that they came into contact with LCMV-infected cells. Instead, the T cells acted as if they did not see the infected cells. Recognition, Doherty and Zinkernagel suspected, required the presence of some other protein on the surface of an infected cell. Further research showed that T cells must recognize two separate signals on an infected cell. One is

Peter C. Doherty (top) and Rolf M. Zinkernagel (bottom) shared the 1996 Nobel Prize for Physiology or Medicine.

the signal of a foreign invader, the virus inside the cell. The other is the "self" signal from the cell's MHC antigens. In Doherty and Zinkernagel's experiments, the T cells were looking not just for virus-infected cells but also for cells having the MHC antigens characteristic of the first strain of mice. The T cells could not recognize MHC antigens from the new strain and so did not mount an immune response. This concept of simultaneous recognition of both self and foreign molecules formed the basis for a new understanding of cellular immunity, the Nobel Assembly said. "Taken in all, the clarification of the recognition mechanisms of the T-cells within the cellular immune system has fundamentally changed our understanding of the development and normal function of the immune system and, in addition, has also provided new possibilities for the selective modification of immune reactions both to microorganisms, and to self tissues."

Later research confirmed the findings by Doherty and Zinkernagel and identified the biochemical mechanism by which dual recognition occurs. Confirmation took almost 20 years and required some of the most sophisticated tools of biotechnology.

Immunologists established that in cells infected with a virus, a small subunit of the virus becomes attached to the MHC proteins to form complexes. The cell then transports these complexes to its surface, where they are exposed to cytotoxic T cells. The T cells have highly specific surface receptor sites that must attach to both the viral antigen and the MHC proteins in order for cell killing to occur. The discovery also led to advances in many areas of clinical medicine. These included efforts to strengthen the immune system's response against infections and certain forms of cancer and to diminish its activity in autoimmune diseases such as rheumatoid arthritis, multiple sclerosis, and diabetes. In these latter conditions the immune system apparently fails to recognize an individual's own body tissue as self. It thus begins to destroy joint, nerve, pancreatic, and other tissue. Researchers have begun using cytotoxic T cells to kill viruses in bone marrow before it is transplanted into a recipient. They also have begun developing vaccines, including those for certain forms of cancer and AIDS, that stimulate the production of cytotoxic T cells.

—Michael Woods

■ ANTHROPOLOGY AND ARCHAEOLOGY

AWARD	WINNER	AFFILIATION
John D. and Catherine T. MacArthur Foundation Award	Joan B. Connelly	New York City
John J. Carty Award for the Advancement of Science	Patrick V. Kirch	University of California, Berkeley

■ ARCHITECTURE AND CIVIL ENGINEERING

AWARD	WINNER	AFFILIATION
Architecture Firm Award	R.M. Kliment and Frances Halsband	New York City
Edward C. Kemper Award	Harold L. Adams	RTKL Associates, Inc., Baltimore, Md.
Gold Medal of the American Institute of Architects	Richard Meier	New York City
Pritzker Architecture Prize	José Rafael Moneo	Madrid
Thomas Jefferson Award for Public Architecture	Richard Kahan	Urban Assembly, New York City
Thomas Jefferson Award for Public Architecture	Hunter Morrison	Cleveland City Planning Commission
Thomas Jefferson Award for Public Architecture	John Tarantino	Metropolitan Transit Authority, New York City

■ ASTRONOMY

AWARD	WINNER	AFFILIATION
Award for Initiatives in Research	Christopher Stubbs	University of Washington, Seattle
Brouwer Award	Brian Marsden	Harvard-Smithsonian Center for Astrophysics, Cambridge, Mass.
Bruno Rossi Prize	Carl E. Fichtel	Goddard Space Flight Center, Greenbelt, Md.
Catherine Wolfe Bruce Medal	Albert E. Whitford (emeritus)	University of California, Santa Cruz
Harold C. Urey Prize	Emmanuel Lellouch	Observatoire de Paris-Meudon, France
Harold Masursky Award	William Brunk	NASA
Henry Draper Medal	Bohdan Paczynski	Princeton University, Princeton, N.J.
J. Lawrence Smith Medal	Ernst Zinner	Washington University, St. Louis, Mo.
John D. and Catherine T. MacArthur Foundation Award	James R.P. Angel	Tucson, Ariz.
John Scott Award	John C. Mather	Goddard Space Flight Center, Greenbelt, Md.
Julius Edgar Lilienfeld Prize	Kip S. Thorne	California Institute of Technology, Pasadena
Julius Edgar Lilienfeld Prize	Michael S. Turner	University of Chicago, Ill.
Maria and Eric Muhlmann Award	Robert Tull	University of Texas, Austin
Robertson Memorial Lecture	Phillip J. Peebles	Princeton University, Princeton, N.J.
Tom W. Bonner Prize	R.G. Hamish Robertson	University of Washington, Seattle

■ CHEMISTRY

AWARD	WINNER	AFFILIATION
Alan T. Waterman Award	Robert M. Waymouth	Stanford University, Stanford, Calif.
Alfred Bader Award	James P. Collman	Stanford University, Stanford, Calif.
Aminoff Prize	Philip Coppens	State University of New York, Buffalo
Arthur C. Cope Award	Ryoji Noyori	Nagoya University, Japan
Arthur W. Adamson Award	Robert J. Madix	Stanford University, Stanford, Calif.
Award for Chemistry in Service to Society	Ernest L. Eliel (emeritus)	University of North Carolina, Chapel Hill
Award for Computers in Chemical and Pharmaceutical Research	Harold A. Scheraga	Cornell University, Ithaca, N.Y.
Award for Creative Invention	Rangaswamy Srinivasan (retired)	IBM Corp.
Award for Distinguished Service in the Advancement of Inorganic Chemistry	John E. Bercaw	California Institute of Technology, Pasadena
Award for the Industrial Application of Science	John H. Sinfelt (retired)	Exxon Research and Engineering Co.
Coblentz Award	X. Sunney Xie	Pacific Northwest Laboratory, Richland, Wash.

AWARD	WINNER	AFFILIATION
E.V. Murphree Award	Arthur W. Westerberg	Carnegie Mellon University, Pittsburgh, Pa.
Earl K. Plyler Prize	Roger E. Miller	University of North Carolina, Chapel Hill
Earl K. Plyler Prize	David J. Nesbitt	JILA (Joint Institute for Laboratory Astrophysics), Boulder, Colo.
Enrico Fermi Award	Martin Kamen (emeritus)	University of California, San Diego, and University of Southern California, Los Angeles
Ernest Guenther Award	Kenneth L. Rinehart	University of Illinois, Urbana-Champaign
Francis P. Garvan-John M. Olin Medal	Karen W. Morse	Western Washington University, Bellingham
Frank H. Field and Joe L. Franklin Award	Charles L. Wilkins	University of California, Riverside
Franklin Medal	Richard E. Smalley	Rice University, Houston, Texas
High Polymer Prize	Frank Bates	University of Minnesota, Minneapolis
International Balzan Foundation Prize	Alan J. Heeger	UNIAX Corp. and University of California, Santa Barbara
James Flack Norris Award	Julius Rebek	Scripps Institution of Oceanography, La Jolla, Calif.
Joel Henry Hildebrand Award	Harold L. Friedman (emeritus)	State University of New York, Stony Brook
Killam Lifetime Achievement Award	Stephen Hanessian	University of Montreal, Que.
Nakanishi Prize	Frank H. Westheimer (emeritus)	Harvard University, Cambridge, Mass.
National Medal of Science	Norman Davidson (emeritus)	California Institute of Technology, Pasadena
National Medal of Technology	Stephanie L. Kwolek (retired)	E.I. du Pont de Nemours & Co.
Peter Debye Award	Robin M. Hochstrasser	University of Pennsylvania, Philadelphia
Priestley Medal	Mary L. Good	U.S. Department of Commerce
Ralph F. Hirschmann Award	Murray Goodman	University of California, San Diego
Ralph K. Iler Award	Charles F. Zukoski IV	University of Illinois, Urbana-Champaign
Roger Adams Award	K. Barry Sharpless	Scripps Institution of Oceanography, La Jolla, Calif.

■ EARTH SCIENCES

AWARD	WINNER	AFFILIATION
Arctowski Medal	Raymond G. Roble	National Center for Atmospheric Research, Boulder, Colo.
Arthur L. Day Prize and Lectureship	James G. Anderson	Harvard University, Cambridge, Mass.
Charles Whitten Medal	Donald L. Turcotte	Cornell University, Ithaca, N.Y.
Henry G. Houghton Award	David W. Fahey	National Oceanic and Atmospheric Administration
James B. Macelwane Medal	Dara Entekhabi	Massachusetts Institute of Technology, Cambridge
James B. Macelwane Medal	David R. Hanson	Cooperative Institute for Research in Environmental Science, Boulder, Colo.
John Adam Fleming Medal	Neil D. Opdyke	University of Florida, Gainesville
Maurice Ewing Medal	Jean-Guy E. Schilling	University of Rhode Island, Kingston
National Medal of Science	Wallace S. Broecker	Columbia University, New York City
Pioneers of Underwater Acoustics Medal	William A. Kuperman	Scripps Institution of Oceanography, La Jolla, Calif.
Roger Revelle Medal	Wallace S. Broecker	Columbia University, New York City
Tyler Prize for Environmental Achievement	Willi Dansgaard (emeritus)	University of Copenhagen, Den.
Tyler Prize for Environmental Achievement	Claude Lorius	French Institute of Polar Research and Technology, Grenoble
Tyler Prize for Environmental Achievement	Hans Oeschger (emeritus)	University of Bern, Switz.

■ ELECTRONICS AND INFORMATION SCIENCES

AWARD	WINNER	AFFILIATION
Bower Award and Prize for Achievement in Science	Frederick P. Brooks, Jr.	University of North Carolina, Chapel Hill
C & C Prize	Albert Cho	AT&T Bell Laboratories
C & C Prize	Akira Hasegawa	Osaka University, Japan
George E. Pake Prize	Donald R. Scifres	SDL Inc.
John Von Neumann Medal	Carver A. Mead	California Institute of Technology, Pasadena

Killam Lifetime Achievement Award	Stephen Cook	University of Toronto, Ont.
Kyoto Prize	Donald E. Knuth (emeritus)	Stanford University, Stanford, Calif.
Louis E. Levy Medal	Whitfield Diffie	Sun Microsystems, Inc., Mountain View, Calif.
Louis E. Levy Medal	Martin E. Hellman	Stanford University, Stanford, Calif.
National Medal of Science	James L. Flanagan	Rutgers University, New Brunswick, N.J.
National Medal of Science	Richard M. Karp	University of Washington, Seattle
National Medal of Technology	James C. Morgan	Applied Materials, Inc.
National Medal of Technology	Peter H. Rose	Krytek Corp.
Silver Medal in Engineering Acoustics	James E. West	AT&T Bell Laboratories

■ ENERGY

Karl W. Boör Solar Energy Medal	David E. Carlson	Solarex, Newtown, Pa.
Robert E. Carter Award	Robert E. Carter	Idaho National Engineering Laboratory, Idaho Falls

■ ENVIRONMENT

Dennis Puleston Conservation Award	Marty Van Lith	Brookhaven National Laboratory, Upton, N.Y.
G. Evelyn Hutchinson Medal	Bob Hecky	Environment Canada
Goldman Prize	Bill Ballantine	New Zealand
Goldman Prize	Edwin Bustillos	Mexico
Goldman Prize	M.C. Mehta	India
Goldman Prize	Amooti Ndyakira	Uganda
Goldman Prize	Marina Silva	Brazil
Goldman Prize	Albena Simeonova	Bulgaria
Greenman Award	Yoichi Kaya	Keio University, Japan
Greenman Award	Meyer Steinberg	Brookhaven National Laboratory, Upton, N.Y.
Greenman Award	Wim Turkenburg	State University of Utrecht, Neth.

■ LIFE SCIENCES

Award for Scientific Reviewing	Paul Harvey	University of Oxford, Eng.
Award in Molecular Biology	Michael S. Levine	University of California, San Diego
Award in Molecular Biology	Richard H. Scheller	Howard Hughes Medical Institute, Boston, Mass., and Stanford University, Stanford, Calif.
Award in Molecular Biology	Thomas C. Südhof	Howard Hughes Medical Institute and University of Texas, Dallas
Bower Award and Prize	Ralph L. Brinster	University of Pennsylvania, Philadelphia
Charles Doolittle Walcott Medal	Mikhail A. Fedonkin	Russian Academy of Sciences, Moscow
Elliott Cresson Medal	Irwin Fridovich	Duke University, Durham, N.C.
Elliott Cresson Medal	Joe M. McCord	University of Colorado, Denver
Franklin Medal	Mario R. Capecchi	University of Utah, Salt Lake City
Gilbert Morgan Smith Medal	Isabella A. Abbott	University of Hawaii, Manoa
John D. and Catherine T. MacArthur Foundation Award	Barbara Block	Monterey, Calif.
John D. and Catherine T. MacArthur Foundation Award	Thomas L. Daniel	University of Washington, Seattle
John D. and Catherine T. MacArthur Foundation Award	Richard E. Lenski	Michigan State University, East Lansing
Killam Lifetime Achievement Award	David MacLennan	University of Toronto, Ont.
Kyoto Prize	Mario R. Capecchi	University of Utah, Salt Lake City
Lemelson-MIT Prize	Herbert Boyer	Genentech, San Francisco, Calif.
Lemelson-MIT Prize	Stanley Cohen	Stanford University, Stanford, Calif.
Louisa Gross Horwitz Prize	Clay Armstrong	University of Pennsylvania, Philadelphia

Louisa Gross Horwitz Prize	Bertil Hille	University of Washington, Seattle
National Medal of Science	Ruth Patrick	Academy of Natural Sciences, Philadelphia, Pa.
Richard Lounsbery Award	James E. Rothman	Memorial Sloan-Kettering Cancer Center, New York City
Selman A. Waksman Award	Carl R. Woese	University of Illinois, Urbana-Champaign

■ MATERIALS SCIENCE AND ENGINEERING

Ellis R. Lippincott Award	Giuseppe Zerbi	Politecnico di Milano, Italy
Francis J. Clamer Medal	James R. Rice	Harvard University, Cambridge, Mass.
Prize for Industrial Applications of Physics	Mark Ketchen	IBM Corp.

■ MATHEMATICS

Award in Mathematics	Andrew Wiles	Princeton University, Princeton, N.J.
Helmholtz Medal	Manfred R. Schroeder	University of Göttingen, Ger.
National Medal of Science	Stephen Smale (emeritus)	University of California, Berkeley

■ MEDICAL SCIENCES

Albert Lasker Award for Special Achievement in Medical Sciences	Paul C. Zamecnik	Worcester Foundation for Biomedical Research, Shrewsbury, Mass.
Albert Lasker Basic Medical Research Award	Robert F. Furchgott (emeritus)	State University of New York, Brooklyn
Albert Lasker Basic Medical Research Award	Ferid Murad	Molecular Geriatrics Corp., Lake Bluff, Ill.
Albert Lasker Clinical Medical Research Award	Porter W. Anderson, Jr. (emeritus)	University of Rochester, New York
Albert Lasker Clinical Medical Research Award	John B. Robbins	National Institutes of Health, Bethesda, Md.
Albert Lasker Clinical Medical Research Award	Rachel Schneerson	National Institutes of Health, Bethesda, Md.
Albert Lasker Clinical Medical Research Award	David H. Smith	David H. Smith Foundation
Bolton L. Corson Medal	Shiriki K. Kumanyika	University of Illinois, Chicago
Distinguished Scientist Award	Alfred Wolf	Brookhaven National Laboratory, Upton, N.Y.
Distinguished Service Citation of the American Medical Association	David Bickham	Edmond, Okla.
Distinguished Service Citation of the American Medical Association	Robert G. Cox	Louisville, Ky.
Distinguished Service Citation of the American Medical Association	Eldon E. Huston	Des Moines, Iowa
Distinguished Service Citation of the American Medical Association	Otha W. Linton	Potomac, Md.
Distinguished Service Citation of the American Medical Association	Robert G. Mickey	Austin, Texas
Free-Electron Laser Prize	Gerald Hanson (retired)	World Health Organization
Free-Electron Laser Prize	Philip Palmer	University of California, Davis
Friendship Award	Arthur Lim	Singapore National Eye Centre
Gregory Pincus Medal	Robert F. Furchgott (emeritus)	State University of New York, Brooklyn
Gregory Pincus Medal	Salvador Moncada	University College, London
Japan Prize	Bruce Ames	University of California, Berkeley
Japan Prize	Masao Ito	Institute of Physical and Chemical Research, Japan
Japan Prize	Takashi Sugimura (emeritus)	National Cancer Centre, Tokyo
Lemelson-MIT Lifetime Achievement Award	Wilson Greatbatch	Clarence, N.Y.
National Medal of Technology	Johnson & Johnson	New Brunswick, N.J.
Olympic Prize for Sports Science	Jeremy N. Morris (emeritus)	University of London

Public Welfare Medal	George W. Thorn (emeritus)	Harvard University, Cambridge, Mass., and Howard Hughes Medical Institute, Boston
Research Achievement Award	David Kritchevsky	Wistar Institute, Philadelphia, Pa.
Robert A. Welch Award	Koji Nakanishi	Columbia University, New York City
Sloan Prize	Mark Davis	Stanford University, Stanford, Calif.
Sloan Prize	Tak Mak	Ontario Cancer Institute and University of Toronto
Troland Research Award	Richard Ivry	University of California, Berkeley
Von Békésy Medal	Peter Dallos	Northwestern University, Evanston, Ill.

■ OPTICAL ENGINEERING

C. Raymond Kraus Medal	Roland Winston	University of Chicago, Ill.
Engineering Excellence Award	Gary Blough	Rochester Photonics Corp.
Engineering Excellence Award	Teddi Laurin	Laurin Publishing Co.
Esther Hoffman Beller Medal	Donald O'Shea	Georgia Institute of Technology, Atlanta
Japan Prize	Charles Kuen Kao	Chinese University of Hong Kong

■ PHYSICS

Accelerator Prize	Jeffrey S. Hangst	Aarhus University, Denmark
Achievement in Asia Award	Wei Ching-Ming	Academia Sinica, Taipei, Taiwan
Albert A. Michelson Medal	William D. Phillips	National Institute for Standards and Technology, Gaithersburg, Md.
Aminoff Prize	Hugo M. Rietveld	Dutch Reactor Center, Petten, Neth.
Aneesur Rahman Prize	Steven G. Louie	University of California, Berkeley, and Lawrence Berkeley National Laboratory
Aneesur Rahman Prize	Donald H. Weingarten	IBM Corp.
Arthur Schawlow Prize	Erich P. Ippen	Massachusetts Institute of Technology, Cambridge
Arthur Schawlow Prize	Charles V. Shank	University of California, Berkeley
Arthur Schawlow Prize in Laser Science	Theodor W. Hänsch	Max Planck Institute, Germany
Award for Initiatives in Research	Matthew P.A. Fisher	University of California, Santa Barbara
Dannie Heineman Prize	Donald Eigler	IBM Corp.
Dannie Heineman Prize	Roy J. Glauber	Harvard University, Cambridge, Mass.
Dannie Heineman Prize	Harry W. Lehmann	University of Hamburg, Ger.
David Adler Lectureship	John D. Joannopoulos	Massachusetts Institute of Technology, Cambridge
Edison Medal	Floyd Dunn (emeritus)	University of Illinois, Urbana-Champaign
Edward A. Bouchet Award	Larry Gladney	University of Pennsylvania, Philadelphia
Edwin H. Land Medal	Donald R. Scifres	SDL Inc.
Enrico Fermi Award	Ugo Fano (emeritus)	University of Chicago, Ill.
Fluid Dynamics Prize	Louis N. Howard	Florida State University, Tallahassee
Fluid Dynamics Prize	Parviz Moin	Stanford University, Stanford, Calif.
Free-Electron Laser Prize	Charles A. Brau	Vanderbilt University, Nashville, Tenn.
Fritz London Prize	Moses H.W. Chan	Pennsylvania State University, University Park
Fritz London Prize	Eric A. Cornell	National Institute of Standards and Technology, Boulder, Colo.
Fritz London Prize	Carl E. Wieman	University of Colorado, Boulder
Gertrude S. Goldhaber Prize	Q. Joan Harris	Massachusetts Institute of Technology, Cambridge
Gold Medal of the Acoustical Society of America	Ira Dyer	Massachusetts Institute of Technology, Cambridge
Heinrich Hertz Medal	Martin A. Uman	University of Florida, Gainesville
I.I. Rabi Prize	Eric A. Cornell	National Institute of Standards and Technology, Boulder, Colo.
I.I. Rabi Prize	Wolfgang Ketterle	Massachusetts Institute of Technology, Cambridge

AWARD	WINNER	AFFILIATION
Irving Langmuir Prize	Jack H. Freed	Cornell University, Ithaca, N.Y.
J.J. Sakurai Prize	Thomas Appelquist	Yale University, New Haven, Conn.
J.J. Sakurai Prize	William A. Bardeen	Fermi National Accelerator Laboratory, Batavia, Ill.
James B. Macelwane Medal	Stephen A. Fuselier	Lockheed Martin Corp.
James Clerk Maxwell Prize	Thomas M. O'Neil	University of California, San Diego
John D. and Catherine T. MacArthur Foundation Award	Nathan Seiberg	Princeton, N.J.
John Price Wetherill Medal	Federico Capasso	AT&T Bell Laboratories and Lucent Technologies
John Wheatley Award	Manuel Cardona	Max Planck Institute, Germany
Lars Onsager Prize	Robert H. Kraichnan	Los Alamos National Laboratory, N.M.
Maria Goeppert-Mayer Award	Margaret M. Murnane	University of Michigan, Ann Arbor
National Medal of Science	C. Kumar N. Patel	University of California, Los Angeles
Oliver E. Buckley Prize	James S. Langer	University of California, Santa Barbara
Penning Award	James E. Lawler	University of Wisconsin, Madison
Quantum Electronics Award	Robert L. Byer	Stanford University, Stanford, Calif.
Quantum Electronics Prize	Claude Cohen-Tannoudji	College of France, Paris
Quantum Electronics Prize	Sune Svanberg	Lund Institute of Technology, Sweden
Robert R. Wilson Prize	Albert J. Hofmann	European Laboratory for Particle Physics (CERN)
Robert R. Wilson Prize	Andrew M. Sessler	Lawrence Berkeley National Laboratory, California
Simon Ramo Award	Michael A. Beer	Princeton University, Princeton, N.J.
Surface Structure Prize	John B. Pendry	University of London
Tom W. Bonner Prize	John D. Walecka	College of William and Mary, Williamsburg, Va., and Continuous Electron Beam Accelerator Facility, Newport News, Va.
W.K.H. Panofsky Prize	Gail G. Hanson	Indiana University, Bloomington
W.K.H. Panofsky Prize	Roy F. Schwitters	University of Texas, Austin
W.K.H. Panofsky Prize	Henning Schröder	Deutsches Elektronen Synchrotron (DESY), Hamburg, Ger.
W.K.H. Panofsky Prize	Yuri Zaitsev	Institute of Theoretical and Experimental Physics, Moscow
Wallace Clement Sabine Award	A. Harold Marshall	University of Auckland, N.Z.
Will Allis Prize	Chun Chia Lin	University of Wisconsin, Madison
Xanthopoulos Award	Carlo Rovelli	University of Pittsburgh, Pa.

■ PSYCHOLOGY

AWARD	WINNER	AFFILIATION
John D. and Catherine T. MacArthur Foundation Award	Vonnie C. McLoyd	Durham, N.C.
Troland Research Award	Keith R. Kluender	University of Wisconsin, Madison
Troland Research Award	Joseph E. Steinmetz	Indiana University, Bloomington
Troland Research Award	Steven G. Yantis	Johns Hopkins University, Baltimore, Md.

■ SCIENCE WRITING

AWARD	WINNER	AFFILIATION
AAAS-Newcomb Cleveland Prize	Patrick Callaerts	*Science*
AAAS-Newcomb Cleveland Prize	Walter J. Gehring	*Science*
AAAS-Newcomb Cleveland Prize	Georg Halder	*Science*
Andrew Gemant Award	Alan P. Lightman	Massachusetts Institute of Technology, Cambridge
Archie Mahan Prize	Stanley Whitcomb	California Institute of Technology, Pasadena
Archie Mahan Prize	Robert Spero	California Institute of Technology, Pasadena
Forum Award	Martin Gardner	—
Georg von Holtzbrinck Prize	Herbert Cerutti	*Neue Zürcher Zeitung*
Science Writing Award	Sandra Blakeslee	*New York Times*
Science Writing Award	Eric J. Chaisson	Tufts University, Medford, Mass.

Science Writing Award	K.C. Cole	*Los Angeles Times*
Science Writing Award in Acoustics	Lawrence A. Crum	University of Washington, Seattle
Science Writing Award in Acoustics	Christopher E. Ruckman	Naval Surface Warfare Center, Bethesda, Md.
Science Writing Award	A. Richard Immel	—
Science Writing Award	Peter Narins	University of California, Los Angeles

■ SPACE EXPLORATION

Gerard P. Kuiper Prize	Michael J.S. Belton	Kitt Peak National Observatory, Arizona
James B. Macelwane Medal	Jonathan I. Lunine	University of Arizona, Tucson
Presidential Early Career Award	Andrea Donnellan	Jet Propulsion Laboratory, Pasadena, Calif.
Presidential Early Career Award	Ellen Stofan	Jet Propulsion Laboratory, Pasadena, Calif.

■ TRANSPORTATION

F.E. Newbold Award	Paul M. Bevilaqua	Lockheed Martin Corp.
Gibbs Brothers Medal	William B. Morgan	Naval Surface Warfare Center, Bethesda, Md.
National Medal of Technology	Charles H. Kaman	Kaman Corp.
Spirit of St. Louis Award	Robert G. Loewy	Georgia Institute of Technology, Atlanta

■ OTHER AWARDS

Award for Behavioral Research Relevant to the Prevention of Nuclear War	Alexander L. George (emeritus)	Stanford University, Stanford, Calif.
Award for International Scientific Cooperation	Harold K. Jacobson	University of Michigan, Ann Arbor
Award for Public Understanding of Science and Technology	Carl Sagan	Cornell University, Ithaca, N.Y.
Award for Scientific Reviewing	Jeffrey S. Banks	University of Rochester, N.Y.
George Gamow Memorial Lecture Award	Albert Bartlett (emeritus)	University of Colorado, Boulder
Japan Prize	Joseph Engelberger	HelpMate Robotics
Japan Prize	Hiroyuki Yoshikawa	University of Tokyo
Leo Szilard Award	David Hafemeister	California Polytechnic State University, San Luis Obispo
Leo Szilard Award	Thomas L. Neff	Massachusetts Institute of Technology, Cambridge
Lewis Thomas Prize	Freeman Dyson (emeritus)	Institute for Advanced Study, Princeton, N.J.
Mentor Award for Lifetime Achievement	Lawrence I. Gilbert	University of North Carolina, Chapel Hill
National Medal of Science	Paul A. Samuelson (emeritus)	Massachusetts Institute of Technology, Cambridge
National Medal of Technology	Ronald H. Brown (posthumous)	U.S. Department of Commerce
Nicholson Medal	Fang Lizhi	University of Arizona, Tucson
Philip Hauge Abelson Prize	William D. Baker	AT&T Bell Laboratories
Public Welfare Medal	William T. Golden	Carnegie Commission on Science, Technology, and Government
Westinghouse Science Talent Search	1. Adam Ezra Cohen	Hunter College High School, New York City
	2. Carrie Shilyansky	San Marino High School, San Marino, Calif.
	3. Nicholas Karl Eriksson	Sentinel High School, Missoula, Mont.
	4. Davesh Maulik	Roslyn High School, Roslyn, N.Y.
	5. Emily Beth Levy	North Miami Beach Senior High School, North Miami Beach, Fla.
	6. Dev Edward Kumar	Texas Academy of Mathematics and Science, Denton, Texas
	7. Ann Clair Seiferle-Valencia	Farmington High School, Farmington, N.M.
	8. Dylan Micah Schwindt	Montezuma-Cortez High School, Cortez, Colo.
	9. Rose J. Payyapilli	Midwood High School at Brooklyn College, Brooklyn, N.Y.
	10. Whitney Paige Bowe	Lawrence High School, Cedarhurst, N.Y.

OBITUARIES

Calvin, Melvin
April 8, 1911—Jan. 8, 1997

U.S. chemist Melvin Calvin studied the structure and behavior of organic molecules and was awarded the 1961 Nobel Prize for Chemistry for having determined the steps by which carbon is converted to carbohydrates, an important mechanism in the process of photosynthesis. Calvin, educated at the University of Minnesota (Ph.D., 1935), began investigating the photosynthetic process in the late 1940s while serving as director of the Bioorganic Chemistry Group at the Lawrence Radiation Laboratory at the University of California, Berkeley. Taking advantage of newly developed tools—chromatography and the radioactive isotope carbon-14—to carry out his experiments, he fed radioactive carbon dioxide to the green algae

Melvin Calvin

Chlorella and followed its path through a cycle of reactions, now eponymously called the Calvin cycle. After devoting almost 15 years to elucidating this pathway, Calvin served as director of the Laboratory of Chemical Biodynamics at Berkeley (1960–80), where he turned his attention to conjectures such as the origins of life on Earth and the possibility of life elsewhere in the universe. He also conducted research into the development of alternate fuels. In addition to the Nobel Prize, Calvin received the National Medal of Science (1989) and the Priestley Medal of the American Chemical Society (1978), and he was elected to the National Academy of Sciences (1954). Over the years he was the author of more than 500 papers and a number of books, including *The Path of Carbon in Photosynthesis* (1957; with J.A. Bassham) and *Following the Trail of Light: A Scientific Odyssey* (1992).

Chapman, Douglas G.
March 20, 1920—July 9, 1996

Canadian-born U.S. biomathematical statistician Douglas Chapman used his expertise in analyzing data to create scientifically based proposals that would help in the conservation of marine mammals, particularly whales. In 1960 the numbers of fin whales inhabiting Antarctic waters were dwindling, and the International Whaling Commission (IWC) asked Chapman to join a "special committee of three" with fisheries specialists K. Radway Allan and Sidney J. Holt to devise a new method to calculate whaling quotas. Specifically, the committee was asked to evaluate data from the whaling industry, such as catches and number of whaling boats, and to formulate proposals that would permit whal-

ing while allowing depleted populations to recover. When the committee presented its findings in 1963, principal whaling nations such as the U.S.S.R. and Japan felt that the quotas were too conservative. Years of arguments between whaling and non-whaling nations in the IWC ensued, while whale populations continued to decrease. Chapman remained steadfast in his support of his original recommendations. He led the scientific committee of the IWC from 1965 to 1974 and joined the U.S. Marine Mammal Commission in the 1970s, serving as its chairman from 1976 to 1981 and remaining a scientific adviser until 1993. In 1979 and again in 1982, he joined members of the IWC who supported a moratorium on whaling and were critical of the few countries that continued to engage in whaling on a limited scale during this period. Chapman also helped to introduce the "precautionary principle," a precept based on the idea that by the time environmental threat had been proved, attempts to reverse the damage would be too late. In 1949 Chapman earned a doctorate in mathematics from the University of California, Berkeley, and he joined the faculty of the University of Washington as a mathematics professor that same year. He retired in 1984.

Cray, Seymour R.
Sept. 28, 1925—Oct. 5, 1996

U.S. electronics engineer and computer designer Seymour Cray led the design of the world's first transistor-based computer and was recognized as the father of the supercomputer industry. After graduating (1950) from the University of Minnesota, Cray went to work for Engineering Research Associates (ERA), a leading digital

Charles Brenton Huggins and research assistant Betty Hathaway

computer company. In 1957, when ERA was taken over in a series of corporate mergers, Cray left to help found Control Data Corp., which became a major computer manufacturer. At Control Data he led the design of the CDC 1604, the first commercial computer to replace vacuum tubes with smaller transistors. Cray had purchased the transistors at a local electronics store. Eager to pursue his vision of building the fastest computers in the world, Cray left Control Data in 1972 and founded Cray Research, Inc. His company's first supercomputer, the Cray-1, which came out in 1976, was 10 times faster than any other computer on the market. Ever-faster and more powerful designs followed, including the Cray-2 (1985) and the Cray Y-MP (1988). In 1989 Cray established Cray Computer Corp., which was eventually forced to file for bankruptcy (1995) as advances in technology made it possible for smaller computers to reach the processing speeds of much larger supercomputers. Undaunted, however, Cray opened another company, SRC Computer Inc., in August 1996, only two months before his death as a result of injuries sustained in a car crash.

Erdos, Paul
March 26, 1913—Sept. 20, 1996

Hungarian mathematician Paul Erdos pioneered the fields of number theory and combinatorics and was regarded as one of the century's greatest mathematicians. At the age of 20, he discovered a proof for a classic theorem of number theory that states that there is always at least one prime number between any positive integer and its double. After receiving (1934) a Ph.D. from the University of Budapest,

Erdos was awarded a postdoctoral fellowship at the University of Manchester, Eng. In 1938 he immigrated to the United States. On fellowship at the Institute for Advanced Study in Princeton, N.J., Erdos founded the study of probabilistic number theory with Aurel Wintner and Mark Kac and proved important results in approximation theory with Paul Turan. Erdos and Atle Selberg astounded the mathematics community in 1949 by giving an elementary proof of the prime number theorem—for more than 50 years it had been assumed that no elementary proof could be given. After spending much of the 1950s in Israel, Erdos traveled almost constantly, earning a reputation as a restless "wandering scholar" who collaborated with hundreds of mathematicians on a variety of problems. "Another roof, another proof," was his legendary motto. In later years Erdos worked primarily in the field of combinatorics, an area of mathematics fundamental to computer science. When he won the Wolf Foundation Prize in 1983, he gave fellow mathematicians most of the prize money he received. He also received many honorary degrees and was a member of the Hungarian Academy of Sciences (1956), and he was a foreign associate of the academies of the United States (1979), India (1988), and the United Kingdom (1989). At the time of his death, Erdos had published more than 1,500 mathematical papers.

Huggins, Charles Brenton
Sept. 22, 1901—Jan. 12, 1997

Canadian-born U.S. surgeon and medical researcher Charles Huggins specialized in the surgical and therapeutic treatment of cancer of the prostate and mammary glands and shared (with Peyton Rous) the 1966 Nobel Prize for Physiology or Medicine for discovering the influence that hormones have on the onset and growth of certain forms of human cancer. His work demonstrated that cancer cells are not necessarily autonomous and self-perpetuating and that some depend on chemical signals such as hormones to survive. This insight led to the development of hormone therapy as a treatment for endocrine-dependent tumors. Huggins graduated from Harvard Medical School (M.D., 1924) and began his career as a surgeon at the University of Michigan. In 1927 he joined the faculty at the University of Chicago, where he served (1951–69) as director of the university's Ben May Laboratory for Cancer Research. Although initially involved in urology research, Huggins became intrigued in the early 1930s by discoveries being made in the field of cancer research by the German biochemist Otto Warburg, who won a Nobel Prize in 1931. Through his own research, Huggins discovered that the growth of prostate cancer could be stemmed by lowering levels of androgens, the male sex hormones, either by removal of the testes or by administration of diethylstilbestrol, a synthetic female sex hormone. In 1944, recognizing that the adrenal glands were compensating for the loss of androgens in some treated patients whose prostate cancer recurred, Huggins performed the first complete removal of the adrenal glands, although this was considered a radical treatment to be used only as a last resort. Huggins turned his attention to breast cancer in the 1950s and showed that removal of the ovaries and adrenal glands combined with cortisone-replacement therapy was beneficial to 30–40% of women who were treated. His work led to the development of a test to distinguish between two types of breast cancer—one that was hormone-dependent and the other not—which helped determine the patients who would benefit from this treatment. Huggins became involved in the 1960s controversy over whether birth control pills stimulated the growth of cancer of the breast and other reproductive organs, and he maintained that data collected throughout 30 years of research did not support this link. In addition to the Nobel Prize, Huggins received a number of awards, including the Lasker Clinical Research Award in 1963. He was also the author of a number of books, notably *Experimental Leukemia and Mammary Cancer: Induction, Prevention, Cure* (1979).

Kuhn, Thomas S.
July 18, 1922—June 17, 1996

U.S. philosopher of science Thomas Kuhn was the author of *The Structure of Scientific Revolutions* (1962), one of the most widely read and influential books in 20th-century social sciences, humanities, and philosophy. Kuhn studied physics at Harvard University, where he earned (1949) a

Ph.D. in physics. He remained there as a junior fellow, then taught at the University of California, Berkeley, Princeton University, and the Massachusetts Institute of Technology. His first book, *The Copernican Revolution* (1957), was a study of the development of Renaissance heliocentrism. His second book, *The Structure of Scientific Revolutions,* argued that scientific work and thought are defined by "paradigms" consisting of formal theories, classic experiments, and trusted methods. Scientists use the resources of paradigms to refine theories, explain puzzling data, and establish increasingly precise measures of standards and phenomena. Confidence in paradigms, however, can be eroded by unresolvable theoretical problems or experimental anomalies, and the accumulation of such difficulties eventually creates a crisis that can be resolved only by revolutions in which new paradigms are formulated to replace the old. The overthrow of Ptolemaic cosmology by Copernican heliocentrism and Newtonian mechanics by quantum physics and general relativity are both examples of fundamental paradigm shifts. The book received polite but not extravagant reviews and significant criticism when it first appeared. By the mid-1960s, however, it had clearly become one of the most influential works in post-World War II scholarship. It revolutionized the history and philosophy of science by inspiring accounts that gave increased weight to external social and cultural factors in shaping scientific work and thought and made the term *paradigm* part of common English. Kuhn's collection of essays, *The Essential Tension* (1977), was followed by his last book, *Black-Body Theory and the Quantum Discontinuity*

(1978), a highly technical study that some considered an implicit rejection of his earlier work.

Leakey, Mary Douglas
Feb. 6, 1913—Dec. 9, 1996

British-born archaeologist and paleoanthropologist Mary Leakey made a number of significant finds of prehuman fossils in East Africa, discoveries that helped to supplant the formerly held notion that the human species evolved in Asia. Through her work as an excavator and an illustrator of tools found at various archaeological sites in England, she met archaeologist Louis Leakey; they were married in 1936 and shortly thereafter left for an expedition to East Africa, an area that became the central location of their work. Her skill at the painstaking work of excavation surpassed her husband's, whose brilliance lay in interpreting and publicizing the fossils that she uncovered. Her first important find was made in 1948 on Rusinga Island in Lake Victoria, Kenya. There she unearthed the skull of *Proconsul africanus,* an 18 million-year-old apelike creature. Her next major discovery was made on July 17, 1959, at Olduvai Gorge, the now-famous ravine in the Great Rift Valley of Tanzania. The jaw of the early hominid *Zinjanthropus* (now *Australopithecus*) *boisei* that she teased from its 1,750,000-year-old resting place brought worldwide recognition to the couple, although the claim that this was the "missing link" between primitive ape-men and early humans was later disproved. Not long after this find, the Leakey team discovered in a nearby spot in Olduvai Gorge skull fragments more similar to a modern human's, designated *Homo habilis*. After her husband's

Mary Douglas Leakey and husband, Louis Leakey

death in 1972, Leakey continued her work in Africa. In 1978 at Laetoli, a site about 48 km (30 mi) south of Olduvai Gorge, she made what she believed was her most important find, a trail of several sets of hominid footprints preserved in volcanic ash that were approximately 3.5 million years old. These prints provided evidence that hominids walked in an upright position at a much earlier date than had previously been thought. Leakey retired from fieldwork in 1983 and in 1984 published an autobiography, *Disclosing the Past*.

Mazia, Daniel
Dec. 18, 1912—June 9, 1996

U.S. cell biologist Daniel Mazia studied the structure, division, and regulation of cells and was best known for having isolated the cellular structures involved in mitosis (the process by which chromosomes within the nucleus of a cell double and divide), research that he carried out in 1951 with Japanese biologist Katsuma Dan. Mazia, who was interested in all aspects of cell reproduction, focused on a variety of other issues in cellular biology, such as the role of DNA in chromosomes and the function of the centrosome, an organizing structure of the cell. He carried his enthusiasm into the classroom, where he was a stimulating and inspiring lecturer. Mazia was raised in Philadelphia and studied zoology at the University of Pennsylvania (A.B., 1933; Ph.D., 1937). After graduation he was a National Research Council fellow at Princeton University and at the Marine Biological Laboratories in Woods Hole, Mass. Between 1938 and 1950 he taught at the University of Missouri, taking time out to serve in World War II. Mazia joined the faculty of the University of California, Berkeley, where he was professor of zoology until his retirement in 1979. He then moved to Stanford University and was professor emeritus of biological sciences at the Hopkins Marine Station in Pacific Grove, Calif. Mazia was a member of the National Academy of Sciences and the American Academy of Arts and Sciences, and he served one term as president of the International Cell Research Organization of UNESCO.

Mott, Sir Nevill Francis
Sept. 30, 1905—Aug. 8, 1996

British physicist Sir Nevill Francis Mott shared the 1977 Nobel Prize for Physics with Philip Anderson and John Van Vleck for research into the electronic properties of noncrystalline, or amorphous, solids. This work showed that amorphous materials, which are easier and less expensive to manufacture than crystalline substances, could be used in such electronic tools as computers, pocket calculators, and transistor radios. Although originally interested in the theoretical aspects of quantum mechanics, Mott focused on the practical applications of this knowledge. His interest in science was inspired by his parents, who studied at Cavendish Laboratory with J.J. Thomson, the discoverer of the electron. After receiving a master's degree in 1930 from the University of Cambridge, Mott became a fellow and lecturer at Gonville and Caius College, Cambridge, serving there later (1959–66) as master. In 1933 he moved to the University of Bristol as a professor of theoretical physics, and in 1948 he became director of the physics laboratories there. He then was appointed Cavendish professor of physics at Cambridge, a position he held from 1954 until he retired in 1971. During his tenures at Bristol and Cambridge, Mott staffed his laboratories with world-class scientists, who made significant contributions to solid-state physics. Mott also published such influential books as *The Theory of Atomic Collisions* (1933; with H.S.W. Massey) and *Electronic Processes in Ionic*

Crystals (1940; with R.W. Gurney). He was elected a fellow of the Royal Society of London in 1936 and knighted in 1962.

Peterson, Roger Tory
Aug. 28, 1908—July 28, 1996

U.S. ornithologist, author, conservationist, and wildlife artist Roger Tory Peterson wrote the pocket-size field guides that were instrumental in stimulating U.S. and European interest in the study of birds. His illustrations emphasized the features that would aid in identification of each species and used arrows to indicate key characteristics; he grouped birds on the basis of their resemblance to one another instead of by species; and he included descriptions that were short and to the point. Peterson became interested in nature, and especially birds, when he was a young boy. His seventh-grade science teacher encouraged him to apply his meticulous attention to detail to the drawing of birds. Peterson studied in New York City at the Art Students League (1927–29) and the National Academy of Design (1929–31). He then taught (1931–34) at the Rivers School, Brookline, Mass., and worked (1934–43)

Roger Tory Peterson

for the National Audubon Society. A fellow birder, impressed with Peterson's knowledge, had suggested that he produce a guide, and in 1934 *A Field Guide to the Birds* was published—after having been rejected by at least four publishers. The initial print run of 2,000 sold out within two weeks. Many other books followed, some in the field guide series and others of a more general nature, among them *A Field Guide to Western Birds* (1941), *Birds over America* (1948), *A Field Guide to the Birds of Britain and Europe* (1954; coauthored with Guy Mountfort and P.A.D. Hollom), and *Wild America* (1955). Peterson's books sold in the millions and were translated into at least a dozen languages. His awards included the New York Zoological Society Gold Medal (1961), the World Wildlife Fund Gold Medal (1972), and the Presidential Medal of Freedom (1980). He was twice nominated for the Nobel Peace Prize. In 1986 the Roger Tory Peterson Institute of Natural History was founded in Jamestown, N.Y.

Reichstein, Tadeus
July 20, 1897—Aug. 1, 1996

Polish-born Swiss chemist Tadeus Reichstein identified the steroid hormones of the adrenal cortex and studied their structure and biological effects. For his role in this discovery, he shared the Nobel Prize for Physiology or Medicine in 1950 with Philip S. Hench and Edward C. Kendall, who carried out independent research on steroids. Reichstein showed that the adrenal cortex, the outer portion of the adrenal glands, located at the upper ends of the kidneys, produces many hormones. He and his colleagues isolated and examined about 29 of them, including cortisone, which was

discovered to be an anti-inflammatory agent useful in the treatment of arthritis. Reichstein graduated (1920) with a degree in chemical engineering from the Federal Institute of Technology, Zürich, where he obtained a Ph.D. two years later. In 1930 he became an instructor there, and he had risen to the level of associate professor by the time he left in 1937. His early research with Nobel Prize-winning chemist Hermann Staudinger included identifying the chemicals in coffee that impart flavour and aroma, work that provided the basis for the development of powdered coffee. He also devised a method for synthesizing (1933) vitamin C in the laboratory, a procedure that remained widely in use in commercial production of the vitamin. In 1938 Reichstein moved to the University of Basel and was appointed director of the Pharmaceutical Institute; in 1946 he became head of the newly created Institute of Organic Chemistry. There he studied plant-derived glycosides, chemicals that have a wide range of biological effects, to determine their usefulness as pharmaceuticals. This work also was important in plant classification. Although he retired in 1967, Reichstein conducted significant research into his 90s.

Sagan, Carl Edward
Nov. 9, 1934—Dec. 20, 1996

U.S. astronomer and exobiologist Carl Sagan studied such diverse aspects of the solar system as the conditions of planetary surfaces and atmospheres and the possibility of extraterrestrial life; he stimulated popular interest in these subjects through his enthusiastic writings, lectures, and televised presentations. An avid reader of science fiction as a boy, Sagan developed an

Carl Sagan

interest in astronomy early in life. He studied at the University of Chicago, where he earned four degrees (A.B., 1954; B.S., 1955; M.S., physics, 1956; and Ph.D., astronomy and astrophysics, 1960). After graduation he lectured at the University of California, Berkeley, and at Harvard University before moving to Cornell University, Ithaca, N.Y., in 1968. There he became director of the Laboratory for Planetary Studies and (1970) professor (from 1976 David Duncan professor) of astronomy and space sciences. Some of Sagan's earliest theories about planetary conditions concerned Mars and Venus, predictions that were confirmed by unmanned space probes during the late 1960s and '70s. Sagan was involved in designing experiments to be carried out on a number of these planetary missions. Intrigued since his graduate-school days by the question of the way that life on Earth originated, Sagan conducted experiments showing how various organic molecules could be produced from a simulated gaseous atmosphere of primitive Earth. Sagan's willingness to speculate about the possibility of life elsewhere in the universe helped to gain credibility for the search for extraterrestrial life. He also perceived the threat that the nuclear arms race posed to humanity, and in 1983 he coauthored an article warning about the possible consequences of a nuclear exchange. Although scenarios, such as an atmospheric cooling dubbed "nuclear winter," predicted by the authors were shown to be unlikely, the article spurred discussion of this serious topic. Sagan was a prolific writer of popular science and won a Pulitzer Prize in 1978 for *The Dragons of Eden: Speculations on the Evolution of Human Intelligence*. His passion for science was contagious, and his ability to inspire others to share that interest became evident when the TV series "Cosmos," a program he narrated and helped to write, began airing in 1980 and became an immediate success.

Salam, Abdus
Jan. 29, 1926—Nov. 21, 1996

Pakistani physicist Abdus Salam shared the 1979 Nobel Prize for Physics with Steven Weinberg and Sheldon Lee Glashow. Each had independently formulated a theory explaining the underlying unity of the weak nuclear force and the electromagnetic force, two of the four basic forces of nature. This so-called electroweak theory showed that the two forces are actually manifestations of a single fundamental force and laid the groundwork for the development of an as-yet-unachieved unified field theory, in which all four forces of nature (including the strong nuclear force and gravity) are described in terms of a single framework. Salam was the first person from an Islamic country to win a Nobel Prize. He received the highest scores ever recorded on an entrance examination to the Punjab University system and entered Government College at Lahore to study mathematics (M.A., 1946). Salam won a scholarship to the University of Cambridge, where he took highest honors in mathematics and physics (B.A., 1949) and received a doctorate in theoretical physics (1952). He went on to teach in Pakistan (1951–54), but frustration at the dearth of research opportunities in his native land prompted him to return to Cambridge. In 1957 he became professor of theoretical physics at the Imperial College of Science, Technology, and Medicine, University of London, and carried out research there until his death. Salam, who was interested in the education and professional development of scientists in Third World countries, helped found the International Centre for Theoretical Physics in Trieste, Italy, a research institute set up to train young scientists from less-developed countries. He served as director of the

Abdus Salam

institute (1964–93) and president (1994–96) and was involved in a number of international and national committees, such as the United Nations Advisory Committee on Science and Technology (1964–75) and Pakistan's Atomic Energy Commission (1958–74). He was elected a fellow of the Royal Society in 1959 and was the recipient of many awards, including the Copley Medal (1990).

Snell, George Davis
Dec. 19, 1903—June 6, 1996

U.S. immunogeneticist George Davis Snell was a winner, with Baruj Benacerraf and Jean Dausset, of the 1980 Nobel Prize for Physiology or Medicine for research into the genes that determine proteins located on the surface of cells that control the body's immune response to foreign tissue grafts. This work enabled transplant surgeons to make better matches between organ and tissue donors and the intended recipients and thereby reduce the threat of graft rejection. Snell conducted his experiments at the Jackson Laboratory in Bar Harbor, Maine, where he spent most of his professional career studying mammalian genetics. He was educated at Dartmouth College, Hanover, N.H. (B.S., 1926), and Harvard University (Sc.D., 1930). After graduating he received a National Research Council fellowship to work at the University of Texas at Austin with the future Nobelist Hermann J. Muller, who was using X-rays to produce mutations in the chromosomes of fruit flies. In 1935 Snell moved to the Jackson Laboratory and studied X-ray-induced mutations in mice. In the 1940s he changed his focus to the genetics of organ and tissue transplantation, collaborating with the British geneti-cist Peter Gorer. In experiments carried out in mice, the two scientists identified the chromosomal location of genetic factors responsible for tissue rejection. The group of proteins that these genes encode, called the major histocompatibility complex, is found in all higher vertebrates, where it plays an extremely important role in the rejection of not only foreign tissue grafts but also many other foreign substances. Snell was credited with coining the term *histocompatibility* (*histo,* from the Greek word meaning "web," denotes tissue). He was elected to the American Academy of Arts and Sciences in 1952 and to the National Academy of Sciences in 1970.

Ter-Pogossian, Michel M.
April 21, 1925—June 19, 1996

German-born U.S. medical physicist Michel Ter-Pogossian developed the concept of positron emission tomography (PET) and applied this theory in designing and building the PET scanner, a diagnostic imaging tool used to visualize both anatomic structure and physiological activities within the human body. During the 1970s the "father of PET" led a research team of physical scientists, chemists, and physicians who developed the PET concept. His research improved many other techniques of medical imaging as well. Ter-Pogossian, the son of a prominent Armenian family that fled to France during World War I to escape persecution, was born in Berlin. As a student during World War II he was involved in the French Resistance, and after finishing his undergraduate degree at the University of Paris (B.A., 1942), he studied with Irène Joliot-Curie at the Radium Institute (now the Curie Institute) in Paris (1943–46). He earned (1950) his doctorate in nuclear physics from Washington University, St. Louis, Mo., and joined the university's Mallinckrodt Institute of Radiology, where he remained throughout his career. There he made improvements in X-ray tomography, radiation therapy, and brachytherapy, including the building of a tool called the "pogo," which delivers radiation therapy for cancers of the cervix and uterus. His research also resulted in a new form of nuclear medicine gamma camera called the Ter-Pogossian camera. By recognizing the potential of using short-lived radioactive tracers to study chemical processes of the body, he was able to form the foundation of PET-scanning technology. The tracers used in PET scanning, such as oxygen and carbon, are short-lived isotopes of chemicals normally found in the body. Because these tracers become active participants in biochemical activities, PET scanning can provide important information about biochemical functions as well as the anatomic information that other forms of imaging, such as ultrasonography or computed tomography, can provide. Ter-Pogossian served as an adviser to various U.S. Department of Energy and National Institutes of Health committees and as an editorial board member of several scientific journals, including the *American Journal of Roentgenology.*

Thimann, Kenneth Vivian
Aug. 5, 1904—Jan. 15, 1997

British-born U.S. plant physiologist Kenneth Thimann isolated and purified the plant hormone auxin and identified it as a chemical messenger with principal roles in regulating plant growth. After receiving (1928) a doctorate in biochemistry from

417

Imperial College, University of London, Thimann joined the faculty of the California Institute of Technology in 1930 and began conducting research to isolate the universal growth substance that was known to control plant growth toward light and against the force of gravity. A few years earlier Dutch plant physiologist Frits Went had extracted the growth-stimulating substance from seedlings. Thimann demonstrated that auxin not only stimulated cell growth but also exerted an inhibitory effect on it. He identified the three main functions of auxin—cell elongation (with James Bonner), root formation (with Went), and bud growth (with Folke Skoog). Thimann's elucidation of the chemical structure of auxin allowed the hormone to be synthetically manufactured and put to use for a variety of purposes in farming and horticulture. For example, by spraying fruit trees with auxin prior to harvest, growers could prevent the premature falling of fruit (especially apples). Auxin was also found useful in promoting the joining of grafts and, in high concentrations, in controlling weeds. Thimann also investigated other aspects of plant physiology such as the formation of pigments in plants, the role of various wavelengths of light in photosynthesis, and the mechanisms involved in plant aging. He continued his research at Harvard University (1935–65) and moved to the University of California, Santa Cruz, where he served (1965–72) as the founding provost of Crown College. He was a member of the U.S. National Academy of Sciences and the American Academy of Arts and Sciences and published more than 300 research papers and a number of influential books, including *Phytohormones* (1937;

with Went), and *Hormone Action in the Whole Life of Plants* (1977).

Todd (of Trumpington), Alexander Robertus Todd, Baron
Oct. 2, 1907—Jan. 10, 1997

Scottish organic chemist Alexander Todd, who studied the chemistry of a variety of chemicals involved in life processes, was awarded the 1957 Nobel Prize for Chemistry for his discovery of the structure and synthesis of the nucleotides that are subunits of nucleic acids—the hereditary material of cells. His work provided the foundation for further studies into the physical structure and biological function of nucleic acids, particularly the discovery of the double-helical structure of DNA by James Watson, Francis Crick, and Maurice Wilkins. Todd received doctorates from the Universities of Frankfurt, Ger. (1931), and Oxford (1934). He held posts at the University of Edinburgh, where he was one of the first chemists to study the structure of vitamin B_1 (thiamine). Although his method for synthesizing the vitamin was not the first, it proved the most well-suited to industrial application and is still used in manufacturing. From 1938 to 1944 he continued his research at the University of Manchester, Eng., studying the chemistry of a variety of compounds, including vitamin E, substances found in marijuana and hashish, and nucleosides and nucleotides. Todd temporarily interrupted his research during World War II to develop and produce gases to be used in chemical warfare. He accepted the chair in organic chemistry at the University of Cambridge, where he spent the greater part of his career (1944–71) and carried out his most important work. During this time Todd synthesized

the nucleoside adenosine as well as adenosine diphosphate and triphosphate (ADP and ATP), nucleotides that are not subunits of nucleic acids but are responsible for energy production and energy storage in plant and animal cells. He also established the structure of the coenzyme flavin adenine dinucleotide (FAD) and was involved in working out the structure of vitamin B_{12}. Todd was knighted in 1954, created a life peer in 1962, and made a member of the Royal Order of Merit in 1977. His autobiography, *A Time to Remember: The Autobiography of a Chemist*, was published in 1983.

Tombaugh, Clyde William
Feb. 4, 1906—Jan. 17, 1997

U.S. astronomer Clyde Tombaugh discovered the planet Pluto, the ninth planet in the solar system and the only one found in the 20th century. Tombaugh was 24 years of age when he made the discovery in 1930 at Lowell Observatory in Flagstaff, Ariz. At that time he had had no formal training in astronomy, only a keen interest that had been sharpened by his first glimpse of the heavens through his uncle's telescope. After finishing high school, Tombaugh built his own telescope according to specifications published in a 1925 issue of *Popular Astronomy*. Using this instrument, he made observations of Jupiter and Mars and sent sketches of these planets to Lowell Observatory, hoping to receive advice about his work. Instead, he received a job offer. Tombaugh's assignment was to locate the ninth planet, a search instigated in 1905 by astronomer Percival Lowell. To carry out this task Tombaugh used a 33-cm (13-in) telescope to photograph the sky and an instrument called a blink comparator to examine the plates for signs of moving celestial bodies. On Feb. 18, 1930, Tombaugh pinpointed Pluto, and on March 13 Lowell Observatory announced the discovery of a new planet. After his discovery Tombaugh attended the University of Kansas on a scholarship, returning each summer to the observatory until completing (1938–39) his M.A. in astronomy. Upon graduating he returned to the observatory and continued his patrol of the skies, cataloguing more than 30,000 celestial objects before he left in 1946. His observations of Mars led him to conclude in 1950 that the surface of the planet was pitted with craters as a result of its proximity to the asteroid belt, a prediction borne out by images taken by the Mariner 4 space probe in the 1960s. Tombaugh also taught at Arizona State College, Flagstaff, and at the University of California, Los Angeles, and he worked as an astronomer and optical physicist at White Sands Proving Grounds near Las Cruces, N.M., where he helped set up an optical tracking system to follow ballistic missiles. He joined the faculty of New Mexico State University in 1955 and there instituted a major program of planetary research. He retired in 1973 but remained involved as an observer and adviser at the university. In 1980 he published, with Patrick Moore, *Out of the Darkness: The Planet Pluto.*

Whittle, Sir Frank
June 1, 1907—Aug. 8, 1996

British aviation engineer Frank Whittle was a pioneer in the field of jet propulsion, which he used to develop aircraft that could fly at faster speeds and higher altitudes than airplanes of the 1920s. Whittle patented the turbojet engine in 1930 and in 1936 formed the company Power Jets to build and test his invention. The engine was tested on the ground in 1937 and made its first flight in the Gloster E.28/39 aircraft on May 15, 1941. Whittle's was not the first jet-propelled aircraft to lift off, however. The German engineer Hans Pabst von Ohain, who had independently conceived of the jet engine, had flown the first jet-propelled aircraft on Aug. 27, 1939. After the start of World War II, the British Air Ministry contracted Whittle's company to produce aircraft for the Royal Air Force (RAF), although up to that time the British government had shown little interest in Whittle's invention. Growing up, Whittle was influenced by his father, a mechanic known for his inventiveness. Whittle joined the RAF as an apprentice at the age of 16 and soon entered RAF College, Cranwell, as a cadet. He wrote a thesis on "Future Developments in Aircraft Design" and graduated in 1928. He then served as a flying instructor and a test pilot and continued his studies at the RAF engineering school and the University of Cambridge, where he delved into mechanical sciences. He was promoted to air commodore near the end of the war and retired from the RAF in 1948, the same year he was knighted. In recognition of his work, Whittle was awarded a tax-free gift of £100,000 by the British government. He subsequently served as a consultant for various organizations, including the British Overseas Airways Corporation (1948–52), the Shell Group (1952–57), and Bristol-Siddeley Engines (1961–70). He moved to the U.S. in 1976 and the following year began work as a research professor at the U.S. Naval Academy at Annapolis, Md.

Wilkinson, Sir Geoffrey
July 14, 1921—Sept. 26, 1996

British chemist Geoffrey Wilkinson was the corecipient, with Ernst Fischer, of the 1973 Nobel Prize for Chemistry for work in organometallic chemistry in which the "sandwich" structure and properties of molecules known as metallocenes—with a metal atom between two flat hydrocarbon rings—was identified. Their explanation of this previously unknown manner in which metals and organic substances could merge opened up new areas of research. Wilkinson was studying for his Ph.D. at the Imperial College of Science and Technology, University of London, when he was recruited (1943) to work with the Atomic Energy Project in Canada. After teaching at the University of California, Berkeley (1946–50), the Massachusetts Institute of Technology (1950–51), and Harvard University (1951–55), he returned (1956) to Imperial College, where he served as professor (Sir Edward Frankland professor from 1978) of inorganic chemistry until becoming professor emeritus in 1988. He continued with his research until his death. Wilkinson's work on organometallic compounds led to discoveries having significant industrial applications—among them, catalysts used in producing low-lead fuels and the compound known as Wilkinson's catalyst, which aided in the development of methods for synthesizing pharmaceutical chemicals. With F.A. Cotton, Wilkinson published a textbook, *Advanced Inorganic Chemistry* (1962), that became a standard. He completed his work on its sixth edition the week before he died. Wilkinson was elected a fellow of the Royal Society in 1965 and was knighted in 1976.

RECENT BOOKS OF SCIENCE

The following list includes 47 recent books in English in 1996 that have been judged significant contributions to learning in their respective areas of science. Each citation includes a few lines of commentary to indicate the tenor of the work. The citations are organized by broad subject area, using the appropriate parts of *Encyclopædia Britannica*'s Propædia as an outline.

Matter and Energy

David Arnett, *Supernovae and Nucleosynthesis: An Investigation of the History of Matter from the Big Bang to the Present,* a description of the physics of galactic and stellar evolution from the origin of matter and the synthesis of helium and hydrogen to the creation of atomic nuclei.

Huw Price, *Time's Arrow and Archimedes' Point: New Directions for the Physics of Time,* an application of the paradoxes of quantum theory to the symmetry of time and "backward causation," showing that the future influences the past.

Sidney Perkowitz, *Empire of Light: A History of Discovery in Science and Art,* a history and appreciation of light from its oldest detectable manifestation (infrared cosmic background radiation) to its relation to the physiology of vision.

Giuseppe Bertin and C.C. Lin, *Spiral Structure in Galaxies: A Density Wave Theory,* a theory that characterizes spiral galaxies as wave rather than material phenomena and takes note of similarities between these spirals and hurricanes.

The Earth

Jerry Dennis, *The Bird in the Waterfall: A Natural History of Oceans, Rivers, and Lakes,* a medley of scientific observation, folklore, historical anecdote, and sailors' yarns about wave physics, the hydrosphere, and the phenomenon of biological adaptation as exemplified by the dipper, the bird in the waterfall.

Cindy Lee Van Dover, *The Octopus's Garden: Hydrothermal Vents and Other Mysteries of the Deep Sea,* a firsthand account of Earth's last frontier, the unknown terrain 2,750–3,660 m (9,000–12,000 ft) below sea level, and its flora, fauna, and geologic profile, with a description of the rigors of deep-sea science.

David Laskin, *Braving the Elements: The Stormy History of American Weather,* an account of efforts, from the rain dance to computer models, to influence or understand the U.S.'s turbulent weather, with a consideration of the effects of industrial pollution and other human interactions.

Ian Thornton, *Krakatau: The Destruction and Reassembly of an Island Ecosystem,* the description of a catastrophic volcanic eruption in 1883 and its aftermath as animal and plant species reestablished themselves.

J.D. MacDougall, *A Short History of Planet Earth: Mountains, Mammals, Fire, and Ice,* an overview of the 4.5 billion-year life span of Earth's landmasses and seas, a history gleaned from rocks and fossils.

Life on Earth

Steven J. Dick, *The Biological Universe: The Twentieth-Century Extraterrestrial Life Debate and the Limits of Science,* a chronicle of the ongoing search for intelligent life elsewhere in the universe.

Stephen L. Buchmann and Gary Paul Nabhan, *The Forgotten Pollinators,* a description of the 100 million-year-old coevolution of plants and insects that stresses the economic and ecological importance of insect pollinators and urges research leading to conservation.

David E. Fastovsky and David B. Weishampel, *The Evolution and Extinction of the Dinosaurs,* current thinking on dinosaur origins, diversity, and extinction that calls into question traditional ideas.

Alan Feduccia, *The Origin and Evolution of Birds,* a detailed history and an analysis of avian evolution, presenting evidence for birds' relatively rapid development from tree-dwelling rather than ground-dwelling progenitors.

Alexander F. Skutch, *The Minds of Birds,* a characterization of the mental and emotional lives of birds, based on 60 years of observation of 9,000 species, that, without anthropomorphizing, offers examples of a rich array of avian cognitive and emotional abilities, such as memory, counting, and a strong aesthetic sense.

Frans de Waal, *Good Natured: The Origins of Right and Wrong in Humans and Other Animals,* an argument that ethical and altruistic behaviors are neither exclusive to humans nor recent but rather are fundamental adaptive and decision-making characteristics essential to species survival.

David Quammen, *The Song of the Dodo: Island Biogeography in an Age of Extinctions,* a description of islands as protectors of biodiversity and as laboratories for the study of species distribution that expresses concern over the escalating pace of species extinction and collapsing ecosystems.

John Leslie, *The End of the World: The Science and Ethics of Human Extinction,* a philosopher-scientist's musings on the imminence of doomsday, both human-induced (pollution, nuclear war) and cosmic (asteroids).

Theo Colborn, *Our Stolen Future: Are We Threatening Our Fertility, Intelligence, and Survival?—A Scientific Detective Story,* an account of the threat to plant and animal heredity caused by chemicals still in common use, warning of the dangers to the fetus from these endocrine-attacking substances.

Colin Tudge, *The Time Before History: 5 Million Years of Human Impact,* a reflection on the symbiotic relationship between humans and ecological and planetary forces over time that comments on the effects of agriculture and "depletion hunting" (and, more recently, industrialization) on the Earth's deep planetary rhythms.

Tom Athanasiou, *Divided Planet: The Ecology of Rich and Poor,* a skeptical view of the value of recycling and energy conservation as agents for halting environmental degradation without first controlling the growth of industrialized nations.

Human Life

Rick Potts, *Humanity's Descent: The Consequences of Ecological Instability,* a dynamic view of human evolution, theorizing that the prehistoric climate was chaotic and unstable, rather than static, imposing on early humans the need to assume adaptive behaviors in order for the species to survive.

Alan Walker and Pat Shipman, *The Wisdom of the Bones: In Search of Human Origins,* a story of the discovery and piecing together of a 1.5 million-year-old fossil skeleton, possibly the missing link, that folds into the narrative a concise history of paleoanthropology.

Paul Mellars, *The Neanderthal Legacy: An Archaeological Perspective from Western Europe,* a reassessment of the contributions made by the Neanderthals to the anatomically modern populations that succeeded them.

Philip Kitcher, *The Lives to Come: The Genetic Revolution and Human Possibilities,* an account of the revolution in genetics and its ethical implications, beginning with the identification of the role of DNA and culminating in the Human Genome Project.

Stanley Coren, *Sleep Thieves: An Eye-Opening Exploration into the Science and Mysteries of Sleep,* a collection of facts, rumors, and folklore about sleep, with warnings on the economic and social costs of sleep deprivation and the threat to health and safety.

John J. Medina, *The Clock of Ages: Why We Age, How We Age: Winding Back the Clock,* a molecular biologist's characterization of human aging that examines the ambiguity of death (Is "brain dead" dead?), the ethics of aging and death, and the way aging takes place in each human biological system.

Daniel C. Dennett, *Kinds of Minds: Toward an Understanding of Consciousness,* a philosophical investigation of the properties and qualities of human and animal minds that speculates on the nature of consciousness and the place of language.

Daniel L. Schacter, *Searching for Memory: The Brain, the Mind, and the Past,* an analysis of memory, what it is, how it works, and how factors such as aging or trauma affect it, with descriptions of varieties of memory and of the cognitive psychologists, clinicians, and neuroscientists who promote an understanding of its mechanics.

Human Society

Heather Pringle, *In Search of Ancient North America: An Archaeological Journey to Forgotten Cultures,* a visit to nine geographically and culturally diverse prehistoric sites in North America, where archaeologists have recently begun to recognize and carefully document the social complexity of these early societies.

Art

Barbara Maria Stafford, *Good Looking: Essays on the Virtue of Images,* studies of the relationship of art to the visualizing capabilities of computers, exploring the influence of science, philosophy, and ethics on what is viewed and how it is viewed.

John Hix, *The Glasshouse,* an account of the development of the glasshouse from its origins as a box for protecting a delicate plant to such virtuoso 19th-century structures as the Crystal Palace and large royal conservatories in the heyday of botanical collecting.

Technology

Edward Tenner, *Why Things Bite Back: Technology and the Revenge of Unintended Consequences,* an account of the unforeseen, often unfortunate, developments that stem from some of humankind's medical, chemical, biological, and mechanical achievements.

Stephen Fenichell, *Plastic: The Making of a Synthetic Century,* a history of plastic, from its origins as Parkesine in England (1862), that describes present-day efforts to make it biodegradable and to reduce its toxicity.

Sophia Behling and Stefan Behling, *Sol Power: The Evolution of Solar Architecture,* an argument in favor of emulating indigenous cultures by extracting maximum benefits from minimum resources and urging the use of solar auxiliaries to reduce depletion of the Earth's nonrenewable resources.

Richard Turton, *The Quantum Dot: A Journey into the Future of Microelectronics,* a look into the past at the microchip, into the present at the quantum dot (a created crystal with the wavelike properties predicted by quantum physics), and into a future where "designer atoms" will have unimagined power and capabilities.

Francisco Asensio Cerver, *New Bridges: Thematic Architecture,* a collection of photographs and descriptions of 15 bridges built within the past decade, illustrating the harmony between architecture and engineering, aesthetics and pragmatism.

Robert Buderi, *The Invention That Changed the World: How a Small Group of Radar Pioneers Won the Second World War and Launched a Tech-* nological Revolution, an account of the combined research efforts of Great Britain and the U.S. that culminated in the development of radar.

Gregory J.E. Rawlins, *Moths to the Flame: The Seductions of Computer Technology,* a discussion of computer technology and its effects on society and culture, speculating on the potential threat to privacy and ethics.

The History of Mankind

Frederick W. Lange (ed.), *Paths to Central American Prehistory,* contributions by specialists in pre-Columbian art, history, and archaeology that attempt to fill in gaps in the history of Honduras, El Salvador, and Panama from the Paleo-Indian period to the Spanish invasion.

The Branches of Knowledge

Clifford Pickover (ed.), *Fractal Horizons: The Future Use of Fractals,* essays on the variety of potential applications of fractals with examples of their contributions to fine art, music, medicine, and fashion.

Anthony Aveni, *Behind the Crystal Ball: Magic, Science, and the Occult from Antiquity Through the New Age,* a survey of the occult, superstition, magic, and science from the era when they were part of the same discipline to modern times.

John Horgan, *The End of Science: Facing the Limits of Knowledge in the Twilight of the Scientific Age,* a hypothesis presented through interviews with distinguished scientists that there are no more unexplored scientific frontiers with the possible exception of the search for a Final Unifying Theory.

Rocky (Edward W.) Kolb, *Blind Watchers of the Sky: The People and Ideas That Shaped Our View of the Universe,* sketches of Western thinkers and observers whose hypotheses about the cosmos laid the foundations of modern astronomy.

David Oldroyd, *Thinking About the Earth: A History of Ideas in Geology,* a synthesis of historical views of geology from the days of early maps to modern seismology and geochemistry.

Fritjof Capra, *The Web of Life: A New Scientific Understanding of Living Systems,* a proposal for an interdisciplinary "systems" approach to new discoveries in the biological, physical, psychological, and social sciences that would integrate them into a single context more intelligible and more meaningful to the layperson.

David Philip Miller and Peter Hanns Reill (eds.), *Visions of Empire: Voyages, Botany, and Representations of Nature,* a collection of essays on the sociology of scientific knowledge, describing the behavior of 18th-century European scientists and explorers when they discovered the indigenous peoples and plants of the Pacific.

William Agosta, *Bombardier Beetles and Fever Trees: A Close-Up Look at Chemical Warfare and Signals in Animals and Plants,* a study of chemical ecology and the uses of organic chemicals by plants and animals to poison, communicate, attract and repel, and camouflage, with suggestions that humans might substitute some of these natural chemicals for synthetics to reduce pollution from chemically intensive activities.

—Jean S. Gottlieb

CONTRIBUTORS TO THE SCIENCE YEAR IN REVIEW

Richard A. Anthes

Earth Sciences: Atmospheric Sciences. President, University Corporation for Atmospheric Research, Boulder, Colo.

George F. Bertsch

Physics: Nuclear Physics. Professor of Physics, University of Washington.

William A. Blanpied

Science Policy. Senior International Analyst, National Science Foundation, Washington, D.C.

Harold Borko

Electronics and Information Sciences: Computer Systems and Services. Professor Emeritus, University of California, Los Angeles.

John M. Bowen

Medical Sciences: Veterinary Medicine. Associate Dean for Research and Graduate Affairs and Professor of Pharmacology and Toxicology, College of Veterinary Medicine, University of Georgia, Athens.

Paul J. Campbell

Mathematics. Professor of Mathematics and Computer Science, Beloit College, Beloit, Wis.

David E. Collins

Materials Science and Engineering: Polymers. Graduate Research Assistant, School of Materials Engineering, Purdue University.

Dave Dooling

Space Exploration. Owner, D² Associates, Huntsville, Ala.

Rolfe C. Erickson

Earth Sciences: Geology and Geochemistry. Professor of Geology, Sonoma State University, Rohnert Park, Calif.

Jean S. Gottlieb

Recent Books of Science. Freelance Editor; Historian of Science.

Robert Haselkorn

Life Sciences: Molecular Biology and Genetics. F.L. Pritzker Distinguished Service Professor, Department of Molecular Genetics and Cell Biology, University of Chicago.

Charles King Hoyt

Architecture and Civil Engineering. Senior Editor, *Architectural Record.*

Lawrence W. Jones

Physics: Elementary-Particle Physics. Professor of Physics, University of Michigan, Ann Arbor.

John Patrick Jordan

Food and Agriculture: Agriculture (in part). Director, Southern Regional Research Center, USDA-ARS, New Orleans, La.

Lou Joseph

Medical Sciences: Dentistry. Medical Writer, Des Plaines, Ill.

Ronald H. Kaitchuck

Astronomy. Professor of Physics and Astronomy, Ball State University, Muncie, Ind.

Allan P. Katz

Materials Science and Engineering: Ceramics. Technical Team Leader for Structural Ceramics, Air Force Research Laboratory, Materials Directorate, Wright-Patterson Air Force Base, Ohio.

George B. Kauffman

Chemistry: Applied Chemistry. Professor of Chemistry, California State University, Fresno.

David B. Kitts

Earth Sciences: Paleontology. Professor Emeritus, Department of History of Science, University of Oklahoma, Norman.

Rebecca Kolberg

Medical Sciences: General Medicine. Senior On-line Editor, Time Life Medical.

Walter R.L. Lambrecht

Physics: Condensed-Matter Physics. Associate Professor, Department of Physics, Case Western Reserve University, Cleveland, Ohio.

Patricia Brazeel Lewis

Food and Agriculture: Agriculture (in part). Public Relations Consultant, New Jersey Agricultural Experiment Station, Rutgers University, New Brunswick, N.J.

Charles Lydeard

Life Sciences: Zoology. Assistant Professor of Biology, University of Alabama, Tuscaloosa.

Melvin H. Marx

Psychology (in part). Distinguished Visiting Professor of Psychology, Western Carolina University, Cullowhee, N.C.

Richard Monastersky

Earth Sciences: Oceanography. Earth Science Editor, *Science News,* Washington, D.C.

Franz J. Monssen

Electronics and Information Sciences: Electronics. Retired; formerly at City University of New York, Queensborough Community College.

Charles S. Mueller

Earth Sciences: Geophysics. Geophysicist, U.S. Geological Survey, Golden, Colo.

Gerhardt Muller

Transportation. Professor, Intermodalism, U.S. Merchant Marine Academy, Kings Point, N.Y.

Norman Myers

Environment. Honorary Visiting Fellow, Green College, Oxford, England.

Larry L. Naylor

Anthropology. Associate Professor, University of North Texas; Director of Cultural Sensitivity and Research Center, Denton.

Stuart L. Pimm

Life Sciences: Ecology. Professor of Ecology, University of Tennessee, Knoxville.

Marla Reicks

Food and Agriculture: Nutrition. Associate Professor, Department of Food Science and Nutrition, University of Minnesota.

John Rhea

Defense Research. Washington Bureau Chief, *Military & Aerospace Electronics.*

C. Paul Robinson

Energy (in part). President and Laboratories Director, Sandia National Laboratories, Albuquerque, N.M.

Mark R. Rosenzweig

Psychology (in part). Professor of Graduate Studies, Department of Psychology, University of California, Berkeley.

Frank B. Salisbury

Life Sciences: Botany. Professor of Plant Physiology, Plants, Soils, and Biometeorology Department, Utah State University, Logan.

Robert R. Shannon

Optical Engineering. Professor Emeritus, University of Arizona, Tucson.

Lawrence J. Shimkets

Life Sciences: Microbiology. Professor and Head of Microbiology, University of Georgia, Athens.

Leslie Smith

Earth Sciences: Hydrology. Professor of Earth and Ocean Sciences, University of British Columbia, Vancouver.

Michael B. Smith

Chemistry: Organic Chemistry. Professor, Department of Chemistry, University of Connecticut, Storrs.

Ben P. Stein

Physics: Atomic, Molecular, and Optical Physics. Science Writer, American Institute of Physics, College Park, Md.

Hans Georg Stern

Electronics and Information Sciences: Computers and Computer Science. Professional Expert, Los Angeles Unified School District, Calif.

Robert E. Stoffels

Electronics and Information Sciences: Telecommunications Systems. Consultant, Glen Ellyn, Ill.

Kevin P. Trumble

Materials Science and Engineering: Metals. Associate Professor of Materials Engineering, Purdue University, West Lafayette, Ind.

Philip R. Watson

Chemistry: Physical Chemistry. Professor, Department of Chemistry, Oregon State University, Corvallis.

James D. Wilde

Archaeology. Archaeologist, Headquarters, Air Force Center for Environmental Excellence, San Antonio, Texas.

Charles H. Winter

Chemistry: Inorganic Chemistry. Associate Professor, Department of Chemistry, Wayne State University, Detroit, Mich.

Joan B. Woodard

Energy (in part). Vice President, Energy, Environment, and Information Technology Division, Sandia National Laboratories, Albuquerque, N.M.

Michael Woods

Scientists of the Year: Nobel Prizes. Science Editor, Block News Alliance.

CONTRIBUTORS TO THE ENCYCLOPÆDIA BRITANNICA SCIENCE UPDATE

David M. Gates

The Biosphere and Concepts of Ecology (in part). Emeritus Professor of Biology, University of Michigan, Ann Arbor.

Glenn Patrick Juday

The Biosphere and Concepts of Ecology (in part). Associate Professor of Forest Ecology and Alaska Ecological Reserves Coordinator, University of Alaska, Fairbanks.

Michael John Kingsford

The Biosphere and Concepts of Ecology (in part). Senior Lecturer in Marine Biology, University of Sydney, Australia.

INDEX

This is a three-year cumulative index. Index entries for review articles in this and previous editions of the *Yearbook of Science and the Future* are set in boldface type, *e.g.,* **Astronomy.** Feature articles appear under the article title and are identified as such. Entries to other subjects are set in lightface type, *e.g.,* radiation. Additional information on any of these subjects is identified with a subheading and indented under the entry heading. Subheadings in quotes refer to feature articles on that topic. The numbers following headings and subheadings indicate the year (boldface) of the edition and the page number (lightface) on which the information appears. The abbreviation "*il.*" indicates an illustration.

Astronomy 98–252; **97**–276; **96**–322
 asteroids **96**–77
 honors **98**–404; **97**–407; **96**–468
 "How Old Is the Universe?" **97**–32

All entry headings are alphabetized word by word. Hyphenated words and words separated by dashes or slashes are treated as two words. When one word differs from another only by the presence of additional characters at the end, the shorter precedes the longer. In inverted names, the words following the comma are considered only after the preceding part of the name has been alphabetized. Names beginning with "Mc" and "Mac" are alphabetized as "Mac"; "St." is alphabetized as "Saint." Examples:

 Lake
 Lake, Simon
 Lake Placid
 Lakeland

A

AAAS: see American Association for the Advancement of Science
Aalto, Alvar
 architecture **97**–275
Aborigine (people)
 anthropology **96**–312
 scientific illustration **97**–136, *il.*
abortion
 RU-486 pill **96**–415
abscisic acid
 botany **96**–394
absorption (phys.)
 X-rays **98**–102
absorption bands
 asteroids **96**–82
abstract reasoning
 robots **98**–160
AC-130 gunship
 Bosnian mission **97**–295
accident and safety
 sleep deprivation **98**–51
 transportation **98**–393; **96**–452
 see also disaster
acetaminophen
 warning labels **96**–417
acetic acid
 chemical synthesis **97**–292
 wine **96**–187
Acheulean technology (anthro.) **96**–311
acid rain **97**–326; **96**–385
 mass extinction theory **98**–278
acidophile **98**–17
acoustic impedance
 aerogels **96**–158
Acoustic Thermometry of Ocean Climate, or ATOC **97**–307
acoustics: see sound
acquired immune deficiency syndrome: see AIDS
ACS: see asparagus crude saponin
activation
 molecular biology **98**–328
Active Desktop (operating system) **98**–295
actual density
 universe expansion **97**–42
actuator (electromechanical device)
 robot design **98**–158
ADA: see American Dental Association
adaptation (biol.)
 mass extinction **97**–78
 Neanderthals **98**–141
adaptive optics **97**–369
ADD: see attention deficit-hyperactivity disorder
adduct
 environmental pollution effect **98**–113
adenine
 DNA repair **96**–399
 translation **97**–344
adenosine triphosphate, or ATP
 molecular biology **96**–402
Adleman, Leonard **96**–410

Adobe Systems Inc. (Am. co.)
 computer software development **97**–314
Advanced Earth Observing Satellite, or ADEOS **98**–273, *il.*
advanced mobile phone system, or AMPS **98**–301; **96**–361
Advanced Photo System, or APS **90**–357
Advanced Photon Source, or APS **98**–97, 101, *il.*
Advanced Research Projects Agency: see Defense Advanced Research Projects Agency
advection (hydrology) **97**–307
Aedes aegypti (mosquito) **98**–275, *il.*
"Aerogels: The Lightest Solids" (feature article) **96**–146
aerosol
 global cooling effect **97**–296
 Jupiter-comet collision **96**–98, *il.* 99
aflatoxin **97**–330
Africa
 anthropology **98**–240; **96**–310
 archaeology **98**–247
 El Niño effects **96**–358
 "Indigenous Science: A Star in Africa's Future?" **96**–160
 Ordovician Period **97**–84
 science policy **97**–381
African hypothesis
 human origins **97**–266
Ageratum conyzoides: see goatweed
aggression
 beauty-behavior study **96**–51
 female masculinization **96**–228
aging
 memory **98**–371
 oral disease **97**–363
 osteoporosis **98**–348
 whales **97**–20
Agrani Satellite **97**–394
agriculture: see Food and agriculture
Agriculture, U.S. Department of, or USDA **98**–312
 dye-based insecticides **97**–291
 veterinary medicine **97**–366
AIDS, or acquired immune deficiency syndrome **98**–343; **97**–361
 cubanes **96**–331
 East Africa **97**–380
 information systems **96**–370
 medical research **96**–415
 molecular biology **97**–345
 organic chemistry **98**–261; **97**–286
 U.S. science policy **97**–387; **96**–461
AIDSLINE **96**–370
Aiken, Howard **96**–83
air-abrasive technology, or kinetic cavity preparation **97**–363
air exchange: see ventilation
air pollution: see pollution
air-traffic control: see aviation
air transport: see aviation
Airbus Industrie (Eur. consortium) **98**–397
aircraft: see aviation
Akashi Kaikyo (bridge, Japan) **96**–321

Akseyonov, Mikhail **97**–268
Alamo breccia
 geologic sciences **98**–278
Alaska (state, U.S.)
 botany **96**–394
 oil spill **98**–51, *il.* 53; **96**–380
albatross *il.* **98**–46
Alcoa: see Aluminum Company of America
alcogel
 metal oxide aerogels **96**–150
alcohol
 abuse **96**–441
 manufacturing
  aerogels **96**–149
  wine production **96**–180
 testing **97**–398
alendronate
 osteoporosis treatment **98**–348; **97**–359
ALERT, or Automated Local Evaluation in Real Time
 flood forecasting **96**–356
Aley, Thomas
 "Caves in Crisis" (feature article) **97**–116
Alfvén, Hannes Olof Gösta (obit.) **97**–414
algae
 cave microclimate **97**–126, *il.* 129
 coral reef degradation **96**–29, 403, *il.* 29
 eukaryote discovery **96**–397
 organic chemistry **97**–285
 see also individual genera and species by name
algorithm (math.) **98**–340
ALH84001 (meteorite) **98**–252, 325, 331, 387, *il.* 252
Ali, Muhammad **98**–239
alkaliphilic microbe **98**–17
alkane
 solvents **98**–260
allele
 animal genome mapping **96**–387
allelopathy
 biological pest control **98**–180
allergy
 air pollution **96**–386
Alpe Arami
 geologic sciences **98**–277
"Alpha" (space station) **96**–447, *il.*
Alpha chip (computers) **96**–364
alpha/proton/X-ray spectrometer, or APX
 Mars Pathfinder **96**–141
ALS: see amyotrophic lateral sclerosis
Altamira (cave, Sp.)
 cave art **97**–126
alternating-current dynamo **98**–78
alternative energy **98**–310; **97**–325
Alternative Futures, Task Force on (U.S.)
 national laboratories **98**–381
alumina
 aluminum smelting **97**–353
 dental use **97**–363
aluminum **97**–352
 rice cultivation **98**–182
Aluminum Association (Am. org.) **97**–352
Aluminum Company of America, or Alcoa
 Audi A8 **97**–353
aluminum nitride
 light-emitting diodes **96**–438
ALV: see Autonomous Land Vehicle
Alvarez, Luis **96**–90
"Alvin" (submersible) **96**–26
Alzheimer's disease **98**–345; **97**–356; **96**–413
amalgam **98**–351
AMANDA, or Antarctic Muon and Neutrino Detector Array **96**–123, *il.* 120
amber
 DNA preservation **96**–396
Ambulocetus (mammal) **97**–14, *ils.*; **96**–351
Amelio, Gilbert **98**–294; **97**–316
America Online, or AOL
 Internet **98**–295, 296; **97**–313
American Anthropological Association **96**–312
"American Anthropologist" (Am. journ.) **96**–312
American Association for the Advancement of Science, or AAAS **98**–380
American Cave and Karst Museum (U.S.)
 cave restoration **97**–133
American Center (Paris, Fr.)
 architecture **98**–317, *il.*
American Chemical Society **96**–327
American Dental Association, or ADA
 health care legislation **97**–362
 managed-care programs **98**–350
American Heritage Center (Laramie, Wy., U.S.) **96**–319, *il.*
American Indian: see Native American
"American Journey 1896-1945" (CD-ROM) **97**–320
American Museum of Natural History (N.Y.C., N.Y., U.S.) **98**–297
"American Presidency Full-Text Database" (elec. pub.) **98**–298
"American Presidency, The" (multimedia disc) **98**–298
"American Psychologist" (Am. journ.) **98**–370
American Railroads, Association of
 transportation **97**–398

American Telephone & Telegraph Company, or AT&T (Am. co.)
 Magic Link **96**–363
 satellites **96**–374
 technological innovations **98**–85
 telecommunications industry **97**–324
 see also AT&T Bell Laboratories
American Veterinary Medical Association, or AVMA **97**–420
americium (chem. element)
 discovery **97**–292
Ames Research Center (Mountain View, Calif., U.S.) **98**–165
amino acid
 bacterial prey attraction **96**–397
 botany **96**–392
 combinatorial synthesis **96**–333
 protein synthesis **97**–343; **96**–340
ammonia **98**–34
ammonium hydrosulfide **98**–34
ammonium ion
 microbiology **96**–397
ammonium salts **96**–337
Amonix Inc. (Am. co.)
 solar energy **96**–369
Ampato, Mount (mt., Peru) **98**–244
amphibian
 environmental discontinuity **97**–329
 evolution **97**–84
amphioxus
 vertebrate evolution **96**–405
AMPS: see advanced mobile phone system
Amtrak, or National Railroad Passenger Corporation (Am. ry. system) **96**–320
 electric rail **98**–394
 rail subsidies **97**–398; **96**–383, *il.*
amyotrophic lateral sclerosis, or ALS, or Lou Gehrig's disease
 drug approval **97**–356
 Scripps Research Institute **97**–216
"An 2440, L'" (Mercier)
 futurism **98**–5
anaerobic bacterium **98**–127
analogy (molecular biol.) **97**–217
anatomy
 female spotted hyena **96**–226, *il.* 231
 Neanderthals **98**–139
 scientific illustrations **97**–137, *il.* 139
"Anatomy" (Gray)
 scientific illustrations **97**–141, *il.* 140
Andes Mountains (mts., S.Am.)
 tectonic patterns **97**–302
Andrews, Michael *il.* **98**–359
androgen
 sex differentiation **96**–228
androstenedione
 gender characteristics **96**–229
Anfinsen, Christian Boehmer (obit.) **97**–414
Angell, Marcia **98**–238
angiogenesis
 tumor treatment **97**–218
angiogram **98**–105
angiotoxicity
 nutrition **96**–389
angle-dependent light scattering
 aerogels **96**–152
animal: see zoology
animal behavior
 sex differentiation **96**–228
 whales **97**–18
Animal Medicinal Drug Use Clarification Act (1994, U.S.) **96**–420
animat
 robotics **98**–166
Ankarapithecus meteai **98**–240
Announcement of Opportunity (NASA proposal) **96**–145
"Annual Review of Psychology" (journ.) **98**–374
anode effect
 aluminum smelting **97**–353
anomalocaridids, or Anomalocaris canadensis
 fossil discovery **96**–404
anomaly (weather)
 Atlantic Ocean **98**–285
 river flow **98**–283
ant
 attack *il.* **96**–248
 mutualism **97**–338
Antarctic Muon and Neutrino Detector Array: see AMANDA
Antarctica
 geology **96**–348
 ice shelves **98**–287
 neutrino detection **96**–124
 ozone hole **98**–274; **97**–296, 402; **96**–346
antenna (elec.)
 "Galileo" project **98**–33
 new technology **98**–318
 telecommunications systems **98**–302
anthocyanin
 molecular genetics **96**–392
anthropoid, or Anthropoidea **98**–240
Anthropology 98–240; **97**–266; **96**–310
 "Archaeology of Us, The" **97**–158
 information systems **96**–371
 recent books **98**–421

ACKNOWLEDGMENTS

16
(Top) Douglas Peebles—Westlight

16–17
(Bottom) Y. Arthus-Bertrand—Peter Arnold,
Inc.

17
(Top) Galen Rowell—Peter Arnold, Inc.

26–27
Illustration by John Berkey

52
Adapted from information obtained from *Body-
rhythms: Chronobiology and Peak Performance,* © 1994 Lynne Lamberg, p. 197, William Morrow and Company, Inc., New York

72
Rainbow; (inset) Clement Mok—CMCD, Inc.

73
(Top, left) Chris Rogers—Rainbow; (top, right)
Corbis/Bettmann; (center) C. Bruce Forster—
AllStock; (bottom) Lass—Archive Photos

105
David Davies—National Institutes of Health;
image based on data collected on beamline 4A

at the National Synchrotron Light Source,
Brookhaven National Laboratory, from Dyda,
et al., Science, vol. 266 (1994), pp. 1981–1986

115
Adapted from information obtained from *Our
Stolen Future: Are We Threatening Our Fertility, Intelligence, and Survival?: A Scientific Detective Story,* © 1996 Theo Colburn, Dianne
Dumanoski, and John Peterson Myers; Dutton,
a division of Penguin Books

129
Adapted from information obtained from
"Bioremediation," Ronald M. Atlas, University
of Louisville, *Chemical & Engineering News,*
vol. 73, no. 14, pp. 32–42, April 3, 1995

134–135
Illustration by Matt Mahurin

142
Adapted from information obtained from *The
Last Neanderthal: The Rise, Success, and
Mysterious Extinction of Our Closest Human
Relatives,* © 1996 Ian Tattersall, based on an
illustration by Diana Salles; Macmillan, USA

268
Photographs, Clemens Bechinger, Suzanne

Ferrere, Arie Zaban, Julian Sprague, and Brian
A. Gregg; National Renewable Energy Laboratory, Golden, Colorado

330
From "Crystal Structure of a Group I Ribozyme
Domain: Principles of RNA Packing," Jamie H.
Cate, Jennifer A. Doudna, *et al.,* reprinted by
permission of *Science,* vol. 273, no. 5282, pp.
1678–1685, September 20, 1996

368
From "Yttrium and Lanthanum Hydride Films
with Switchable Optical Properties," J.N. Huiberts, R. Griessen, J.H. Rector, R.J. Wijn-
gaarden, J.P. Dekker, D.G. de Groot, and N.J.
Koeman, reprinted by permission of *Nature,*
vol. 380, no. 6571, pp. 231–234, March 21,
1996. © Macmillan Magazines Ltd.

374
The Neuro-Developmental Center; illustration
by Tim Nichols